Longbourn's Angels

By
Sue Barr

Chapter One

All of Meryton waited with bated breath when the party from Netherfield Park entered the assembly room at the Red Lion Inn. Elizabeth Bennet, dancing with Samuel Watson, missed the initial introductions given by Sir William Lucas, master of ceremonies for most of Meryton's public social events. This minor oversight did not worry her in any way. Given the fact her father was the largest landowner in the area, she knew she would, at some time during the evening, make their acquaintance.

As she and Mr. Watson waited to go down the line, she noticed the much talked about Mr. Bingley was as good-looking and gentlemanlike as her friend Charlotte Lucas had reported earlier in the week. She was not wrong in saying he had a pleasant countenance and easy, unaffected manners. Mr. Bingley's sisters carried themselves with an air of decided fashion, although Elizabeth felt they were quite overdressed for a simple country assembly. The older man, whom she learned later was married to Mr. Bingley's eldest sister, looked the gentleman, but his fastidious attendance to a hidden flask in his coat pocket soon put paid to that observation. However, it was the third gentleman of the group who grabbed Elizabeth's attention.

Upon laying eyes upon him and hearing his name, she felt a faint fluttering of excitement. Never in her life, had she seen such perfection in male beauty. Tall and broad-shouldered, he towered over the rest of his party. Raven curls, grown a touch too long to be thought fashionable, skimmed the top of his crisp, white cravat, while piercing blue eyes beneath dark brows, scanned the room, drawing together to form a small frown. His face was savagely beautiful, his lips firm and sensually full.

She was extremely glad she had worn one of her newer gowns and taken extra care with her toilette. Normally Elizabeth's maid braided and pulled her hair into a simple bun, but this evening Sarah had managed to pin the riotous curls into some semblance of order, securing them in place with various pins and decorative flowers. Although Jane was the undisputed beauty of the family, Elizabeth felt for once she could stand with her head held high, knowing she looked her very best.

It wasn't long before Mr. Bingley asked Charlotte to dance and they joined the set. From where she danced, Elizabeth could plainly see Mamma was not at all pleased with this turn of events, but her glare turned to smiles when the affable young man solicited Jane's hand for the next two.

As pleasant and friendly Mr. Bingley was upon first acquaintance, his friend did not enjoy the same praise and good thoughts from the citizens of Meryton. He danced only with the ladies of his party and spent the rest of the evening stalking about the edges of the room, ignoring anyone who dared to attempt polite conversation with him, refusing all introductions to other patrons of the assembly.

It came as no surprise to the gentlefolk of Meryton the most outspoken against him was Mrs. Bennet, whose dislike of his general behavior was sharpened into a particular resentment when the following incident took place.

Obliged by the scarcity of gentlemen to sit down for two dances, Elizabeth became aware the handsome gentleman had paused in front of her. Would he notice her and ask for a set? Mr. Bingley, dancing with Jane, broke from the line to implore his friend to join the set. With no intention of listening to their conversation, Elizabeth could not avoid the two friends when they paused no more than a few feet from where she sat.

"Come, Darcy," Bingley said, "You must dance. I hate to see you standing about when you could be enjoying the company of a pretty girl."

Could this be the Mr. Darcy she had heard so much about?

"You know I detest dancing unless I am particularly acquainted with my partner. At such an assembly as this, it would be insupportable. Besides, there is not any woman in the room whom it would not be a punishment to me to stand up with."

"You are so frustratingly fastidious," cried the younger man. "These people are my neighbors. Can you not, for my sake, soften your attitude for one dance? Truly Darcy, I never met with so many pleasant girls in my life, and several of them are uncommonly pretty."

"You are dancing with the only handsome girl in the room," said Mr. Darcy, looking toward the dance floor. Elizabeth noted where he directed his attention and felt a slight thaw in her disgust. Someone who thought Jane was beautiful could not be all bad.

"I agree. She is the most beautiful creature I ever beheld! Regardless, you will not detract me from my mission. I must have you dance." Bingley cast his gaze around and it fell on Elizabeth, who looked away, embarrassed at having almost been caught listening in on their conversation. "I say, there is a young lady sitting down just behind you who is quite pretty. Miss Bennet will know who she is. Do let me ask my partner to introduce you."

Elizabeth worked hard to regulate her breathing, counting

to ten while mentally preparing a positive response when asked to dance. By the time she reached three, she realized there had been no answer from Mr. Darcy, other than, 'Which do you mean?' Without thought, she glanced up and found him staring directly at her. Thinking him vexed with his friend, she sought to alleviate his discomfort by smiling. Upon catching her eye, he withdrew his own and coldly said, "She is tolerable; but not handsome enough to tempt me. I am in no humor at present to give consequence to young ladies who are slighted by other men. Return to your partner and enjoy her smiles, you are wasting your time with me."

Stunned, cheeks burning with mortification, Elizabeth could not even form words in her mind at his brutal observation. Mr. Bingley opened his mouth to argue further when a familiar figure stepped in front of both gentlemen.

"Excuse me. I believe you owe my sister an apology."

"I do not know who your sister is," Darcy replied, giving the younger man a haughty glare.

"She is the one whom you find barely tolerable, and not handsome enough to dance with."

Oh dear, this could get messy. Elizabeth hurried to join them. By this time, a second gentleman had come alongside and he also glared at Mr. Darcy.

"If you require introductions, sir, you are cordially invited to join us outside. My brother and I will introduce you to our fists. You will find they are not tolerable as well."

"Michael! Gabriel!" Elizabeth stepped in their midst. "Apologize to this gentleman at once."

"He insulted you, Elizabeth," Michael ground out between clenched teeth, his steely gaze never wavering from Mr. Darcy's.

"He deserves to be horsewhipped for saying such things about a lady to whom he has not been introduced," Gabriel added, and gently tried to move his sister aside. "It was extremely rude."

"I agree, Gabriel. Would you like to take the first punch?"

"No, you are the elder Michael, you may go first."

"Stop!" Elizabeth shook off Gabriel's hand, stood her ground, and stared her brothers down. "There will be no punches thrown, nor whippings given, and you will apologize to the gentleman."

"No need, Miss Elizabeth. I will apologize."

She shot a hard glare over her shoulder in the direction of Mr. Darcy, deciding he was not so handsome after all. "We have not been introduced, sir. You will not address me until you are. I am of a mind to let my brothers have at you."

"You are the Bennet twins!" At Mr. Bingley's astonishing outburst, Elizabeth looked at the young man who stood open-mouthed, completely forgetting his dance with Jane. "You were two years ahead of me at Cambridge. I have heard much about the two of you."

"As we have of you," Michael Bennet said in a decidedly cool voice, keeping his attention on Mr. Darcy. He looked at him from head to toe and back up again to stare him directly in the face. "Because we are Cambridge men, I know you have a younger sister," – Mr. Darcy gave a violent start – "and would like to pose a hypothetical question. If someone wholly unconnected with your sister said within her hearing, she was not handsome enough to dance with, what would you do?"

"I would be tempted to call them out onto the field of honor." Mr. Darcy turned his somber gaze to Elizabeth and gave her a polite half-bow. "Although we have not been properly introduced, please allow me to apologize for the insult I levied in your direction. It was not well done, and I am heartily ashamed of my words."

She longed to turn and leave without acknowledging his apology, convinced it was given because he'd been called out, not because he felt any regret over his odious words.

However, she was raised as a gentlewoman and would behave like one.

"Apology accepted, sir." She gave him an equally polite curtsy, then without so much as a by your leave, grabbed an arm of each of her brothers, and dragged them to the other side of the room.

"Promise me you will seek retribution with Mr. Darcy this evening. The next set is starting, and Jonathan Lucas awaits me at the refreshment table."

"We promise," the brothers said in unison. She could only hope they would keep their promise and made a mental note to follow up with more explicit directives when they got home. Her brothers were too clever by far, and just because they promised not to take action at the assembly did not mean they would not exact vengeance on the man in the following days or weeks. She paused and turned back to them. "Do not think you are relieved of this promise once the clock strikes midnight."

From their slight reaction, she knew she had struck a chord. The Bennet brothers were known to be protective of their sisters. Mrs. Bennet bemoaned their actions, saying no eligible young man would ever darken the door to Longbourn for fear of facing the wrath of Michael and Gabriel, Longbourn's resident guardian angels. With any luck, Mr. Darcy would be gone from the area after a short visit with his friend. Satisfied her brothers would behave, she continued to the refreshment table and her next dance partner.

Once her dance with Mr. Lucas was complete, she found herself with Jane in a quiet alcove. By tacit agreement, they both stayed out of their mother's sight and hearing.

"Whatever happened, Lizzy? One minute I was enjoying a dance with Mr. Bingley, the next I knew, I was alone in the middle of the dance floor watching our brothers stand toe to toe with Mr. Darcy."

Elizabeth heaved a heartfelt sigh at the memory.

"Oh, Janie. I had such high hopes when I heard his name. Our cousin Peter has often spoken of him."

"I remember. All of it was good, and our brothers were slightly in awe of him. He took first in almost every subject at Cambridge."

"True, but no one has yet to beat our father's record."

"Father excelled because at the time he had no inclination to become a landowner as Uncle Edgar was still living, and Papa wanted to remain at the university and teach."

"I was only five when our uncle died, and I still remember the library."

"We all know you will never judge a man by his purse or status. If he has more than two shelves full of books, your heart will be his for the taking."

"You know me well, dear sister."

"Enough procrastinating." Jane took hold of her hand. "What happened between Mr. Darcy and our brothers?"

Even though her pride had been pricked and tender feelings trampled on, Elizabeth presented a bright smile and rendered her version of events. She even managed to have Jane stifle a giggle when she came to the part of her brothers asking who would throw the first punch.

"Poor Mr. Darcy," she murmured. "We shall have to be extra vigilant with our brothers. They will not take this slight lightly, even though he did apologize."

"He tendered an apology, not because he regretted his remarks, but because he was called out over his manners. I believe if no one had taken him to task, he would never have felt any remorse or changed his mind. He thinks too highly of himself, and the company he keeps is but a reflection of his true self."

"Mr. Bingley is an amiable young man."

"That may be so, but his sisters act as though they live in

a sphere of rarified air. If their noses were held any higher, I would have to climb a ladder to see if a falcon's nest was lodged in them."

"Lizzy!"

"You know I speak the truth. As it is, a flock of small birds might well take flight out of Miss Bingley's turban at any moment. Look! You cannot miss her in the crowd. The feathers jump and twist with each word she speaks."

Jane did take a quick glance over her shoulder and then turned back to her sister, her eyes dancing with merriment.

"For shame, Elizabeth. Now I will fight all evening to suppress a grin when I look at her."

"I plan on not looking at her at all."

"Elizabeth Bennet, remember you are a lady and will be polite to all you meet. Do not lower yourself to their level. Remember what Susannah said last year when that horrid little man declared your nose was too thin for his liking."

"He would have been better off picking new friends instead of picking his nose?"

"No, the other thing she said."

"Shall I call on Sebastian to defend your honor?"

"Lizzy, be serious. I was speaking of her teaching us the stratagem of projecting tranquility. Never let strangers see the turmoil of your heart and mind."

"Rest easy, Jane. I remember. 'Be a swan, my dear Miss Bennets. Calm and sedate as you float about in the pond of humanity while your feet paddle like mad beneath the surface.'" Elizabeth snuck a glance around the corner of the alcove in the direction of Miss Bingley and her sister. "Frankly, I prefer 'Ponder and deliberate before making a move.'"

"You are talking as though they are our mortal enemies."

Elizabeth looked at her sister and impulsively took both of Jane's hands in hers.

"I give you leave to like Mr. Bingley. He is a very amiable young man. However, his sisters…" She pursed her lips and shook her head from side to side to emphasize her point. "Given the fact they have not spoken to a single person outside their own party, shows they hold us all in contempt."

"You know I trust your instincts and will approach them with caution." Jane turned to leave the alcove but not before asking, "What of Mr. Darcy?"

"What of him?"

"Are we to avoid him as well?"

"At this exact moment, I am uncertain. We shall have to see if his apology was genuine and made a determination based on his future behavior."

Jane's next partner arrived to escort her to the dance floor, and Elizabeth waved her sister off with a wide smile. She caught sight of Mr. Darcy prowling about the edges of the ballroom, a scowl marring his handsome face and sighed. How was it such a handsome man, who seemed to have no earthly worries, could be so miserable?

***

"Badly done, Darcy." Bingley prodded the dying fire with an iron poker.

"I am aware. You need not beat the horse dead." Darcy laid his head against the back of the chair and blew out a heavy sigh. He made a colossal mistake by misinterpreting Miss Elizabeth's smile. With whispers abounding throughout the room of his wealth and property, he immediately thought she was being coy and flirtatious. Her brothers, making their sentiments known, had abused him of that notion. "Lord save us, from overprotective brothers."

"In this matter, I would suggest you are the pot talking about the kettle." Darcy nodded in agreement. He could not dispute the fact he was very protective of his younger sister, Georgiana. And for good reason, as he discovered to his detriment this past summer. He dimly noted Bingley was still talking. "They are protective because you behaved like an ass – which is something you do far too often lately."

"I am sorry if I put you into an uncomfortable situation."

"These people are going to be my neighbors, and hopefully friends. Could you not have been more friendly? Truly, Darcy, what did they do to earn such obvious disdain? They are no different than the people you deal with at your estate. The village of Lambton is not much bigger than Meryton. Do you treat the landed gentry around Pemberley like you did Sir William or even Mrs. Long?"

"No, I do not."

"You realize Caroline will now follow your lead and believe it her right to condescend and belittle anyone she meets. I shudder to think of how she will behave if she thinks any young woman in this area looks twice in your direction."

"I am not her betrothed. I am not even her friend. I am here at your bequest. Please remind her of that fact."

"I can remind her until I am blue in the face from lack of air. She listens only to you, and you prevaricate in putting her in her place."

"Because it is not my place. I suffer her company because you require a hostess in order to invite guests for dinners and other entertainments. Although, with your sister Mrs. Hurst in residence, why not send Miss Bingley packing? Preferably far, far away. Would the Hebrides be too far, this time of year?"

Charles chuckled, then turned serious.

"Louisa is a terrible hostess. She is far more interested in her jewelry than pouring tea and making conversation. No, I am stuck with Caroline until I marry."

"Then prepare yourself for a miserable three months. She

may have her sights set on me, but she also has lofty goals for your future as well, and if you think she will allow you to settle with a gentleman's daughter when she sees a titled lady in your future, think again."

"Darcy, she does not have a titled daughter in my future, she envisions your sister gracing my arm at future events."

"She does not!"

"Not only does she wish to secure the position of Pemberley's mistress, but she also wants me to court your sister."

"Georgiana is not yet sixteen!"

"I am aware and as much as I like your sister, I do not think of her in such a manner."

"Which, for your health, you will continue to do so. It is bad enough I had to—"

Darcy stopped abruptly, almost divulging the fact his sister had nearly eloped this past summer. If he and his cousin Richard had not arrived at Ramsgate two days earlier than planned, they would not have been able to save her from the greedy clutches of George Wickham, his late father's godson, an unrepentant rake who seduced her for her marriage portion of thirty thousand pounds. Even though she heard with her own ears how Wickham had pursued her for money, her tender heart was badly bruised, and given her age, she found it hard to stop loving him. Time was the only thing Darcy knew would cure her. That, and the wise counsel of their Aunt Lucinda, Lady Matlock.

"We should explore the estate tomorrow." Bingley's whimsical tone brought him out of his troubled thoughts. "With any luck, we might find ourselves near Longbourn."

"Where is this Longbourn, and who lives there?"

"Longbourn is the estate which abuts Netherfield, where your double trouble nemesis and their sisters reside." Bingley gave him a wicked grin. "With further luck, we might stumble across the fair Miss Bennet."

Darcy felt a pinch of alarm. Bingley had a habit of falling in and out of love with each new angel he met.

"I must caution you against raising the young lady's expectations. This is not London. Society is very limited here and what is acceptable in town is not acceptable here."

"Surely, I can appreciate the company of a beautiful woman without her thinking I am about to fall on bended knee. I enjoyed our dances and would not mind getting to know her better. Nothing more, nothing less."

"I still think you should keep your distance. At least until you know more about her family."

"Always worried about connections, eh Darcy?"

"You cannot think only of yourself, Bingley. You must also consider your sister and make sure your actions do not hinder her chances at making a good marriage."

On that note, he took his leave and made for his rooms. After his nightly ablutions were complete, he dismissed his valet and warned him to ensure both his doors were locked.

"Is there anything else you need before you retire, sir?"

"No, that is all, Jenkins. Thank you."

His trusted valet slipped from the room, and Darcy finally took himself to bed. As tired as he was, his mind whirled with the evening's revelations. He had finally met the famed Bennet brothers, known for their quick wit and equally quick tempers. Staunchly supportive of those they deemed the underdog, they had made a name for themselves at Cambridge defending those who were bullied. Although Darcy had already graduated, he heard of their escapades via Bingley and admired them based on the good reports his friend brought with him whenever he visited. However, he had metaphorically put his foot in it regarding their sister. He was heartily ashamed of what he'd said. All breath had leeched from his body when they'd posed the question of how he would have reacted if the lady in question had been his sister. Georgiana.

If she overheard a stranger say she was barely tolerable, and not handsome enough to tempt a man to dance, she would have been utterly destroyed. There would have been no road to redemption for the man who expressed such pompous words. Despite his turmoil and self-disgust, he finally fell into a restive sleep with dreams centered around a young woman with fine eyes.

LONGBOURN'S ANGELS

Chapter Two

The next morning, as was her custom, Elizabeth rose early to enjoy a quiet walk and think about what happened the night prior. She had started her familiar climb to Oakham Mount when a twig snapped behind her. With deceptive ease, which came from much practice, she slid her hand into a hidden leather pocket, fingers curling around a small dagger's hilt. Upon turning, she was relieved to find the intruder was none other than her eldest brother.

"Elizabeth, you know Father is uncomfortable with you walking alone. Especially now, with the militia quartered so closely to our land."

"I am not unprepared, Michael." She withdrew the sheathed blade from her pocket. "I pray I shall never have to use it in the manner you and Gabriel taught me." At his surprised look, she added. "I have another in my boot, as well."

"Good. Like you, I hope you never have to use them. Still…" he paused, "I would feel better if you asked one of the footmen to accompany you until the militia move on. These men are trained for battle and if an unsavory sort came across you during your morning walk, you may not stand a chance, even with the element of surprise."

"Mayhap I could beg your company during my walks. You are much better company than a footman who would never dare enter into conversation with the daughter of his employer."

Elizabeth missed the carefree days of their childhood, before her gangly brothers went to school and university, returning as grown men.

"I have too many things which require my attention." Upon seeing the downturn of her mouth, he added, "If I am able, I will join you."

She rewarded him with a wide, happy smile.

"Why did you follow after me this morning?"

"I wished to ensure my sister did not suffer from any further repercussions following the confrontation we had with Mr. Darcy."

Elizabeth looped her arm through Michael's and gave him an affectionate little shoulder bump.

"I will admit, his comment did give me pause. As a gentleman firmly entrenched within the first circle of society, he is well aware of what is currently in vogue amongst the beau monde. To be found tolerable, but not handsome enough to tempt a gentleman of his caliber for even one country dance, was a blow to my confidence."

"Frankly, Lizzy, I am surprised by what he said. Peter knows Mr. Darcy and has nothing but praise for the gentleman. Let us hope this one time is an aberration of his character. Having said that, I still want to take him outside and remind him, as only a brother can, how his words have consequences."

"You and Gabriel must not act on your feelings. We need to show these new neighbors we are above their behavior."

"I assume you are including the ladies of Netherfield Park in this assessment?"

"Most assuredly. Mr. Bingley's sisters think very well of themselves, and I would be surprised if they make any effort to form lasting friendships within our small village. They think they are above our company."

Having reached the top of Oakham Mount, the siblings sat on a large outcropping of rocks and marveled at the sunrise.

"At times like this, I am in awe at the complexity of God's creation," Elizabeth said with a contented sigh. "How the colors of the clouds, the sun, and the valley below blend perfectly against the canvas of the sky."

"I agree. In the vastness of His glory, we are but tiny ants, scurrying about."

Elizabeth laid her head on Michael's shoulder. "Tiny ants that despair when there are not enough gentlemen to dance with at local assemblies. How I wish we were not at war with so many countries."

"Such is the way of man, Lizzy. Always striving to achieve more land, more power, and more wealth."

"I am satisfied with our little corner of the world. What more could a girl like me hope for."

Michael stood and held out his hand to help her up.

"You can hope for a husband who will love you as you are, and make it better for your future children and grandchildren."

"What if I never married? What if I am content in becoming the perfect aunt who plays the pianoforte ill, and spoils all her future nieces and nephews."

The siblings began to make their way back to Longbourn, soon reaching the path which led to Longbourn's gravel drive.

"You will marry, Lizzy. You would be a marvelous mother."

"I, at least, would not suffer from phantom vapors and spasms."

"Our mother has always had a nervous disposition. She does not know any better."

"I assure you, she does."

Their conversation was interrupted by the sound of horses on the main road. Elizabeth's surprise was great when Mr. Darcy and Mr. Bingley turned the corner and cantered toward them. She quickly smoothed her brow. It would not do for Mr. Darcy to see her scowling. If he found her only barely tolerable when she smiled, there was no telling what he might think if she looked disgruntled.

***

The minute Darcy and Bingley reached the gates to Longbourn, Darcy's attention was caught by the sight of Miss Elizabeth Bennet, looking delightfully feminine tucked against her brother's side. Upon her seeing him, a slight scowl rested briefly on her face, reminding him of his terrible insult the night prior. He had dug a very deep ditch with this young lady and needed to make further amends. His sense of honor demanded no less.

"Good morning, Mr. Bennet, Miss Elizabeth," Bingley said upon reaching them.

Darcy echoed his friend's greeting after they had dismounted. They joined the siblings as they walked toward Longbourn, their horses trailing behind them.

"What made you decide to lease Netherfield Park?" Michael Bennet asked Bingley.

"I wish to learn how to run an estate. Darcy agreed to take time out of his busy schedule and teach me the fundamentals of land management."

"You could find no better place to learn. Netherfield Park is a profitable estate. You should not be too overwhelmed as you learn the basics."

"I would very much like to meet your father. As the second largest landowner in Meryton, next to Netherfield Park, he will have great insight—"

"Largest landowner."

"I beg your pardon?"

"Longbourn is the largest estate in the area."

"Oh… my sister, Caroline assured me our estate is twice the size of Longbourn."

"Your sister is a skilled cartographer?"

"No sir, she is not."

"Then, she has spoken with your steward?"

"I cannot say, that is… I do not believe she did."

"She must have spoken with someone. You arrived only yesterday, mere hours before the assembly."

Bingley had the decency to flush.

"Miss Bingley gleaned this information from some of your neighbors during the course of the evening," Darcy finally revealed, uncomfortable with the inquisition his friend was being put through.

Michael Bennet looked directly at Darcy, then shifted his gaze to Bingley.

"It is said he that utters slander, is a fool. In my opinion, the second person who further spreads that slander, without verifying the truth is either foolish, or vindictive."

"On behalf of my sister, I apologize to you and your family." Bingley gave Michael a half-hearted smile.

"Apology accepted. We do not broadcast our wealth, much like your good friend with his five satellite estates, along with one more in Scotland."

Darcy barely stopped his mouth from dropping open. How did Michael Bennet know so much about his business?

"Darcy could own the King's palace for all I care," Bingley said. "I have never based our friendship on material things. He is simply one of the best men I know."

"Thank you, Charles," Darcy said, grateful for Bingley's simplistic approach to their friendship. It was what drew them close. God knows, his sister was not the reason.

By this time, they had passed through the gate which led to Longbourn.

"Would you gentlemen care to break your fast with our family?"

Before Darcy could utter one word Bingley accepted. Not surprising as his main goal for their early morning ride was to see the ethereally beautiful Miss Bennet. Darcy slid a glance at Miss Elizabeth, making note of her slightly horrified expression at the realization her brother had invited them into their hearth and home. However, he would not repine how their morning was unfolding. His goal was to extend a more refined apology to the lady he'd so grievously insulted the night before.

Michael Bennet turned to his sister.

"Lizzy, would you let Hill know we have guests this morning?"

"Of course. Good day, gentlemen."

She gave them all a polite curtsy, and hurried to the house, stopping only when Darcy called out, "Miss Elizabeth!" When she turned, he handed his reins to Bingley and approached her.

"Although our intent was simply a refreshing morning ride, I will admit I had hoped to see you. I wished to further extend my apologies with regard to my behavior last night."

Elizabeth stood still as he gave her a formal bow.

"Miss Elizabeth Bennet of Longbourn, I regret most heartily the fact I rejected a proper introduction to you. I also regret uttering such vile words within your hearing. I see by your raised brow you are not impressed. They were not the words of a gentleman, and my parents, were they alive, would have been deeply ashamed. In truth, whether you did or did not hear what I said, such disparaging comments should never have been uttered in the first place. My foul mood was no excuse, and I beg your forgiveness."

In silence, Elizabeth considered his words. He noted she flicked a glance over his shoulder. More than likely to see how her brother reacted to his apology. Just as quickly she returned her gaze to his and held it for several heartbeats.

"Apology accepted, sir," she finally said in reply and seemed surprised when he took her hand and raised it to his lips, whispering a heartfelt thank you against her knuckles.

He could not help the feeling of satisfaction at her heightened color before she pivoted on her heel and continued into the house. The fine hair on the back of his neck rose, and he turned to retrieve his horse from Bingley, well aware Michael Bennet glared at him. Anything Miss Elizabeth's brother might have said was interrupted by the appearance of a stable boy, who had come to take the horses.

"Shall we proceed?" Bennet asked with all politeness in his voice and manner.

He and Bingley nodded and followed the gentleman into the house.

***

That same day, the ladies from Lucas Lodge descended upon Longbourn, as was their custom after a quarterly assembly.

"You began the evening well, Charlotte," said Mrs. Bennet. "You were Mr. Bingley's first choice."

"Yes, but we all know he liked his second better," Charlotte replied.

"You mean Jane, I suppose," Mamma said with smug satisfaction.

"None of us were surprised. Jane was the prettiest girl there," Lady Lucas said warmly. Although she did not like the fact her eldest daughter was continually overshadowed by the Bennet sisters, she had a soft spot for them.

"Yes, my Jane made a very good impression, unlike Lizzy."

"I believe Mr. Darcy quickly regretted his observation of our Eliza being only tolerable," Charlotte said with a conspiratorial grin toward her greatest friend.

Mamma fluttered her lace handkerchief in the air, as though waving away a bad smell. "He is such a disagreeable fellow, although he seemed pleasant this morning at breakfast."

The eyebrows of all the Lucas ladies rose upon receiving that news.

"Mr. Darcy took breakfast with your family?"

"He and Mr. Bingley – oh! such an amiable young man – met with Michael and Elizabeth while on their morning walk. My son is a very gracious host and invited them to join us."

"I must admit, this surprises me. Mr. Darcy does not strike me as a social butterfly," Lady Lucas said, her tone speculative.

"Did you know Mrs. Long told me, he sat next to her for half an hour without once opening his lips?"

"Are you quite certain, Mamma?" said Jane. "I saw Mr. Darcy speaking to her."

"Aye, because she asked him how he liked Netherfield, and he could not help answering her."

"Then, it seems Mrs. Long spoke an untruth. As I said before, Mr. Darcy did speak with her, even if it was only to answer a question," said Jane, "Not every gentleman will rattle on about nothing, and he did not know who any of us are, or what our dispositions are like."

"That is true, Mamma," Elizabeth added, glad the discussion of Mr. Darcy's insult seemed to have been forgotten. "We all know Gabriel can talk to anyone, while Michael and Papa stay in the background. As the party from Netherfield become acquainted with us, they may develop more open manners."

"One cannot be surprised that so very fine a young man, with family, fortune, everything in his favor, should think highly of himself," Charlotte mused out loud. "As nephew to an earl and grandson of a duke, he has a right to be proud."

"Charlotte!" Elizabeth exclaimed in mock horror, clutching at her throat in an exaggerated manner. "You are not to side with Mr. Darcy in this, no matter how reasonable your argument. I could easily forgive his pride if he had not mortified mine."

Her dear friend only smiled, knowing she was right.

"Do you think he will attempt a second apology, Eliza?"

"He already has."

Elizabeth grinned at her friend's look of surprise and explained further the gracious apology Mr. Darcy had given her. Their attention was soon drawn across the room. Once again, Mamma spoke of Mr. Bingley dancing twice with Jane after his initial set with Charlotte.

"If I had been allowed to attend the Assembly, Mr. Bingley would have danced with me," Lydia suddenly blurted out. "It is painfully obvious he will dance with anyone."

"Lydia!" Elizabeth hissed in frustration. "Have your lessons on decorum left you already?"

Lydia snorted and slouched in her chair. "Who needs decorum? I am going to be the first of my sisters married, you shall see. Mamma says I am too pretty and lively to stay on the shelf, like Charlotte."

"Lydia Francine Bennet!"

Unbeknownst to the ladies, Michael stood within the door frame, anger rolling off him in waves. Lydia immediately straightened her posture and folded her hands in her lap. Mamma glanced between her eldest son and youngest daughter, clearly torn as to whom she should support. During this, Lady Lucas rose from her chair and stood, shoulders squared and stiff.

"My daughters and I shall take our leave, Mrs. Bennet." Lady Lucas moved toward the door, then turned back to face the woman she had known many years. "Gain control of your youngest daughter, Fanny. You may not have been raised a gentleman's daughter, but that is no excuse for your youngest to behave in the manner you have just allowed."

With a small hand signal, she indicated for both her daughters to precede her from the room. Before she could exit, Michael gently touched her forearm.

"Lady Lucas. On behalf of my family, I extend an apology. I assure you Lydia will attend your home on the morrow and request forgiveness in a manner expected from a gentleman's daughter."

A shadow of a smile flickered across Lady Lucas's face before her lips thinned with anger.

"We shall not be at home on the morrow. A well-written letter will suffice, for now."

"Thank you, Lady Lucas." Michael gave their long-time neighbors a polite bow, and as soon as they had quit the room, he rounded on Lydia. "You will come with me to Father's study and explain your vulgar behavior."

"I will not!"

Lydia crossed her arms across her chest and stuck out her bottom lip. Mamma's eyes widened at such an outright display of disrespect. Elizabeth reasoned her mother had not truly realized how out of control Lydia had become in the past few months. Michael advanced until his boots touched the hem of Lydia's skirt.

"Either you come willingly, or I will pick you up and throw you over my shoulder."

"You are not being fair. Mamma says all the time Charlotte Lucas is not pretty, and will never marry."

"When have you ever heard me say such a thing?" Mamma

protested loudly.

"The day after Mrs. Long's card party, you said, 'Charlotte Lucas is so very plain, and will never find a husband.'"

"Enough," Michael interjected. "Come with me to Father's study."

"You are not my father! I do not have to listen to you!"

"Lydia." Papa's quiet voice cut through the air like a newly sharpened blade. "You have two minutes to attend my study and be seated before my desk. If you are one second late, I will send you to a school in Cornwall."

He swiveled and strode down the hall. Lydia hesitated for one brief moment before she threw herself out of the chair, and scampered down the hall after her father. Michael turned his attention to Mamma.

"Mother, Lydia's behavior is becoming unacceptable. Father and I would like to discuss this with you. Could we, perhaps, meet in your private sitting room later this evening to discuss what must be done?"

"I… yes, I shall meet you directly after we dine."

"Thank you. I know you have all my sister's best interest at heart, and will do everything in your power to ensure their future felicity."

When Michael left the room, Jane shifted in her chair, obviously upset by what had just occurred.

"I believe Lizzy and I should visit with Miss Lucas as soon as possible. We cannot let this wound fester. We have been friends for too long."

"I will come with you," Mamma said. "I know what Lydia did was wrong, but even you must agree, Lady Lucas herself has commented on her daughter's plain face. More than once she has expressed a wish for a daughter like Jane."

"It is one thing for Lady Lucas to acknowledge her daughter's lack of expected beauty when having a private conversation with a friend. However, it is another thing to hear a spoiled fourteen-year-old girl throw such unkind remarks in her daughter's face."

"I know, Lizzy, and I will beg forgiveness from my friend."

Chapter Three

Darcy felt the beginnings of a headache, and the cause of it stood next to him. Ten paces. He had counted them. Their tiny party of five had advanced a mere ten paces into Lucas Lodge before Miss Bingley's lamentations began. He handed the footman his outerwear and condoled himself it was better than the evening prior when they had dined at Haye Park. There, her litany of complaints began before the carriage had even rolled to a stop outside the manor. As to the source of her complaints, her focus remained on the Bennet family, and more specifically, Miss Elizabeth Bennet. Miss Bingley cared not that they were the premier family of the area, and it was all his fault.

Because of his previous ungentlemanly behavior, Miss Bingley now thought it her duty to call out every minor flaw or mistake the young lady made. No one could live under such dedicated, biased scrutiny, and yet, Miss Elizabeth always greeted Miss Bingley with cool politeness no one could fault.

Tonight, he watched Miss Elizabeth from across the room. She was currently enjoying what seemed like a spirited conversation with her friend and neighbor, Miss Lucas, along with Colonel Forster of the ___shire Militia. This was not the first time he'd covertly observed the petite lady. No matter where she went, everyone wished to engage her in conversation. Anyone with eyes and ears could perceive she was popular, and laughter was a common occurrence in all these interactions, a fact which vexed Miss Bingley to no end.

It was also no secret that, at first, he'd not thought Elizabeth Bennet pretty. She was the antithesis of what the beau monde found beautiful. Petite and curvy instead of tall and willowy, mahogany curls with auburn highlights instead of silky winter wheat hair, and everyone within a thirty-mile radius knew of his infamous remark at the assembly. Yet the more time he spent in her company, the more his view changed. She was vivacious and witty. He appreciated the intelligence in her dark eyes, the way they lit up when she was involved in a lively conversation, or in a debate, which was the road most of their encounters traveled.

That she was quite learned had come as a pleasant surprise. The two of them sparred more than once over classic literature, and she was not afraid to defend her point of view. At times he was convinced she voiced an opinion polar opposite of his merely to start a debate. She challenged him, and he found it exhilarating. He was now close enough to hear the conversation between her and the colonel. She implored Colonel Forster to host a ball in order to introduce his new wife to the neighborhood. Her next comment startled him.

"Did not you think, Mr. Darcy, that I expressed myself uncommonly well just now when teasing Colonel Forster to give us a ball at Meryton?"

For a brief moment, a euphoric sense of satisfaction surged through his body at the obvious fact Elizabeth was as aware of him as he was of her.

"You expressed your opinion with great energy," he replied, keeping his expression neutral. "Which is not completely unexpected, as it is a subject which always seems to increase a lady's excitement."

"While such an observation may prove true, a lady's enthusiasm comes from multiple sources of entertainment," she said and gifted him with a wide smile. "Dancing only being one of them."

He could not believe her flirtatious manner in front of others, and his heart began to race. He longed to comment back in like manner but dared not in case he gave rise to unrealistic expectations.

"Speaking of entertainment, I am going to open the instrument." Miss Lucas gave her friend a playful look. One which told Darcy these two ladies were great friends. "You know what follows."

"What have your father's guests done to deserve such punishment?" Elizabeth asked with absolutely no censure in her tone at all. "You know very well I am not as talented as others on the pianoforte, yet you wish to bludgeon their ears with my discordant plunking of the keys."

"You, Eliza Bennet, always delight our neighbors when you play and sing." Miss Lucas took her friend by the elbow and began to steer her toward the instrument.

Elizabeth allowed herself to be drawn away, but not before she turned to him and said, "Now is your chance to quit the room, Mr. Darcy." At his raised brow, she added playfully. "Never say I did not warn you."

With that, Miss Lucas successfully led her friend to the pianoforte, who immediately sat down and entertained the guests. Darcy, having heard many examples of exquisite playing, knew Elizabeth's performance was not perfect by any means, and yet he found her rendition of a fast-paced Scottish air thoroughly delightful. Again, he found himself wishing she had better familial connections and a larger marriage portion. He could well imagine this lively woman gracing the halls of Pemberley and many a night spent in such a fashion, yet it was not to be. For Georgiana's sake, he had to make a prudent marriage. One his family could solidly support and stand behind. A simple country maiden would not do. However, there was nothing to stop him from admiring her from afar, as long as he did not act on whimsical impulses.

"I can guess the subject of your reverie."

Darcy barely suppressed a grimace when Miss Bingley, wearing an overpowering scent that could fell an elephant at one hundred paces, situated herself by his side.

"I should imagine not," he replied.

"I am certain you hold the same criticisms as me as you listen to poor Miss Eliza hammer away on that instrument. It is painfully obvious she has not had any training." He made no comment as Elizabeth's playing did not bother him. "Can you not hear how she fudges and slurs her way through the more intricate parts?"

"I am not sure to what you refer. I find her rendition of this song delightful."

"Delightful! If I did not know you better, Mr. Darcy, I would think you were joking."

"I always speak the truth, Madam."

"I did not know your former disgust had changed to admiration. Should I wish you joy?"

"I have no intention of marrying any time soon."

"Such a relief," Miss Bingley said and tapped his arm playfully with her closed fan. "You had me very apprehensive with regard to your future happiness."

"You will have no doubt of my intentions when I do decide to marry," – her smile turned sly, making him more determined than ever to make his meaning clear – "as your family will be the first amongst my friends to be introduced to the future Mrs. Darcy."

Miss Bingley paled as his words hit home; however, she was a creature of the ton and knew when to retreat – for the moment – and her inherent nature to censure the entire neighborhood, especially the Bennet family, quickly reasserted itself into their conversation. Darcy listened with perfect indifference while she chose to entertain herself in this manner, and as his composure convinced her all was safe, at least with regard to Miss Eliza Bennet, her caustic wit flowed long.

***

After a song or two, and before she could reply to the entreaties of several guests to sing again, Elizabeth slipped away to find her friend, and they enjoyed a rousing tête-à-tête, comparing notes on the party from Netherfield.

"I see Mr. Bingley's admiration for Jane has not diminished," Charlotte observed.

Mr. Bingley had once again sequestered Elizabeth's eldest sister in a quiet corner, paying no attention to anyone else in the room.

Charlotte spent the next few minutes watching Jane and Mr. Bingley before turning to Elizabeth.

"You must speak plainly with Jane and advise her to ensure Mr. Bingley knows of her warm regard," she finally said. "While it is undoubtedly clear Bingley likes your sister, he may never do more if she does not give him some encouragement."

"I believe she would, but our brothers have cautioned her with regard to Mr. Bingley's past proclivities." A small gasp escaped Charlotte's mouth and Elizabeth hastened to allay her fears. "He is not a rogue, but Michael was careful to let Jane know Mr. Bingley has a tendency to pay particular attention to the prettiest girl in the room, but goes no further than light flirtation. He cautioned her to not take his compliments to heart, but to enjoy his company while he is here in Meryton."

"They do not believe he is sincere in his attentions?"

"Only Mr. Bingley knows if his heart is engaged or not,

and it is up to the gentleman to make his expectations known. As for now, she does help him on, as much as her nature will allow. She does not want to give rise to gossip and be branded as impertinent. That is my duty."

"You are impertinent, Eliza. It is part of your charm. My only advice for Jane, given our societal restrictions, is to make the most of every half-hour where she commands his full attention. When she has secured his affections, then she will have the leisure of falling in love as slowly as she chooses."

"You set an almost impossible task before my sister. They have known each other only a few short weeks," Elizabeth kept her voice low, aware others might hear their conversation. "Not nearly enough time for any woman to understand a gentleman's character, and my sister is naturally cautious, especially when in full view of our mother."

"I fully understand her natural trepidation, and wish Jane success with all my heart, however, if they married tomorrow, she has as good a chance of happiness as if they had courted for a year. You and I both know pleasure in marriage is entirely a matter of timing and circumstance. There are moments when I think it is better to know as little as possible of the defects of the person with whom you are to pass your life."

"Now, I know you are saying things to vex me," Elizabeth declared. "You would never behave in such a manner. I believe one should know as much as possible about their future partner in life. Could you imagine, accepting the proposal of someone who only gave the appearance of being a gentleman, and once trapped within the bonds of matrimony, you discover they are a knave and a rake of the first order?"

"Within the perimeter of Meryton's boundaries, there is no chance anyone's son could deceive us with their character."

"Which is why the Netherfield party is so interesting. We do not know who they truly are beneath their masks."

"You believe they wear a mask in public?"

"I do. For example, take Miss Bingley," Elizabeth said and carefully directed Charlotte's attention toward the proud woman. "She is desperate for us to believe she is popular amongst the members of the ton, yet she continually looks to Mr. Darcy for approval. He does have access to the first circle and chooses to ignore her. It is painfully obvious he is friends with Mr. Bingley and suffers the sister's company. If Miss Bingley had the social standing she claims, she would rarely look at Mr. Darcy, and would treat him with a sense of *ennui*."

"How do you know these things?"

"You forget Jane's and my friendship with Susannah, and how the three of us deepened our bond at Miss Tyler's Academy. More than etiquette was taught in those hallowed halls, and my esteemed friend is a fount of knowledge with how the le bon ton behaves."

"Who could have imagined such a profitable friendship would spring from your act of heroism?"

"I did not jump in the river because a duke's daughter was drowning. I foolishly jumped into the river because I saw a girl struggling to survive."

"His grace has been very kind since that incident, and I still remember the summer when I was invited to attend Brighton with you and Jane. I was so frightened of the ocean."

"You soon forgot your fear when we did a bit of sea bathing. The duke was determined to teach his daughter how to swim, and we reaped the benefits of his kindness."

"You most definitely did reap the benefits." Charlotte cut her a quick side glance. "I could scarcely believe when you told me his grace invested ten thousand pounds in your name."

"I thought you inadvertently informed your brother

Jonathan before I attended my last term at Miss Tyler's academy. I was certain he had set his sights on me as his future companion."

"Oh, Eliza, you are so precious. I know of when you speak. Papa had strongly advised my brother to look toward his future and find a wife, and I will admit, Jonathan's musings did flow in your direction. At least they did until he realized you would never be more than a close friend. You will recall his attention soon shifted to Sarah Pettigrew."

"I do recall, and then it moved to Arabella Long, Harriet Harrington, Clarice—"

"Stop!" Charlotte laughed. "You make it sound like my poor brother is a notorious rake when he was nothing more than a young man trying to find a suitable wife."

"He is not a rake. Anyone who knows him will agree he is first and foremost a gentleman, and Miss Meredith Goulding is worthy of his attention. They are an excellent match."

"I agree. Mamma is over the moon with their courtship, and I adore Miss Goulding. She will make an excellent mistress of Lucas Lodge."

***

"I see the denizens of Meryton greet Eliza as if she is the prodigal daughter returned."

Jane looked across the room and saw her sister encircled by a group of ladies and some gentlemen. All were smiling, and very noticeably enjoying themselves.

"Elizabeth returned a little over a month ago," Jane said with a smile. "The week prior to the assembly, in fact."

"Had she been wandering about the countryside with a band of gypsies?"

Jane felt a quick flash of anger, her legendary control over her emotions slipping more and more in the company of Miss

Bingley. Not for the first time, she wondered how such an amiable man as Mr. Bingley could have such a termagant for a sister. Then, she thought of the disparity between her and Elizabeth compared to Lydia, and her anger cooled.

"Elizabeth has been gone for the better part of the year on an extended tour of Ireland and Scotland with a friend she made at Miss Tyler's Academy for Young Women," Jane informed Miss Bingley, whose eyebrows nearly disappeared beneath her hairline upon receiving the information.

"Did I hear you correctly? Miss Tyler's Academy?"

"Lizzy and I both attended *la Bonne Chance Académie*," Jane said with affection, calling the school by its well-known moniker.

"Is this not the school you and Louisa tried to get into, Caroline?" Mr. Bingley had come alongside and joined the conversation. "Miss Tyler is notoriously fastidious over who is allowed entrance."

"Apparently not!" Miss Bingley replied with a disgruntled sniff. "Both the Miss Bennets attended her academy."

"As they should, Sister. Their father is a gentleman and the Bennets have owned their land for generations. These facts alone qualify them for admittance."

"It is notoriously expensive. I am perplexed over how they could afford such a luxury."

"My father can well afford to educate his children. Michael and Gabriel have themselves attended Eton and Cambridge," Jane said smoothly. "Please excuse me, I see my mother wishes me to attend her."

After giving Miss Bingley a graceful half nod of her head, Jane turned and glided across the room toward Mrs. Bennet.

"What are you about, Caroline? You were abominably rude to Miss Bennet."

"Oh, fie! As if that piece of fluff has anything in her head except what her next gown shall look like," Miss Bingley muttered, uncaring if anyone heard her.

"That piece of fluff converses fluently in five languages, Miss Bingley. How many do you speak?"

Miss Bingley jerked around to find not one, but two Bennet men glaring at her.

"I speak French and some Italian, Mr. Bennet," she said, addressing the patriarch of the Bennet family, carefully ignoring his formidable eldest son.

"So, you speak four languages then," Michael said.

"No sir, only three. English, French, and Italian."

"You forgot one, Miss Bingley," Mr. Thomas Bennet said in a low voice. "You most assuredly speak serpent. Your venom is perfectly pronounced."

Both men gave the Bingley siblings a curt bow and joined Mrs. Bennet and her eldest daughter across the room.

"Caroline," Bingley said in a hard voice, "Keep your vile opinions to yourself. They are not welcome here, and soon; we shall not be either. The Bennets are the leading family in Meryton. You would do well to remember this fact."

"They may be the leading family in this backwater town, but they are nothing to the people we associate with in town. As long as they remain here, in the wilds of Hertfordshire, they reign supreme. However, if they dared showed their face in town, the Bennet sisters would remain firmly on the shelf. Unwanted and unwed."

"Why do you think they shall remain unwed?"

"Charles." Caroline spoke his name in a tone reminiscent of their mother when they were younger. Patient, yet exasperated. "I was informed Miss Bennet and her sisters will receive a share of their mother's portion, which is a paltry five thousand pounds, split between them on her death and I assume their father has not managed to save anything worth reporting toward their marriage portion. If he had, Mrs. Bennet would have crowed about it the minute we were introduced at the Meryton Assembly. Regardless of their manifold attractions, no man wishes to marry a woman who comes into the marriage with nothing but the bonnet on her head." Caroline shook her head as if she pitied the ladies of Longbourn. "No, brother, they will have a very hard time finding a man who could look past all that."

LONGBOURN'S ANGELS

Chapter Four

When dinner was finally announced, Elizabeth found herself placed at the midway point of the table next to Gabriel, with Michael directly across from them. Next to him sat Maria Lucas, who practically swooned. It was no secret the young miss held a tendré for the future master of Longbourn.

Elizabeth did not judge the young girl for her affection, for both Michael and Gabriel were fine specimens of male beauty. They had the height and breadth of shoulders similar to Papa, and the same handsome mien. Maria was not the first girl to sigh over the Bennet brothers. Elizabeth could only hope the impressionable girl would remember to eat, or else the punch she consumed when her mother was not looking would affect her in ways she would not appreciate in the cold light of morning.

Mr. Darcy had the place of honor to the right of Lady Lucas, and next to him was Charlotte. The gentleman from Derbyshire would be hard-pressed to enjoy Lady Lucas's company, but of her eldest daughter, he could not complain. Like Jane, Charlotte was a calm presence in a turbulent sea of absurdity. Mr. Bingley sat to the left of Lady Lucas, next to Mamma.

Elizabeth allowed her gaze to flow to the other end of the table where the patriarch of Lucas Lodge held court. Sir William was quite proud of his presentation at St. James and was more than excited to inform new acquaintances of his elevation in society. By the pinched look on Miss Bingley's face, Elizabeth knew the overdressed woman wished to be anywhere but where she sat.

Her gaze flew across the table to Jane, seated beside Michael, and they shared a smile. It seemed her eldest sister also realized Lady Lucas had placed Mr. Darcy and Mr. Bingley, two very eligible single men near her eldest daughter. Their hostess further pushed forward her not-so-subtle endeavors by placing Mamma in their midst.

Well played, Lady Lucas. Well played.

Mamma, emboldened by more than one glass of wine, tittered, and laughed, extolling the virtues and beauty of Jane to Mr. Bingley. She did not bother to lower her voice, and the blushes which stained Jane's cheeks throughout the meal bore testament to the fact she clearly heard every word spoken and was mortified by them. Finally, when Mamma began telling the story of how a gentleman had written a poem for Jane on the occasion of her fifteenth birthday, Papa cleared his throat. Quite unexpected and quite loud, it caused Mamma to pause and look at her husband.

"I apologize, Lady Lucas," Papa began as he placed his napkin on his plate. "It seems as though a piece of food became lodged in my throat." He lifted his glass and took a sip of wine, clearing his throat again. "Ahh... much better. Forgive my interruption."

"Are you well, Mr. Bennet?" Mamma's widened eyes and short gasps of air betrayed her panic.

"Perfectly fine, my dear," Papa soothed, "How do you like your pheasant?"

She looked down at her plate as though she had never laid eyes on what was arranged before her.

"It... it is quite delicious."

"Mayhap you should entreat Lady Lucas for the receipt.

You always set a lovely table, and this would be a fine addition to your growing collection."

"Indeed, I will," Mamma exclaimed with enthusiasm and turned her attention to the lady of the house, the conversation about Jane's hopeful swain forgotten. "I shall beg for this tomorrow when we visit, Lady Lucas."

With the crisis of Mamma's runaway tongue averted Elizabeth felt the tension leave her shoulders. She caught the look Papa gave Michael and knew her father would be having words with their mother once they were back home. Even though Longbourn was prosperous, and Michael a competent landowner, Mamma sometimes behaved as though she would be tossed into the hedgerows when Papa died. Not only that, but Gabriel would be taking over Netherfield once Mr. Bingley's lease expired. In no way did their mother have to worry so much.

***

After dinner, the men enjoyed their port brandy while the women retreated to the main drawingroom. Sir William regaled Misters Hurst, Bingley, and Darcy with more stories of his investiture into knighthood. Their father, seated by the fireplace, watched their discomfort with joy while enjoying a splendid glass of smuggled brandy while his sons, across from him spoke quietly.

"I do not like how Bingley monopolizes Jane's attention. He allows no other gentleman near her, yet makes no promise of fidelity."

"This is but a repetition of how he behaved while in university. I did not approve of it then, and I most definitely do not approve of it now, given it is our sister whom he dangles on a pretty thread of promise."

"We cannot just stand around and watch Jane fall further in love if he does not have honorable intentions."

"I have a plan," Michael finally said.

"Well… go on," Gabe urged when his brother remained frustratingly silent.

"We need to enlist the aid of Samuel Watson and Jonathon Lucas."

Gabe began to smile.

"I believe I know where your mind is headed, and agree."

Later that evening…

"May I have this dance, Miss Elizabeth?"

Mr. Samuel Watson, at the none-too-subtle urgings of his two good friends, stood in front of their sister and held out his hand.

"Thank you, Mr. Watson. I would be delighted to dance a reel with you."

Elizabeth, engaged in a lively debate with Mr. Darcy on the merits of Cowper over Byron, gave the gentleman a small curtsy and walked to the cleared area of the room to line up. Next to her were Jane and Michael. Mr. Bingley moved to where his friend stood, alone, and watched them dance, his expression one of a wounded puppy.

The next set was just as lively, where Jonathan Lucas gained Jane's hand while Gabriel swung Elizabeth out onto the dance floor. By the end of the evening, she and Jane had danced four dances and were completely exhausted when Papa called for the carriage. It was not until the sisters, preparing to exit the coatroom, heard their father speak with his sons.

"You had better hope your sisters never realize what you did this evening with regard to Mr. Bingley and Mr. Darcy."

"We were looking after their best interests."

"Were you now?" came Papa's amused question. "Is that not my job?"

"Gabriel and I know of their character from university, Father. We do not want to see our beloved sisters get their hearts broken by men who will forget them the minute they return to London."

"And you are positive this will be the only outcome of their venture, here in Meryton?"

"Father, Bingley is known for courting and making love to beautiful women, yet he does not go further. There are many broken hearts between London and Scarborough. He has yet to mature into a man willing to settle down."

"I do not believe you can say the same about his great friend."

"Darcy thinks himself above us all. He suffers our company because Bingley wishes to make a good impression."

"While I agree with you about Mr. Darcy, I believe you have pegged his friend wrongly."

"I stand by my observations, and Gabriel agrees. Mr. Bingley desires to make a good impression but he is, and always has been, under the thumb of his sisters and they have no respect for any of us. They will steer him back to London and do their best to make him forget about Jane."

"Poor Jane," Papa murmured.

"If our sisters knew what we did, I would hope they realize it is for their own good—"

"And when did you become the arbiter of our happiness, Michael Thomas Bennet?" Elizabeth finally heard enough and shook off Jane's cautionary hand to confront her brothers. "Am I to understand you and your friends danced with Jane and me to keep Mr. Bingley and Mr. Darcy at bay?"

"Yes," Michael stated, his chin lifted in calm defiance.

"You," Elizabeth said, poking her brother hard in the chest, "had no right to interfere. Jane and I are rational creatures, capable of crafting our own opinions. If this is how you truly feel and believe, then you should lock us in our bedchamber, as we obviously cannot make a sane decision without your input."

"That is not what—"

"No? You judged them based on actions from when they were young men. Shall we revisit some of your decisions when you were first at university, learning how to be a proper gentleman? Shall we judge your behaviors and the manner in which you treated young ladies? Shall we call upon Abigail Long, and ask what she thinks of your high-mindedness?"

"Enough, Lizzy," Papa interjected.

"No, Father, she is correct," Gabriel said and wrapped Elizabeth in a warm hug. "I am sorry. Michael is sorry. We should not have interfered unless we knew you to be in absolute danger."

"The one you should apologize to is Jane. I care not for Mr. Darcy and his opinions, but our sister likes Mr. Bingley a great deal, and you may have cost her an admirer."

"Come, the carriage has arrived. Your mother will be along shortly and then we shall leave." Their father turned to his sons, who were putting on their riding capes as the trio of gentlemen would ride alongside the carriage. "Tomorrow morning, Michael," he said in a low voice, "you shall attend my study, and fill me in on what Elizabeth alluded to with regard to Abigail Long."

Michael visibly paled but nodded in deference. It was while their father was helping his wife into the carriage that Gabriel dared speak with his brother.

"Are you going to tell Father the truth?"

"He will demand no less from me."

"You promised Miss Long you would never reveal her secret."

Michael turned to Gabriel, his eyes glittering in the moonlight with unshed tears.

"Father is honorable, he will not judge her too harshly, and the events set in motion were constructed in such a way as to protect her honor. Soon, she will reside with her aunt in Surrey, away from the gossiping tongues which would have ruined her forever."

***

"Elizabeth does not know the complete story, only what Miss Long and her parents have allowed to slip out."

Michael and his father were in the study, a cheery fire lending warmth to the cluttered room filled with Mr. Bennet's books, periodicals, and personal journals.

"Fill me in, and spare no details."

"It is rather personal, Father."

"You are my son, and from the way Lizzy spoke, your honor could be called into question. You would be wise to keep nothing from me, no matter how embarrassing."

"The embarrassment is not mine, but Miss Long's."

"Regardless, you will tell me all."

His father leaned back in his chair and clasped his hands over a still-trim stomach, and waited. Michael sighed heavily and sat in the chair opposite his father's desk.

"As you know, Miss Long and I had entered into an informal courtship. However, after her return from visiting friends this past summer, she showed obvious signs of disinterest. What I did not know then, and found out too late, she had become involved with a prolific womanizer."

"Is he from around here?"

"He is from Derbyshire. I have not met him personally,

but I am very aware of his unsavory reputation. He made a name for himself at Cambridge, and not in a good way."

"Let us thank the good Lord this fiend is nowhere near my daughters. Now, please inform me why Miss Long did not break off the courtship when her heart was engaged elsewhere?"

"From my limited understanding, she met him while visiting friends in Ramsgate, and he turned her head with pretty words and empty promises. One evening, after too many glasses of wine, she and the gentleman had an intimate encounter. Upon her return to Meryton, she waited for him to follow as promised, and speak to her uncle about their secret engagement. Before a month had passed, she was certain of two things. Her secret fiancé was not about to honor his promise, and she was very likely enceinte. Desperate to speak with the father of her child, she convinced her uncle to allow another trip to Ramsgate, whereupon she tracked the reprobate down, only to find him courting a young heiress from the north. He had absolutely no time for a penniless trollop, as he called her. He then smugly told Miss Long he would soon be married and enjoying the grand life of gentleman with his wife's portion, which was thirty thousand pounds. Apparently, they were leaving for Gretna Green in a few days. Miss Long returned home, not knowing how to tell her family."

Mr. Bennet shook his head, his expression one of deep sadness.

"How did you find all this out? This is not something the family would broadcast to their neighbors and friends."

"I came across her on the bridge which connects our estate to theirs. She was going to jump into the rocks by the rapids. Needless to say, I could not allow her to take her own life, and told her I would help her find a way to come through this with her honor intact."

"Whatever for? The child is not yours."

"She is still my friend and someone I thought would have made a suitable Mrs. Bennet. Regardless, I offered her family a solution where Miss Long and I would have a public argument, at which point she would end the courtship. To help facilitate our ruse, she leaves for Surrey next week to get over her professed heartache and will stay with her aunt's cousin. No one has knowledge of her indiscretion, other than her family, myself, Gabe, and now you. I will never divulge her secret."

"I wondered why you quit your courtship. You went above and beyond what was required."

"Father, if you had seen how completely defeated… the way she swayed on the side of the bridge…" Michael shuddered. "I could not have lived with myself if I had not done something."

"I, of all people, understand exactly why you felt you must lend aid to a young lady. If I had not done so when I was your age, you and your brother would never have been born." His father leaned forward on his desk and held Michael's gaze. "You know your public disagreement with Miss Long did not show you in a good light."

"Father, I will not suffer any severe consequences from our perceived discord, however, Miss Long would have, which is why I behaved as the one who forced her to call off the courtship. This allowed her a valid reason to flee Meryton without anyone being the wiser to her true cause."

"You are a good man, Michael. I am exceedingly proud of you."

"Thank you, I knew you would understand." Michael rose to his feet, knowing the discussion with his father was at an end. "What will you tell Lizzy?"

"I will tell her to mind her own business. What happened between you and Miss Long is private, and I will not have her harangue you over perceived misdeeds."

"You know Lizzy can hold onto a grudge tighter than a child with a new penny?"

"I know very well, and will caution her to not make snap judgments, for one day this character foible may cost her dearly."

Chapter Five

"Mamma, do we have plans to visit Aunt Philips this morning?" Lydia asked one morning when the ladies were breaking their fast. "I cannot contain my curiosity for news about the militia."

"Why would you want to know more about the militia?" Jane asked.

"Because I know they will all be handsome."

"There is not much you can do about their handsomeness, Lydia. You are not yet out in society, and therefore, will not meet any officers," Elizabeth said calmly.

"It is not fair. You and Jane are already out while I am forced to stay in the schoolroom." At this, Lydia turned to her mother. "Mamma, I demand to be allowed to come out. I am nearly fifteen! It is not fair I have to wait."

Mrs. Bennet was prevented from replying by the entrance of a footman.

"A note has arrived from Netherfield Park for Miss Bennet," he announced and handed Jane the missive. "Their servant has been instructed to wait for an answer."

"Well, Jane. Who is it from?" Mamma eagerly called out, her eyes sparkling with pleasure, completely disregarding her youngest daughter.

"It is from Miss Bingley," Jane murmured as she quickly perused the note.

"What does she have to say?"

Jane obliged her mother and read the note out loud.

My dear friend,

If you are not so compassionate as to dine with Louisa and me, we shall be in danger of hating each other for the rest of our lives, for a whole day's tête-à-tête between two women can never end without a quarrel. Come as soon as you can on the receipt of this. My brother and the gentlemen are to dine with the officers.

Yours ever,
Caroline Bingley

"This could have not come at a worse time," Mamma cried out in frustration.

"Whatever do you mean, Mamma?"

"Both riding horses were sent to the farrier today, and your father and brothers have already left for St Albans with the carriage. We have no suitable conveyance to take you to Netherfield Park, and you cannot walk. I am positive it is going to rain again."

"This means we cannot even visit Aunt Phillips!" Lydia produced an impressive pout, her bottom lip jutting forth like a birdhouse perch. "It is so boring here. I hate this family."

For once, Mrs. Bennet did not placate her coddled baby. Her focus remained on Jane who, deep in thought, tapped the letter against her bottom lip.

"There is always Nellie. She is not fleet of foot, but I do not mind leaving as soon as possible to accommodate her pace."

"I think it quite rude for Miss Bingley to send an invitation for you alone. What would she think if we had an intimate dinner party and invited only her eldest sister?" Mamma continued to fuss and huff. "She should have extended an invitation to Elizabeth as well. What kind of manners does this young lady have?"

"My pride is not injured at being excluded. I do not have the same incentive as my dear sister."

"Lizzy!" Jane protested as her cheeks tinged the lightest shade of pink.

"None of these trifles matter. Miss Bingley made certain to extend an invitation when the gentlemen were out." Mamma stood and placed both hands on her hips, her brow furrowed in thought. "Take along a small valise with something you can change into after you arrive. I will not have it said my daughter does not know how to dress for dinner."

"What a thoughtful suggestion."

"I shall have one of your brothers attend after dinner to escort you home. I do not need you riding poor Nellie in the dead of night."

"Thank you, Mamma." Jane placed her flatware across her plate. "Come help me find a suitable gown, Lizzy."

Bang.

Lydia mulishly kicked the table leg at her frustration of being left out. Jane and Elizabeth ignored their petulant little sister, gracefully rose to their feet, and quit the room. The door had barely closed behind them when Mamma was heard to say, "You may go directly to your room and not come down until tomorrow. Also, forget about visiting with Maria Lucas as you will not be leaving the confines of Longbourn for the next week."

Lydia's outraged squawks faded as the two older sisters mounted the steps to the second floor.

"Father will not be pleased about Lydia's latest dustup," Elizabeth murmured. "She continues to act out."

"Our sister wants what we have without earning the privilege," Jane said when they reached the top of the stairs.

"What else should I take with me?"

"I suggest you pack something to plug in your ears," Elizabeth said once she and her sister were alone in their room. "I have an inclination the superior sisters will not be kind. Expect an inquisition the Spaniards would admire."

"You, Elizabeth Bennet, are as prejudiced toward them as you perceive them to be about you. If they ask about our family, I will not hide our heritage."

"How lovely. Will you inform them Gabriel was bequeathed Netherfield Park from Papa's sister Mrs. Harding, and they are his tenants?"

"I would not wish to make them uncomfortable in my presence."

"Can you imagine Miss Bingley's expression when she realizes a member of the dreaded Bennet family is her landlord?"

"I am not afraid of her Lizzy. You know I can hold my own."

"I do. My only question is this. Does she know you can hold your own?"

Less than an hour after Jane departed from Longbourn, a thunderstorm ripped through the shire. Fierce winds tore limbs from trees, scattering debris around Longbourn and the rain fell so fast and heavy, Longbourn's graveled drive soon resembled a small pond. Elizabeth stood, gazing out the window in the direction of Netherfield. Her mother came alongside and wrapped an arm around her middle. Elizabeth rested her head on her mother's shoulder.

"Do not worry so much, my dear. Jane left in plenty of time. I do not believe she was caught in the storm."

"We cannot know for certain. I pray she arrived safely. She is so susceptible to chills and colds."

"I join you in your concern." Mamma gave her a squeeze. "Jane will send word if something untoward happened. Until then, let us not borrow trouble by worrying."

Both of their attention was arrested by the sight of the Bennet carriage coming through the gate. As it reached the covered portico, the skies opened again, and rain fell at a steady pace, not letting up until morning. Jane was well and truly stranded at Netherfield.

The following morning, breakfast had only begun when a servant from Netherfield brought the following note for Elizabeth:

My dearest Lizzy,

I find myself very unwell this morning. Despite my best efforts to arrive at Netherfield Park ahead of the storm, I still managed to get thoroughly soaked not a half mile from the house. My kind friends will not hear of my returning home till I am better. They insist also on my seeing Mr. Jones, therefore do not be alarmed if you should hear of his having been to me, and excepting a sore throat and headache, there is not much the matter with me.

Yours, &c.,
Jane.

"Well, my dear," said Mr. Bennet, after Elizabeth had read the note aloud, "if your daughter should have a dangerous fit of illness and die, it would be a comfort to know it was all in pursuit of Mr. Bingley."

"Jane will not die from a trifling cold," Mamma said in a calm voice. "None of us expected such a terrible storm and, when I approved of her visit, I was certain she would arrive before the weather changed. Nellie must have plodded slower than expected. Miss Bingley will ensure our Jane is taken good care of, although I would not mind for Lizzy to ride over and lend her comfort."

"I will go with you, Lizzy," Gabriel said. "It is a good excuse as any to check the house and grounds for any visible signs of damage."

Soon, Elizabeth, and Gabriel were on their way to Netherfield, a small trunk strapped onto the carriage carrying a few things Jane might need if she were too ill to come home. They pulled up to the front of the house and after Gabe helped Elizabeth descend from the carriage, they both turned to peruse the façade of the manor.

"The new slate roof remained intact." His gaze flowed from right to left. "I cannot see any damage to the windows or exterior cornices, either."

They had just reached the top stair when the front entrance door was opened by Netherfield's butler, Cardston.

"Good morning, Mr. Bennet, Miss Elizabeth."

"Good morning, Cardston," Gabe replied. "Everything safe and sound after yesterday's storm?"

"Yes, sir. There are some minor incidentals Mrs. Nicholls will submit in her report to your uncle."

"Excellent."

By this time, Elizabeth and Gabe had come fully into the front foyer and they both stopped, mouths slightly agape at what they beheld.

"Cardston," Gabe began, then paused as he took in the complete room. Almost everywhere they looked there were urns and statues of varying sizes, fake potted palms, and silks of all colors draped across ornately carved chairs. Two fake pillars, for lack of a better description, had been placed beside the doors which led to the main floor drawing room. "Are the Bingleys planning a themed party?"

"No, sir."

Gabe looked at Elizabeth, and all she could do was shrug. There was no accounting for some people's tastes.

"Are any other rooms decorated in the *Chinoiserie* style?" Elizabeth asked before Gabe suffered a fit of apoplexy.

"Only the public rooms, miss. As per the lease agreement, the private rooms have remained untouched."

"Thank goodness for small mercies," Gabe grumbled. "I am now eternally grateful Father had Uncle Phillips add the clause that no room was to be changed by either structure, paint, or wallpaper. Can you imagine what she would have done if allowed?"

By she, Elizabeth knew her brother meant Miss Bingley.

After asking Cardston to have a footman take the trunk to their sister's assigned room, Elizabeth and Gabriel were shown into the breakfast parlor, where all but Jane were assembled. Mr. Bingley and Mr. Darcy stood when they entered. Miss Bingley and the Hursts remained seated.

"Miss Eliza, what brings you to Netherfield before proper calling hours?"

"My sister Elizabeth and I have come to see Jane, Miss Bingley," Gabe answered in his sister's stead. There was no doubt, by his tone, he would not abide anyone insulting his sister. Least of all any resident of Netherfield Park who desecrated rooms with such garish furnishings.

"Would you care for some tea?" Miss Bingley asked, finally remembering her manners.

"I thank you, but no," Elizabeth replied. "How is our sister?"

"I am afraid Miss Bennet slept ill, and although she was awake when I last checked, she was not well enough to join us for breakfast." Miss Bingley sounded sincere, which surprised Elizabeth. No doubt the lady of the house was doing her utmost to impress their guest from the north.

"Would you be so kind as to take me to her? My heart and mind will not rest until I have seen for myself how she fares."

"Of course." Miss Bingley dabbed her mouth with a linen

napkin and rose to her feet. "Allow me and Louisa to escort you to her room."

As the three women prepared to exit the breakfast parlor, Elizabeth looked at Gabe.

"Do you wish to join us, brother?"

"I would not dare intrude on your time with Jane. I will stay here and visit with the gentleman. Let me know when you wish to leave."

Elizabeth only bowed her head in acknowledgment and hid a smile. She knew her brother would begin his own interrogation. If she weren't so concerned for Jane's health, she'd loved nothing better than to be the proverbial fly on the wall, listening to their conversation.

***

The door had barely closed before a footman poured a cup of coffee for Gabriel. With a word of thanks, he accepted the hot beverage and settled back in the chair he had chosen, directly across from Mr. Darcy, and to the left of Mr. Bingley. He cast a quick glance at Mr. Hurst, who paid them no mind, concentrating solely on his overflowing plate of food.

"Was there any damage to Longbourn from the storm?" Mr. Darcy asked.

"Not that I could tell. My father and brother will ride the estate later this morning and assess the damage."

"I have been riding the border between Netherfield and Longbourn, and am very impressed with how well the land is managed. How long has Longbourn been in your family?"

"For over seven generations."

"I say, the Bennet history is as rich and deep as yours, Darcy," Bingley exclaimed.

"My family does have deep ties to our land," Darcy said with a slight nod of his head.

"Peter tells me Pemberley is quite the sight to see." Gabe watched the master of that great house carefully. "He opines it might be more impressive than Chatsworth."

"I will own I am proud of Pemberley," Darcy conceded. "However, it is not as grand as Devonshire's home. Few are."

"Peter's opinion may be skewed by the fact he was not particularly fond of the late duke. For myself, I did not talk to him long enough to form an opinion."

"You met his grace?" Bingley asked, his mouth dropping open in surprise.

"My brother and I, along with Peter, were invited to a house party hosted by their son, the Marquis of Hartington. While there, we met his father."

"You have mentioned Peter a few times. Does he have an estate here in Hertfordshire?"

"He does, it lies just outside the borders of Meryton, fondly called by us locals as the great house at Stoke. He uses it mainly for hunting parties, and quick summer escapes from town. His father's estate is in Derbyshire."

"Where in Derbyshire?"

"About thirty miles west of Pemberley."

Gabe suppressed a grin. Darcy had put the pieces together, confirmed by his next question.

"Would your friend, by chance, be Peter Chilton?"

From the blank expression on the faces of Bingley and Hurst, neither of them knew who Peter Chilton was, but Darcy most certainly did and Gabe held that man's gaze, knowing an adjustment in attitude would soon follow.

"How is it you know the Chilton family?"

"Peter is the only son of my father's eldest sister, Aunt Poppy."

It was a small movement, but Darcy's left eyebrow twitched. Better and better. Everyone in the upper echelons of society knew Patricia 'Poppy' Chilton. She was married to

Daniel Chilton, the Earl of Haywood. Gabe heard movement in the hall and knew the ladies would be joining them in a few minutes. He looked at Darcy, allowing his disdain for the man to show completely on his face.

"Do you wish now you had given consequence to a young lady who was not slighted by other men but had sat out two sets because there were not enough gentlemen to dance with?"

***

While Darcy mulled over the information gleaned from his conversation with Gabriel Bennet, Miss Elizabeth returned to the breakfast room and informed her brother Miss Bennet was indeed miserable with the beginnings of a dreadful cold.

"What do you wish to do, Lizzy?" Gabriel Bennet asked his younger sister.

Darcy found himself waiting, breath held, for her answer.

"Jane has a slight fever, which may or may not turn into something more. Although I wish to take her home, I think it prudent she remains abed for the rest of today, and tomorrow morning we can reassess the situation."

"Miss Eliza, do you wish to remain here, with your sister?" offered Miss Bingley, earning a surprised look from Darcy. "I can have Mrs. Nicholls prepare the chamber next to your sister's."

"Thank you, Miss Bingley. I would dearly love to stay and tend my sister." Miss Elizabeth turned her attention back to her brother. "I will send a note tomorrow morning, either for the carriage or for you to bring Mr. Jones if Jane's cold worsens."

Miss Bingley instructed a footman to relay her direction to the housekeeper to prepare a room.

"I will return to Longbourn, and inform Father of Jane's

illness."

"Have one of our footmen bring over Hill's draughts. I wish to ease Jane's discomfort as soon as possible."

Gabriel bade farewell to the Netherfield party before asking his sister to walk him to their waiting carriage. Almost as soon as the door to the breakfast room closed behind them, Mrs. Hurst and Miss Bingley began to disparage the Bennet family.

"I have an excessive regard for Jane Bennet," Mrs. Hurst said upon the Bennet sibling's exit. "She is a very sweet girl, and I wish she were well settled with all my heart. But with such low connections, I am afraid there is no chance of it."

Darcy remained at the window and watched Miss Elizabeth bid farewell to her brother, waving at the carriage as it trundled down the gravel drive, their natty horse trailing behind.

"I think I heard dear Jane say their uncle is an attorney in Meryton," Miss Bingley said.

From the reflection in the windowpane, Darcy could see Miss Bingley looking in his direction when she spoke of the Bennet family and immediately knew this particular conversation had been staged to inform him and Charles how unsuitable the Bennet ladies were.

"Yes, and the other one lives somewhere near Cheapside," Mrs. Hurst replied and scrunched her nose as though she'd smelled something foul.

"Much too far from Grosvenor Street for us to worry about whether we might run into them by chance," added her sister, and they both laughed heartily.

You will rue the day you slighted both Miss Bennets. Like lightning, the random thought flashed through Darcy's mind while simultaneously acknowledging he already did.

"If they had uncles enough to fill all Cheapside," cried Bingley, "it would not make them one jot less agreeable."

"Charles!" Miss Bingley cried out. "How can you be so obtuse? Having such low connections will materially lessen their chance of marrying men of any consideration in the world. Is that not so, Mr. Darcy?"

"If it were true, yes," replied Darcy, ignoring the frustrated look his friend threw in his direction.

It seemed Bingley was unaware of Peter Chilton's identity. Not unusual as the viscount and his father preferred a tight circle of friends who avoided Town and kept mostly to their country estate. Something Darcy understood intimately. There were very few people he could bear to be in company with for any length of time and completely empathized with the earl's penchant for keeping his own counsel and avoiding most social engagements. Ironically, Darcy was one of the few select gentlemen the Chilton's invited to their estate when they did hold small house parties and dinners.

His attention was diverted by the sound of someone entering the room, and he turned with the anticipation of seeing Miss Elizabeth again. His hopes were dashed when a footman entered the room and told Miss Bingley the young lady had gone upstairs to tend her sister and asked if her hostess would be so kind as to send a maid when everyone gathered for dinner.

Darcy remained restless for most of the afternoon. Even riding the estate with Bingley to assess the damage from the storm did not settle his nerves. They only quit jangling later that evening when Miss Elizabeth stepped into the main drawing room and took a seat on the divan.

"How is your sister, Miss Elizabeth?" Darcy asked, experiencing a rush of pleasure when she raised her fine eyes and looked directly at him.

"She is resting at the moment, Mr. Darcy. I thank you for your concern."

"Do you think she will need to see the apothecary tomorrow?"

"Anxious to whisk the vermin out the door?"

"I beg your pardon?" He drew himself to his full height and glared at her.

"Pray, excuse my poor attempt at humor. I am not being a gracious guest." She ran a tired hand over her forehead, and it was then he noticed the fine tension lines. "I suspect Jane will recover nicely, but she is susceptible to chills, and I cannot do anything but wait and see how she fares through the night."

"Apology accepted Miss Elizabeth. I ask because if she does succumb to a fever, I will send an express for my personal physician to attend."

Her gaze snapped back to him; eyes widened in surprise.

"I… I thank you, but I do not believe that will be necessary."

"What are the two of you talking about so secretively?" Miss Bingley called out from where she sat alone on a small sofa near the fireplace.

"I was asking Miss Elizabeth how her sister fared."

"Oh yes, I was meaning to ask the same thing myself." Miss Bingley directed her attention to Miss Elizabeth. "How is *dear* Jane? Did she rest at all this afternoon?"

Idly, Darcy wondered how often would Miss Bingley call Miss Bennet 'dear Jane?' If his cousin Richard were here, they could turn this into a drinking game. One drink for a 'dear Jane,' and two for Mrs. Hurst playing with her bracelet.

"My sister slept for most of it, and she has a bit of a fever. I am hoping it will subside so we can go home tomorrow."

"There is no need to hasten your departure," Bingley chimed in. "Miss Bennet must remain until she is at no risk of further infection. We have more than enough room, and I am sure my sisters would enjoy your lively manners and company whilst she recovers."

Both Miss Bingley and Mrs. Hurst shot their brother a dark look. Darcy bit the inside of his cheek to suppress an outright grin and project his practiced aloof mien. Also, from his vantage point, he could not help but notice how Miss Elizabeth's fine eyes twinkled with mirth. It seemed she was very aware of how the Bingley sisters viewed her company.

Cardston finally announced dinner was ready for serving and because they dined in one of the smaller rooms, Darcy was seated between Miss Elizabeth and Miss Bingley. The frisson of delight he'd felt when they first sat down, soon dissipated like a morning fog. Miss Bingley rudely dominated the conversation, at no time allowing him the freedom to converse with Miss Elizabeth. It seemed the lady did not mind, as she kept up a steady discourse with Hurst. Hurst! of all people. A more disinterested man he did not know, yet the normally social recluse chortled twice and outright guffawed once during the meal.

His second chance of speaking with Miss Elizabeth was shot down when she returned directly to her sister's bedside following dinner and did not come down until later in the evening. He was about to excuse himself from the card table and bid his hosts a good night when she glided into the drawing room, a book in hand. Mrs. Hurst had already excused herself for the evening and her place sat empty.

"Miss Elizabeth," Hurst called out unexpectedly. "Will you join us in playing cards?"

"Miss Eliza Bennet," Miss Bingley said before Elizabeth could reply, "despises cards. She is a great reader, and takes no pleasure in anything else."

"I do not believe I asked you, Caroline," Hurst said pointedly. "Unless Miss Elizabeth has the power to throw her voice across the room and sound exactly like you – shrill and whiny."

Darcy clearly heard Hurst mutter the last three words under his breath and fought back a smirk. Unaware of the hidden comments which only Darcy seemed to have overheard, Miss Elizabeth spoke directly to Miss Bingley.

"I take great pleasure in many things, reading being one of them. I resent you thinking I would not wish to play cards without canvassing my own opinion on the matter."

"Brava, Miss Elizabeth," Hurst exclaimed. "You may be my partner. I am certain we will hold our own against Caroline and Darcy."

Elizabeth hesitated for a brief second before placing her book on one of the side tables and taking Mrs. Hurst's vacated chair. Charles pulled up a small chair and sat between his sister and brother by marriage.

"I say. This should be fun. Darcy, Hurst, and Caroline have played together so often, they know each other's playing strategies. You are the dark horse in this game, Miss Elizabeth."

"Your theory works against me as much as it does against them," Miss Elizabeth said with a light laugh. "I shall endeavor to hold my own and not make Mr. Hurst rue the day he requested my participation."

They cut the deck to see who would lead the deal, and the game commenced. A half-hour later, a delighted Miss Elizabeth took the final trick with the two of diamonds.

"How is it you still possess trump?" Miss Bingley demanded.

"I am afraid Miss Elizabeth hid her card sharp light beneath a bushel," Darcy said. "She is very talented at cards. We have met a master at the game."

Elizabeth ducked her head, her cheeks turning a delightful shade of pink.

"I am pleased you were my partner, Miss Elizabeth." Hurst pushed back his chair and stood, having made it known he was leaving to join his wife. "You have a standing invitation to be my whist partner."

"I thank you, Mr. Hurst." Elizabeth rose to her feet as well. "I shall bid you all good evening. I promised Jane I would not tarry too long from her side."

Darcy automatically stood when Miss Elizabeth did, and could not help but note the blush on her cheeks from his praise had not abated. About to offer to escort the lady to her sister's room, he was stopped when Bingley spoke up.

"Now that you are done playing cards, and Hurst is off to bed, what say you to a game of billiards?"

Darcy's eyes flicked to Bingley, then back to Miss Elizabeth, who was already at the door. He'd look the fool if he hurried to catch her.

"I shall meet you in the billiard room in five minutes."

Bingley bounded out of the room, leaving him and Miss Bingley alone.

"Eliza Bennet," said Miss Bingley, once the two of them were alone, "continues to insert herself where she is not wanted. I would not be surprised if she loitered outside the drawingroom, waiting for my sister to leave so she could join our card game."

"Come, Miss Bingley," replied Darcy, "how can you think she lingered in the hall for the sole purpose of playing cards? When she came into the room, she had a book in her hand. Something which you pointed out before your brother, Hurst, asked her to be his partner in whist."

It was obvious Miss Bingley did not like his mild chastisement, but he no longer cared. He was tired of her continual sniping at a woman who had done nothing more than behave in a polite manner in the face of subtle insults.

He bid Miss Bingley good night, intent on joining Bingley in the billiards room. As he neared the door, he noticed the book Miss Elizabeth had left behind, and without thought, picked it up. He turned the book over in his hand and saw it was *The Iliad*, written in the original Homeric Greek. What other talents did the lady hide? A wolfish smile crossed his face. A man could spend years plumbing the depths of such a woman.

.

LONGBOURN'S ANGELS

Chapter Six

Elizabeth walked around the drawing room in search of her father's book, positive the last place she had seen it was when she placed it on a side table before playing cards. One of the maids must have removed it to the library, unaware the treasured classic did not belong to Mr. Bingley.

She snorted softly. No one would ever assume such a book was Mr. Bingley's. He would be the first to admit he did not read such tomes. Rather, they would assume it was Mr. Darcy's. She turned on her heel and made her way to the library, coming to a complete halt upon seeing the man himself seated by the fire, reading her book. Unsure if she should politely ask for the book, or pretend she had not seen him, Elizabeth hesitated at the door. Her decision was made when Mr. Darcy looked up.

"Miss Elizabeth," he said upon standing and giving her a polite nod.

"Mr. Darcy," she replied with an equally polite half-curtsy.

"I was enjoying your book," Darcy glanced down at the leather-bound tome and smiled. "It has been at least six years since I last read it, right before…"

He paused and the silence stretched between them.

"Before…?" Elizabeth prompted gently, somehow knowing he was in the midst of a fond memory.

"Oh! Forgive me I should have returned this to you first

thing this morning." He stepped away from the chair and handed her the book. "Before my father passed, I read to him every night. *The Iliad* was one of his favorites."

"My condolences, Mr. Darcy," Elizabeth said and accepted the tome. "I did not mean to bring up such unhappy memories."

His gaze flew to hers and she was surprised at the emotion so clearly etched upon his features.

"They are not sad memories. Anything which brings my father to mind is welcome." He drew himself to his full height and gave her a curt bow. "Good day, Miss Elizabeth."

For a brief moment, she stood holding the book and listened to him stride down the hall and call a footman to bring him his outerwear. What was it about this man that held her interest? He was aloof, haughty, and demeaning to those he thought below him, and yet… she found him so very handsome and her heart ached whenever she remembered his awful words at the assembly.

She is not handsome enough to tempt me.

***

The next day found Jane was feeling much better but not well enough to risk a cold carriage ride home, even though it was only five miles of smooth roads.

"I ab sorry to be such a bodder," Jane croaked from beneath three layers of blankets.

"There is nothing to be done about it now," Lizzy soothed and took back the glass of water she had given her sister along with some draughts Hill yesterday afternoon. "Gabriel said Mr. Jones will attend to you later today to ensure your cold has not decided to migrate into your chest like last time."

"I ab certain, *cough* *cough*, it is only id by head. My dose feels as dough it has rags stuffed id it."

"It is a good thing I understand you when your 'dose' is fully stuffed up, dear sister," Elizabeth chuckled. At her sister's frown, she placated her with, "I will leave you in peace and let Hill's medicine do its work."

Confident her sister would sleep for a few hours Elizabeth decided to escape outside and tour the garden paths Aunt Harding had laid with such loving care when she lived here with her husband before his untimely passing two short years ago.

She had rambled about for less than fifteen minutes when coming around the corner of a hedge, she nearly ran into Mr. Darcy.

"Miss Elizabeth," he exclaimed and quickly grabbed her elbow to keep her from tripping backward. "Forgive me, I was not paying attention."

"There is nothing to forgive, Mr. Darcy. It is not as though I wear a bell, warning others of my approach."

"There are some people I would like to bell—" He stopped mid-sentence. "That is neither here nor there. May I join you on your walk?"

"You may." He turned and extended his elbow, whereby she threaded her arm around his and laid her hand lightly on his forearm. "What had you so engrossed you were unaware of your surroundings, and do not feel the need to answer if that was too personal a question."

"I have no secrets, Miss Elizabeth, and will gladly share my thoughts as they were pleasant, though disturbing."

"Now, I am intrigued."

"I have just received a letter from my sister." At her quizzical look, he explained further. "She turned fifteen this past August and while she is still a young girl, there are times when she surprises me with how much and how fast she is growing up."

"I understand completely, sir. You have yet to meet our youngest sister, Lydia. She is only fourteen and has much growing to do. Not physically. She is already as tall as Jane, but maturity-wise, she is very young."

"My sister, Georgiana, is also tall for her age. People look at her and do not realize she is not yet out in society, and because she is quite shy in company, they mistake her shyness as rude behavior."

"Oh, dear," Elizabeth exclaimed softly. "She is not the only one who is wrongly perceived. I would hazard to guess the same can be applied to you?"

"I am shy," Darcy started to say, then he paused. "However, you have experienced me being haughty and rude, so I cannot fall back on the premise of being shy."

"Our initial meeting was unique, Mr. Darcy. There is no other way to describe it and it might turn out to be a blessing or it might turn out to be a curse."

"For the sake of my sanity, I hope it turns out to be a blessing because I enjoy your company very much."

"Thank you," she managed to say without a single wobble in her voice and then remained silent as they traversed the path for a short while.

Soon, they both roused themselves enough to begin a conversation about their favorite books and authors. Their thought-provoking discussion came to a sudden halt with the appearance of Miss Bingley and Mrs. Hurst.

"Mr. Darcy," Miss Bingley called out. "If we had known you wanted to walk the park, we would have joined you. You did not have to traverse the area on your own."

"I am not alone, Miss Bingley."

Mr. Darcy gave a pointed glance at Elizabeth, who had removed her arm from his and now stood a little apart. She did not want to stoke the fires of Miss Bingley's jealousy when it came to the gentleman from Derbyshire.

"You arrived just in time, Miss Bingley. I was about to bid Mr. Darcy adieu and return to my sister."

"How is dear Jane, today?" Miss Bingley asked before she slid beside Mr. Darcy and looped her arm around his. "There is nothing worse than being sick with a cold."

"She is resting at the moment, which is why I came outside to enjoy the fresh air. And, although her head is quite stuffy, I am certain by tomorrow we can go home and let her recover in her own bed."

"That would be for the best," Miss Bingley simpered and looked up at Mr. Darcy. "We, all of us here at Netherfield, hope for her speedy recovery."

Mr. Darcy disentangled their arms.

"I am also returning to the house. I have some correspondence that must go out with tomorrow's post." He extended his bent arm to Elizabeth. "May I escort you, Miss Elizabeth?"

"Thank you, Mr. Darcy."

Not willing to cause a scene, she demurred and once again placed her gloved hand on his forearm, ignoring the dropped bottom lip of the younger Bingley sibling. Elizabeth struggled not to laugh. Miss Bingley pouted nearly as well as Lydia.

She allowed the gentleman to lead her back into the house, all the time wondering if it were her imagination that her back felt as though it were on fire from the heated glare Miss Bingley gave her as they walked away. No matter. That lady's fascination for Mr. Darcy was not Elizabeth's priority. Her only concern was for her elder sister.

Upon entrance into Jane's room, she was glad to see her awake and feeling much better now that the draughts had begun to take effect.

"Lizzy," Jane warbled upon seeing her sister enter the room. "I ab glad you are back."

"You look better even though you still sound terrible,"

Elizabeth said and pulled up a chair to sit by Jane's bedside.

"I ab feeling better, even dough by dose is still stuffed." Jane coughed once and sneezed twice. "Believe it or dot, I ab on de mend."

"You do not need to convince me," Elizabeth said gaily. "It is Mr. Bingley you have to persuade. I do not believe he wishes you to leave Netherfield. At least, not yet."

"For whatever reason? It is dot as though I cad have visitors."

"I believe he wishes for you to linger for a few days. Maybe come down in the evening for a nice hot drink and pleasant company." Elizabeth pulled the covers up around Jane's neck when she laid back down. "I think he is pining for your company."

"I would rather be healthy whed I see hib dext."

"Fret not, dear Jane. Sleep well. I shall come back and check on you after dinner."

"Thank you," Jane mumbled, her eyes already closing in sleep.

Elizabeth looked down at her fair sister, her cheeks flushed with a slight fever. Jane's cold was distressing, but given how fast the symptoms had come on and how quickly they seemed to be departing, she was confident she and her sister could return home on the morrow. That left only one night to circumnavigate the eclectic group which currently resided beneath the eaves of Netherfield Park. She took a deep breath, squared her shoulders, and quit the room before making her way to where everyone would gather before they dined.

**

Darcy kept himself busy writing his promised letter to Georgiana while Miss Bingley, seated near him, watched the progress of his letter, and repeatedly pulled at his attention with messages to his sister. Mr. Hurst and Mr. Bingley were at Piquet, and Mrs. Hurst was observing their game. Miss Elizabeth, who had only just returned from checking on her sister, seemed content to stay in the background and watch.

I remain dear sister, a prisoner in the gilded cage known as Netherfield Park. Today is Day 27 of my confinement and Miss B continues to praise every little thing I say or do. I am tempted to do something completely outrageous, only to see if she declares it the most wondrous thing since the birth of our Lord and Savior.

Forgive my pernicious nature, Georgie. Four weeks in the lady's company is enough to drive any sane man crazy. She has once again asked me to remind you how much she longs for your company. In that regard, she is not alone. In a few short weeks, I shall return to London and spend Christmas with you and our family.

"How delighted Miss Darcy will be to receive such a letter!"

Darcy made no answer. To do so would only invite more interruptions and unwanted conversation.

"You write uncommonly fast."

He stifled a frustrated sigh. It seemed she was not going to leave him alone.

"You are mistaken. I write rather slowly."

Has our lady aunt continued —

"How many letters you must have occasion to write in the course of the year! Odious letters of business as well!"

"It is fortunate, then, this is my burden and not yours."

"You must tell your sister I long to see her again."

"I have already told her so once, by your desire."

Has our lady aunt continued to guide you in household budgets and responsibilities of being mistress of a grand estate? You may think sixteen is too young to learn such things, but before you know it, you will be making your curtsy and I will be holding off all kinds of hopeful gentlemen who will flock to our door, seeking your hand in marriage.

I cannot believe I have just written those words. It seems as though it was only yesterday, I held you in my arms and welcomed you to our family. I was so afraid I would drop you. What twelve-year-old boy knows how to properly hold a baby? But our mother was confident I would never let you down, and I have done my very best to uphold my part of our joint sibling agreement. You, to look beautiful. Me, to protect you — always.

He paused briefly, his quill having become dull, and pulled open the drawer to search for a knife. He should have known Miss Bingley would not leave him in peace.

"Oh, Mr. Darcy, let me mend your pen for you."

"Thank you, but I always mend my own."

He was silent and cut a sideways glance at Elizabeth, who had taken up some needlework. By the slight smile gracing her face, he was fairly certain she was vastly amused at the conversation which had been passing between himself and Miss Bingley.

"Tell your sister I am delighted to hear of her improvement on the harp and let her know that I am quite in raptures with her beautiful little design for a table, and I think it infinitely superior to Miss Grantley's."

"Will you give me leave to defer your raptures till I write again? At present, I have not room to do them justice."

"Oh! it is of no consequence. I shall see her in January. But do you always write such charming long letters to her, Mr. Darcy?"

The urge to answer her question with complete honesty was almost his undoing. He chose to ignore her and finish his letter.

I have spent the last ten minutes in the most insane conversation loop of my entire life. How can a woman attend one of the best seminaries money can buy and still remain an addlepated fool? Forgive me, my dear. I am at the end of a very tense rope and if it were not for Miss Elizabeth Bennet – also an unwilling guest of Mr. Bingley's – I think I might run mad.

You would like Miss Elizabeth, dearest. Her father's estate borders Bingley's and her sister fell ill when she got caught in a downpour on her way to dine with Miss Bingley and Mrs. Hurst. Miss Elizabeth has come to nurse her sister back to health. She is witty and vivacious. There are times when I think she spouts an opinion not her own just to see how I will defend my point of view.

His quill hovered over the pressed paper. Before it dribbled ink, he carefully placed it in the inkpot. He had almost written, actually placed into tangible words, how he would like to introduce Georgiana to Elizabeth when the ramifications of where his thoughts led had him pause. True, she was a gentleman's daughter. In that, they were equal and her family had excellent connections on their father's side, but the mother… If his family raised any objections, it would be for their close ties to trade. Was he willing to look past all that? Would his growing infatuation with Miss Elizabeth hurt his sister's chance of making a spectacular marriage? With her marriage portion, Georgiana could aspire as high as a duke – not that they littered the ground like ripened apples, waiting for wealthy maidens to come along and scoop them up.

He chastised himself for becoming distracted and quickly finished his letter. When that business was over, he applied to the ladies for the indulgence of some music. Miss Bingley almost ran to the pianoforte, joined by Mrs. Hurst who sang with her sister. While they were thus employed, Elizabeth turned over some music books that lay on the instrument. Was she acting coy, hoping he would ask her to perform for him? He had greatly enjoyed her playing that night at Lucas Lodge and would not mind hearing her again.

Miss Bingley must have been aware of his secret longing because she did not give up the instrument and began to play a lively Scotch air. This was his chance to claim Miss Elizabeth's full attention and he approached her.

"Do not you feel a great inclination, Miss Elizabeth, to seize such an opportunity of dancing a reel?"

She smiled but made no answer. He repeated the question, with some surprise at her silence.

"Pardon me," she replied, her eyes flashing with unspoken humor. "I was attempting to craft a witty reply and could not come up with anything. I blame it all on lack of sleep."

"Your care for your sister is admirable."

"Last night she had a touch of fever and I could not leave her side until it broke, so I beg forgiveness if I am not very lively this evening. Now, despise me if you dare."

"Indeed, I do not dare."

There was a mixture of sweetness and archness in her manner which made it difficult for him to be affronted by her manner. Darcy had never been so bewitched by any woman as he was by her. He really believed, were it not for the inferiority of her connections, he should be in some danger.

Chapter Seven

The next afternoon, both Gabriel and Michael attended Netherfield Park to provide an escort for their sisters, and once Jane was settled in her own bedchamber, she continued to recuperate at a rapid pace. She felt well enough to attend service on Sunday, enjoying a brief conversation with Mr. Bingley before the family made their way home for a light repast. During this meal, Mr. Bennet cleared his throat, withdrew a letter from his inside pocket, and set it on the table beside his plate. Six sets of eyes turned in his direction, and no sound was heard other than Mamma's finger tapping her knife. A nervous tic she exhibited when her husband teased indiscriminately.

"Are you not curious as to whom this letter is from?" Papa finally queried, his eyes twinkling with amusement.

"You will tell us when you are ready, Mr. Bennet."

Mamma picked up her fork and speared another succulent piece of lamb into her mouth. Jane, Elizabeth, and Lydia remained silent, while Michael and Gabriel leaned back in their chairs. Apparently, they also had no idea who had written their father.

"Mother will outlast you, Father," Michael finally said, and Lydia snorted. "You may as well tell us, or we will be sitting here until Aunt and Uncle Gardiner arrive for Christmas dinner."

"For shame, Michael. We would only have to wait until four in the afternoon tomorrow for your mother to budge."

"I did not know you were a prognosticator, Father," Gabe teased. "Care to enlighten the rest of us, or shall we turn to the stars to divine what you already know?"

"About a month ago, I received this letter, and about a fortnight ago, I answered it, for I thought it a case of some delicacy and requiring early attention." Mr. Bennet's eyes sparkled, a sure sign he was enjoying the banter with his family, and he outright grinned when all of his children turned their eyes heavenward at his capricious sense of humor. "It is from my cousin, Mr. Collins, who, if we had not been blessed with our sons, could have turned you out of this house as soon I met with my eternal reward."

"Has he written you often?"

"This is the second one I have received from him, and have enjoyed both of them immensely." At their questioning looks, he elaborated further. "He is somewhat full of himself and the way he expresses himself makes me giddy to meet the man in person."

"We are to meet him?"

"Yes, tomorrow afternoon in fact. Here, let me read his missive. I think you will find it most diverting."

Papa pulled out his reading glasses, settled them on the end of his nose, and flicked open the letter.

Dear Sir,

The disagreement subsisting between yourself and my late honored father always gave me much uneasiness, and I have frequently wished to heal the breach. I was recently ordained and have been so fortunate as to be distinguished by the patronage of the Right Honorable Lady Catherine de Bourgh, widow of Sir Lewis de Bourgh, with a valuable living in Kent.

As a clergyman, I feel it my duty to promote and establish the blessing of peace in all families within the reach of my influence; and on these grounds, I flatter myself that my present overtures of good-will are highly commendable and not lead you to reject the offered olive branch of familial friendship.

"He has a certain… flourish in his writing style," Elizabeth offered when their father looked up to see their expressions.

"Lord, he uses ten words when one will suffice," Lydia grumbled and was pleased when the rest of the family chuckled at her observation.

"I will spare you the rest of his letter, but suffice to say, this verbose gentleman will be here by four o'clock tomorrow afternoon, and plans to stay until the Saturday, se'ennight following."

"Nearly two full weeks. I must speak with Mrs. Hill, and have the guest room aired out." Mamma rose from her chair and pinned her husband in place with an angry glare. "Thank you, husband, for allowing me one day to prepare for our guest. At least you did not break the news to me over breakfast tomorrow morning."

"Would you be so very angry with me if I had?" Papa asked cheekily.

"Thomas Bennet, you vex me greatly, and yes, I would have been extremely angry."

"Then, it is a good thing I gave you plenty of notice."

"Of all the…!" Mamma exclaimed, and huffed her way out of the room.

"Papa, you were very unkind." Jane chastised her father before placing her napkin on her plate. "I shall go assist Mamma."

She rose gracefully from the table and quit the room.

"I will admit, I now feel guilty, for when even Jane has the temerity to censure me, I most definitely am in the wrong."

Mr. Bennet took stock of all his remaining children and sighed. "I shall make amends to your mother. I promise."

The next afternoon at precisely four o'clock, a small hired carriage clattered down Longbourn's drive and pulled to a jarring halt, nearly throwing the passenger forward over the horses.

"Have a care, man!" the black-garbed gentleman cried out, his one hand holding down his hat, the other clutching a dark travel bag.

Only Mr. Bennet, Michael, and Elizabeth greeted Mr. Collins. Because the day bore threatening clouds, Mrs. Bennet remained firm in her decision Jane would not be exposed to the cold and wet, which meant she, and Jane, along with Gabe and Lydia, waited in the parlor where tea would be served.

Mr. Collins climbed awkwardly out of the carriage and, not wishing to relinquish his travel bag to grab the appropriate handles and gracefully disembark, he very nearly ended up on his behind as a result. Once safely on the ground, he straightened his black overcoat and faced the trio of cousins. He gave them all a very low bow, nearly tipping over in the process. Elizabeth worked hard to keep a smile from appearing and dared not look at her father. She knew he would find their cousin's behavior exceedingly diverting.

"Mr. Collins, at your pleasure, sir," Mr. Collins said upon straightening to his full height.

"Welcome to Longbourn, Mr. Collins. I am your host and cousin, Thomas Bennet. This is my daughter, Elizabeth—"

"The rumors of your beauty were not exaggerated, Cousin Elizabeth."

Her goodwill toward her new cousin stretched a bit thin at his unwelcome flattery. She held back a sigh. They should have expected such behavior, given the language of his letter. Papa continued with his introductions.

"And, this fine young man is my son, Michael."

An expression of disappointment crossed Mr. Collins' face as his gaze waffled between Elizabeth and Michael. "Cousin Elizabeth is married?"

"None of my daughters are married. Michael is my son by birth."

"How wonderful." Mr. Collins's expression lightened and he smiled wide. "I had hoped to find favor with one of your amiable daughters. I have been told you have three."

"My daughters are not looking for suitors, Mr. Collins." Papa's mouth thinned in anger. "In light of this revelation, I believe you should climb back up into your carriage and return to Kent immediately."

"I cannot do that. Lady Catherine expects me to stay a full two weeks and return with a bride. She has already said she is willing to greet her and help her settle in the parsonage at Hunsford."

"Then, she will be disappointed on many levels because you will not remain here, and you will not find a bride among my daughters."

"Cousin Thomas, I humbly apologize for having misspoken. I am still willing to offer the olive branch of friendship and heal the breach between our two families."

"Let me sleep on this, and I will advise you in the morning. I suggest you do not unpack completely. You may have to leave early in the morning if I am not satisfied with your behavior."

Mr. Collins bowed low again and turned toward Elizabeth. "May I escort my cousin Elizabeth into the manor?"

By pretending she had not heard his ridiculous request, nor seen him sidle closer, Elizabeth looped her arm through Michael's, who squeezed it tight to his body. He had seen the oaf's awkward attempt to take his sister's arm.

"I am certain you would like some time to refresh yourself before meeting the rest of the family," Papa said, firmly moving Mr. Collins toward the house, away from his daughter. "Our man, Griggs, will have a footman escort you to your room and have water brought up. A bath would be quite refreshing after such a long trip."

Mr. Collins followed a footman up the stairs to the guest wing. As soon as he was out of sight and hearing, Mr. Bennet spoke with their butler.

"Griggs, I want you to assign a footman to remain outside Mr. Collins's room each night. I do not wish to find him wandering into the family wing by mistake."

"I will see the matter is taken care of."

"Excellent. When Mr. Collins is fully refreshed, he can be escorted to the main parlor."

"Very good, sir." Griggs gave a nod of the head and withdrew.

Papa sighed heavily. "I had such high hopes he would behave in a manner that would be highly entertaining, but I see I will have to be on guard during his visit."

"Do not forget our resident guardian angels," Elizabeth teased.

"Aye, Father. Gabriel and I will keep a watchful eye on our cousin. Between the three of us men, he should not get into too much trouble."

"We can only hope." By this time, they had reached the parlor. "I must have a word with you, Mrs. Bennet, about our guest."

"Is he a pleasant young man?" Mamma asked.

"Yes, and no." At his wife's look of disappointment, Papa continued. "When he saw Elizabeth, his eyes lit up like a child on their birthday."

"Is that not flattering?"

"My dear wife, when you meet the young man, you will see for yourself. I do not think he has had much opportunity to be in the company of ladies and has much to learn in the way of manners."

"Oh… how disappointing."

Mamma poured her husband a cup of tea and prepared it the way he liked best. Mr. Collins joined the family about an hour later, whereupon Papa then introduced his family, starting with his wife.

"I am ever your humble servant, Mrs. Bennet."

When Papa reached Jane, Mr. Collins gasped audibly.

"I am well pleased to meet you, Cousin Jane," Mr. Collins said with great enthusiasm.

He made to sit next to her but was forestalled when Michael and Gabriel plopped down on either side of their sister. The only seat available was next to Lydia, which Mr. Collins took with little or no grace.

While they waited for dinner to be announced, Papa took the time to get to know his cousin better. He may as well have talked to a wall. No matter what topic he introduced, or asked of his verbose cousin, everything circled around Lady Catherine de Bourgh, Mr. Collins's patroness. There was no part or portion of his life the great lady did not control.

The following day, Mr. Collins joined Jane and Elizabeth, along with Lydia on an excursion to Meryton. Their youngest sister had regained some of her privileges and was beyond excited to escape the confines of Longbourn, even if it was only a walk to the busy market town.

It was upon entry into the village the attention of the three sisters was caught by their Aunt Phillips, in conversation with two gentlemen outside of Miss Watson's Tea House. As soon as the sisters greeted their aunt, she wasted no time introducing them to Mr. Denny, a member of the ____shire Militia quartered outside of Meryton, and to Mr. Wickham, who had accepted a commission in corps that very afternoon. Elizabeth immediately felt a tug of attraction, noting his handsome features and athletic build, and could not help but think the charming gentleman would look very handsome in regimentals.

The whole party was still standing and talking together when the sound of horses drew their notice, and Darcy and Bingley were seen riding down the street. On distinguishing the ladies of the group, the two gentlemen came directly towards them and began the usual civilities. Bingley quickly dismounted and sought Jane's company.

"Miss Bennet. I am glad to see you taking in the fresh air so soon after your terrible cold. I was a little anxious when I distinctly heard you sneeze at service the other day, and worried you may have ventured from your chambers too soon."

"Thank you for your concern, Mr. Bingley. I am afraid it was not my cold that brought on the sniffles. I am sensitive to certain fragrances."

Elizabeth kept her expression neutral during their exchange. The whole Bennet family knew Miss Bingley's perfume caused Jane discomfort. Mr. Darcy also dismounted and bowed politely to Jane and herself, and when he turned to acknowledge their aunt, his gaze fell on Mr. Wickham. Elizabeth happened to see the countenance of both as they looked at each other and felt an odd sort of astonishment at the result. Both changed color. One turned white, the other red. Mr. Wickham, after a few moments, touched his hat, a salutation which Mr. Darcy did not return. Instead, he remounted his horse and rode off toward Netherfield. Meanwhile, Mr. Bingley, having missed what transpired between his friend and Mr. Wickham, took his leave, and joined Mr. Darcy.

"Isn't Mr. Wickham handsome, Elizabeth?" Lydia asked, uncaring if her voice carried on the breeze to the object of her admiration.

"Lydia, lower your voice," Elizabeth hissed under her

breath. "In mixed company, a lady does not speak about a gentleman's countenance whilst standing on a street corner. Conversations of this matter should be discussed when we are at home, in the privacy of our own rooms."

"Lord, you are all so boring. No wonder you and Jane are not married!"

With a toss of her head, Lydia flounced to their aunt's side and proceeded to ask the gentleman all sorts of impertinent questions about their daily life in the militia.

***

The next evening found the Bennet siblings and Mr. Collins at their Aunt Phillips's house, being jostled from all sides in the crowded room.

"Remind me again why we agreed to come?" Gabe groused as another red-coated gentleman stepped around them to join his fellow officers.

"We have always come to our aunt's soirees," Elizabeth said as she surveyed the full room. "I would assume the officers are starved for good company as not one of them declined her invitation."

"They came not only for the benefit of the pleasant company but also for good food. Why pay for a meal at an inn when one is provided for free?"

"We all know military men do not make decent wages, at least, not enough to support a family and children. I, for one, do not mind their company. They provide some social color in an otherwise bland landscape."

"As long as you do not dabble in painting a picture with any of these unknown men," Michael warned as yet another officer pushed his way through the crowd. "We must move from this location. I swear, it is busier than the North Road from London."

"I agree," Jane said quietly. "Most of our aunt's guests are gathered here where the food and card tables are set up."

Both sisters followed Michael toward a smaller parlor while Gabe and Mr. Collins chose to stay in the main drawing room. Mr. Collins because he had been asked to partner with Aunt Phillips in a game of cards, their brother because he wished to become better acquainted with Colonel Forster. Once Elizabeth and Jane were comfortable, Michael offered to get them each a glass of punch. Gabe joined him at the refreshment table and whispered a name in his ear.

Punch sloshed onto the floor when Michael whirled around, his gaze sweeping the room.

"Where?"

"He went to join Jane and Elizabeth."

"Here, take these," Michael said and handed the sticky glasses to Gabe. "I do not trust him with any woman, let alone our sisters."

Michael made his way to the parlor and Gabe murmured into the air, "Do not mind me, brother. I will take care of this punch, while you take care of another punch."

He grinned at his own humor, knowing if it came down to fisticuffs, he would stand back-to-back with his brother against the piece of slime which had slithered in the direction of their beloved sisters.

Chapter Eight

Michael stood within the door frame of the smaller parlor and cast his gaze about the room, coming to a halt when it landed on the group of three in a far corner. His sisters had their backs to him, talking with an officer whom he recognized immediately.

Wickham!

A red haze misted over Michael's eyes and he breathed deeply several times through his nose in an attempt to control his anger. As much as he wanted to severcly maim the cur who ruined Miss Long's life, they were in a crowded room. However, it was imperative he remove that useless heap of sheep dung from the presence of his beloved sisters. On silent feet, he approached them and listened in for a few minutes, his anger growing exponentially with each untruth that dripped out of the dastard's mouth.

"The late Mr. Darcy was my godfather and excessively attached to me. Upon his death, he bequeathed me, upon its next availability, the parish in Kympton. He meant to provide for me amply, and thought he had done so; but when the living came open, it was given elsewhere."

Michael heard Elizabeth's soft inhale, an indication she was about to ask a question. He forestalled her by joining their conversation.

"Pardon me for interrupting," he said, sounding contrite

when he was nothing but. "I require further clarification of these allegations you so casually tossed into your conversation with my sister."

He came alongside Elizabeth and kept his unwavering gaze on Wickham, who paused for one brief moment before speaking.

"The informality in the terms of the bequest gave me no hope from the law."

"How informal, exactly?"

"A man of honor could not have doubted the intention, but the current Mr. Darcy chose to treat it as a merely conditional recommendation, and has asserted I forfeited all claim to the living."

"*Had* you forfeited all claims?"

"It was his father's dearest wish I receive this living." Michael hoped his sisters noticed that Wickham did not answer his question directly. Instead, he continued to heap grievance upon grievance against Darcy. "When it became vacant two years ago, it was given to another man. I cannot accuse myself of having really done anything to deserve to lose it. I have a warm, unguarded temper and may have sometimes spoken my opinion of him, and to him, too freely for his liking. I can recall nothing worse regarding my behavior which he could accuse me of. But the fact is, we are very different sorts of men, and he hates me."

"Your behavior is well known at Cambridge, which leads me to believe Mr. Darcy, the son, is also aware of your base nature and acted accordingly." Wickham's eyes widened at Michael's mention of them attending the same university as he and Darcy. "Elizabeth, would you please excuse us? I would like to have a candid conversation with this gentleman."

"If you think to shield me from hearing how badly Mr. Darcy has behaved toward Mr. Wickham, you will be disappointed," his sister said firmly.

Michael evaluated her rigid posture and, seeing the determined lift of her chin, lightly shrugged his shoulders and faced the red-draped officer. He hoped his sister's ears would not burn for days with what he was about to impart to the lecherous man who had dared importune a cherished member of his family.

"The living became open two years ago?"

"Yes, and I wrote Darcy to tell him I was available at his leisure."

"And where did you attend seminary? Have you curated for any other rectors in preparation for your new position?"

"Uh… no, I have not taken orders. I had no notion of when the living would become vacant."

"Yet, you told my sister, and I will repeat your exact words, '*the church ought to have been my profession. I was brought up for the church.*' Why were you not ordained and working in some parish if this is the case?"

Michael had the uncanny knack of never forgetting a conversation. Sometimes his gift was a blessing, and sometimes it was a curse. However, when he noted the whisper of a cringe cross Elizabeth's features, he was thankful he had brought Wickham's lies to light. So blinded by the officer's good looks and smooth manners, she very likely believed Wickham's tale of woe.

"None of us can know when someone will die. The living at Kympton may not have become available for years. I had to have some occupation."

"And what was your occupation in the five years since Mr. Darcy senior died? I am aware you received a bequest upon his passing. One thousand pounds, if I remember correctly."

"How did you know that?"

"It is common knowledge," Michael lied smoothly. He knew because, since this past summer, he'd been quietly gathering information about the cad.

"I thought to study the law."

"An admirable ambition, and yet, here you are in the uniform of the militia. Did you not study for the bar or clerk for some barristers while you waited for your living to fall open?"

"I did not."

A droplet of sweat appeared on Mr. Wickham's temple and slowly weaved its way through his sideburns. The gentleman himself flicked it away and cast his gaze around the room. It was painfully obvious he wished to end the inquisition and move on. He lifted his hand and raised his chin, as though someone had caught his attention.

"One of my comrades is waving me over to the card tables. I shall bid you adieu. Miss Elizabeth," he said and took her hand in his, bowing low over their joined fingers. She gave a start and Michael inherently knew the walking dead man had squeezed them lightly before releasing her hand. "Mr. Bennet."

Wickham gave Michael and Jane a curt nod and strode off to the other side of the room.

"It is a good thing he left while he still had kneecaps," Michael heard himself say with a growl. "If he had annoyed you further, Gabriel and I would have had to take matters into our own hands."

"Michael!" Elizabeth exclaimed. "You must stop threatening every new gentleman who comes into our vicinity."

He turned to face his sister, and her countenance paled in the face of his anger.

"That man is no gentleman! You have no idea how debauched he is, and when I heard he was here and saw him circling around you, looking for your soft underbelly, I nearly asked Uncle Phillips if I could borrow his gun."

"I was in no danger! We were having a conversation in the middle of a room full of people."

"And how did Mr. Darcy come into your conversation? How long did Wickham wait before he began to tell you his sad story? One minute? Two? I would hazard a guess not more than ten minutes before he tickled your ears with things you wished to hear."

Never, in their entire life, had he spoken so harshly to her. By this time, Gabriel had joined them.

"I see you sent Wickham off with a flea in his ear."

"Aye, he was telling our sister how he was meant for the church and how Darcy denied him a valuable living."

"The church!" Gabriel emitted a harsh laugh, and both Jane and Elizabeth stared at them in wonder. "The day Wickham is responsible for the spiritual health of any person is the day the sun does not rise in the morning." He paused, seeing the sheen of tears in his sister's eyes. "Do not berate yourself, Lizzy. That particular snake has charmed many people. I would not be surprised if he is the natural son of the Father of Lies. You had no reason not to believe his lying tongue."

"Somehow Wickham knew you did not care for Mr. Darcy and moved in for the kill. I am uncertain why he is telling you such false tales, but I think my brother and I should pay Mr. Darcy a visit. To warn him Wickham is in the area."

"He already knows." Elizabeth had finally quelled her tears and found her voice. "He and Mr. Bingley came upon us yesterday when we all walked to Meryton to have tea with Aunt Phillips."

Michael and Gabriel looked at one another and nodded.

"Did Mr. Darcy acknowledge you in any way when he and Mr. Bingley came upon you?" Gabriel asked.

Elizabeth thought carefully before answering. "He did, but it was extremely brief as almost immediately his gaze fell upon Mr. Wickham. I remember this because I was astonished at how red Mr. Darcy's face turned and how pale Mr. Wickham became."

"Interesting," Michael murmured and shared another glance with his brother. "Evidently, Wickham noticed Mr. Darcy's interest in Elizabeth."

"Mr. Darcy is not interested in me," Elizabeth exclaimed. "His acknowledgment of my presence was polite and required. There was nothing special in his attention."

"And yet, Wickham made note of it, which is why he targeted you specifically tonight."

"I do not believe he targeted me."

"No? Did he not eschew the company of every lady here and come sit beside you as soon as he entered the room?"

"I... he..." Elizabeth's shoulders sagged as the hard truth hit her. "I was so foolish and felt flattered he sought my company. I am as empty-headed as Lydia."

"No one is as empty-headed as Lydia," Gabriel said and curled an arm around Elizabeth's shoulders, drawing her close for a brotherly hug. "You had your head turned by a handsome rake, and now that you know the truth of his character, you will proceed with caution."

By this time, the card party had broken up, and Mr. Collins joined them.

"Am I correct, based on what I heard from that officer," Mr. Collins began, indicating Mr. Wickham with a nod of his head. "He is acquainted with Mr. Darcy?"

"You are correct, Mr. Collins," Elizabeth replied.

"I had no idea the nephew of my noble patroness was in Meryton. I must write her immediately and let her know her daughter's betrothed is very nearby."

"Mr. Darcy is engaged?" Elizabeth exclaimed.

Mr. Collins answered in the affirmative, then launched into a grand soliloquy of the attributes of Lady Catherine's only daughter, Miss Anne de Bourgh.

Before Michael quit the room to warn his aunt and uncle about Wickham, he saw Lizzy lean into Jane and heard her whisper, "Poor Miss Bingley."

***

Elizabeth and Jane walked amicably around the garden which ran the length of Longbourn's gravel drive, protected by thick, manicured shrubs, talking over what happened with Mr. Wickham which led to Mr. Collins' startling news about Mr. Darcy.

"Has Mr. Bingley said anything to you with regard to Mr. Darcy's betrothal?"

"Not a word, but he is a very good gentleman and if Mr. Darcy asked him to keep his confidence, he would comply. He is not one to gossip."

Unlike his sisters, Elizabeth could not help thinking with a touch of malice. Judge not, lest ye be judged, came a still small voice that sounded too much like Grandmother Bennet to be comfortable. Mentally, she shook her head. She had wasted far too much time on the residents of Netherfield. It was time to reclaim her peace of mind and happiness and think of more pleasant things, such as her and Jane's invitation to visit with Lady Susannah in the new year.

The two sister's attention was diverted by the arrival of the very party they had been discussing. Mr. Bingley and his sisters came with a personal invitation for the ball at Netherfield, which was fixed for the following Tuesday. The two ladies were delighted to see their dear friend again and repeatedly asked what she had been doing with herself since their separation. Determined to suffer the Bingley sisters with a level of controlled insouciance that would make Jane proud, Elizabeth smiled until her cheeks hurt.

When Mamma hinted at their staying to dine, the Bingley sisters rose from their seats so fast, they took everyone by surprise, claiming prior commitments. Elizabeth wondered why the supercilious duo had even deigned to stay the obligatory fifteen minutes. She remained firm in her opinion they would rather have tossed the invitation through the window of the carriage in the direction of the manor, while their driver whipped the horses to flee the contaminated grounds of Longbourn.

"Oh! Jane," Mamma enthused after their hasty exit. "Such a compliment to you, my dear. Mr. Bingley flattered us greatly by bringing his invitation in person rather than having a servant drop off a ceremonious card. I am certain Lady Lucas will not receive her invitation in person."

"Mamma, will I be allowed to attend the ball?" Lydia asked.

"Of course, my love, it will be such a grand affair."

"I would speak with Papa before you make any plans," Elizabeth cautioned. "He has said Lydia will not have a soft come out until she is at least sixteen."

"That is almost two years away!" Lydia wailed. "I will be an old hag by the time Father lets me out of the school room. I may as well sit on the shelf next to you and Jane."

"Lydia, my love, I will speak with your Papa and see if he will allow you to attend for at least the first part of the ball. Although, Mr. Bennet might restrict your sets to family only. Your brothers will surely grant you one set each, and of course, Uncle Phillips if he is in attendance."

Lydia huffed and slouched in her chair, crossing her arms across her chest. "Who wants to dance with stuffy old Uncle Phillips?"

"An undeserving young girl who receives permission to attend a ball before she is officially out," Elizabeth said. "That is who."

Lydia responded by sticking out her tongue before turning her attention to her mother, completely ignoring her two eldest sisters. Leaving Mamma and Lydia to talk about the ball, Elizabeth and Jane conversed quietly in the corner about their most recent guests.

"I know you like Mr. Bingley, but surely you cannot want Miss Bingley for a sister."

"I am certain Miss Bingley improves upon further acquaintance. Mr. Darcy would not stay in their company for such great lengths of time if she did not have pleasing manners."

Elizabeth's mouth threatened to drop open in surprise. Her eldest sister always looked for the good in everything, but to say Miss Bingley was pleasant... Elizabeth internally huffed, the notion was patently ridiculous. The steely glint in Jane's eye indicated her opinion would not change unless something drastic happened, proving that more than one sister in the Bennet family could be stubborn in their sentiments. Regardless, Elizabeth plowed on with her point.

"I truly believe he stays in their midst for the sake of Mr. Bingley, and nothing more."

"Be that as it may, Mr. Bingley's sisters are always pleasant to me, and I wish to know them better." Jane stood, her back ramrod straight. Unbending. "If Mamma asks, please advise her I will be in the stillroom."

Elizabeth felt remorse, hating the fact she had upset her beloved sister. While her method of burning off frustration was to walk, Jane channeled her disappointments in the still room, creating perfumes, sachets, and medicinal oils for the family. Even her outlet for anger benefited others. For her sister's sake, Elizabeth prayed the ladies of Netherfield proved worthy of such steadfastness.

Jane had not been gone more than five minutes when Mr. Collins entered the room. Upon seeing Elizabeth, he joined her, sitting too close for her comfort on the couch.

"I heard a carriage. Did I miss meeting some of your illustrious neighbors?"

"Mr. Bingley and his sisters brought an invitation to their ball."

"I have never been to a ball before." Mr. Collins lifted a hand to his mouth and gasped. "Forgive me. I should not assume I was invited."

"Of course, you were invited, Mr. Collins," Mamma declared. "The invitation was for the Bennet family, and you are my husband's cousin."

"I might not be the lightest of foot, but I intend to honor each of my cousins with a dance." Still speaking with Mamma, Lydia glanced over her shoulder at his announcement. Oblivious to her abject look of horror, focused solely on Elizabeth, Mr. Collins continued, "With regard to the first set, I was wondering—"

"Oh, look at the time. I promised Jane I would bring some huckleberry leaves to her for scalding." Elizabeth jumped to her feet. "Pray, excuse me, Mr. Collins."

Before he could utter another word, she fled the room, fervently hoping he would not follow.

Chapter Nine

Ever since the invitation to the ball had been extended, the skies had opened and a deluge of rain fell for five straight days. Not even their family tradition of Stir it up Sunday alleviated Elizabeth's frustration of having her walks curtailed, although some of the nuts had been chopped to a fine powder by the time she was finished. Mamma was also in a dither. The continuous rain prevented her from taking the carriage to Meryton to obtain whatever she deemed necessary for Jane's dress. She also fretted over Lydia's gown, as this would be her first official ball, having been granted permission to attend the first half and dance with family members only. Papa would return Lydia back to Longbourn after the supper hour.

Mrs. Bennet's exasperation was felt in equal parts by all the Mister Bennets, who would rather have been anywhere but inside the house. In order to escape animated conversations about ribbons, lace, length of sleeves, and lack of shoe roses, they took refuge in their father's well-stocked library to read or play chess, with Elizabeth frequently joining them in a bid to escape their persistent cousin. It was there he finally tracked her down.

"Cousin Elizabeth, I have found you."

Elizabeth paused, her white bishop in hand poised over the chessboard.

"I did not realize I was lost, Mr. Collins."

"You are uniformly delightful."

"What did you need to see Lizzy about, Mr. Collins?" Papa queried from his comfortable chair by the fireplace. He knew of her frustration, and had found it amusing – for the first few days – but now, even the edges of his temper were beginning to fray.

"I sought out my cousin's company in order to request her hand for the first two sets at Mr. Bingley's ball."

Elizabeth flashed a look of panic toward Gabriel, seated across from her at the chess table. Without even looking in the direction of their cousin, Gabe said, "Lizzy's first sets have already been spoken for."

"By whom?"

Impudent man!

"Excuse me, Gabe. I need to put your King in check before I address Mr. Collins." Elizabeth dropped the chess piece onto the board, feeling a surge of satisfaction at her brother's incredulous look. She then stood to face her cousin. "I am not required to divulge this information to anyone save my father, Mr. Collins. Suffice to say, it is none of your business, and you will see for yourself on the night of the ball."

She fervently hoped one of her brothers or Papa would stand up with her because, as of this exact moment, she did not have a partner for the opening sets.

"This is not to be borne," Mr. Collins sputtered. "You will mind your sharp tongue in the future, Elizabeth."

The silence which descended upon the room was almost measurable. Papa carefully placed a bookmark in his book, set it on the side table, and rose to his feet. He was at Mr. Collins's side in two strides, causing the younger man to crane his neck in order to meet his elder cousin's steely gaze.

"What is not to be borne?" Papa asked, his voice deceptively soft. "Who are you to tell my daughter to mind her tongue?"

"I have determined Elizabeth suits me best. She is next in age and beauty to Cousin Jane and, as her future husband, I naturally assumed she would open and close the ball with me."

Elizabeth dropped back into her chair, shocked at the audacity of the man. His outlandish explanation fully explained why he had dogged her every step these past few days.

"Lizzy," Papa said without turning around, "Please join your mother and sisters. Your brothers and I need to have a conversation with Mr. Collins."

"I respectfully request to stay, Father."

Papa cut her a quick glance and winked. She did her very best not to smile when Mr. Collins's mouth flopped open in surprise. As it was, she clearly heard Gabe cut short a gurgle of laughter. She dared not look in Michael's direction.

"When and where did this betrothal take place?"

Papa returned to his chair while Mr. Collins swallowed hard, and began to speak.

"I have not yet asked for Elizabeth's hand in marriage," he began by way of explanation. "But I have made my intentions perfectly clear."

Michael straightened in his seat and made a noise that almost sounded like a growl. His grey eyes narrowed and his hand curled into a fist on the arm of the chair. Mr. Collins began to get a panicked look about him.

"Never mind my son. Carry on. I am fascinated with what you are telling me."

"As I saying, before being rudely interrupted," Mr. Collins dared to glare in Michael's direction, whose unwavering glower remained focused on the bumbling parson. "Your esteemed daughter has not shown any inclination that she would refuse my offer."

"I realize your father and I had an acrimonious relationship, and cannot fault you for wishing to heal the breach in our family." Papa held up his hand when Mr. Collins opened his mouth to speak again. "I do, however, take umbrage with the notion you believe you have an understanding with my daughter, especially when I explicitly informed you, upon your arrival, none of my daughters were seeking a husband."

"But, if I take Elizabeth to wife, when you leave this mortal coil, your family will have the comfort of knowing one of their own inherits Longbourn. The entail was designed for this very thing."

The room fell silent, broken only by the snap and crackle of the fireplace.

"Mr. Collins, you not the heir to Longbourn. You are not even the heir presumptive." Mr. Collins gasped and stumbled back a step. "Your father did not tell you the entail was broken when my son came of age?"

"No sir, he passed on four years ago in a fire that not only burned everything our family owned but also took his life. If there was any paperwork, it was lost in the fire."

"This explains much of your behavior. I have all the documents and will have my brother Phillips give you notarized copies of everything. I am sorry you were not made aware of these facts."

Knowing that her father needed to have a private conversation with their cousin, Elizabeth decided it was time for her to take her leave.

"Mr. Collins, while I thank you for the honor you wished to bestow on me, I would never have said yes to your proposal of marriage."

"Never?"

"I do not love you, sir, and will only marry a man who can hold my heart in tender care." Mr. Collins continued to gape, his mouth hanging open. She did not wish to cause him further embarrassment unless provoked, so she turned her attention to her father. "I believe I will join my sisters."

"Are you forfeiting the game, Lizzy?" Gabe called out, his voice hopeful.

With a sly grin, she leaned over the chess table and said, "There is only one move open, dear brother, and then you are in checkmate."

Gabe studied the board and grimaced before tipping his king. Elizabeth straightened and moved toward the door. When Mr. Collins stepped aside, allowing her to exit gracefully, she bobbed him a quick curtsy. No need to be rude to the poor man.

***

That night, Mr. Collins was strangely absent, and over dinner, Papa asked Mamma if she had had any inkling Mr. Collins had hopes of marrying Elizabeth.

"No, not at all, although it would not be a bad thing. Men are thin on the ground here in Meryton, and a better offer might not come her way."

"I have no desire to marry Mr. Collins," Elizabeth said and continued to cut up her roast beef. "I do not love him, and he most certainly does not love me."

"What has love got to do with this? He has a valuable living. He told me himself he brings in almost five hundred pounds a year, and you are talented in the still room and can grow a garden. You could increase his profit by at least ten or twenty pounds."

"I will not marry Mr. Collins, Mamma."

"Mrs. Bennet, we discussed this earlier. Elizabeth shall not be forced to marry someone she does not esteem."

"But her future would be secure—"

"No."

"How can you be so thoughtless? If some unfortunate calamity befell our family, she would have a husband and a stable home." Mamma dragged a lace handkerchief from within her sleeve and used it to dab tears from her eyes. "Elizabeth should do her duty and marry Mr. Collins. Esteem will not keep a roof over her head, or food in her belly if all of you die."

At this declaration, the Bennet men exchanged glances before Papa asked, "When do you expect all three of us to cock our toes upward, Mrs. Bennet?"

"Oh, how you love to vex me. You could be in a horrific carriage accident, or a dread disease could spread, just like it did through Buckinghamshire five years ago, and take you all. Then where would I be? I shall tell you. I would be begging for comfort and food from my brothers, and when they grow tired of me, they will toss me out into the street."

"I wonder where our sisters are during all this?" Gabriel murmured, earning a narrow-eyed glare from his irate mother.

"I believe I am secure in Hunsford," Elizabeth whispered, low enough to escape her mother's censure, but not her father's.

Papa shook his head at Gabe and Lizzy, indicating he would deal with their mother without any commentary from his children. He then turned his attention back to his frivolous wife.

"Have you forgotten there is no entail on Longbourn? Should the unthinkable happen to me and our sons, Jane inherits Longbourn and Netherfield goes to Elizabeth. There is no requirement for Elizabeth to marry a man she does not want."

"Mr. Bennet! You have no compassion for my nerves."

"For once, you are one hundred percent correct. I have no compassion for your nerves. You have become a self-indulgent woman without the sense of a goose." Although Papa had not raised his voice, everyone seated around the table knew he was very angry. "It is my fault. I should have insisted you focused more on your duties as mistress of Longbourn and less on gossiping with your sister and buying useless fripperies for our youngest daughter."

When Mamma opened her mouth to speak, Papa forestalled her by raising his hand.

"Being mistress of an estate is more than being a good hostess, which you are. I cannot take that away from you. When it comes to entertaining, you excel, but when was the last time you visited our tenants or created baskets of much-needed items for them? When was the last time you attended our still room, ensuring we have enough oils and medicinal supplies for the year or prepared soaps and sachets? What, exactly, do you do with your day when you are not gadding about, gossiping with your neighbors?"

Silent tears streamed down Mamma's face.

"You are not fully to blame, Fanny. I have allowed you to become self-absorbed. Well, no more. As of today, Jane and Lizzy will no longer visit the tenants, or see to their needs." Mamma opened her mouth, but Papa cut her off. "It is time your youngest daughter learned how to run a house."

"But… Lydia is only fourteen," Mamma said, casting a frantic glance at her baby when she squawked in protest.

"You have both just made my point, Madam. Jane and Elizabeth were sewing blankets and mending clothes when they were ten. Lydia is four and ten, and still does not know which end of the needle goes into the material first."

"You wish me to teach her?"

"Yes, my dear. And I would not mind if you also took her in hand with regard to the pianoforte. For a woman who plays as well as you, I am surprised you can bear the noise she makes whenever she does attempt to play. Her banging on the keys is as soothing as a blacksmith at work over his anvil."

"I hate the pianoforte," Lydia declared and began to sulk. "It is so boring."

"Everything but shopping is boring to you, Lydia," Michael retorted. "I would rather lock you up in the nursery for a few more years."

"Papa!" Lydia exclaimed at the same time Mamma said, "I have not played the pianoforte in years, Mr. Bennet."

"I am certain you will remember how as soon as you take your place before the instrument. I have fond memories of you playing when we first married. I would like to revisit them." Papa turned his attention over to his youngest daughter. "And you, Miss Lydia Bennet, are relegated back to the schoolroom. I am heartily disappointed with you, young lady."

"What in the world will I do up there? It is so boring."

"A familiar phrase I have become tired of hearing." Papa scowled at Lydia. "I am rescinding my permission for you to attend Mr. Bingley's ball. You can spend the evening sewing blankets for our tenants." Lydia burst into noisy tears. "Fret not, my dear, your exile will end in two years when you attend Miss Tyler's Academy."

At this, his youngest, most spoiled child, pushed away from the table and fled the room. Surprisingly, Mrs. Bennet did not rush to soothe her daughter. Instead, she watched her husband, a soft smile on her face.

Chapter Ten

Elizabeth followed her mother into the ballroom, having passed through Miss Bingley's receiving line relatively unscathed. She had to give the lady credit. Her sneers were mostly muted, but that could very well be attributed to the fact the Bennet family was hustled through as fast as humanly possible. Mamma made her way to her clique of friends, while her father and brothers stood with Jane, whose focus remained on the entrance to the ballroom, where Mr. Bingley would make his appearance once his duties were complete, and claim his promised dance.

Of Mr. Darcy, there was no sign.

Elizabeth entertained herself with the image of the tall gentleman cowering in his bedchamber in order to abstain from dancing. Highly amused with her own imagination, she took in the grandeur of the ballroom, from its glittering chandeliers to the large displays of flowers, placed strategically about the room. She could not fault one thing, everything looked spectacular, even the garish columns. Somehow, they suited the atmosphere of grandeur. As she perused the venue, she spied Charlotte Lucas across the room and joined her. Soon they were deep in conversation.

"Dear Charlotte, I cannot believe it has been almost a week since I saw you last. The rain kept all of us at home, as I am sure it did your family."

"Father worried about the chickens, but our man of all work had mended the roof to the coop earlier this fall, so they remained safe and warm." Charlotte slid a coy look at Elizabeth and said, "What surprised us most was the appearance of Mr. Collins."

After the meeting in Mr. Bennet's study, Mr. Collins had found solace in visiting Lucas Lodge as much as possible, given the inclement weather.

"His visit to Longbourn did not get off to an auspicious beginning," Elizabeth said with a small grimace.

"Your rejection of his proposal was one of the first things he mentioned," Charlotte confided and looked startled when her friend's eyes flashed with anger.

"First, he never proposed, he assumed." Elizabeth let out a long sigh. "I was not going to say anything and embarrass him."

"I believe he needs a gentle, yet firm touch to move him in the right direction."

"Pardon my impertinence, has his conduct been acceptable?"

"At first he was in a dither," Charlotte chuckled. "However, I have sat with him a few times, and helped guide his thoughts in a different direction."

Understanding began to dawn on Elizabeth.

"Are you trying to… Has he made an offer?"

"Not as of this moment, but I do expect one."

"Are you certain this is a choice you wish to make? Although educated, I would not say he is a learned man, and he is very much under the thumb of his patroness, Lady Catherine de Bourgh."

"At this juncture, she reigns supreme because she is the only person from whom he seeks advice. Once a wife has settled in, and her counsel is heard more than his patroness, things will change."

"Miss Elizabeth."

A deep voice caused Elizabeth to startle, and she turned to see Mr. Darcy standing by her side.

"Mr. Darcy," she said with a polite curtsy.

"Would you do me the honor of being my partner for the supper set?"

"I… that is…" Mr. Darcy had taken her so much by surprise in his application for her hand, she floundered for words. A nudge from Charlotte's elbow reminded her the gentleman awaited a reply. "I will. Thank you, sir."

He turned and walked across the ballroom floor. She could not tear her eyes away from his tall, athletic form, which disappeared through a door leading to the card room.

"I dare say, you will find him agreeable," Charlotte soothed, in an attempt to console.

"Agreeable or not, I am wondering why he would ask me to dance. If you recall, I am not handsome—"

"What?" Charlotte asked when she abruptly stopped talking.

"My brothers chastised me for regurgitating his remarks."

"They are not wrong in this regard. The gentleman has already tendered two apologies, and I believe him asking you to dance proves he has revisited those opinions, and now finds you very tolerable."

Their conversation came to a natural close when Gabe arrived to lead Elizabeth out onto the floor for the first set of dances. Down the line, she saw Jane with Bingley and Charlotte with Mr. Collins. Miss Bingley stood alone near the edge of the dance floor, glaring at the door Mr. Darcy had gone through, her lips pressed thin and tight. It was patently clear Miss Bingley had fully expected Mr. Darcy to open the ball with her. The fact he had not even looked at her, nor came by her side for conversation, kept the fire lit beneath woman's pot of simmering anger.

Later that evening, when the musicians began to play the opening bars for the supper set, Elizabeth watched Mr. Darcy's steady approach to claim her hand. Charlotte could not help but caution her.

"Do not allow your *piqué* over his blunder from the assembly to make you appear unpleasant, Eliza. He is a man of some consequence who has singled you out for his attention. He has danced with no other lady this evening, not even his hostess."

Her good friend's use of the word 'consequence' reminded Elizabeth of the assembly in October, whereupon the gentleman said, *I am in no humor at present to give consequence to young ladies who are slighted by other men.* What changed his opinion of her? The only thing they agreed upon was Shakespearean plays and a love of the outdoors. She had no time to ponder this further as he had arrived.

"I believe this is our set, Miss Elizabeth."

Elizabeth made no answer and took her place, very aware of the ripple of surprise moving through the crowd. They stood for some time without speaking. Half amused and half disgruntled, she imagined their silence would last through the two dances. How boring. Her lips curved into a smile, thinking of Lydia's favorite complaint.

It may have been a little spark of mischief, or it may have been the extra cup of punch she drank before their dance that made her decide the greatest punishment she could bestow on her taciturn partner, would be to oblige him to talk.

"The musicians, hired by Miss Bingley, are very talented," she began in her quest to make him converse.

"She was fortunate to gain their services on such short notice."

"Very true. Her brother allowed only two weeks to make such detailed arrangements."

They went down the line and then stood again, facing each other. They were not even halfway through their first set and he still did not speak willingly. His steady gaze made her slightly uncomfortable, and she huffed out a frustrated breath. The light puff of air moved the hair on her forehead, and his eyes tracked the movement of her unruly curls. A wave of self-satisfaction washed through her body. So, the man from Derbyshire did notice things around him.

"It is your turn to say something now, Mr. Darcy. I talked about the dance, and you ought to make some kind of remark on the size of the room or the number of couples."

He smiled and she was not prepared for the set of dimples which magically appeared at the corners of his mouth.

"Do you... perhaps always talk while you are dancing?"

"It would look odd if we were entirely silent for half an hour together."

They met in the middle and briefly touched hands, turning a slow circle.

"And you feel our time is better spent conversing, rather than simply enjoying the dance itself."

"I believe we are talented enough to do both."

"How odd, for I thought that is exactly what we were doing," Mr. Darcy said close to her ear as she turned beneath his outstretched arm.

Her whole body warmed, from the top of her head to the tips of her toes and she forgot what she was going to say next. As a result, they were again silent till they had gone down the dance. While she cast about for another topic to introduce, he asked, "Do you and your sisters often walk to Meryton?"

"Yes.' Unable to resist the temptation, she added, "When you met us there the other day, we had just been forming a new acquaintance."

Immediately, the smile which had been teasing the corners of his mouth disappeared, and his features transformed into an impenetrable mask. Elizabeth, for all her delight in teasing, was exceedingly remorseful she had brought a certain unnamed gentleman into their conversation. When Darcy finally spoke, the previous ease she'd come to enjoy in their light discourse was completely absent.

"Mr. Wickham is blessed with such happy manners as may ensure his making friends. Whether he is capable of retaining them is less certain."

"Count your blessings in that you lost his friendship," Elizabeth said softly.

Something akin to surprise flickered in his eyes before he went back to an expression of cool, assessing calm. He opened his mouth, as though to speak further, but at that moment Sir William Lucas, on noticing Mr. Darcy and Elizabeth waiting their turn to go down the line a final time, stopped to give them his regard.

"I see you have finally asked our dear Eliza to dance. Even though it is evident you belong to the first circles of society, your fair partner will not disgrace you, and the honor may be repeated more often when a certain desirable event takes place." Here, the amiable gentleman directed their attention down the line to where Jane danced with Mr. Bingley. "What congratulations will then flow in! But, let me not interrupt you, sir. You will not thank me for detaining your delightful partner."

Elizabeth perceived Mr. Darcy was no longer listening. It seemed as though Sir William's allusion to Mr. Bingley and Jane unsettled him, and his attention remained riveted upon the other couple. When their turn to move down the line came up, he recovered himself enough to speak.

"Sir William's interruption has made me forget what we were talking of."

"Hard to believe as we were speaking of Mr. Wickham."

"I respectfully request you do not bring his name up in conversation with me."

"You may rest assured I do not speak of him with admiration." She felt Mr. Darcy's fingers stiffen in her light clasp. "My brothers ensured I was made aware of his reprehensible past."

"Wickham would not have liked that, one bit."

"No, indeed. He did not." She tilted her head and assessed her dance partner. There was so much about this man she did not know. "Will you remain in Hertfordshire through the winter?"

"I will spend Christmas with my sister."

"In London?"

"Yes."

"I would imagine your evenings will be filled with parties and elegant company."

"Where are these questions leading, Miss Elizabeth?"

She was startled by the harshness in his tone.

"My sole purpose is to have a pleasant conversation with my dancing partner."

"One dance does not give you carte blanche with regard to my social calendar."

Elizabeth felt the sting of his rebuke and, lifting her chin in defiance, met his haughty glare with one of her own.

"Then, Mr. Darcy, when next we meet, let us limit our conversations to the weather. Far be it from me to assume a friendship with someone who believes my condition in life is so decidedly beneath his own."

She said no more, and they went down the other dance and parted in silence.

***

Two days later, Darcy strode toward his bed chamber in his London residence, and for the first time in six long weeks, allowed his shoulders to relax. Down the hall, Bingley's man sorted out his belongings, his master having been invited to stay with Darcy instead of a hotel room. Bingley fully intended to return to Hertfordshire, and for this reason, he had not wanted to open Hurst's house for the two weeks he was in town on business.

Before the ball had ended, Darcy knew it was imperative he remove Bingley from the sphere of the Bennets. The poor, hapless fool could not see beyond the dazzling beauty of Miss Jane Bennet, who blithely followed her mother's dictates. Coming by horseback for dinner when a storm was brewing should have been Charles' first indication the young woman was as mercenary as her mother.

He paused briefly in thought. The Bennet family had excellent family connections with regard to their family. Why had they not taken advantage of them? With her beauty, Jane Bennet would have been snapped up before one full season was over. He halted his thoughts. Good connections notwithstanding, she held no affection for his friend.

His valet entered the room and began to put away his master's clothes and personal effects. It was Jenkins who had quietly informed him, once Charles left for London the next morning, Mrs. Bennet had arranged for their family's carriage to be called last when the ball ended. It was plain she had endeavored to keep her eldest daughter in Bingley's vicinity to the very end.

Darcy needed no further impetus to separate his friend from that family and agreed with Miss Bingley to follow her brother to town and do everything in their power to keep him there. Together with Mrs. Hurst, they decided it was best for Charles to stay at Darcy's house for the next few weeks, which would allow him time to wean Bingley from his unhealthy fascination with the fair-haired beauty. Safe from the allure of Jane Bennet and her mercenary mother, they would wait for another angel to catch his eye and then advise him to close Netherfield for good and give up the lease.

Once Darcy had refreshed himself, he went down to his study to sort through his correspondence. His secretary was very efficient and had forwarded important documents to Hertfordshire for his perusal and direction, but there remained numerous letters and requests which needed some attention before he could justify a full day of leisure.

He had finished going through his stack of invitations, separating them into three piles – Decline, Accept, and Consider – when Bingley knocked on the door.

"I see you are hard at work," Bingley said upon entry.

"I am certain you will be deluged with invitations once your return to town is made known," Darcy said and moved to the cabinet where he kept his good port and brought out two glasses. Filling them both, he handed one to Bingley and took the chair opposite of him.

"Caroline will respond to them," his friend said with little or no emotion. "It is what she lives for."

"Your sister wishes nothing but the best for you, Charles."

Bingley drank a large portion of his port, before cradling the half-empty glass between the palms of his hands.

"Does she? Or is her concern and care solely for her own advancement?"

"Valid point," Darcy conceded. "Your success in society is also hers, and vice versa."

"I still do not understand why all of you quit Netherfield Park and followed me here. I told Caroline and Louisa I planned to return the week following St. Nichol's Day. None of this makes any sense."

Darcy hesitated briefly, wondering if he should wade into the issues of Miss Jane Bennet without the input from

Bingley's sisters. He really had no stake in this game, other than a desire to see his friend find a woman who loved him for himself and not for how deep his pockets were.

"Can you not shed some light on this subject? I am stuck here in town for the next two weeks for business reasons only. If I did not have important meetings with my solicitors and investors, I would never have left Hertfordshire."

"I did not realize you still had investors. I thought you sold all your father's interest in his company."

"That is what I tell Caroline. She is adamant we wash the stain of trade from our shoes, but I am loathed to part with such a lucrative income. Also, I wish to establish a partnership with an established import/export company. Gardiner Shipping & Emporium is turning a profit at a dizzying rate, and many people are scrambling to invest in his company. This is why I had to come to town, I am slated to meet with him next week. After that, he is unavailable until the new year. He always visits family over Christmas, so the timing was crucial."

"I am intrigued, Bingley. Would you mind if I accompanied you to this meeting? I am always looking for ways to diversify my income portfolio."

"I do not mind, at all."

Chapter Eleven

Without conscious thought, Elizabeth looped her arm through Jane's. Even though the air was cool, the sun still shone, and because they were moving at a steady pace, the two girls remained warm. She dared to sneak a peek at her sister, noting no tears had yet to fall but knew they would. When all the candles were extinguished and Longbourn lay in silence, her sister wept into her pillow over the amiable young man who, two weeks prior, had danced with her three times. Tantamount to a proposal in any circle of society. Indeed, all of their family and friends had thought for certain he would, at the very least, request a courtship.

As it was, the Bennet family via their servants, learned Mr. Bingley had left for London the morning after the ball, and his sisters, along with Mr. Darcy, followed the very next day. Not one resident of Netherfield Park farewelled the families who had extended the hand of friendship. Without saying a word, the Bingleys, Hursts, and Darcy had shown how deep their disgust of Meryton's society went.

"Mr. Bingley could still return alone," Elizabeth offered, inherently knowing her sister's thoughts were on him, and all which had preceded the night of the ball. "He knows enough families in the area now he does not require his sister as hostess."

"Stop it, Lizzy. He has already been gone a fortnight, and Miss Bingley made it very clear they would not return this winter. A lot can happen in six months."

Elizabeth knew her sister was referencing the letter Caroline Bingley had written to Jane, wherein she relayed there was nothing left behind in Hertfordshire they would miss, and their brother was actively courting Miss Darcy. There was some truth to the hateful shrew's missive of misery. Miss Bingley loathed Meryton and its environs and would not miss anything left behind, however, Elizabeth did not believe the ambiguous reference to a future alliance with the Darcy family. Mr. Darcy would never allow his sister to marry someone so far beneath her station. His family was of the upper ten thousand in society, while Mr. Bingley – although amiable – was still the son of a tradesman who had not yet acquired property. Miss Bingley's verbal blathering was nothing but a dream she clung to, not realizing it would never happen. Her heart's desire was promised to another.

"I believe the amiable Mr. Bingley will return before Christmas, and fall before you on bended knee," Elizabeth reiterated, not only to bolster Jane's mood but her own.

"Thank you for trying to lift my spirits, however, I hold no hope from that quarter. Mr. Bingley had plenty of time to state his intentions. We had many opportunities and quiet conversations where he could have broached the subject, yet he chose to remain silent, and not once did he speak of plans to leave for London."

"Mayhap because he did not want to leave your side. Not even for a half-day."

"Our brothers did warn me of his fickle behavior, and I was a fool to think he would change for me."

"In a perfect world, he would have."

"Do you realize, the whole time he was in residence at Netherfield, he never called upon me at Longbourn?"

Elizabeth had no chance to answer because Jane continued speaking. "Think about it, Lizzy. He came with friends to dine, and with his sisters to deliver an invitation to the ball, but not once did he go out of his way to specifically seek out my company. Our brothers were right. I was a pleasant diversion, nothing more."

Determined to steer their conversation down a different road, Elizabeth pressed her sister's arm into her side and said, "I have written Susannah, and informed her we are coming to town with our aunt and uncle the week after Christmas."

"And what was her reply?"

"Expect an invitation for tea almost as soon as we arrive, even though we are staying with her for a month complete in February. She has promised to make it worth our while, reminding us to bring our best gowns for their annual ball."

"What Susannah proposes sounds like the perfect solution for both of us. I desperately need some time away from Longbourn, and Mamma's laments over Mr. Bingley's continued absence."

"I, too, am weary of our mother haranguing you."

"Maybe we could entice our brothers to escort us to the duke's ball in February," Jane said as they turned in tandem to walk back toward Longbourn. "We are then guaranteed at least two dances."

"After the fiasco at Lucas Lodge, I am not sure I want our dear brothers to dance with us." Upon hearing a gentle chastisement from her sister, she continued. "Also, if you believe your dance card would remain empty longer than it takes for the musicians to warm up for the first set, you are a fool."

"I doubt my ability to judge people, Lizzy. I still do not know what to make of Mr. Bingley."

"I am of the opinion his sisters held much sway in him not returning, and Mr. Darcy had a hand in this iniquitous affair."

Jane sighed.

"Lizzy, have you not even once considered Mr. Bingley did not promise me anything tangible because he actually *is* courting Miss Darcy."

"Need I remind you Miss Darcy is nearly the same age as Lydia? She has not been presented and most definitely is not out. This is but a pipe dream of Miss Bingley's. If she were to tell me the sky is blue, I would look out the closest window to see for myself. You cannot trust her words."

"Regardless, I think both of us could use some extra cheering up."

"You know Susannah will have hopeful gentlemen lined up for you to look over. She is determined to have you marry well."

"I... I am not ready."

Elizabeth gave Jane's arm a soft squeeze.

"Then, we shall tell her, and enjoy our time by attending the theater and shopping for some extracts you can use to make new perfumes. Susannah wants only what is best for you."

"She has turned out to be a true friend," Jane said, smiling slightly as she thought about Lady Susannah. "Who would have thought, given the inauspicious way you met?"

The sisters, by tacit agreement, bypassed the house and continued walking down the garden toward the stillroom.

"It is not every day a gentleman's daughter rescues the daughter of a peer from a rampaging horde of horses and rising floodwaters," Elizabeth said and waited for her sister's response. She did not have to wait long.

"Your story gets larger with each re-telling."

"True. When her horse reared on the bridge and threw her into the river, my only thought was to get her to shore, and once I was no longer terrified and had caught my breath, I was so glad Michael and Gabriel taught me to swim. Her sturdy riding habit had soaked through and the weight of the material was dragging her under the water." Elizabeth grinned up at her sister. "Thank goodness for poor gentlemen's daughters who can only afford cotton muslin dresses. Much lighter when submerged in murky water."

"You are incorrigible."

"Yes, and I am unrepentant about that fact."

***

The month of December began its inevitable march toward the end of another year, and Darcy joined Bingley in his meeting with the owner of Gardiner Shipping, listening most attentively when Mr. Edward Gardiner laid out the facts of how his business ran, and what investors could expect in return for their money. The canny businessman did not sugarcoat the perils, what with pirates and the French navy standing between England and the countries Gardiner conducted business with. In turn, he also did not exaggerate the profits which could be expected with each successful shipment.

Although impressed with Gardiner's intelligence and good manners, there was something intangible that niggled at Darcy's conscious when the gentleman smiled or canted his head a certain way. After two in-depth meetings, both Bingley and Darcy gladly became partners in his burgeoning company and planned for further meetings between their solicitors after Gardiner's return from visiting his brother-in-law's estate in the country.

After their business meeting, the two men retreated to Darcy's study for a congratulatory drink. They had not been there too long before Bingley's mind turned to the fair-haired maiden in Hertfordshire.

"Why am I still here?" Bingley threw himself into a

comfortable chair near the fireplace. "I should be in Hertfordshire, trying to steal a kiss from Miss Bennet under the mistletoe."

"You need to move on, my friend. Find some other pretty lady to kiss."

"I could not kiss another lady when my mind is set on Miss Bennet. She is an angel, come to earth for me to fall in love with."

"Charles, I studied her most assiduously, and remain constant in my belief she did not return your affection."

"How can you say that? She was always pleasant and smiled at me when I entered the room."

"Do you not recall our first night in Meryton? Even then I said she smiled too much. Miss Bennet likes you; I will accede that much, but nothing more. If anyone loves you, it is the mother, and she has five thousand reasons to wish you for a son."

Eventually, after a joint effort by Darcy and both sisters to tell their brother what they had witnessed themselves of Mrs. Bennet's behavior and vulgar proclamations at the Netherfield ball, Bingley agreed to quit the lease and promised to make an appointment with his solicitor to affect the change.

Darcy truly felt sorry for his friend, and there were times his frustration knew no bounds when the normally cheerful Bingley spent an inordinate amount of time staring off into space, his expression pensive. It was time for all of them to return to their normal social routine and for the first time since his father passed, Darcy was glad his family always hosted an annual Twelfth Night party. It was the perfect venue to help his friend start the year anew.

The Bingley family arrived — fashionably late as always. After divesting themselves of their outerwear, they joined Darcy, Georgiana, and their guests in the main drawing room.

Greetings were exchanged and as soon as she could arrange a quiet moment, Miss Bingley approached Darcy for a quasi-private conversation.

"I must ask your opinion on a delicate matter, Mr. Darcy."

Darcy was not pleased with her cloying attention for two reasons. Well, for a myriad of reasons, but two were most prevalent in his mind. First, she always stood too close for his personal comfort and her perfume gave him headaches. Second, her separating them from the rest of the party gave an air of intimacy he had no wish to foster. He would never offer for Miss Bingley. Not even as his mistress. He would rather lay with a cold fish.

"I have received a letter from Miss Bennet. She is in town, and intends to call on us."

"You should have expected this. You enjoyed a friendship with her in Hertfordshire, she will naturally expect to call on you when she is in town."

"I am aware of polite civilities, but I do not want Charles to accidentally run into her. What should I do?"

"I will invite him to continue to stay here for a few more weeks. I would not worry about Miss Bennet when, or if she comes to visit."

Miss Bingley murmured her thanks, then turned her gaze to where her family stood talking with Georgiana.

"They make a lovely couple, do they not?" she queried, her voice still low.

Darcy also surveyed the group.

"Yes, your sister married well, and seems content."

Miss Bingley's mouth pinched, and her nostrils flared.

"My sister did the best she could."

Surprised at her tone, Darcy ruminated on Miss Bingley's words, realizing – too late – she had been speaking about Bingley and Georgiana.

"While your brother is one of my closest friends and I

have great respect for him, my sister will not be courted until after she has been presented, and makes her debut."

"I cannot wait for dear Georgiana's presentation. It will be such a delight to take her shopping for all the ball gowns she will require."

"Why would you be involved in my sister's preparation, Miss Bingley? You are the sister of my friend, not family." Darcy asked, his voice bitingly cold. "My aunt Matlock will take care of all the details, and sponsor her presentation."

Miss Bingley stiffened and, finally, stepped back a pace.

"Forgive me for inserting myself where I am not wanted."

He ignored her tightened lips and gave a perfunctory bow before moving to stand with his family.

"You look like my general the night before he has to pass sentence on one of his soldiers," his cousin Richard said after his mother whisked Georgiana away to greet Lord and Lady Addlesworth. "Ever since you returned from Hertfordshire, you have gone about with such a long face, one would think all the joy has been sucked out of your life."

"I have finally reached the end with Bingley's sister, and was more abrupt than I intended."

"Oh, ho! Shall I break out the good brandy, or commiserate? Bingley is your best friend; how do you think he will take the news of you breaking his sister's heart?"

"I have told him, more than once, I will never marry his sister. Even if I came across her without a stitch of clothing, in my bed, and a dozen witnesses gathered about."

"And, he did not challenge you to a duel?"

"We have spoken on this topic at length, and he assured me if there was even a hint of scandal between our families, Miss Bingley would be shipped off to Scarborough before her trunks were packed."

"Let us hope he does not need to follow through with his promise. With Georgiana coming out in a few short years, our family does not need to become embroiled in a scandal."

"We were lucky to avoid one last summer."

"How does our Georgie fare? She still seems unsure of herself. Look at the way she stays close to the mater's side."

Richard half nodded his head in the direction of his mother in conversation with Lord and Lady Addlesworth. Darcy's heart clenched at the sight of his sister, with her hands clasped tightly – most likely to stop them from visibly trembling – her body stiff with fright. Her shyness, which prior to Wickham's treachery had been painful to observe, now seemed debilitating. He should not have asked her to attend this dinner, even though it was held in their own home where she knew she was safe.

"Excuse me," Darcy said to his cousin. "I must attend my sister."

He took his leave and walked toward Georgiana. Upon reaching her side, he lightly touched her arm and she cast a startled glance up at him. Leaning into her, he asked in a sotto voice, "Are you well, sweetling?"

"I…" she began, and her eyes welled with tears. "I am uncertain."

"Come with me. Let us see if Mrs. Whittaker can make you a restorative tea."

Without fuss, he led Georgiana from the room and asked Burke, who quickly came to their side, if he would have Mrs. Whittaker attend them in Georgiana's room. Once they reached her suite, he gathered her in his arms and hugged her close.

"It was too soon to ask you to attend such a large gathering. I am sorry."

"It is not your fault, William. I am hopeless and useless."

Darcy placed his hands on her slender shoulders, and held her away from him, in order to look her square in the eyes.

"You are not hopeless, nor are you useless. You are a

young lady who took a mighty blow to her self-esteem and has yet to recover fully. I have complete faith you will rise above this, and make yourself proud."

"Do you not wish for me to make you proud?"

"How could you make me any prouder of you than I already am?" Her eyes widened. "What you struggle with is how you look at yourself. You have no need to impress me, or Richard, or anyone else, for that matter."

She flung herself back into his arms and squeezed tight, her cheek pressed into his chest.

"Oh, William! I have been so worried you would hate me after Ramsgate."

She began to sob openly, wetting his waistcoat and jacket thoroughly. He stroked her hair and whispered soothing words, bringing to mind the one and only time he, as a young boy, had wept in his mother's arms the day his beloved grandmother had died. A quiet knock on the door had them separate, and he handed her a linen handkerchief from his pocket. Upon his acknowledgment of the knock, Mrs. Whittaker entered the room with a tray of biscuits, and a fresh pot of hot chocolate.

"I thought Miss Darcy might like some chocolate, rather than tea. I hope you do not mind, sir."

"Not at all, Mrs. Whittaker. Could you please let Miss Darcy's maid know my sister is retiring for the evening and requires her attention?"

"Yes, sir," Mrs. Whittaker said with a polite nod of the head, before leaving the siblings alone.

"You do not wish for me to return to the party?"

"I think it best you enjoy your chocolate and get a good night's rest. I will explain to Lady Matlock and Richard you have come down with a megrim, and I urged you to have an early night." He moved toward the door, then turned. "Good night, Georgiana. I shall see you in the morning."

"Good night, William. I love you."

"And I love you, Georgiana."

LONGBOURN'S ANGELS

Chapter Twelve

Jane waited for Molly, one of Aunt Gardiner's maids, before descending the stairs of Mr. Hurst's townhouse to her uncle's waiting carriage. Both ladies were silent as they climbed into the vehicle and began to make their way to Gracechurch Street. A few blocks from Mr. Bingley's home, Jane rapped the carriage roof with her small parasol, and after the driver opened the little window between them, asked if he would please stop at the park they were passing by.

Almost immediately the carriage drew to a halt.

"Thank you," Jane said, as the coachman helped her out of the carriage before turning to lend aid to Molly. "I am going for a short walk to clear my mind. There is no need for you to attend us."

"I cain't leave you alone, Miss Bennet. There ain't no accountin' fer what might be out there." He held up his hand when it looked like Jane might protest. "Yer uncle would have me hide ifin I let you walk without protection."

"You are correct, Mr. James. I find I am not thinking clearly at this moment and will inform my uncle about your diligent care." She looked at Molly. "Do you mind taking a turn with me? I need to gain a semblance of control before I see my family."

"After the afternoon you had, Miss Bennet, I'm not surprised you need t'gather your strength."

"Thank you, Molly." Jane looked toward Mr. James. "I will stay, at all times, within your sight."

With that, she and Molly turned and strolled down the well-kept path. As promised, they stayed in sight of Mr. James and soon took refuge on a park bench near one of the many bushes which showed a promise of pretty spring blossoms. Jane used this time to reflect on the conversation she had with Miss Bingley and Mrs. Hurst not more than twenty minutes past. It all began as soon as she followed the butler into the front parlor after presenting her card.

"Miss Bennet, I am all astonishment. Did you not receive my letter?"

Jane, who had begun to advance further into the room, now paused, taken aback by the brusque tone of her hostess. She also took note neither Miss Bingley, nor Mrs. Hurst, rose to greet her properly, nor did they invite her to take a seat.

"I did—"

"Louisa." Miss Bingley angled her body to face her sister. "You recall our discussion of Miss Bennet's letter not long after we left Hertfordshire. I specifically asked you to check our calendar when she mentioned the days she might be in town."

"I do, Caroline. In fact, I remarked she could not have picked a worse time to come to London."

"Given our close friendship in Meryton, I thought it only polite to give your family a courtesy call," Jane explained while she twisted the cords of her reticule tight around her fingers. "I asked my uncle if I could have the carriage for a half-hour in order to pay my respects."

"Forgive me, Miss Bennet, I tend to forget things which are not important. Would this be the uncle who is in trade? Where did you say he lived again?"

"Gracechurch Street."

"Oh yes. In *Cheapside*." Caroline sneered. "How could I

have forgotten? Well, no matter. Louisa and I are about to depart for our daily visit to Mr. Darcy's house where that gentleman, along with our dear Georgiana and Charles, await our pleasure."

"Please forgive my intruding. I will take my leave. I have only to say I wish you a good day." Jane signaled her maid to head toward the front entry.

"Miss Bennet." Miss Bingley's call halted Jane before she turned to quit the room. "I am surprised you would dare show your face after I explicitly informed you of my brother's interest in Miss Darcy."

"I did not come to visit your brother."

"Please," Miss Bingley scoffed and her sister snorted. "You and your mother were quite vocal about trapping my brother. How you would throw rich men in the path of your pathetic sisters. Thank goodness Charles never held any deep regard for you and saw past your deceptively sweet face. Once he was back in town, it took but a moment for us, and Mr. Darcy, to encourage him to close Netherfield Park. He is seeing his solicitor this week to give up the lease."

Jane stood in stupefied silence. Her brothers had warned her, yet every word Miss Bingley spoke was a physical blow to her heart, and she knew not how to defend herself. It was then Caroline Bingley delivered her *coup de grâce*.

"Do not come to my sister's home again. You will not be received, and if you have the temerity to acknowledge us on the street, or in a shop, we will cut you direct. You mean nothing to us, Miss Bennet. You never have, and never will. You may see yourself out. Our butler will ensure the door is locked behind you."

Oh, how Jane wished Lizzy had come with her and not stayed back to tend to their sick cousin. Jane could not help but wonder how her brave sister would have handled such an outright attack. With that thought in mind, she gathered her tattered dignity around her like a shield and addressed the ladies of the house.

"Cut me if you wish, Miss Bingley, but remember this. I am a gentleman's daughter, and no matter how many ways you cut the social pie you remain the daughter of a tradesman."

Jane gave the sisters an exaggerated curtsy, one she had practiced for her court presentation less than five years ago. Then, head held high, shoulders back, she sailed out of the room, her maid right behind.

She now knew, with certainty, those two women had never been her friends and experienced nothing but disgust in her presence. She berated herself for not listening to Lizzy when she tried to warn her about their attitude.

If she were to tell me the sky is blue, I would look out the closest window to see for myself. You cannot trust her words.

Jane's musings were cut short by a high-pitched scream. She immediately stood and glanced around the area, spying a little girl on the ground near a tree, holding her ankle. As far as she could tell no one else was nearby to lend aid, so she hurried to the child.

"Are you hurt?" she asked, kneeling next to the girl without thought of how it would soil her own dress.

"I fell from the tree and hurt my foot," the child said between body-shaking sobs.

"Let me take a look," Jane said and stripped off her gloves. She began to gently probe the girl's ankle, which already showed signs of swelling. "Are you here by yourself?" she asked in a very gentle voice, doing everything she could to keep the girl from becoming more frightened.

She was surprised no one had yet to make an appearance and claim the child, whose clothing gave hint to her family being wealthy. Usually, children of peers or wealthy tradesmen had an army of servants guarding their offspring.

"I snuck away from my governess and Papa," the girl said with a hiccup. Her sobs had slowed to small shuddering breaths and sniffling. Jane reached into her reticule and pulled out the handkerchief Lizzy had given her for Christmas. Not saying a word, she handed it to the girl, who thanked her in a subdued voice before vigorously wiping her nose. "She always behaves silly around Papa. I think she wants to be my new Mamma."

"Someone is coming, Miss Bennet," Molly warned, and Jane rose to her feet, ready to explain what happened.

Neither of them was prepared for the handsome man who careened around the large bush, which hid a portion of the path, his expression one of panic.

"Cassandra!" he exclaimed and ran toward them. "Step away from my daughter," he demanded upon reaching them. "I will have your hides if you have harmed her."

"You'll haf t'go through me ifin you try t'hurt them ladies."

The coachman stepped in front of Jane and Molly, fairly bristling with indignation. Jane touched his elbow, smiled up at the man and urged him to step back.

"Mr. James, I admire you coming to ensure our safety, but I am of the opinion Miss Cassandra's father is anxious and does not know who we are, or how we came to be in his daughter's company."

The man lifted his daughter in his arms and faced them, his handsome face flushing a dull red at Jane's gentle chastisement.

"I apologize for my outburst. My first and only concern was for the safety of my daughter."

"I am aware of that, sir. Your daughter apparently fell from this tree and told me she hurt her foot. I hope you do not mind, but I checked her ankle and it is, indeed, beginning to swell. You may wish to have a physician treat it further."

Jane slid a glance at Molly and began to pull on her gloves. "I believe we should return to my uncle's house. He will wonder what has taken us so long."

She gave the gentleman a polite curtsy, as did Molly. Mr. James remained standing straight and tall, not moving one inch. Jane knew he would follow quietly behind, making sure no one bothered them before they reached the carriage.

"Miss," Cassandra's father called out, and she paused before turning to face him. He attempted to smile, but it came out as a bit of a grimace. "May I have your name and address in order to express a proper thank you?"

"My name is Miss Bennet, and I am currently staying at my uncle's residence. His name is Mr. Edward Gardiner, and his address is number twenty-three Gracechurch Street."

Jane did not wait to learn the gentleman's name or to see if he was horrified where she laid her head at night. She had had enough prejudice leveled against her family today to last a lifetime. Instead, she returned to the carriage, her walk forgotten, and was home in time for tea.

***

The next day, a surprise visitor made his appearance at twenty-three Gracechurch Street. Elizabeth had gone to Hatchard's to purchase a copy of the highly anticipated new book by A Lady, and Mrs. Gardiner and Jane were happily situated in the parlor when the butler entered the room and asked if they were at home for a gentleman. Lambert handed Aunt Maddie an elegant, embossed calling card displaying the gentleman's name. Her only reaction was a raised eyebrow when she turned it over to read the address.

"Jane, did you happen to learn the name of the gentleman, whose daughter you lent aid yesterday?"

"No, Aunt, I did not. Our conversation was very short, and centered around his daughter."

Her aunt tapped the card against the palm of her hand.

"I will presume, then, this gentleman is Miss Cassandra's father. Shall we invite him to join us for tea?"

"I would not mind. I wish to know how his daughter fairs after her mishap."

"Very well."

Aunt Madeline informed Lambert to escort the gentleman to the parlor and have the housekeeper prepare fresh tea with biscuits. It was only after he entered the room did Jane remember how handsome the man was. Gone was his look of anger and anxiety, replaced with one of concern and genuine kindness.

"Pardon me for intruding without any form of invitation, but I wanted to personally express my fervent thanks to Miss Bennet for the aid she lent my daughter the other day," the smartly attired gentleman said to Aunt Madeline.

"Thank you, sir. Seeing as we have breached almost every level of propriety, may I introduce myself and my niece to you?" Aunt Madeline asked in her normal, unhurried manner.

"Indeed, I would be honored. There seems to be a perfect symmetry in our introduction, even though it wandered off the path of proper behavior."

Both Jane and her aunt smiled at his allusion to how he entered their lives, and also at his valiant attempt to alleviate the ensuing awkwardness of strangers trying to behave as though intimately acquainted.

"I am Mrs. Edward Gardiner, and this is my husband's niece, Miss Jane Bennet. She is visiting us from her father's estate in Hertfordshire."

The gentleman gave both ladies a very proper bow before replying, "I am Henry Bradford—"

They were interrupted by the housekeeper bringing in the tea tray. Aunt Madeline indicated Mr. Bradford was to take a seat, and he sat in the chair next to Jane. Once settled, he continued with, "You already know my daughter's name, Cassandra. In fact, everyone in the park knows her name. I called out many times before I finally found her in your company."

"I believe, sir, that may have been what caused her to tumble out of the tree. Not that you were the cause," Jane hastened to assure him when his lips thinned. "If I may explain. I am not censuring you. I think, in fact, she was trying to climb down and simply lost her footing. If she is anything like my sister, she can lose herself in the moment, and time simply slips by.

Jane had no intention of telling the man his daughter was hiding from her governess. She did not know the dynamics of the family, and she knew children often saw things differently than adults.

"Frankly, I had no idea Cassandra could even climb a tree. She is far more interested in her books and music. She rarely ventures outside."

"May I ask how old your daughter is?"

"She is eight... going on ten and eight," Mr. Bradford said with a groan.

At his apparent distress, Jane laughed and Mr. Bradford looked at her in surprise.

"Forgive me, Mr. Bradford. My closest sister, Elizabeth, seems to be very much like your Cassandra. By the time she was eight, she spoke fluent French and Italian, and voraciously read any book or periodical my father had in his library – in several languages." At the gentleman's raised brow, she held back another wide smile. "She is a bit of a savant when it comes to languages."

"Your sister is a bluestocking?"

"If you are asking if she is educated beyond what others deem normal, then yes, she would be considered as such, which is not surprising as our father, before he inherited Longbourn, was a Cambridge Don. And yet, she does not use her intellect as a cudgel. If you were to meet her today, you would find her the most composed, polite lady in the room."

The hall clock struck the quarter-hour and Mr. Bradford, after placing his teacup on the small table, stood to face Aunt Madeline.

"Mrs. Gardiner, thank you for accepting a stranger in your home, and for the tea." He turned toward Jane. "Miss Bennet, you have no idea how much I appreciated the care you took of my daughter. You were calm and collected and helped contain her fear, for she told me later, the pain was something she had never experienced before. For the past few days, all I have heard is, 'Miss Bennet this,' and 'Miss Bennet that.' You made quite the impression. She is convinced you are a fairy princess, for no mortal woman could be so beautiful and kind."

Jane knew her cheeks had flushed with embarrassment and kept her gaze trained on the floor. Her aunt smoothly interjected. "My niece is a sensible young woman, and it would not matter who the person was. If you were in trouble, she would lend assistance. It is her nature."

"Miss Bennet." Jane raised her gaze and met Mr. Bradford's. "By way of a thank you, may I request the pleasure of your company, and that of your uncle and aunt, at my home for dinner Tuesday next? Cassandra is expected to have better mobility by that time, and I know she would love to see you again."

"Your wife does not mind you inviting strangers to dine?" Jane could not stop herself from asking.

"I am a widower, Miss Bennet. My daughter and I live alone."

Alarmed at the uptick in her heart rate, Jane managed to reply with a steady voice. "If my aunt and uncle have nothing planned for the evening, I would be delighted."

"I can safely say we have no engagements for next Tuesday. The Parkers were obliged to cancel their ball," her aunt replied warmly. "Jane's sister, Elizabeth is also staying with us. Would you mind if she joined our party for dinner?"

"Not at all. I know you will consult your husband, Mrs. Gardiner, so please send a confirmed acceptance to the address on my card. Also, because Cassandra wishes to be the hostess, we will eat earlier than normal town hours. Would six o'clock suit you?"

"That would be acceptable. With four children of our own, we also tend to keep earlier hours." Aunt Madeline glanced at Jane. "Would you be so kind as to escort Mr. Bradford to the front door while I have Lambert retrieve his outerwear?"

"Yes, Aunt, of course."

She rose to her feet and followed Mr. Bradford from the room, standing in the front vestibule while he shrugged on his coat, and thanked the footman for his hat and walking cane.

"I look forward to our dinner engagement, Miss Bennet, and will give you fair warning, Cassandra has a plethora of questions to ask." Jane's eyes widened, and Mr. Bradford smiled. "Nothing too indiscreet, I am sure. She longs for elegant female companionship, so do not be surprised if your conversation revolves around a desire to pin her hair up like a young lady."

Anything further Mr. Bradford might have said was put on hold as Aunt Madeline joined them, and together, they bid the gentleman farewell.

Jane wandered into the front parlor and watched him board his carriage. The vehicle was well sprung, its pitch-black body gleaming in the sun from an expensive, high gloss finish. There was no identifying crest or decal on the door, but she made note of the familiar stylized **BCC** anchored above the rear wheel casing. The irony of the fact Mr. Bradford's carriage had been made by the Bingley Carriage Company was not lost on her.

The elegant equipage rumbled down Gracechurch Street, and she ruminated on Mr. Bradford's short visit. Polite and congenial, he had not talked about his family, other than to praise his daughter, and gave no indication he sought Jane's company for anything other than friendship. She moved away from the window and returned to her needlework in the parlor, resolved to put her heart in abeyance. She did not need another wealthy man toying with her feelings. The last one had nearly broken her.

LONGBOURN'S ANGELS

Chapter Thirteen

Elizabeth returned from Hatchard's and could not help but notice the elegant carriage moving away from her uncle's house, and hurried inside, finding her way to the family parlor.

"Elizabeth, would you like Mrs. Seggie to bring you some tea?"

"That would be lovely, Aunt Madeline," Elizabeth said as she pulled off her bonnet before handing it to the maid. "I am parched."

"Your shopping expedition was successful?"

"Partly. The novel I wanted had not arrived, so I placed my name on a waiting list. The clerk promised it would arrive within the week. This way, I will have a new book to read when Jane and I are at Susannah's."

"If you find the book a good read, may I borrow it when you travel with Aunt and Uncle to the Lake District this summer," Jane asked

"Absolutely," Elizabeth said and gave her sister a sly smile. "So… did anything exciting happen whilst I was out trying to spend all my pin money? Jane, have you anything to share with your most beloved sister? The one who keeps ALL your secrets."

"Mr. Bradford, the gentleman whose daughter I lent aid to last week, came by to express his thanks."

"He invited us all to dinner next Tuesday. I find I am quite curious as to who he is."

"Why do you say that, aunt?"

"His card shows an address on Grosvenor Square."

"Grosvenor Square?" Jane gave a small start and turned pale. "He must reside very close to Mr. Hurst's townhouse, which is on Grosvenor Street."

"Grosvenor Street is longer than you realize." Aunt Madeline gave Jane a small smile. "I would not worry about running into a certain family, and even if you did, hold your head high, my dear. You did nothing wrong."

"If anyone should worry, it is I," Elizabeth teased. "Have you forgotten Mr. Darcy resides on Grosvenor Square? That great gentleman might suffer a fit of apoplexy if he witnesses me disembarking from a carriage to dine with someone who lives within sight of his home."

"You are too harsh on Mr. Darcy," Jane said quietly. "I do not believe he holds you in as much contempt as you think."

Aunt Madeline cleared her throat to get their attention.

"Enough about gentlemen who do not appreciate the Bennet sisters. Given we are to attend a very upscale address next week, a trip to Madame Etienne's is required. Nothing too flashy, but our gowns must be elegant." When Elizabeth and Jane both began to object, Aunt Madeline raised her finger to silence them. "I will brook no opposition. Consider this my early birthday gift to both of you."

A few days later, the ladies were spending a quiet afternoon, using the time to catch up on their correspondence with friends and family. They were interrupted when a footman brought in a hand-delivered note for Elizabeth, who upon reading it, gave a soft murmur of approval. Jane looked up from her writing slope.

"Who is the note from, Lizzy?"

"It is from Susannah." Elizabeth placed the letter on her lap and smiled at Jane. "She invites us to join her on Bond Street tomorrow afternoon before having tea at a lovely pastry shop, she recently discovered."

"We have nothing on our calendar, except the final fitting for our dresses We might be able to squeeze in a bit of shopping for some accessories while there. I could use a new reticule, now that I think on it."

"Perfect. I shall send a reply at once unless you had previous plans, we were not aware of, Aunt Madeline." Elizabeth acknowledged their aunt, who replied she had no engagements on the morrow which required her niece's attention. "I shall reply directly, then."

The next afternoon found the three friends browsing the windows of some unique boutique stores, trying to decide which one they would enter before visiting the pastry shop. Having decided to attend an elegant haberdashery, their entrance was stalled by the exit of two ladies. Both of whom came to a complete stop, blocking the entrance.

"Do you smell something, Louisa?" asked the one lady. "It reminds me of country mushrooms, which tend to spring up where they are not wanted."

Jane had gone completely still, her face chalk white. Elizabeth merely watched the two sisters make complete fools of themselves, and Susannah… well, she narrowed her eyes and Elizabeth would not have been surprised if she removed her glove and slapped Miss Bingley across the face, before challenging her to a duel of honor.

Fortunately, for them, Miss Bingley and Mrs. Hurst said not another word. They turned their offended noses high in the air and walked around the three friends without further acknowledgment.

"Well," Susannah said, her manner bemused instead of offended. "I must say, she is a saucy minx. I have never before been called a country mushroom. Does she have any idea how great a faux pax she performed?"

"She holds herself in very high esteem," Elizabeth answered.

"They are the sisters I wrote about this fall, Miss Bingley and her sister, Mrs. Louisa Hurst," Jane said with a resigned sigh. "If you recall from my letters, Mr. Bingley leased Netherfield Park, the estate which abuts Longbourn."

"As witnessed here today, the contempt his sisters hold for Jane and me is plainly evident," Elizabeth said, her tone casual, although she seethed with a deep anger at the treatment her sister and friend received. "However, given the careful assessment that Miss Bingley gave your ensemble Susannah, I imagine she is confused as to who you are."

Her friend nodded in agreement. "Based on her behavior, she would never expect a duke's daughter to befriend ladies like you and Jane. Oh, this makes me want to do something absolutely naughty."

"No," Jane said firmly. "When the two of you get your heads together, even fallen angels tremble with fear. I beg you to leave Miss Bingley alone. She is entitled to her opinion, and I have no further wish to gain or lose her favor."

Susannah looped her arm through Jane's.

"My dear friend. I have no wish to give you grief and promise I will not go out of my way to bring Miss Bingley to her knees. However," Susannah turned Jane to face her and looked her directly in the eye. "If she crosses my path, and the opportunity presents itself, I will not back down. On that, you have my word."

"Dear Susannah," Jane said. "What am I going to do with you?"

"Absolutely nothing except help pick out the best hat this delightful shop offers."

Susannah kept her arm around Jane's and led both sisters into the shop. Soon the three friends were laughing and enjoying each other's company, the ugly encounter forgotten.

***

Jane did everything she could to remain calm while her uncle's carriage slowed to a halt in front of an elegant townhouse. Hands clenched on her lap, she focused on her breathing, bringing to mind the face of Cassandra, and the fact it was for her they were here.

"Oh, Janie. Mr. Bradford's house is quite stunning."

"Yes, it is. I hope we do not become lost in finding the dining room."

"We are here, my dears," Uncle Edward said and waited for his man to open the carriage door. He quickly stepped out and turned around to hand out each of his ladies.

A liveried footman descended the stairs and, after a courteous bow, led them back up to the front entrance where an austere butler awaited. With every step mounted, Jane's anxiety rose. By the time she reached the door, her heart was nearly in her mouth. Each beat hammering at her throat.

I cannot do this. I cannot do this.

The spell was broken by a soft, high giggle and an excited, "Miss Bennet. You have come!"

At the sound of Miss Cassandra's voice, all panic melted away, and the smile Jane bestowed on the young girl was genuine.

"Miss Bradford, you are obviously feeling better, although I would not want you to re-injure your ankle."

She said this because, as much as Cassandra tried to contain her excitement, she was practically dancing from one foot to the other. She calmed a bit when her father laid a gentle hand on her shoulder.

"Welcome to my home, Mr. Gardiner, Mrs. Gardiner,

Miss Bennet, and…" he cast a glance at Lizzy. "May I assume this is Miss Elizabeth Bennet?"

"You are correct, sir." Lizzy dipped a quick curtsy, while their aunt and uncle returned Mr. Bradford's polite greeting and made the proper introduction.

"Crenshaw," Mr. Bradford turned to the butler. "Advise Mrs. Porter we shall dine within the half hour."

"Very good… sir."

Crenshaw left his post by the door, moving across the foyer in search of Mrs. Porter, whom Jane assumed could not be far away, and Mr. Bradford asked his daughter to lead the way to the drawing room. Jane felt her sister nudge her in the arm with her elbow while they walked, and she spared Lizzy a quick glance.

Lizzy arched her one eyebrow, a trait she shared with Papa, and nodded at the elegant furniture and paintings. "Mr. Bradford has excellent taste in décor, and he is handsome – which you conveniently forgot to tell me."

"Hush, Lizzy. He might hear you."

"I will behave. So far, I am quite impressed and will do nothing to ruin your chance of a good friendship."

"I seek nothing from Mr. Bradford," Jane whispered.

"I was speaking of his daughter," Lizzy whispered back and nudged her again, letting Jane know she was teasing.

Aunt Madeline partially turned before they reached the drawing room, and leveled a censorious look in their direction. Jane's cheeks warmed. She and Lizzy were no better than Lydia, whispering behind people's backs. She straightened her posture even further and nodded at her aunt, a nonverbal acknowledgment that she and her sister would behave like the ladies they were. She heard a very quiet, 'Sorry,' from Lizzy as they entered the room.

The dinner was delightful, if not simple. Miss Bradford had chosen every dish served, which comprised all of her favorites and one of her Papa's. Jane was enchanted by the little girl, amazed at how poised she was at the tender age of eight.

Miss Bradford, for the occasion, sat at the head of the table, while her Papa sat at the other end. Jane, as the guest of honor, sat to her right, Elizabeth to her left. Aunt and uncle were seated near Mr. Bradford. The table was small enough that everyone conversed easily, and Jane was pleased to hear Mr. Bradford engage her uncle and aunt with no hint of condescension. Meanwhile, Lizzy entertained his daughter with stories of Longbourn and Meryton. Through it all, Miss Bradford peppered them both with questions about their sister and brothers.

"I would love a brother or sister. What is it like?" she asked between the first and second courses.

"Loud," Lizzy replied

"Lizzy," Jane chastised softly. "I grant you at times the noise level is more than we like, but it is lovely to know you always have someone you can talk to, and share your thoughts with."

"Miss Bradford," Lizzy leaned closer to the little girl, as though departing a great secret. "My beloved sister Jane is the gentlest person I know, however, it is a well-known fact our dear Jane, when pushed beyond her limits, can hold her own in a sisterly argument."

"That was but one time," Jane protested.

"Truth, in fact, it was only one time, and because you are normally so soft-spoken, Lydia stopped her caterwauling the minute you raised your voice." Lizzy sat back and smiled. "It was the most glorious, five minutes of peace I shall never forget."

"Miss Lydia is your youngest sister?"

Both Jane and Lizzy turned their heads toward Mr. Bradford, eyes widening when they realized he had been listening quite attentively to their conversation. Jane should have known he would keep a close eye on relative strangers conversing with his only child. Her cheeks warmed again while Lizzy chuckled.

"Yes, Lydia is the youngest, although she dearly wishes she were the oldest."

"And why is that?"

"At the grand age of fourteen, she has decided she knows everything she needs in life to succeed and is determined to be the first of her sisters to marry." At Mr. Bradford's slightly shocked look, Lizzy hastened to add, "Not that she will have the opportunity. Our father and brothers would never allow anything to happen to her. She is quite safe to admire gentlemen from afar."

"You also have brothers, Miss Bennet?"

"We do, Michael and Gabriel are our eldest brothers."

"Dare I worry avenging angels might descend upon my home?"

"On is the avenging angel, the other is the messenger," Jane replied, a hint of humor coloring her voice.

"What my sister is attempting to say in her own delicate way, is this," Lizzy interjected. "If a gentleman dared overstep his bounds, Longbourn's angels spring into action. Gabriel brings the tidings of upcoming woe, and Michael brings the woe."

Mr. Bradford chuckled. "I am in favor of this, and would like to meet your brothers one day."

The thought of Mr. Bradford wishing to meet her family gave Jane much pleasure, yet she fought those feelings. She did not know the man well enough to judge whether he was being merely polite, or earnest in his intention.

"Papa, may I show Miss Bennet my new pianoforte?"

Because of Miss Bradford's age, the gentlemen did not stay back to enjoy their port and joined the ladies. By nine o'clock, the little girl could barely hide her yawns, and Uncle Edward indicated it was time his family took their leave.

"Thank you, Mr. Bradford, for a pleasant evening," Uncle Edward said, once they were all gathered near the front entrance. "Miss Bradford, you were a very elegant hostess, and the meal you provided was delicious."

Even though she was practically asleep on her feet, Cassandra smiled wide and looked up at her father, who nodded in agreement. Jane's heart melted a little further at the sight of a loving father and his daughter. Clearly, Mr. Bradford was a good man.

Their hosts bade them all good night, and before Jane could exit, Miss Bradford broke from her father and ran to Jane, who bent down to receive a fierce hug.

"I love you, Miss Bennet. You are the nicest lady I have ever known, and I am glad you are my friend."

"I will always be your friend, Miss Bradford." Jane gave her a little squeeze, then stood. "I think you should stand with your Papa. A lady always holds herself tall with a little bit of elegance when saying good night to guests."

"Yes, Miss Bennet."

The young girl immediately returned to her father's side and waved at them when they were ready to depart. Jane waved back and dared to look at Mr. Bradford, whose gaze never left hers.

"You are in deep trouble, Jane," Lizzy teased, once the two sisters were settled in the bedchamber they shared at their uncle's house.

"Whatever do you mean?"

"Not only does the daughter love you, but the father is well on his way to losing his heart."

"No, I will not tread down that road again."

"I agree. There will be no walking this path. I think you will suffer a landslide. He at least is a man who knows what he wants, not a puppy who plays the game of love."

"Lizzy!"

"I speak the truth and you know it. I give you leave to like Mr. Bradford. He is a true gentleman. Look how he treated our aunt and uncle this evening. He is clearly very wealthy and likely in the upper ring of society, yet he treated them with care and consideration."

"He did, indeed."

"I do not blame you if you proceed with caution, dearest, but do not paint him with the same brush as Mr. Bingley. It would not be fair to Mr. Bradford. He needs to be accepted on his own merits."

"I do not know if I could bear another heartbreak, Lizzy. Even though I was warned about Mr. Bingley's fickle nature, I could not believe he left without saying a word. It was like we had never met, or spent time together."

"I am beginning to understand Mr. Bingley is a bit of a dreamer. He is charming and amiable, but he has yet to become a man who makes his own decisions."

"I agree, Lizzy." Jane became pensive. "When he does come into his own, he will be a wonderful husband and father, however, it will not be with me. He did not love me enough to stay and grow together."

"Sad, but true, Jane."

The sisters fell into silence, which turned into a restive sleep.

***

"Papa," Cassandra mumbled, half asleep and desperately trying to stay awake to ask her father a question.

"Yes, my love."

Henry pulled the cover over his daughter's slight body and tucked in the edges before kissing her forehead.

"I really like Miss Bennet and Miss Elizabeth."

"I like them as well."

"Will we see them again?"

"Would you like to see them again?"

"Yes, very much."

"Then, I will see what I can do."

"Thank you, Papa. I love you."

"I love you too, sweetling."

He would have given her another soft kiss, but his precious child had already fallen asleep, a contented smile gracing her face. He made his way to his own bedchamber, stopped in front of the fireplace, and looked up at the portrait of a beautiful woman, an older version of their daughter.

"You would like Miss Bennet, Constance. She is not a titled lady and, from the way her uncle spoke, has no wealth of her own. I find their honesty refreshing, and that is what draws me to her. Miss Bennet's heart is pure and she is kindness herself. I do not think I am wrong to ask for a courtship, to see if we suit. Cassandra is already in love with her, and I am not far behind."

He gave the portrait a small nod and turned to undress before sliding into his bed to dream of a fair-haired lady from Hertfordshire.

LONGBOURN'S ANGELS

Chapter Fourteen

"Miss Bennet!"

Elizabeth looked up from the bookshelf she'd been browsing to find Mr. Darcy standing next to her.

"Mr. Darcy," she said and gave the gentleman a barely polite half-curtsy.

"I did not know you were in town as well."

"As well? What can you mean by that?"

"I am aware your sister is visiting relatives. I did not know you accompanied her."

Anger, lain dormant following Jane's visit with Miss Bingley and subsequent cut on Bond Street, burned beneath her breastbone. Not only had Mr. Darcy aided the viper in separating her brother from Jane, but knew she was currently in the city.

"What think you of this abnormally cold winter?"

Mr. Darcy very nearly gaped at her, and she felt immense satisfaction at having discombobulated him.

"I am sorry, you wish to discuss the weather?"

"I did promise when next we met, I would ensure we spoke of the weather."

"Then, let me not disappoint you. We are indeed having a cold winter. Fortunately, my house is well insulated, with plenty of provisions to keep our rooms comfortable."

"Does Mr. Bingley still reside with you and your sister?"

Elizabeth projected what she hoped was a very innocent look. "Is *his* room all toasty and warm?"

"He removed to his brother's house more than a week ago." Mr. Darcy's eyes narrowed with suspicion. "Why do you ask?"

"No particular reason other than it became a central part of the brief conversation my sister had with Miss Bingley and Mrs. Hurst when she paid them a courtesy call earlier this month."

"A central part of the conversation?"

"They were under the assumption my sister had come for the sole purpose of seeing Mr. Bingley. Anyone with a modicum of intelligence would know my sister never crosses the hard lines of polite society, yet that is exactly what Miss Bingley inferred before she cut the visit short."

"For your sister's sake, I am sorry Miss Bingley was abrupt."

"Why would you care if Miss Bingley conducted herself in a rude manner? It is not as though this pattern of behavior is surprising, and I know very well you have no concern over the feelings of my sister. Miss Bingley made certain Jane was aware of your opinion in this matter."

For what seemed like an eternity, Mr. Darcy stared down at her. His eyes were sharp with intelligence and held absolutely no hint of remorse or shame.

"I will not quibble with you, Miss Elizabeth, over the deportment of my friend's sister. Suffice to say, Mr. Bingley is now with his family, where he belongs."

Of all the… She could not even finish her own thought. Arrogant man! She knew, based on what Jane shared after that disastrous social call, Mr. Darcy was instrumental in convincing Mr. Bingley to abandon Netherfield Park, and her beloved sister was the one who paid the price for his treachery. About to verbally lay into him again, she glanced over his shoulder and noticed Susannah, standing at the end of the aisle. Her friend smiled when she saw where Elizabeth had been browsing for a book.

"I should have known you would be in the classic section, Lizzy."

"Excuse me, sir,"

Elizabeth stepped around Mr. Darcy, treating him as if he were just another patron with whom she had no acquaintance. Once she reached Susannah, she looped their arms together, and steered her friend toward the entrance, chatting gaily as though she did not have a care in the world.

"I am so glad you found me; I find this wonderful place of finding dreams has lost its charm."

"I am shocked," Susannah teased. "Hatchard's is your absolute favorite store to visit. I shall have to mark this on my calendar."

"You absolutely must, for this aberration will never happen again. Now, let me pick up the book I ordered, and then we may depart."

Confident her friend had not even noticed the gentleman left behind; Elizabeth glanced over her shoulder at Mr. Darcy. He had turned to watch them, twin flags of anger high on his cheekbones. She'd been abominably rude, not taking a proper leave of him. Mentally, she shrugged. Turnabout was fair play. He and his party did not take their leave upon departing Meryton. It was only fair he experienced a taste of his own medicine.

***

That evening found Darcy comfortably seated by a roaring fireplace, long legs stretched out before him, mulling over the rancorous encounter with Miss Elizabeth. His initial delight in seeing her, and having a valid reason to engage her in conversation, was completely overshadowed by her righteous anger. He took another sip of his drink. All Caroline Bingley had to do when faced with Miss Jane Bennet was present a polite veneer, deflect all conversation about her brother, and send the placid miss on her way after a gracious quarter-hour visit. But no, it seemed Bingley's sister, convinced of her own superiority, had been cruel and vindictive. No wonder Miss Elizabeth was furious with all of them.

He laid his head on the back of the chair and released a deep sigh. His friendship with Bingley, deep and abiding, was the only reason he suffered the company of the snobby sisters. Yet, there were times he wondered if it were enough. Maybe it was time to limit the interactions with his friend to their club and riding. Upon remembering he was set to dine with Bingley and his family that very evening, Darcy banged his head lightly against the chair. He would attend the dinner, ask Bingley to meet with him sometime during the week at their club, then explain why he needed to put space between their families.

Darcy had a sense of *déjà vu* the minute he stepped into the Hurst's main drawing room the next evening. Similar to Meryton, he had barely cleared the door frame before Miss Bingley attached herself to his side like a limpet. And, if that were not bad enough, she immediately began to brag how she set Miss Jane Bennet out on her ear when she dared to show her face at their townhouse earlier in the month.

"I immediately informed Miss Bennet the visit was a waste of time as Charles was staying with you and Miss Darcy." That explained how Miss Elizabeth knew with certainty Charles had been residing at his house. Miss Bingley continued, not even noticing his silence. "Of course, I have not returned her call. As if I would ever set foot in Cheapside, let alone darken the door of a low-born tradesman." She paused to take a breath, then gasped as if taken with a new thought. "Oh! I must tell you the best part."

"There is a best part to all of this?"

"Oh, yes, Mr. Darcy." She leaned closer, obviously hoping he would reciprocate. When he did not, she straightened and her lips thinned in anger. "Less than a week ago, Louisa and I came across Miss Bennet and her sister on Bond Street, and we cut them direct."

"Are you certain Miss Bennet was aware of your presence?"

"Most definitely. She made as though to bid us a good day before turning pale with fear. Eliza Bennet dared lift her nose at us, impertinent miss."

Inwardly, Darcy grimaced. No wonder Miss Elizabeth treated him with such disdain at Hatchard's. His anger toward her emolliated somewhat, knowing how insulted she must have felt at the hands of Bingley's sisters. It was just bad luck they had crossed paths so soon after the incident.

"Did you say Bond Street?"

"They were not there by themselves. They were accompanied by another woman, dressed in a very expensive manner. She looked somewhat familiar. Likely some wealthy tradesman's daughter, and as I do not muddy my reputation by associating with the lower rings of society, I paid her no mind."

Darcy felt his eyebrows raise at the absurdity of her comment. He recalled Gabriel Bennet subtly telling him of their connection to the Chilton family and tried to remember if there was a sister the same age as the two eldest Bennet girls. His aunt Matlock would know; however, he had no intention of asking. Aunt Lucinda would take that as a sign he was seeking a bride, and he had no wish to start rumors of that nature.

Miss Bingley continued ranting. "I now wish I had confronted her before giving the cut direct."

"Your brother is moving on with his life, as should you."

"You cannot know how much I appreciate your good opinion, Mr. Darcy." Miss Bingley drew closer and whispered, "I shall remember your kind words and take them into my dreams."

He could not help himself. He recoiled in horror.

"Do not read more into my remarks other than taking them at face value. I am your brother's friend. Nothing more."

She straightened her spine and removed her hand from his arm.

"Forgive *my* impertinence, Mr. Darcy. It would not do for you to mistake me for Miss Eliza Bennet by either word or action."

He almost laughed out loud. He would *never* mistake Miss Caroline Bingley for Miss Elizabeth Bennet.

"I should mingle and greet your other guests. It would not do for them to think I am avoiding my friends."

With that, he approached Lord Blake and asked about the new horse he'd purchased a few weeks ago at auction. Darcy remained aloof and distant from Miss Bingley until dinner was announced, and after the men enjoyed their port brandy, he had a quiet word with Bingley, asking if they could meet at their club later in the week, then departed for his own house. He did not care if Miss Bingley felt slighted by the fact that he did not return to the drawing room.

***

That same night, Mr. Bradford dined with Jane and her family. Cassandra, much to her disappointment, had remained at home with her governess. Upon hearing this, Jane worried the little girl would be upset on two fronts. The first reason, Miss Bradford loved coming with her Papa when he took Jane for walks in the park nearby. The second reason, his daughter truly did not like or trust her governess. Snippets of information continued to slip into their conversation, and Jane sadly agreed that Miss Pope, a recently acquired governess from Kent, did aspire to become the next Mrs. Bradford.

When thinking about that possibility, Jane became disconcerted by her reaction. She did not like to think of another woman on the arm of Mr. Bradford. She wished for the honor to be hers, and hers alone. Upon realizing her feelings had shifted into something more than friendship, she found it very difficult to look Mr. Bradford in the eyes.

"Have I done something to offend you, Miss Bennet?" Mr. Bradford asked almost as soon as he arrived and took a seat next to her on the couch.

Thrilled by the fact they were quite alone in the parlor, her gaze flew to him, and she found him watching her with tender regard. She knew her cheeks flushed, and she dropped her eyes again. His hand found hers, and she forced herself to look up again.

"Might I ask if you would grant me a private interview before dinner?" Mr. Bradford asked in a low voice.

"My aunt and sister have yet to join us, Mr. Bradford. This is about as private as we can manage in such a busy household."

"Then, I will waste no time." Gently, almost reverently, he kissed the back of her hand. "You are the kindest, most generous woman I know, and after gaining consent from my daughter, I humbly ask permission to court you."

Jane's heart rate increased at his request. She had only just come to realize how much she liked the gentleman.

"I would be honored, Mr. Bradford."

"Let me make my intentions clear, Miss Bennet. I already know my own feelings, and my desire is for marriage. This courtship is for you. To give you time to determine your own feelings, to ascertain if they will ever match mine."

"I appreciate the consideration. Please know I esteem you greatly, however, I must confess something before we go further." She tried to release her fingers from his, but he held firm. She had to admit, his unwillingness to let go, for even a minute, warmed her heart. "This past autumn a young gentleman leased the estate next to my father's. Given the limited society in Meryton, we were often in each other's company, and his attention to me was quite singular. So much so, I and my family were certain he would make an offer."

"What kind of attention?"

"At every event where we both were in attendance; he sought my company to the exclusion of everyone else. He also hosted a ball, whereupon he danced three sets with me."

"That is, indeed, singular attention." Mr. Bradford's thumb traced a lazy circle on hers. "I gather, given we are holding hands, mutually admiring each other, this gentleman no longer seeks your company. May I ask what happened?"

"The morning after the ball, Mr. Bingley left for London. The following day, his family along with their guest, quit the estate and joined him."

"They cut off all acquaintance?"

"One of their servants delivered a letter from his sister the day they departed Hertfordshire. I responded in kind to their London address, and heard nothing more until I arrived in town."

"Given your innate good manners, I assume you paid the sister a courtesy call."

"I had just come from their townhouse when you and I met in the park. I had stopped to regain my composure. Miss Bingley and her sister made it abundantly clear they, and their brother, wanted nothing more to do with me."

"I am sorry you were treated with such careless regard.

How do you feel about Mr. Bingley now?"

"Although his intentions were implied, he never made any promises. I can safely say, my heart suffered no lasting harm."

"To hear you say that my dear Miss Bennet, makes me very happy. I cannot give you grief over accepting a young man's attention. I was married myself."

"I would like to know more about your wife. That is if you are comfortable talking about her."

"I do not believe there was a time in my life when Constance was not a part of it. We practically grew up together and had a great friendship. Marriage seemed the logical step, and when she turned eighteen, we married."

"You were happy?"

"Yes. One year after we married, we had Cassandra, and the rest you know. I never thought my heart would be touched again until I met you. I love you, Jane, and hope one day, you will come to love me."

"At this moment in time, I do not know if what I feel is love. However, I am not averse to examining these feelings. I know I look forward to seeing you and am greatly disappointed when you cannot come to visit."

"Then, I shall have to make a more concerted effort to visit daily."

"Do not forget to bring your daughter. She is just as important to me as you are."

Mr. Bradford leaned forward and brushed her lips with his. Startled, she gasped, and he chuckled softly.

"I will not say I am sorry for stealing a kiss. I have longed to do that ever since we first met."

"Mr. Bradford!"

"You must call me Henry. We are well past formalities. We have kissed, you know."

"Humph… if you call that peck a kiss."

"Is that a challenge, Miss Bennet?"

"I thought you said we were past formalities, Mr. Bradford."

Henry released her fingers only to bring his hand up to cup her cheek. Slowly, ever so slowly, he leaned into her again, his gaze never leaving hers.

"One word from you will stop me, sweet Jane."

She pressed her lips together. That was until his lips met hers, then she became completely swept up in the moment. Too soon for her liking, they separated. Henry touched his forehead to hers before dropping a feather-light kiss on her brow.

"I believe I will need direction to your father's estate."

Jane's heart sank. Would Mr. Bradford survive her mother's nerves or her father's capricious sense of humor? Would Michael and Gabriel take one look at him and toss him out the door? Henry must have sensed her disquiet, because he took her hand again, and brought it to his lips.

"What is your concern, love?"

"I must warn you of my family." She attempted to withdraw her hand but, once again, he did not release his hold. "My mother… she is a woman of mean understanding, little information, and uncertain temper. When she is discontented, she fancies herself nervous. She is also very dedicated in her quest to have her daughters marry well."

Jane glanced up at him, to try and gauge his reaction. She was rewarded with a wide smile and sparkling eyes. She dropped her gaze and focused on their clasped hands.

"Your mother is not alone in this quest. Do you have any other concerns?"

"My brothers."

"Are they highwaymen? Blackguards? Vandals? I know they bear the name of angels, but this does not mean they have the same attributes."

"Oh no!" Jane's eyes flew once more to his. "It is just…

they are so very protective of their sisters."

"As they should be." Henry raised her chin with his finger and held her gaze. "What truly bothers you?"

Jane chewed the inside of her lip, trying to find words to describe her eclectic family.

"Miss Bennet. I will be forced to kiss you again if you continue to mangle your beautiful lip." With a small gasp, her mouth dropped open, and Henry took advantage, kissing her soundly. "I did warn you," he teased. "Now, out with it. What has you so worried?"

"Papa is, to some extent, cavalier in his attitude. He is a good father but allows my mother to behave inappropriately at times. In our small community, our neighbors are used to her outbursts, but to strangers, she appears vulgar and uncouth." Jane took a deep breath. "My youngest sister, Lydia, is spoiled and her manners are atrocious."

"That is all?" Jane nodded. "Thank goodness. I thought you were going to tell me you had hobgoblins in your family, and our children would have to wear hats all their lives to hide their green ears."

She stared at Henry for almost a full minute before she began to laugh. He quickly joined her, and this was how Lizzy found them, her eyebrow lifting slightly when they quickly disengaged their hands.

"I am pleased you make my sister laugh, Mr. Bradford. At times, Jane is too reticent with her feelings."

"I find I am delighted with all facets of your sister's personality, Miss Elizabeth."

Their conversation was interrupted when Aunt Madeline entered the room and asked them to follow her to the dining room. Later in the evening, after a delicious meal and good conversation, Jane and Elizabeth accompanied Henry to the front hall, where he shrugged into his great coat, and waited for his carriage to be brought around.

"I had a wonderful evening." He caught and held Jane's gaze. "As you know, I have some important business matters to attend to and will be away for a few days. May I call upon you as soon as I return, Miss Bennet?"

"Yes," Jane said with a tremulous smile. "I look forward to your return."

"Good night then, Miss Bennet. Miss Elizabeth."

He gave them each a polite half-bow and stepped out into the night.

Chapter Fifteen

Two days later, Henry's equipage turned through the gates to Longbourn. He had taken one of his more subdued carriages, with no family crest on the door, as he did not want to give rise to gossip when Jane's neighbors learned of their courtship. Upon arrival, Henry presented his card, the one which displayed only his name and address to Mr. Bennet's butler. He used them to conduct business in London's east end as deals were more easily negotiated if his rank was not front and center. He was quite content with everyone thinking he was nothing more than a wealthy gentleman.

"Mr. Bennet," Henry said and gave Jane's father a very polite half-bow.

"Mr. Bradford." Bennet returned his introduction with a nod of the head. "I have heard mention of your name through my daughter's letters and have a fairly good idea why you have descended upon Hertfordshire. However, that is all speculation. I would like to know, in truth, why you are here."

"I will not waste your time, Mr. Bennet. Miss Bennet and I have entered into a courtship."

Bennet's one eyebrow rose, reminding Henry of Miss Elizabeth. He smiled at how the eyebrow lowered and turned into a frown.

"Usually, when a man comes courting, he asks permission. He does not tell the young lady's father the deed is done and now seeks his blessing."

"Forgive my impertinence, but I am aware Miss Bennet is of age. Permission is not required; however, her dearest wish is that you and I are amicable with one another."

"Hmmm…" was all Bennet said as he resumed his seat behind a massive desk, waving his hand in the direction of a comfortable chair directly opposite him. "Jane wants everyone to get along, and spends most of her time as a peacemaker."

"I am aware and it is one of the traits I like best about her."

"Not her beauty or womanly form?"

Henry leveled a narrow glance at Jane's father, very aware of the delicate trap he had laid at Henry's feet.

"I will not insult your intelligence by saying your daughter's beauty did not draw me in. Only a blind man would pass her by without a second, or third look. Even then, he would turn around if he heard her voice." Bennet chuckled, and Henry pushed forward. "What drew me to your daughter was her kindness. She came to the aid of my daughter without one thought of dirtying her gloves or tearing her gown and calmed my daughter's fears. Not many ladies would lower themselves to give aid to a stranger. At least, not the ladies who parade the park in front of my home."

"Yes, I noticed you reside on Grosvenor Square." Bennet tapped the card with his finger. "Am I to assume you are wealthy?"

"I am."

"Jane does not have a large dowry. It is substantial, by Meryton's standards, but not the beau monde."

"I do not require an infusion of cash. When my wife passed, her settlement was set aside for our daughter Cassandra, and I have more than enough for my future wife and children."

"Jane wrote you were raising your daughter on your own. Although we did not know your wife, please accept our condolences."

Henry merely bowed his head in acknowledgment and when Bennet offered him a drink, he accepted, settling back into his chair to assess the man who started to push back his chair in order to pour them each a brandy. So far, his identity had remained secret, which suited him fine. Once he and Jane were more established in their courtship, he would reveal all. What Henry had not counted on was Jane's brother knowing him by sight.

"Lord Holcomb!" Michael paused at the door to his father's study, clearly startled to recognize the man seated across from his father.

"Lord Holcomb?" Bennet said, surprise lending an unpleasant color to his tone. "I thought your name was Henry Bradford."

"It is, Mr. Bennet. I am also Lord Holcomb."

Bennet's eyes narrowed and his steely gaze pinned Henry to his chair.

"I see, and how far up the realm's ladder rests your title?"

"I am an earl."

"This does not bode well for you, Lord Holcomb. You began our conversation under the blanket of subterfuge."

"I wished for you to know the man, not the title."

Unflinching, Henry held the older man's gaze.

"I am seriously displeased by this turn of events," Bennet muttered, and both Michael and Henry frowned.

"You are displeased I am courting your daughter?"

Henry could not believe how this interview was turning out. Was Jane's father gone mad?

"I would be a fool to discourage your interest." Bennet leaned back in his chair and tapped the bottom right drawer of his desk. "This means I shall have to bring out the good brandy, and not the one I foist off on my neighbors."

The room fell silent, excepting the snap and crackle of the fireplace. Then, Henry began to chuckle.

"I now see where your second eldest daughter gets her sense of humor. I think I am going to like your family very much, Mr. Bennet."

"You may call me Thomas, or Bennet – although it becomes confusing when my sons are in the vicinity."

"Thank you, Bennet. Please call me Holcomb, and if the blessed event I fervently hope for takes place, I would ask you to call me Henry."

"Blessed event?" Michael asked.

"Holcomb here has requested permission to court Jane."

"I believe he wishes for something more," Michael said in a dangerous tone.

"Your sister is well aware I wish to marry her. The courtship is to help her become more comfortable with me."

"Her hesitancy is natural, given what happened this autumn," Mr. Bennet murmured.

"She told me about Mr. Bingley."

"I am sure she was generous in her description of the young pup. She sees the good in everyone, even when they insult her in a very egregious manner."

"Pardon?" Henry's head cocked to one side as he perceived Bennet was, in an oblique manner, trying to tell him something Jane would never reveal. "Is there something important I should know?"

"Has Jane told you Mr. Bingley's sisters gave her, and Elizabeth, the cut direct on Bond Street?"

"No, sir, she did not." A righteous fury swept through him at the thought of someone assaulting his Jane in any manner. "Not one word."

"I am not surprised," Bennet said, smiling softly. "Jane is very much the lady and does not gossip. She is also a gentle soul, and their acrimonious behavior is hard for her to digest as she would never think to retaliate in the same manner."

"Oh, I do not know about that, Father," Michael said with a wry grin. "If Jane is motivated enough, she will stand up for herself. Although I think we can all agree, it takes a lot to get our sweetest sister angry. Do you remember the incident with Miss Maria Lucas?"

"Yes. If I recall correctly, she would rather have had Lizzy's sarcasm directed at her rather than Jane's righteous anger," Mr. Bennet said and shook his head at the memory.

"What did she do?" Henry could not imagine Jane losing her temper over anything. Not realistic, he inherently knew, but she was always so composed, serene, like a placid lake.

"Miss Maria had a terrible row with our youngest sister," Michael began. "To paint an accurate picture, I should tell you my sister Lydia is a determined, strong-willed girl, and likes to get her own way. She was not innocent in this altercation, by any means. As it was, during the argument, Miss Maria, ripped off Lydia's bonnet and tore it to pieces. Jane, who was also in the garden with them, witnessed the whole affair. She simply walked up to Miss Maria, removed the young lady's bonnet from her head, laid it on the ground, and stepped on it."

"No!"

"Oh, yes. She then picked up the squashed bonnet, and tied the ratty thing back onto Miss Maria's head before calmly saying, *'Do not forget the preserves your mother asked for when you take your leave.'* Miss Maria and Lydia both stood, mouths agape, their argument forgotten." Michael chuckled at the recollection. "Not one of them ever breathed a word of it. Had I not been sitting by an open window, none of us would ever have known."

Henry ruminated on what Jane's brother shared, and the longer he thought, the more amused he became.

"What has you smiling, Lord Holcomb?"

"I was thinking still waters run deep."

"You allude to Miss Bennet's temperament?"

"I do. I was, at first, amazed she would lose her temper over anything, and in my mind, likened her personality to a calm, placid lake." Both Mr. Bennet and Michael nodded at his description. "However, if you are any kind of angler, you know beneath the surface of some waters, there are strong currents and eddies, which catch you unaware. I believe Miss Bennet is like that."

"She is, at that. Well, Michael," Bennet said, leaning back in his chair. "Bring over some glasses in order for us to enjoy the good brandy I promised. We must celebrate our Jane finding a man worthy of her affection."

While Michael brought out three glasses and proceeded to fill them, Bennet continued his conversation with Henry.

"I think, for the time being, we will not tell my wife about your title. She tends to get over-excited and will not be able to contain her spasms and fluttering if she knew she might be tasked with planning a peer's wedding."

"You mean, her daughter's wedding."

"No, your lordship, I meant a peer's wedding. The only thing on this planet which could displace Jane in her mother's affection is a son who brings a title into the family. Mrs. Bennet would do everything in her power to make you the happiest man."

"If Miss Bennet accepts my courtship and proposal, exchanging her name from Bennet to Bradford is the only thing that would make me happy. The rest is all fluff."

"Yes, well, fluff is what my wife excels at."

"Mr. Bennet… I, ah…" Henry hesitated. "Your daughter is not aware of my title, either."

Bennet's eyes widened, while Michael's narrowed.

"You have not told Jane you are an earl?"

"It did not come up in conversation."

"I find that hard to believe," Michael said. "Introductions had to occur at some time where you let others know who and what you are."

"Believe me, or not, this did not come up. Our initial introduction was through my daughter, Cassandra, who is eight. Your daughter lent her aid after she was injured in the park. When I arrived at Gardiner's household to extend my thanks, the housekeeper entered the room right after I told them my name was Henry Bradford."

"Let me get his straight. Neither my brother and his wife, nor my two daughters know you are an earl. Jane has written of your invitation to dine. Did not your residence give them pause?"

"An acquaintance of theirs lives on the same street. I believe your family thinks I am a wealthy landowner, same as him. Technically, they are correct."

"You allude to Mr. Darcy, I presume."

"Your daughters never told me his name."

Henry admitted to being startled by this tidbit. Once again, satisfaction coursed through his body at the confirmation that his Jane, and her sister, were not name-droppers. They judged people on the merit of their behavior, not wealth or rank.

"Elizabeth must be fit to be tied, landing on the same street as Mr. Darcy," Michael said, his voice amused. At Henry's questioning look, Michael expanded. "The very first night Mr. Darcy arrived in Meryton, there was a local assembly. Unfortunately, he attended with Bingley. While Bingley made love to our sister," – Henry frowned, and Michael briefly paused – "his great friend stalked the edges of the dance floor, and before the night was out, insulted Elizabeth in a very personal way."

Henry was surprised by this declaration. He knew Darcy to be a consummate gentleman.

"I see your doubt and will tell you what happened. Bingley pointed out Elizabeth, who was seated at the time, saying she was a pretty sort of girl, and he should ask her to dance. Darcy looked directly at my sister and said, she was 'tolerable but not handsome enough to tempt him to dance.' He then blathered on about not giving consequence to a woman who was slighted by other men."

"Please tell me your sister did not hear him spout such balderdash."

"She most assuredly did, along with many of our friends and neighbors."

"I cannot fathom him behaving in such a fashion, and wonder if he is in need of corrective lenses. Anyone with eyes can see your sister, Miss Elizabeth, is more than pretty." Henry shook his head and wondered what Darcy had been thinking to say such a thing. In public, no less. "If I see him at our club, I must have words with him."

"Have no fear, Holcomb. Lizzy let him know what she thought of his abject rudeness and was so effective in her chastisement, he apologized twice. She then took my brother and me to task for attempting to protect her."

A mental picture of Elizabeth standing toe to toe with, not only Darcy but her brothers, struck Henry's funny bone, and he started to laugh. "I would have paid good money to see your sister take on all you fine gentlemen. Having said that, the party from Netherfield did not leave a good impression on your small village. Shame on them."

"We are better off without them. Life has gone back to normal. At least, as normal as Meryton can be with red coats strutting like puffed-up peacocks down our streets. Fortunately, they are decamping to Brighton this spring and things will settle down."

"I cannot believe the fool left without securing her hand." All three gentlemen knew to whom Henry alluded. "She has assured me her heart suffered no lasting damage and was very receptive to my proposal of a courtship."

"Then, we had best plan for what we hope happens next."

The three gentlemen spent another hour discussing future plans and expanding the boundaries of their burgeoning friendship. Although he was given the invitation to stay the night and meet the rest of the family, Henry declined, anxious to return to Town, and Jane.

***

"What does Charlotte say in her letter, Lizzy?" Jane asked as she folded a chemise and laid it in her trunk. The two sisters were leaving later in the afternoon for their planned visit with Susannah.

"She writes..." Elizabeth smoothed the folded paper and began to read out loud.

'Mr. Collins spends much of his spare time in the garden, attempting to colonize a bee hive. Lady Catherine expressed a fondness for honey during one of our visits and he is most anxious to curry her favor in all things. Unfortunately, he did not research what type of apiary is required, or what types of flora and fauna are the preferred food source. He is beside himself with worry, and I have awakened at night, only to hear him sneaking down the stairs to fuss over them when he should be at slumber. Needless to say, he is quite discomposed from lack of sleep and worries. I have written my father, asking him to send a book on bees so Mr. Collins may study the art of beekeeping, and perchance achieve a modicum of success.'

"Thank goodness Charlotte is patient. Further down, she writes about how much she enjoys being the mistress of her own home and is quite content. For that, I am glad."

"Does she still expect you to join her father and sister when they travel to Hunsford for Easter?"

"Yes, she does and, funnily enough, I am looking forward to our visit." Elizabeth laughed a bit at the notion. "I find I am exceedingly curious as to the nature of Lady Catherine de Bourgh. I am sure Sir William and Miss Maria, or rather Miss Lucas as she is now called, will be in awe. Like his new son-in-law, Sir William appreciates rubbing shoulders with those of a higher rank."

Aunt Madeline entered the room and sighed at the sight of open trunks and scattered bits of clothing.

"I shall miss you, girls. It was lovely having you here this past month, and the children will be desolate when you are gone."

"We are not leaving the country, Aunt Madeline. You know Jane and I will visit as often as we can. In fact, let us make plans to take the children to visit the British Museum and see the artifacts brought back from Egypt. I, for one, cannot wait to see the Rosetta Stone."

"That sounds wonderful, Lizzy. The boy's tutor instructed them to write an essay on some historical fact. We can use this excursion to broaden their minds and please their teacher at the same time."

"James is eleven, he very likely will want to explore the mummy exhibit, and Philip enjoys anything to do with rare animals. I am sure there will be many things to appeal to young boys."

"Not only young boys," Jane teased. "You are as bad as Papa and Gabriel when it comes to history, Lizzy. I am certain we shall have to drag you out of the museum, along with Philip and James."

"I will not deny your claim, Jane. The only thing I like better is rare books."

"Of that, I am well aware," her sister exclaimed with a laugh. "I refuse to attend a bookstore with you. Never again, I promised myself after I waited over two hours while you browsed the shelves."

"You cannot blame me, Jane. The owner had just received a shipment of rare manuscripts which he claimed had come from the Ottoman Empire. However, enough of this. We should decide on what day we will attend the museum."

Aunt Gardiner checked her social calendar, and the ladies picked a convenient date for all involved before Elizabeth and Jane finished packing the remainder of their belongings. The duke's carriage was set to arrive for them later that afternoon. Once complete, they joined their aunt to enjoy a final tea before joining their friend, Susannah.

LONGBOURN'S ANGELS

Chapter Sixteen

"Tell me more of the gentleman who leased Netherfield Park," Lady Susannah said while pouring tea. "So bemused by his sister's behavior, I completely forgot to ask you about him."

Almost immediately upon their arrival, their hostess joined them in the private sitting room situated between their allocated bedchambers. As they had done for years, the first few hours were spent bringing each other up to date with their lives and families.

"Your letters this autumn were full of dinners and local gatherings, then you ceased writing of them completely."

"There is not much more to impart," Jane began. "If you recall, I wrote Mr. Bingley was going to host a ball near the end of November, which he did, and within two days of the event, they decamped for London."

"All of them?"

"Yes."

"With no advance warning about their plans to close the house?"

Elizabeth picked up the conversation thread.

"The first hint we had of their departure was a cryptic letter Miss Bingley wrote to Jane, wherein she stated her brother was close to offering for Miss Darcy."

"Fitzwilliam Darcy's sister?"

"The very same." Elizabeth immediately remembered her last encounter with the gentleman, and how she'd effectively kept Susannah from meeting him. "Are you acquainted with Mr. Darcy?"

"Not acquainted, *per se*. Any young lady out in society knows who Mr. Darcy is."

"Do you remember our trip to Hatchard's?"

"Of course, you practically fled the area as though the hounds of Hades were on your heels."

"Do you recall a gentleman standing in the aisle near me?"

"Vaguely. He had his back to me, so I did not see his face."

"He was none other than Mr. Darcy."

"No! And you did not say one word."

"As usual, we were not having a pleasant conversation. I steered you out of the establishment before he could see who accompanied me."

"Whatever for?" Susannah appeared a little shocked by her friend's actions.

"I do not want him, and by extension the Bingleys, to know we have such high-placed friends. You saw firsthand the way Miss Bingley treated Jane and me. If they knew who you were, they would toady up to us, and I would rather have them as enemies than false friends. At least then the relationship has some honesty."

"Mr. Darcy is a very good prospect for a husband. Even my father would not mind if I set my cap for him, although he avoids most balls, and I have yet to see him attend Almack's. Everyone knows he does not favor dancing."

"You do, indeed, know Mr. Darcy." Elizabeth tried to laugh, but it came out sounding bitter. "His abhorrence of dancing was the first thing the citizens of Meryton made note of."

"I sense a story here."

Elizabeth proceeded to tell Susannah of Mr. Darcy's insult and how her brothers had taken him to task. She finished by saying, "Mr. Darcy did apologize, but I believe if my brothers had not confronted him, he would never have acknowledged his rude behavior. He is such a contrast to Mr. Bingley. I cannot understand how they can be such great friends."

"This Mr. Bingley, did he not just come into his inheritance recently?"

"That is our understanding. His father wished the family to purchase an estate and join the ranks of the landed gentry." When Susannah gave her a questioning look, Elizabeth elaborated. "Their father owned the Bingley Carriage Company."

Susannah's brow cleared and she exclaimed, "That is why the name is so familiar. And you say Miss Bingley believes her brother is almost betrothed to Miss Darcy?"

"Yes."

"I find that odd. Not only is Mr. Darcy's sister still in the schoolroom, there is no way the Darcys, or the Fitzwilliams for that matter, would ever accept him as a suitor. She is the granddaughter of a duke and a niece to an earl." Susannah shook her head and took a cautious sip of her tea. "Miss Bingley is a fool if she thinks such an event will happen."

"I believe she hopes with her brother marrying Miss Darcy, her chances to snare Mr. Darcy improve."

With that statement, Susannah began to laugh.

"Elizabeth, you are priceless. Miss Bingley aspires too high. From what I gathered by our unpleasant encounter the other day, not only does she have atrocious taste in millinery, she apparently lives in a vivid imaginary world."

"I wholeheartedly agree she aspires too high and for that, I blame Mr. Darcy," Elizabeth said.

"Whatever for?" Jane asked, her eyes wide.

"Do you not recall me mentioning Mr. Darcy is engaged to his cousin, yet said nothing to his friends?"

"I had forgotten. Oh, poor Miss Bingley."

"Only you, Jane, would feel sorry for a woman who treated you so infamously."

"My curiosity must be satisfied," Susannah said, her voice bright with determination. "I do not dally in loose gossip, so the truth must come out. Did Miss Bingley actually say her brother was engaged to Miss Darcy?"

"Not in those precise words. Let me read you her exact words," Jane stood and went into the dressing room, returning with a letter in hand.

"You brought her letter with you?" Susannah asked, and Jane's cheeks flushed. "Forgive me. It has been so long since you have seen the Bingleys, I am surprised you carry it with you."

"With Lydia having unfettered access to our room, I fully expect her to snoop through every drawer and cubby while we are gone. Bringing Miss Bingley's letter with me was the only way to keep it private," Jane resumed her seat, and, to anyone with a discerning eye, it was obvious the letter had been read many times.

"You do not need to share something so personal." Susannah covered Jane's hand with hers. "This is your private business. I have no right to demand such intimate details."

"Lizzy and I have known you since she was eight and I was nine. I do not think there is much in our life of which you are not aware. Also, I am very confused by Mr... their behavior and could not write about this because I did not know what to say. I might have rambled on for pages and pages, and Papa would have refused to pay the postage."

Susannah leaned back and laughed gaily.

"My Janie, you are delightful. Next time you are confused and need another willing friend to help think things through,

I will pay the postage. You know I can well afford to keep you in paper, ink, and postage fees without a worry."

"I would never presume upon our friendship in such a manner."

"We do not think of you that way," Elizabeth said, reiterating the sister's decision to never abuse Susannah's trust in them. "To us, you are still the girl in braids who decided to swim in a river rather than ride her atrociously huge horse."

"It was the worst, best day of my life. And things continued to improve when I found out Jane and I were attending Miss Tyler's Academy at the same time." Susannah placed her teacup and saucer onto the elegant little table by her chair. "I believe Miss Tyler's eyebrows disappeared into her hairline when I insisted Miss Jane Bennet of Longbourn, share a suite of rooms with me."

"Believe me, the halls still reverberated from the shock waves when I joined the both of you," Elizabeth said in a teasing manner, her emerald eyes sparkling with mirth. "Your father has been so very kind to Jane and me."

"He likes to tell my brother and me that you and Jane are his adopted daughters. Do not be surprised if he wishes to vet whichever man dares ask for a courtship."

"Papa would welcome your father into his study any time, as you well know. They have quite the rivalry going with their chess game."

"Yes, Father pounces on each letter from your father and moves the chess pieces accordingly."

"Mine does the same. When we last saw him, I did not have the heart to tell him in four moves, your father will declare victory."

So focused were the ladies on their discussion, no one realized the dressing room door was ajar, and the maid who had brought up fresh linens heard every word spoken.

"Do you still wish me to read the letter?" Jane asked.

"Yes, but only the part where Miss Bingley wrote of her expectations. I do not need to hear anything further." Susannah said and settled back in her chair to listen closely.

Jane unfolded the paper and after scanning the page to find the correct passage, began reading.

'Mr. Darcy is impatient to see his sister and to confess the truth, we are scarcely less eager to meet her again. I really do not think Georgiana Darcy has her equal for beauty, elegance, and accomplishments; and the affection she inspires in Louisa and myself is heightened into something still more interesting, from the hope we dare to entertain of her being hereafter our sister. I do not know whether I ever before mentioned to you my feelings on this subject, but I will not leave the country without confiding them, and trust you will not esteem them unreasonable. My brother admires her greatly already, he will have frequent opportunities now of seeing her on the most intimate footing, her relations all wish the connection as much as his own, and a sister's partiality is not misleading me, I think, when I call Charles most capable of engaging any woman's heart. With all these circumstances to favor an attachment and nothing to prevent it, am I wrong, my dearest Jane, in indulging the hope of an event which will secure the happiness of so many?'

Her task complete, the maid left the dressing room as quietly as she had entered.

"Well?" Elizabeth demanded. "What do you make of this, Susannah?"

"First, I cannot believe she wrote such drivel. However, I found it interesting she wondered if she had ever before mentioned how she felt on the subject. Truly, if there was an agreement between Mr. Bingley and Miss Darcy, I have no doubt in my mind the news would have been made known to everyone, especially someone she saw as encroaching on her brother. Not to mention, if there was such an arrangement,

Mr. Darcy himself would have spoken to Mr. Bingley, and taken him to task."

"I cannot believe she thought we would trust her every word," Elizabeth said as she set down her teacup.

"Jane, dear. Did you like this Mr. Bingley?" Susannah asked, her voice rife with concern.

"He was everything a young man ought to be. Amiable, handsome…"

"And rich. Do not forget he is so very rich," Elizabeth teased, hoping to keep Jane from becoming too maudlin.

"Lizzy! You know I do not care about those things. I liked him as a person."

"Should I invite him to my parent's anniversary ball?" Susannah asked.

Jane's eyes widened in alarm. "Oh, please do not. I no longer hold him with any affection. Besides, if he wished for my company, it was up to him to seek me out. I am not the one who left Hertfordshire."

"There is my spicy sister. I thought I lost her last year."

Susannah watched her closest friend and her impertinent sister, her mind churning with plans.

"Enough of the Bingleys," she finally declared. "Let us talk about the theater. As you know, my brother insists on escorting all of us for the opening night. It will be a mad crush."

"The marquess does not mind us riding his coattails to the theater?"

"Elizabeth Bennet! How many times must I remind you he said that in jest? He adores you and Jane. In fact, he would cut all acquaintances with almost everybody except the two of you. You are my truest, most genuine friends."

"I am well pleased you think so, as Jane and I are fond of you as well. We suffer your brother for your sake alone."

Lady Susannah Harrington, daughter to the Duke of

Belmont, laughed uproariously. This was how her brother Sebastian, Marquis Grenfell, found them.

"I see Elizabeth has not lost her touch," he teased before giving them all a polite half-bow in greeting. "May I enter the inner sanctum of the Bennet ladies and join you?"

Susannah encouraged her brother to sit on the couch next to her.

"We are discussing the idea of attending the theater. You said you would escort us."

"I did?" He gave the two Miss Bennets a saucy wink.

"Most assuredly. Our Jane was abused most heinously by a Mr. Bingley and we must ensure the gossips go crazy with news of her being seen in your company."

"No, Susannah," Jane began in protest. "I will not have people gossip about our friendship. I would rather not attend any events in your company if that is the end result."

"Miss Bennet — Jane," the marquis said softly. "Your friendship with my sister has never been questioned. Only a fool would see you, or your sister as mercenary."

"Then it is a good thing our mother is not trailing behind us because she would defy your claim. Her only goal in life is to see her daughters married well. Most especially, Jane," Elizabeth teased.

"Is that not the goal of every mother?"

"True, however, our mother has turned it into an art form. For example; at the ball Mr. Bingley hosted, she outright declared to her group of friends that not only did she expect an offer for Jane that very night, but they would marry before Christmas."

"No!"

"Yes! Unfortunately, I was seated across from her alongside Mr. Bingley's close friend, Mr. Darcy. He heard every word."

"Fitzwilliam Darcy of Pemberley?"

"One and the same. Are you acquainted with his friend, Mr. Bingley?"

"I have seen him at various events, and know he and Darcy are close. It is rumored he looks to Darcy for guidance."

"I thought as much," Elizabeth grumbled under her breath.

"I did not mean to casts aspersions on Mr. Bingley's character. He only recently came into his inheritance and truly requires someone to guide him. Darcy is a steady fellow and also has no need for Bingley's wealth. Any advice he gave would be solid and unbiased."

Elizabeth knew her one eyebrow had lifted at the word 'unbiased.'

"You do not look convinced, Lizzy," Susannah noted, seeing the arched brow.

"I am not convinced, and am very much of the opinion Mr. Darcy encouraged Mr. Bingley to abandon Netherfield Park and Jane"

"Lizzy!" Jane exclaimed. "Mr. Bingley did not abandon me. He gave no promise, nor asked for anything further than friendship."

"Miss Bennet, for what it is worth, I think Bingley was a fool," the marquis offered with a smile. Jane grimaced slightly and focused her attention on her hands. "We will stop visiting your torment, and speak of more pleasant topics."

"Mayhap it is a good thing we are attending the theater later this month," his sister said smoothly. "I have heard it is a comedy, and we could use a good laugh."

"I have something to tell you," Jane said, quite abruptly. All attention was given to her, and she twisted her fingers together before taking a deep breath. "I was not certain if I would share the news, for which I am sorry, but it is all so new, and I did not know how to tell you, and—"

"Jane, slow down. I am confident neither Susannah nor I will chastise you." Elizabeth hurried to soothe her distraught sister.

"I am being courted."

All of them gasped.

"By whom?" Susannah finally managed to ask.

"A gentleman I met last month. I did not say anything because Mr. Bradford wished to visit Longbourn before we told anyone. He returned yesterday, and during our walk, gave me the happy news Papa had given his blessing."

The conversation became centered around Jane's courtship. Unbeknownst to them, word of a different engagement had slipped the confines of the duke's residence and began to wend its way through the various households of the beau monde. Barely three days passed before Lady Vernon, an inveterate gossip and contributor to *The Tattler*, heard the news.

Chapter Seventeen

Fitzwilliam Darcy picked up the carefully pressed paper, wondering why his butler felt the need to give him the gossip rag instead of *The Gazette*. He hadn't even started to read when the door to his study burst open, and his cousin Richard stormed in.

"So, have you read it?" he demanded upon entry.

"Have I read what?"

Upon spying the gossip page in his hand, Richard bit out, "I suggest you read the latest *on-dit* this morning. It will not be hard to find as it is the first item at the top of the other trash."

His cousin was not known to become violently angry over gossip, so with mounting trepidation, Darcy turned his attention to the paper and quickly scanned its contents. Soon, his stomach heaved and rolled, and he thought for sure his previously enjoyed coffee would make a reappearance.

It has come to the attention of this author that Miss CB of Grosvenor St is elated over the secret engagement of her brother, CB to Miss D of Derbyshire. So much so, she wrote a letter to a dear friend declaring the fact. Normally, this would not surprise anyone as CB, a very close friend of FD, has been residing at his house in Town… until recently. One might suppose he decamped to his brother's townhouse to maintain a sense of decorum, which is expected when a couple becomes betrothed. However, the young lady in question is only in the first blush of womanhood and has yet to make her curtsy. It makes this author wonder if there is another, more _personal_ *reason for such haste.*

"I must speak with Charles immediately!" Darcy stood and threw the paper onto the desk.

"Where in god's teeth would anyone hear such drivel?"

"I do not know, but I will find out."

Darcy called for his carriage and waited for a footman to bring him his outerwear. It was during this time frame the butler announced the arrival of Mr. Bingley.

"I have not asked Miss Darcy for her hand," were the first words out of Bingley's mouth upon entry into the room.

"It matters not if you did or did not. The gossip about this will be rampant."

"There was mention of a letter." Richard went right to the heart of the matter." Have you spoken with your sister?"

"No, I came here as soon as I read the paper."

"I will speak to her," Richard practically growled out. "This particular rag is very careful about what they write as they have no wish to be sued for slander. If they said there is a letter, then I would place a large wager on that fact. I would like to read this letter myself and know exactly what it says. It could be a matter of interpretation."

"Caroline is at Hurst's townhouse. I will give you the direction." Charles quickly scribbled down the address and handed it to the colonel. "She has not yet seen the article. I brought the paper with me."

"I will return when I have some answers, cousin," was all Richard said to Darcy as he slipped out of the room.

"I know it is early, but I think we could both use a drink."

"Yes!" Charles threw himself into the closest chair and ran a hand through his unruly mop of curls. "What a disaster. I do not even look at Miss Darcy in that way. How could anyone think I would pursue her?"

"She is your type," Darcy said and handed his friend his drink.

"What do you mean by 'my type?' I do not have a type." Bingley frowned into the glass as he spoke.

"Oh, but you do." Darcy took the chair opposite his friend. "Blonde. Blue eyes. Willowy figure. Gentle nature. Good manners." He stopped when Bingley raised his eyes to him. "Does this sound familiar?"

"You have just described Miss Bennet. I could never look at another while my heart breaks over her callous disregard for my feelings."

Darcy felt a pinch of regret over the morose declaration. Not once did he think Miss Bennet showed a callous disregard, his opinion remained firm that Miss Bennet liked Bingley, but did not feel romantic love. If his friend had pressed his suit, it would have been the mother responding to any and all proposals with a resounding yes, not Miss Bennet.

"All of that is behind you now, Bingley. We need to figure out how to mitigate this disaster." His gaze fell to the paper on his desk. "Is there anyone in your sister's social circle who may have heard her say something? Something they carried forward and embellished?"

"Any of her friends would spread gossip if they thought it advanced them socially, except perhaps Miss Grantley. She seems to be a gentle lady. I never could quite figure out why Caroline kept up their acquaintance once they left the seminary."

"Miss Grantley's paternal uncle is a viscount and her maternal cousin is a duke. Your sister courts the highest echelons of society for her future happiness."

"She courts you, as you well know."

"I am sorry, Bingley, but I will never, no matter what happens, ever court your sister, or be coerced into a marriage.

You know I barely tolerate her company for your sake."

"I do know and have told her. She remains stubbornly obtuse to my warnings. You may have to cut her direct to drive your point home."

***

The duke's butler advanced into the room and handed Jane a note. She quickly unfolded the missive, her mouth forming a soft '*o*' as she read it. Quickly, she re-folded the note and stood, tucking it into her skirt pocket.

"Bad news, Jane?" Lizzy queried.

"No, Mr. Bradford is out front and has asked to speak with me."

Lizzy frowned. "Why would he not come inside?"

"I do not know."

Jane asked the footman to find her heavy shawl and meet her by the front door. Adequately attired, she stepped outside and hurried down the steps to where Mr. Bradford waited in his carriage. As soon as he saw her, Henry disembarked and, taking her hand in his, leaned down and kissed her cheek.

"Mr. Bradford, may I invite you inside where it is warmer?"

"I… that is… I came to ask if you would like to go shopping with me. Cassandra's birthday is in a few weeks and I would dearly love a woman's opinion on what to buy a young girl."

"My sister and I have no plans for the afternoon, but come inside while I ask Elizabeth if she will come along as a chaperone."

"Would you mind if I waited in the carriage?"

Alarm coursed through Jane's body and she dropped his hand. Why was Mr. Bradford acting in such an odd manner? It was quite obvious he did not want to come inside the duke's house. The gentleman before her was still a stranger, one she had started to feel great affection for, but his reaction to a simple question was troubling. Had she inadvertently stumbled upon another Mr. Bingley?

"Mr. Bradford." Jane drew the shawl tight around her shoulders. "I have the distinct impression you are unwilling to come into my friend's house, and I am not sure why. I believe there is much about you I do not know and this is, frankly, disturbing."

"Miss Bennet... Dash it all." Henry muttered a faint curse under his breath, and Jane's cheeks turned even redder, and not from the cold. "Pardon my rudeness. You are correct, there are things about me I wish you to know. However, I thought I would have more time before all had to be revealed."

"I do not understand your meaning, sir." Jane took a step backward with the intention of returning to the house.

"Wait! Miss Bennet." Mr. Bradford stepped away from his carriage and touched her shoulder, staying her movement. "I will come with you. All I ask is that you keep an open mind, and allow me a full explanation."

Jane looked him square in the face, her gaze never leaving his. She could see his eyes were clear of guile and decided to trust her instincts.

"I will keep an open mind." They both began to ascend the stairs to the palatial townhouse. "However, I cannot speak for Lizzy."

She was rewarded with his soft chuckle.

"I can ask for nothing more."

Upon their entry into the duke's townhouse, the butler gave Mr. Bradford a low bow and said, "Good afternoon, Lord Holcomb. I am afraid the marquess is at his club."

"Not a problem, Fields. I am here to visit with Miss Bennet. I shall catch up with Sebastian later."

"Very well, my lord."

Jane had come to a complete stop during the exchange and stared at Henry. Who was this man who stood before her, a sheepish grin on his face?

"Lord Holcomb?"

"Yes."

"And, is your daughter Miss Cassandra, or Lady Cassandra?"

"Her proper address is Lady Cassandra."

"When did you plan to tell me?"

"Our wedding night?"

"Henry!"

Jane made to move by Henry and he grabbed both her hands, causing her shawl to slip down to her elbows.

"Miss Bennet… Jane… I did not tell you because I wanted you to love me for myself. Not my titles, not my wealth, not any of the things which do no matter."

"I do love you… at least, I loved Henry Bradford."

"I am still Henry Bradford, darling. I am also the Earl of Holcomb."

"You know that is not what I meant."

"Yes, I do, and it still does not change the fact of who I am."

"Jane, is everything well?" Elizabeth approached, a concerned look on her face. "I worried you were taking too long. Good afternoon, Mr. Bradford. Have you come to spirit my sister away, or shall you be joining us for tea?"

Henry looked at Jane for the answer. How could she deny him anything?

"His lordship will join us for tea," she replied calmly and handed her shawl to the waiting footman.

Lizzy's left eyebrow arched in an elegant manner upon hearing Henry's elevated status, but she said not one word, other than, 'Lovely.'

Once they were all assembled in the parlor, an awkward silence descended upon the three of them. Jane did not know how to start the conversation. All the ease she and Henry achieved over the past few weeks, had vanished. She glanced at Lizzy, surprised she had not broached the subject of Mr. Bradford's title. When her sister met her gaze unflinching, Jane realized her feisty sister meant for her to carry the conversation. For her to figuratively take up the banner and lead the charge.

"My lord," Jane started and was halted by Henry's heavy sigh.

"I have been Henry for weeks now, Jane. Might we forego the honors of my title, at least among friends and family?"

"Very well… Henry." He gave her a grateful smile and a little more of her anger and embarrassment leeched from around her heart. "Please explain why you deceived us in such a manner."

"I did not mean to begin in such a way. When we first met, it was so refreshing to be treated as a simple gentleman. You see, I was born the second son of the previous earl. Five years ago, the whole family gathered for Christmas at the family seat in Buckinghamshire. Cassandra had just turned three, and my wife was expecting our second child. I am not sure if you heard the news of what happened, but it was in all the broadsheets about a deadly influenza that swept through our area, and before the new year came around, my father, eldest brother, and my wife had all succumbed to the disease. We also lost many tenants and servants, and half the village near our estate was wiped out. My brother was unmarried, and so the title fell to me."

"I am exceedingly sorry this happened to anyone," Jane said, her heart wrenching at his many losses.

"Your mother, has she recovered from this?" Lizzy asked.

"My mother passed when I was thirteen, a small mercy for

which I am now grateful. No woman should have to bear the burden of her husband and son dying together."

"Your loss was equally devastating."

"The first few years following were very dark, very chaotic. I survived only to look after my daughter." Impulsively, Henry took Jane's hand in his. "I did not tell you this to garner sympathy. Cassandra and I have adjusted, and part of that adjustment is keeping our life simple."

Their attention was caught by the rustle of silk skirts and the entrance of Lady Susannah, who paused in the doorway. Jane immediately pulled her hand out of Henry's light grip. He stood and gave Susannah a polite nod of greeting.

"Henry! I have not seen you in ages. Did you come by to see Sebastian?"

"I did not." Henry resumed his seat and cast a loving gaze upon Jane. "I came to see Miss Bennet."

"Really?" Susannah smiled and looked at her friend, whose cheeks were stained a rosy red. "My friend has been strangely reticent about her top lofty acquaintances."

"You will not tease Jane about this. She did not know about my title."

Susannah's expression showed she understood, and she took the seat directly across from Henry and Jane.

"As much as I wish I had known who Jane's new interest was, I am glad it is you, dear, dear Henry, although I should have put the pieces together myself. You are the only Mr. Bradford I know. Sometimes I can be quite the dunderhead."

"I, for one, would like to know how all of you became friends," Henry said, his curious gaze encompassing all three ladies.

"It all began when I jumped into a river that threatened to flood its banks and pulled a young lady to safety." After her very brief explanation, Elizabeth folded her hands on her lap and waited for comments.

"I am surprised you removed the stampeding elephants from the story. It had much more excitement than simply jumping into a swollen river to save me," Susannah said, with a grin.

"I personally like the one where she has a mad highwayman chase you into the river and she must fight him off before she can rescue you," Jane teased.

"From what I gather," Henry mused, "Elizabeth saved Lady Susannah, who had somehow fallen into a river."

"Yes," all three ladies said together and then laughed.

"How old were you at the time?"

"Elizabeth was eight, I was nine," Susannah answered.

"I do remember Sebastian speaking of this. Not long after, your father took your family to a sea resort in order to teach you how to swim."

"Yes, and both Elizabeth and Jane were invited to join me. It was the beginning of our great friendship."

"Of course!" Henry playfully slapped his forehead. "You are the sisters Sebastian has spoken of. Now it all makes sense." He cast a warm glance at Jane. "I should have known. My friend has nothing but praise for you and your sister. You are the standard he has set for every lady he looks at when considering a wife."

"Oh, my," Jane murmured. "I did not realize he had set it so low."

"Jane!" three voices chorused before she smiled, and winked at Lizzy.

Chapter Eighteen

"She denies writing any kind of letter, but the orange shrew lies."

It had been a week since Richard began his campaign to find the perpetrator of the rumor which had forced Georgiana to hide at Lord and Lady Matlock's residence.

"And you know this because…?"

"Darcy, it is my job to ferret out information from people who do not want to give up their secrets. She lies, and is unwilling to say to whom she wrote such drivel."

"What will you do now?"

"Well, 'tis fairly obvious this pack of lies was fed to someone, not from our social circles."

"What makes you say that?"

"First, Miss Bingley would never write such hokum to anyone from town. She would be laughed out of every drawing room whose door frame she darkened. Second, it had to be to someone who would not question what she told them, as they would have no way to corroborate her story." Richard paced, reminiscent of a caged tiger. "What about someone from Hertfordshire? Bingley usually has some angel to lose his head and heart over."

Darcy's thoughts immediately flew to Miss Bennet and just as quickly he discarded them. If Miss Bingley had written such an outlandish lie, she would not have had to disabuse

Miss Bennet of her brother's disinterest, nor given her the cut direct on Bond Street.

"There was a young lady he showered attention upon, however," Darcy held up his hand to forestall Richard speaking, "Miss Bingley informed this young woman in person her brother had no intention of furthering their friendship."

"You know this for a fact."

"We had the Bingleys over for dinner the other night, and Miss Bingley specifically told me more details."

"Why?"

Trust Richard to get to the heart of the matter.

"Because I aided Miss Bingley and her sister, once again, in separating Charles from the local beauty."

"She must have been extraordinary. Bingley usually loses attention when another bright shiny ball rolls by."

"She was the only bright shiny ball in the whole shire."

Not true, his heart protested. *Elizabeth outshone them all.*

"Why the frown?" Richard asked.

Darcy smoothed his brow. It would not do for his cousin to analyze his reasoning.

"I was recalling the limited society we were forced into. With only four and twenty families, beautiful women were scarce on the ground."

"Every man wishes for a beautiful wife, Darcy."

"When beauty is the sole currency, the lady has to offer, marrying a wealthy man is her only salvation."

"You are certain there was no correspondence between Miss Bingley and this young woman?"

"Reasonably certain. I am aware the lady was in town earlier this year. She stayed with her family in Cheapside." The slight widening of Richard's eyes indicated he caught the subtle nuance as to why the family had no connections worth mentioning.

"Without invitation, she showed up at Hurst's townhouse, and Miss Bingley was forced to ask her to cease pestering them. Such a blunt conversation would not have been required if this brazen miss was the recipient of the letter."

A restless sense of unease poked at Darcy's conscience upon making that statement. He knew Miss Bennet was not brazen, but how far would a desperate woman be willing to go in order to capture the attention of a wealthy man?

"If it was not the jilted lover from Hertfordshire, then someone else received a letter from Miss Bingley," Richard said, continuing to pace.

"This fictional someone must know somebody," Darcy fumed. "How else would such rubbish make its way to *The Tattler?*"

"I have discovered Lady Vernon dropped the story into the editor's hands."

"Lady Vernon! I rarely see her, let alone speak with her. How in the world did she come by this information?"

"Apparently, servant's tongues have been wagging for weeks over this, and I have been painstakingly following each lead. The next connection is to an upstairs chambermaid from the Duke of Belmont's household."

"I find such a thing hard to believe. His grace has a hard and fast policy if anyone is caught gossiping about the family, they are turned out without reference."

"But, this morsel of gossip was not about his family."

"Why Georgiana? I do not believe they have met her."

"That is what I am about to find out."

"And how do you intend to discover who initiated the gossip?"

"I shall attend the source directly."

"Do you plan on sashaying into the duke's study, and demand he tells you if he whispered an untruth into his maid's willing ear?"

"I am not a complete idiot, Darcy. I have ways and means of finding things out. Give me a few more days, and I will have everything well in hand."

"See that you do. Aunt Catherine wrote a scathing letter, using this unholy incident as yet another reason for me to marry Anne."

"When are you going to tell her, you have no inclination of marrying our cousin?"

"I have told her."

"You have danced around the issue, but not laid down the law. You are a Darcy. Start acting like one. What would your father have done in your stead?"

"You are asking what the man, who was completely bamboozled by George Wickham, would have done with his autocratic sister-in-law?"

"Wickham was a deviation in your father's behavior. You know he never kowtowed to Aunt Catherine. It is one of the reasons she refused to attend Pemberley while he was alive."

Darcy paused at this revelation. How had he missed such a salient fact? Upon the death of his father, his maternal aunt had descended upon his ancestral home, demanding he marry Anne once his six months of mourning were at an end. In his grief, he had not once thought about the timing of her declarations.

"I will confront her when we attend Rosings at Easter."

"This might be the first year I look forward to seeing our aunt."

"Our visit will not be pleasant, not when she discovers I will not be moved to do her bidding." Darcy, in deep thought, rubbed his chin. "If required, I will cut all acquaintance."

"There you go. You never know, Darce, something completely unexpected might occur which will distract the old gorgon."

"Other than Napoleon himself marching up the drive to

Rosings Park, nothing else will deter her."

"Would not that be a sight to behold? I would place wagers on Aunt Catherine defeating the little pissant. Now, on to slaying the other dragon in our life. Who spilled the gossip about dear Georgiana?"

***

"Colonel Fitzwilliam!" Lady Susannah declared upon the gentleman's entry into the drawingroom. "Today is not my usual at-home day, and our butler nearly turned you away at the door."

"I told your man I had to speak with the duke about a very important manner. However, as your esteemed father is away on business, he cannot clear up the mystery I am trying to unravel."

"A mystery? Now I am intrigued, Colonel." Susannah waved for Richard to take a seat. "Is there anything I can do to aid you in your quest?"

Richard began to answer, but at that moment his attention was directed to the large Palladian window overlooking the back garden. Outside, he watched Lord Holcomb walking the paths with Jane on his arm. Lady Susannah noticed where the colonel's attention had gone and waited for the question he would inevitably ask

"Does Lord Holcomb often walk beautiful women around your grounds?"

"No, he does not, however, he has recently entered into a courtship with my guest, and love brings him to our door almost every day."

"I have not seen her before."

"This does not surprise me. Jane and her sister usually visit our family during the summer months, when we escape to our country estate to avoid the heat."

"Do I know their family?"

"I do not believe you do. Their father hates Town and rarely leaves his estate. If it were not for the fact Jane's sister saved my life when I was nine, our family never would have met. I treasure their friendship, greatly." Susannah tilted her head to one side and gave Richard an assessing look. She was under no illusion as to why the colonel had shown up unannounced. What she didn't know was how the content of Miss Bingley's letter had made its way to a notorious gossip rag. "I am certain you did not come to ask about the intrigues of my friend and Lord Holcomb. What brought you to our door, Colonel Fitzwilliam?"

"Are you aware of what was written in *The Tattler* a few weeks ago?" At her nod, he continued. "As a person who is greatly invested in protecting the reputation of the young woman so broadly maligned, I have been searching for the source."

"You mean, you are searching for the letter, because I am right in believing you have already confronted the lady who supposedly wrote it, and she denied all culpability."

"Yes," he answered, seemingly surprised by Susannah's astuteness. "I am loathed to denigrate your household, but the search for those involved has led me to your father's residence."

"Of this fact, you are positive?" She frowned at his news.

"Yes, however, the trail became muddied when a footman I was slated to interview was struck by a carriage. Sadly, he did not survive. His friends knew he had just begun stepping out with a young woman. No one was able to describe his sweetheart, other than she worked for the Duke of Belmont as an upstairs maid."

"So, you do not have hard proof the story began from our home. All you have is conjecture."

"I apologize, Lady Susannah. I do not wish to make false

accusations, but the only remaining trail led me here."

"Colonel Fitzwilliam, I have not been properly introduced to this Miss B mentioned in the gossip rag, but I have heard things which are not complimentary."

"What have you heard?"

"I do not trade in gossip, colonel. My social currency is the hard truth. However, I will say this. If it were me in the middle of this maelstrom, I would cut all ties with the notorious Miss B and her family."

"As we speak, her brother is making plans to visit family in Scarborough. The earliest they can depart is April."

"I believe that would be best for all involved," Lady Susannah said. "Fortunately, Miss Darcy is too young to remain at the forefront of gossip, although there might be some mention when she finally has her come out, nothing your family cannot withstand. It is not as though she eloped with an unsavory rogue."

The disquiet which flickered across the colonel's face happened so fast, Susannah almost doubted what she witnessed. In her peripheral vision, she noticed Henry and Jane making their way back to the house, and did not want an introduction to occur with the astute colonel. Upon learning Jane was from Hertfordshire, he would immediately deduce she was the recipient of Miss Bingley's notorious letter and, in Susannah's mind, Jane was as much an innocent party as Miss Darcy.

"I must beg forgiveness, Colonel. I had not noticed the time and have a few tasks to complete before attending the theater tomorrow. There are always details which require a visit to the modiste with regard to a lady's ensemble."

"I am aware as I have accompanied my mother on many last-minute trips to Bond Street. Thank you for your time, Lady Susannah." Richard stood and gave her a low bow. "I shall see myself out, and wish you a good day."

Having said that, he pivoted smartly on his heel and quit the room. Not five minutes passed before Jane and Henry came in, looking very much in love, followed by Elizabeth, their somewhat indifferent chaperone.

"Was that Earl Matlock's son I saw riding off?" Henry asked once he'd settled next to Jane on the couch.

"It was," Susannah said, with an affirming nod.

"Do you have a beau you have not told us about?" Elizabeth teased.

"I do not. He was here to see Papa, and stopped for a brief chat once he knew Father was not in residence."

"And here I felt guilty leaving you alone in order to traipse about the garden with Jane and Lord Holcomb," Elizabeth teased.

"I have asked you to call me Henry, or just plain old Holcomb."

"I would never presume upon your friendship, Lord Holcomb."

"You may as well give up now, Henry," Susannah said with a laugh. "My brother has badgered Elizabeth to call him Sebastian for nearly twelve years. You will not succeed."

"He might," Elizabeth said and gave Jane a coy look. "I am known to call family members by their first name."

"Lizzy!" Jane protested and her cheeks turned a becoming shade of deep pink. "You are putting Mr. Bradford and myself in an awkward position."

"Very well, dear sister, I will cease and desist, but only because I love you sincerely, and do not want you to fret."

Henry stayed for another hour before taking his leave and once the women were alone, Susannah told them why the earl's son visited earlier, and how the trail of gossip led to one of the duke's staff, described only as an upstairs maid in a relationship with a deceased footman.

"Betsy is the only one we know who lost a beau."

"She must have been working in one of our connecting bedrooms and overheard the conversation. Your staff will not gossip about your family, but they would think nothing of talking about others."

"True." Susannah sat for a few minutes, and Elizabeth knew she was recreating the scene in her mind the afternoon Jane read her letter out loud. "We did not hold back with our opinions and conjectures, knowing we were in a private sitting room, but all it takes is for one door to remain partially open…"

"I do not think we can lay blame. It is as much our fault as hers. We should have been more circumspect of our surroundings."

"I agree. I will speak with her to determine if what we think occurred is true, and tell her to spread a word of caution among the staff. My father's decree of not gossiping includes everything which occurs in our home."

"Please do not dock her pay. Most of these girls support family members."

"Do not worry, Jane. I will speak with her privately. More lives need not be ruined because of Miss Bingley's spiteful words toward you."

"Should we speak further with the earl's son, and tell him about the letter?"

"I honestly do not know. Trying to absolve ourselves from guilt might further exasperate matters." Susannah pursed her lips, clearly deep in thought. "At this moment, it is a juicy bit of gossip, but Miss Darcy is not yet sixteen and will not make her debut for another two years. By the time she makes her curtsy, many new scandals will have diverted the ton's attention."

"I cannot help but feel wretched for poor Miss Darcy," Jane said, her eyes filling with unshed tears. "I wish I had never mentioned Miss Bingley's letter."

"I am surprised Mr. Darcy has not confronted Miss Bingley about this," Elizabeth murmured, more to herself than the other two ladies present.

"I believe he has, with no good results."

The three ladies sat quietly, each consumed with their own thoughts. Jane finally broke the silence.

"Lizzy, we are acquainted with Mr. Darcy. Might we visit his house and give him the letter? Then, it would be his choice if he wished to act on it, or destroy it."

Elizabeth held her sister's gaze for a few minutes, then nodded. "If that is what you wish to do, I will attend his house with you."

"Would you like me to come along?" Susannah asked.

Both Miss Bennets smiled at their friend and shook their head in tandem.

"Thank you, but no," Jane said. "This is something I should do alone." At Elizabeth's playful protest, she added, "Or, as alone as I can be with my sister by my side."

"I am not afraid of Mr. Darcy, Jane. He will not dare chastise you if I am there."

They determined to go to Mr. Darcy's house the next afternoon, and as luck would have it, their brothers arrived just as they were ready to order up the carriage.

Upon seeing their sisters fully dressed, bonnets at the ready, and also upon hearing where they were going and the reason, the brothers determined their sisters would not beard the lion in his den alone. Jane and Elizabeth had a fearsome escort when they arrived at Mr. Darcy's townhouse on Grosvenor Square.

Chapter Nineteen

Darcy glanced down at the presented calling card and told his butler to escort his unexpected guests to the blue parlor.

Michael T. Bennet ~ Longbourn, Hertfordshire

Straightforward, and to the point. Darcy admired that quality in a man, yet wondered why this particular gentleman had come calling. He stood and shrugged into his fitted jacket, and made his way to the parlor. Prior to entering, he remembered Burke had said there were unexpected guests, meaning Michael Bennet had not attended alone. Darcy's pulse quickened to think the second eldest sister may have accompanied her elder brother.

As quickly as the thought entered his mind, he shut it down. He had felt the danger of liking Miss Elizabeth too much in Hertfordshire, and would not revisit those feelings again. Her connections to higher levels of society were tenuous at best, and given the way Georgiana had recently been dragged into the court of gossip, he could ill afford to even consider getting more involved with someone whose condition in life was so decidedly beneath his own.

Although Darcy was prepared to see two Bennet siblings, he was quite unprepared to confront four of them.

"Mister and Miss Bennets," Darcy greeted them. "What brings you to my home?"

In unison, three heads swiveled in the direction of Miss Jane Bennet, who stood pale and trembling near a couch. Ever the gentleman, Darcy was alarmed at how upset she seemed.

"Miss Bennet, are you well? Shall I have my housekeeper bring you a cup of water or a glass of wine?"

"No, Mr. Darcy, I thank you."

Jane Bennet finally sank down onto a couch, her brothers taking their place on either side. Miss Elizabeth moved to a chair closest to where Darcy stood, and with seeming defiance, settled herself in the single chair. Mystified, Darcy also sat, impatient to learn what had brought them to his house.

"Mr. Darcy, I..." Miss Bennet floundered for words before taking in a deep breath. She then lifted her head and held his gaze. "I am very disturbed over what was written about your sister."

"Have you come to gloat over her degradation and ruin?" Darcy almost leaped to his feet. Sheer willpower kept him anchored to his chair. "You will leave my home."

Michael Bennet stood, almost simultaneously with his brother.

"You do not even know why my sister is here," Michael said, his voice dangerously low. "You have constantly judged our family as beneath you, even though we are your equals, in *every* possible way, you can imagine."

"I have asked you to leave my home."

Darcy stood and pulled the lanyard to recall his butler. When he turned to face his unexpected guests, he was surprised to find Miss Bennet standing directly before him. In her extended hand, a letter.

"Do with this what you will. I believe you should be aware of what your friends say and do when you are not in their company."

He took the worn letter, and gave it a cursory glance, easily recognizing Miss Bingley's handwriting. Miss Bennet then left the room with Gabriel Bennet following immediately behind. Michael watched them, then turned his contemptuous gaze upon Darcy.

"I will not forget this, Mr. Darcy. If you ever see me, cross the street. I cannot attest to the strength of my faith and convictions that I will not lay you out if I am ever in your presence again. Come, Elizabeth, we are leaving this house."

"I will follow shortly, Michael." At his hesitation, she stared her brother down. "I wish for some private words with this gentleman before I leave."

Only a fool would think Michael Bennet wished to leave his sister behind, and Darcy was no fool. Filled with righteous anger, he waited to hear what the little upstart had to say.

"I am waiting, Miss Elizabeth."

"Take care where you direct your scorn, Mr. Darcy. I am well aware of how you perceive my family." Miss Elizabeth took a deep breath. "In your hand is the letter which was referenced in the gossip pages. Jane has only ever shared the content of it with me and an intimate friend. Today, after our brothers arrived, they learned we were coming to see you, and the reason why."

"Then how——?"

"How did it make its way to *The Tattler*?" At Darcy's curt nod, Miss Elizabeth continued, "During our visit with this friend, she asked Jane about her state of mind with regard to Mr. Bingley."

"How would she even know about Bingley?"

"Do not be obtuse, it does not become you. Friends write letters, and through their correspondence, our friend knew

Jane had developed strong feelings for Mr. Bingley. When she ceased writing about him, our friend was curious and the contents of the letter entered the conversation. After you read Miss Bingley's letter, you will learn why Jane was confused and hurt. To learn Mr. Bingley had treated her with such casual disregard—"

"Bingley treated her with casual disregard! I watched your sister most attentively and plainly saw she did not return my friend's feelings in equal measure. If she had accepted any kind of proposal from him, it would have been because she did not want to go against your mother's expressed wishes."

"Are you accusing my sister of being mercenary?"

"Everyone in attendance at the ball heard your mother claim your sister would be married to Bingley before Christmas, and how she would throw her other sisters in the paths of wealthy men."

"I cannot fault you on my mother's behavior, it was badly done." Elizabeth closed her eyes, clearly in an attempt to cool her anger. "No matter what you believe, Mr. Darcy, my sister and I have both sworn we will marry only for the greatest of love."

"Love does not fill the belly, Miss Elizabeth."

"True, but it does make life more bearable while cold, hard coin does not make a comfortable bed."

"Enough, what does this have to do with my sister's ruination?"

"We believe a maid overheard our conversation, and from there, gossip spread." Miss Elizabeth glanced at the letter, now crushed in his hand. "Read the letter, Mr. Darcy, and make your own observation."

He smoothed the paper and scanned the contents, anger beginning afresh at what was laid out before him. When he looked up, Miss Elizabeth Bennet had left the room and his house. He stood alone in his resentment.

Later that afternoon, Richard arrived fully dressed in his regimentals, reminding Darcy the family expected him to attend the Dalrymple's ball. His aunt, Lady Matlock, had determined they must show a united front, and not let gossip change how they went about their lives.

"I have in my possession the letter Miss Bingley wrote," Darcy began with no preamble.

Richard halted mid-step, then followed Darcy to his study. "Where is it?"

"In my strong box, where it will stay."

"I would like to see it for myself. I wish to know who started this vicious rumor about Georgie."

"Stand down, Richard. I am aware of who received it and can tell you the recipient is not to blame. Not in this. She only recently learned of the gossip, and immediately brought the letter to me."

"How much did she want?"

"Nothing. She did not request a monetary exchange."

"She must have wanted something. Why else would this travesty have begun?"

"Truly, Richard, she did not ask for money. She gave me the letter, no conditions attached."

"Was it as I suspected? She was one of Bingley's angels?"

"She was, indeed."

"Am I correct in assuming it was the lady from Hertfordshire?" At Darcy's curt nod, Richard continued. "Even though she has proven she is not mercenary, was she that reprehensible you needed to intervene on Bingley's behalf?"

"At the time, I believed she received his attention in a pleasant and amiable manner but her heart remained untouched. Because of that, I could not stand by and see my friend attach himself to a woman who did not return his affection in equal measure. He will find another angel to fill his dreams and bed."

"As long as it is not our dear Georgiana, I care not who Bingley eventually falls in love with. So, what do we do now?'

"Nothing. We strangle the weeds of gossip by giving them no light of day and act as though nothing has happened. Georgiana is safe at Matlock House, and we will be leaving for Pemberley after I return from Kent this spring."

"Well, I will apologize now for the grumbling I am sure to engage in. I wanted, nay, I needed a physical foe to battle. Inaction is not something I am comfortable with."

"Keep your saber sharpened, cousin. I may have need of it when we visit Aunt Catherine at Easter."

"I know with certainty this year my skill with a blade will come in handy. I shall become known as Richard, the dragon slayer."

Richard burst out laughing, and Darcy was a bit mystified by his cousin's apparent delight and eagerness to confront their aunt.

***

For Elizabeth, there was nothing more exciting than attending the theater and losing herself in the middle of a story. Aunt and Uncle Gardiner tried to ensure their nieces enjoyed at least one play when they visited, and Uncle always managed to purchase decent seats. However, situated comfortably in the Duke of Belmont's box, they were assured of an unimpeded view of the stage.

Elizabeth found her toes tapping with excitement. With great effort, she attempted to project a calm façade, similar to Jane, whom she knew was more nervous than excited. To date, Jane and Henry had kept their courtship private, and tonight was their first public appearance together. More than one set of lorgnettes was trained on their box.

She hid a smile. The public might be curious about two unknown ladies in the company of a marquis and an earl, but when the affection between Jane and Henry became known, they would likely turn into a rabid mob. Many society matrons with single daughters would not be happy after tonight. Frankly, Elizabeth did not care. As long as Jane was happy, she was happy. When the curtain at the back of the box was unexpectedly drawn to one side, both sisters were pleased to see Michael and Gabriel step through.

"We did not expect to see you again until tomorrow," Elizabeth teased her brothers after all the greetings were exchanged.

"We spoke with the marquis after we dropped you and Jane off this afternoon," Michael said with a nod toward Sebastian, who was handing Susannah a glass of wine. "He let us know there was plenty of room for more guests and, as you know, Gabriel never turns down a visit to the theater."

"I do know," Elizabeth said and directed a conspiratorial grin toward Gabe. "You will be pleased to know tonight's play is *A Midsummer's Night Dream*."

"Excellent! My favorite play from the bard."

Gabriel politely acknowledged Susannah, then slipped into the chair beside her, quietly asking how her evening was. Soon they were talking like the old friends they had become through the years.

"Ugh…" Michael grunted, catching Elizabeth's attention.

"What is it?" she asked.

"My night is ruined."

With a nod of his head, he drew her attention across the theater. She obliged her own curiosity, dismayed to see Mr. Bingley and his sisters, along with Mr. Hurst seated in one of the lower-tier boxes. How ironic that the amiable young man, who left Jane dangling on faint hopes and unfinished dreams, would attend a play the same night as her.

Elizabeth continued to surreptitiously watch the Bingley family and saw the exact moment Miss Bingley realized the dreaded Bennet sisters were in attendance and seated in a premier box. She nearly laughed out loud at the ensuing chaos as Miss Bingley did everything in her power to ensure her brother did not look up and discover Jane's presence. Dear Papa would howl with laughter at Elizabeth's next letter home, especially when she described the bobbing of Miss Bingley's head, and how the feathers on her turban looked like a fluffy bird trying to take flight.

Elizabeth cast a quick glance at Jane, worried about her reaction if she were to see Mr. Bingley. Not for the first time she thanked God for bringing Henry into Jane's life, and based on the way her sister had been smiling ever since the earl had left uncle's house this afternoon, she was almost one hundred percent certain he had asked for Jane's hand in marriage. She looked upward, and prayed silently, please, do not let Mr. Bingley ruin this night of happiness.

Little did she know, Jane *had* seen Mr. Bingley and leaned into Henry as a result. Upon her edging closer, he smiled and Jane's stomach did a funny little flip.

"What has provoked you to come so near as to entice me with your scent?" he whispered dangerously close to her ear.

"Do you recall my mentioning Mr. Bingley?" she murmured, keeping their conversation away from the others. Henry frowned and nodded. "He is here, in one of the lower boxes."

Henry glanced over his shoulder and scanned the room, then whispered, "Is his sister's gown an atrocious shade of purple with a matching turban?"

"It is one of her favorite colors, next to orange," Jane replied, trying very hard not to giggle. Miss Bingley's fashion sense was, at best, distinctive. "I only bring them to your attention because I would not want you to be caught off guard if they try to reestablish an acquaintance. Especially after they learn the identity of our host."

"Fear not, my dear," Henry said and lifted her fingers to his lips. "As the proud owner of your heart, I can meet the gentleman and his family with equanimity and goodwill."

"Dear Henry, you know just how to soothe my anxiety."

"Do you wish for me to tell them I have gained your consent to marriage, or would you rather wait until we notify our families."

"I wanted to talk with Lizzy right after you proposed this afternoon, but we had no spare time." She held his gaze and smiled. "However, if the occasion calls for you to declare yourself, I will not chastise you in any form."

"Not even with a pouty lip?" he teased. "You know how much I love to kiss that full lower lip."

"Henry!" Jane protested, daring a quick peek over his shoulder to see if anyone heard her cry out. "You are a terrible flirt."

"I am, but only with you, and I will not apologize for that."

***

During the first interval, the gentlemen exited the box to find refreshments for the ladies, leaving Susannah, Elizabeth, and Jane quite alone. Now that there was a semblance of privacy, Elizabeth moved to sit next to Jane.

"Did you see who was seated across the theater?"

"I did," Jane said, her voice filled with regret. She heaved a deep sigh. "I am afraid they will try and opportune us for introductions."

"Whom are we speaking about?" Susannah had moved to sit behind Jane.

"Mr. Bingley and his family are in attendance, and Miss Bingley made note of it," Jane explained.

"From what I have learned of Miss Bingley's nature, I believe we should prepare ourselves for her to, quite literally, knock on our door."

"Must we speak with them?" Elizabeth asked. "If I recall, she and her sister cut us direct. If we refuse them entry, we will be abiding by the rules they set before us."

"Elizabeth, you are so naughty," Susannah teased, smiling wide. "However, I promised Jane if the opportunity rose for me to put Miss Bingley in her place, I would do so. All I ask is for you and your lovely sister to remain polite, and behave as the ladies I know you are. I shall take care of the rest."

Elizabeth took Jane's hand in hers and they held each other's gaze. When Jane gave a slight nod, Elizabeth squeezed her hand and turned her attention to Susannah.

"We will leave whatever happens to your discretion, Lady Susannah."

As if on cue, a knock was heard on the door to their box.

Chapter Twenty

Darcy caught Richard's eye, silently beseeching him to save him from the endless sniping of Miss Bingley. His cousin merely shook his head, refusing to even come near Bingley's sister. He had made his disgust for her behavior very clear. For himself, Darcy had not yet had a chance to speak with Bingley directly about the letter his sister had written. His intentions were to visit Hurst's townhouse tomorrow. Until the rumors died down, Darcy dared not invite Bingley to his house or see him at their club.

As it was, he was shocked when Bingley and his family sought him out at Lady Dalrymple's ball. He was positive they were taking in a play, which was why he had chosen to attend a venue where they were not expected. About to take his leave, to stave off further gossip, he paused when the name Elizabeth Bennet flew off Miss Bingley's tongue.

"What about Miss Elizabeth?" he found himself asking before his brain had engaged enough to stop him.

"She was at the theater. In a premiere box, can you believe it?" Miss Bingley huffed out. "I do not know how she and her pasty sister are acquainted with the Duke of Belmont—"

"The Duke of Belmont!" Darcy exclaimed.

"I was as shocked as you, but that is not all. During the first interval, Charles and I went to greet them"

"Why?"

"Why what?"

"You cut them direct. Why would you now greet them like good friends?"

"Well… we were on good terms whilst in Hertfordshire."

"Were you?" Darcy was astonished at her audacity. "Is that why you wrote Miss Bennet, telling her you do not pretend to regret anything you left in Hertfordshire?"

Miss Bingley gave a small start.

"I do not recall my exact words when I bid Miss Bennet farewell."

"Then, you also do not recall writing you and your sister dared to entertain the idea of my sister becoming yours?" At the widening of her eyes, Darcy forged ahead, anger giving his words the cutting edge of a rapier. "No? Then, mayhap you recall telling Miss Bennet your brother was very capable of engaging any woman's heart, and my relations all wished for the connection as much as your own. Of course, these are not your exact words, I am but paraphrasing."

"How would you know what I wrote?"

Darcy glared down at her, his anger flowing white hot.

"Because I have, in my possession, the very letter where you penned those lies."

Miss Bingley paled before him, swaying slightly on her feet. Darcy wondered if she would swoon, and more to the point, would he do anything to break her fall? He then remembered Georgiana's tears and how she had fled to stay with Aunt Matlock in the aftermath of the devastating column in The Tattler and decided if Miss Bingley fainted, he'd let her crumple to the ground.

"Caroline!" Bingley rushed over to them and grabbed her arm while signaling Mrs. Hurst to give aid. "Here, take Louisa's arm. She will help you to a retiring room."

"I would like to go home, Charles," Miss Bingley said, her voice surprisingly soft.

"Louisa, take care of Caroline. I will call for the carriage and meet you at the front door in a half hour."

The two sisters left the ballroom and an angry Bingley stood facing Darcy.

"What did you say to my sister?" he demanded.

"I told her I have in my possession the letter she wrote. The one which was referenced in *The Tattler*."

Bingley openly gaped, "You have the actual letter?"

"Yes?"

"And you know it was written by my sister?"

"I recognized her handwriting and her signature."

"But she swore she had nothing to do with all this."

"She lied." Darcy pinched the bridge of his nose in an attempt to stave off a headache. "I want nothing more to do with your sister."

"You cannot mean that, Darcy," Bingley almost whispered.

"Because of your sister's vindictive nature, *my* sister's reputation has been dragged through the social gutter. She is not yet sixteen and already her name is synonymous with rumors of an illicit affair with an unmarried gentleman. I do not know what your sister thought to accomplish with such bald-faced lies, other than to viciously hurt a woman who, at one time, held you in great esteem."

"To whom did she write such things?"

Although his expression did not change, Darcy internally cringed over the fact Bingley had no idea to which of his many 'angels' his sister may have penned such a poison letter.

"Miss Jane Bennet," he answered.

"Darcy, I cannot tell you how sorry I am about all this. To think my sister would write such falsehoods to Miss Bennet, and for that lady to gossip about it… I do not know who is more at fault."

"Before you cast judgment on Miss Bennet, I should tell

you she was having a private conversation that was overheard by a maid. In no way did she instigate gossip with anyone."

Bingley ran his fingers through his mop of curls.

"I was going to wait until April to take the family to Scarborough, but I believe it would be best if we left earlier, rather than later."

"I cannot help but agree with you. I will gladly welcome you back when you return, but I must say this before you leave. Your sister is not welcome in any of my homes. Her machinations against Georgiana, as well as her continual clinging to my arm at every social occasion, is abhorrent to me." He almost stopped speaking when his friend's head bowed in defeat. "I have never given your sister reason to believe I would make an offer for her. Her delusions are her own, and I sincerely hope with time away from town, she will reach her own epiphany with regard to what is required for her own happiness."

Bingley raised his head and nodded. "I have told her this, many times. Unfortunately, she is too used to having her own way." He frowned, his eyes trained on the ground but flicking left to right, and back again. Darcy recognized this behavior. It was something Bingley did when trying to figure something out. Suddenly, he raised his head. "My sisters never liked Miss Bennet, did they?"

Caught by surprise, Darcy nearly objected. Yet, his friend needed to know the truth.

"No, they did not and I know, for a fact, they treated her in an exceedingly rude manner."

At Bingley's questioning glance, Darcy proceeded to tell him how his sisters had rushed Miss Bennet from his townhouse, and how they had cut her direct while shopping. Bingley blinked and swallowed hard.

"No wonder we were not allowed access to the duke's private box."

"Pardon?"

"Caroline began acting very strange before the play started, and it soon became obvious she was attempting to direct my attention to another portion of the theater. Of course, I had to see what had her so upset and noticed both Miss Bennets in the Duke of Belmont's box. During the first interval, Caroline and I went to greet them, only to have the footman deny us entrance."

Darcy didn't know if he should be amused or horrified at the idea of Bingley and his sister attempting to enter the duke's box without invitation, having never been introduced to him and his family. The audacity of the two siblings was beyond belief.

Bingley continued. "As you can well imagine, Caroline became distraught, and she proclaimed that she and I were on intimate terms with the Miss Bennets, which we are, and it was them we wished to see."

"I would suspect her entreaties were not received well."

"Not in any way. I attempted to take Caroline's arm and direct her back to our box, but she forced her way past the footman and entered on her own. I could do naught but follow."

Is that not what you always do, my friend? Darcy thought wryly.

"Imagine my surprise when the duke's daughter stood and said, quite loudly I might add, '*Who are you, to barge uninvited into my father's private box? Do you think this is Bond Street, where you can accost people at will? Jasper, remove these people.*' She turned her back on us, and sat next to Miss Elizabeth."

Darcy remembered how Miss Bingley had gloated over cutting the Bennet sisters and some unknown woman on Bond Street. It was patently obvious the woman had been the duke's daughter.

"I was able to steer Caroline from the room and into the outer hall where we were faced with Miss Bennet's brothers,

Marquis Grenfell, and Earl Holcomb. I apologized for our unwelcome intrusion and made to move Caroline along when the earl forestalled me. You will never guess what he whispered in my ear."

That was one guess Darcy did not wish to make and dreaded what might come of it. As long as it did not involve Miss Elizabeth, he could withstand anything.

"He is betrothed to Miss Bennet, and he further said he would never have been so foolish as to leave her dangling in the same manner as I had. Can you believe that? I suppose you were right in your estimation she did not hold affection for me, to have moved on so quickly."

"Even if Miss Bennet did hold you in tender regard, you have been gone from Hertfordshire for over three months. You cannot paint her character with such a broad brush. She is entitled to find happiness with someone else."

"What if she does not love him? He is wealthier than me and titled. Should I warn him she is as mercenary as you thought?"

"Charles, I never said Miss Bennet was mercenary, those were your sister's words. I believed she did not return your affection. Nothing more, nothing less."

"You are right, I suppose."

Bingley then bid him *adieu* and went to call for his carriage, telling Darcy he would write when they reached Scarborough. Not even five minutes passed before Richard returned to his side. He knew his cousin was impatient to know what he said to Miss Bingley. Both of them still smarted from the sting of gossip generated around Georgiana, which was why they had subjected themselves to Lady Dalrymple's ball.

"What had the Bingleys scuttle out of here like rats caught in sunlight?"

"Bingley did not scuttle."

"His waspish sister did. I nearly clapped and cheered."

"This is not the time nor place to discuss such a sensitive topic. We shall have plenty of time when we travel to Kent."

"Well then, I may as well enjoy myself whilst we are here," Richard said as he rocked back on his heels, a wide smile on his face. "I believe I shall ask Miss Ludlow to dance. Her beau had to attend to estate matters and she is bereft of partners this evening. I suggest you do the same."

Darcy did not wish to dance, he did not even want to remain at the ball, but for his sister, he would. He searched through the crowd for a safe, suitable partner, and spied a very happily married Mrs. Brandon, seated next to her equally happily married sister, Mrs. Ferrars. She would do nicely and he was soon bowing in front of them, asking each for a set.

***

Darcy leaned back on the squabs of his carriage and allowed himself to think about something Bingley had said before he left to escort his sister home.

You will never guess what he whispered in my ear.

He had braced himself for the worst and when Bingley said, 'he is betrothed to Miss Bennet,' Darcy had very nearly fallen to his knees. Elizabeth was not betrothed. He breathed it over and over like a mantra. She was not betrothed. He still had time to make amends, but how?

As soon as he arrived at his townhouse, he went to his study and picked up the pile of correspondence he had mentally labeled Decline. He rifled through the various cards and letters until he found the gold-embossed invitation to the Duke of Belmont's annual ball and breathed a heartfelt sigh of relief. He would see Elizabeth Bennet again, and if she were gracious enough, she would grant him a dance.

The week leading up to the ball was interminable. Now that he knew where Elizabeth laid her head at night, he had to restrain himself from saddling up Arion and ride past the duke's house in the vain hope he might see her through a window, or better yet, going for a walk. It seemed when it came to the miss from Hertfordshire, he lost all dignity and decorum and for the first time in his life, the words of a love-sick Romeo made sense.

Did my heart love till now?

He knew his had not.

Finally, the night was upon him and he unconsciously held his breath when he entered the ballroom after traversing through the receiving line. He was thankful his height allowed him to peruse the room with relative ease. His breath released in a soft huff of breath when he spied Elizabeth standing with Miss Bennet and Lord Holcomb near the terrace doors. Mesmerized, he could only stare. She was translucently beautiful. A bright star plucked from heaven's court to shine amongst them. How in the world had he ever thought her barely tolerable?

He straightened his shoulders and began to wend his way through the crowd, never taking his eyes off the prize of Elizabeth Bennet. Her sister leaned toward her and must have said something because Elizabeth turned her head and watched him approach. He was uncertain if she was wary or combative. He had not done himself any favors with his more than haughty behavior.

"Lord Holcomb, Miss Bennet, Miss Elizabeth."

When they had each returned his greeting, he placed his attention on Elizabeth.

"Lovely weather we are having. Do you not agree?" he asked and watched her cock her head slightly to one side. "There is nothing more refreshing than a lovely breeze coming through the terrace doors to keep the ballroom cool."

She stayed silent for so long, he fully expected her to pivot on her heel and leave him standing there. An unexpected sense of relief flowed through his body when she finally spoke in a surprisingly polite manner.

"I agree, the breeze is welcoming, which is why we have chosen to stand in this location. I would not be surprised if it rains later on."

His shoulders relaxed, thankful the impertinent miss would, at the very least, remain polite in his presence. It was time to change her opinion of him.

"Would you do me the honor of dancing the sixth set?"

"You are aware you would be my partner for supper if we danced this particular set."

"I am aware, and look forward to your company." Miss Elizabeth stepped slightly to her left and craned her neck, as though looking behind him. "May I ask what you are doing?"

"I am looking for the marionette strings, for surely Mr. Fitzwilliam Darcy of Derbyshire is not asking Miss Elizabeth Bennet of Hertfordshire to dance the supper set. Someone else must be controlling your actions."

"Lizzy!" her sister admonished.

He tried, he truly did, but he could not stop the grin which graced his face. His reward was her widened eyes and slightly dilated pupils.

Ahh… the Darcy dimples have caught her attention.

He was not a vain man, but he did own a mirror and knew he was handsome. From the time he could crawl, he'd learned his full smile had social currency, and now that he knew she was physically aware of him, he was not averse to spreading some of that non-tangible cash around in his pursuit of Miss Elizabeth Bennet.

"I stand before you of my own free will, Miss Elizabeth, and would be honored if you stood up with me for the supper set."

"In such cases as this, it is, I believe, the established mode is to graciously say yes." His heart plummeted past his stomach and landed somewhere on the floor near his new dancing shoes. She was going to say no. She would forego her pleasure and sit out all dances, simply to avoid partnering with him. He was a fool. So busy castigating himself, he almost missed the remainder of her answer. "However, I am not one to go against societal dictates, and accept your invitation to dance."

He almost wept. Almost. It was all he could do to give her a polite half-bow, thank her, and then find a room where he could lick his wounds in private. Even though she had accepted, she had flayed him alive without lifting one delicate finger.

***

What on earth was Mr. Darcy about? After their confrontation at his home, she was more than surprised when he approached and greeted them. Other than having accidentally entered an alternate universe, something had changed the gentleman's perspective of their family.

"Jane," she asked her sister. "Have I fallen asleep and this is a vivid dream?"

"No, you are wide awake, standing with Henry and me."

"Then, I did not imagine Mr. Darcy asking me for a set."

"You did not."

"Pinch me."

"What?"

"Pinch me. I still think I am dreaming." Jane pinched her arm. "*Ow!* That hurt."

"You did ask."

"Lord Holcomb," Elizabeth said, lightly rubbing the tender flesh above her elbow. "Are you certain you wish to marry this cruel woman?"

"Even more so." Elizabeth pretended to gasp in horror. "It is good to know my future wife knows how to deal with stubborn young ladies."

The musicians began to play the opening chords and Jane and Henry went to line up for the first set of dances. Elizabeth's partner, Lord Ellery, came to claim her hand and they spent a pleasant hour conversing on a variety of subjects, one of them being the fact her brothers were attending his estate for a house party in the next few days. All too soon she took her place in the set, opposite Mr. Darcy. They stood for some time without speaking a word, and she was reminded of their first dance at Netherfield Park.

"It is your turn to start the conversation, Mr. Darcy. The last time, I started by complimenting Miss Bingley's decorations." As he did then, he smiled and assured her that whatever she wished him to say should be said. "No, that will not do. You must have your share in the conversation."

"That is something my aunt would say."

"She insists on having her share in every conversation?"

"She insists on having everything to her liking. She can be quite demanding."

"A family trait, I would imagine."

They moved down the line and did not have a chance to speak further until the dance was near complete.

"How is it that your family is acquainted with the duke's daughter?" he asked when they stood across from one another again.

"I was nine and our family had gone to visit my father's eldest sister in Derbyshire. Aunt Poppy had to attend the closest village for something, and I decided to wait for her near the river which ran through the town. I had barely reached the bridge when a young girl came tearing across from the other side. She had lost control of her horse. Suddenly, the horse reared and she was thrown over the bridge and into the river, which was swollen from recent rains. Without thought, I jumped in and dragged her to shore."

"I can see why the duke and his family have made you part of their family."

"As Susannah likes to say, it was the best worst day of our lives. I have always been grateful I was there at the right time."

"As a person who has come to value your friendship, I understand her sentiments."

Elizabeth smiled and enjoyed the rest of the set and during supper, where she and Mr. Darcy sat with not only Jane and Lord Holcomb but also Sebastian, Susannah, and the duke and duchess. She could not help thinking back, once again, to Netherfield Park, where she and Mr. Darcy had also sat through a dinner, where neither of them had been comfortable. Given the sense of calm emanating from Mr. Darcy, it was clear he also preferred their current company.

When Susannah looked at her and waggled her eyebrows, Elizabeth gave her head a soft shake. She held no hope for someone like Mr. Darcy pursuing her. She knew he only asked for a set because, while in Hertfordshire, he had made it abundantly clear he would only dance with someone he was acquainted with. She was not handsome enough to tempt him to take their friendship further.

Chapter Twenty-One

"I see you are already packed. I have only begun," Elizabeth said upon entering Jane's bed chamber. "I am going for a walk before the day gets away from me."

"I have only my small personal items to put away. Henry wishes to leave for Longbourn at first light tomorrow." Jane tucked one of her hair combs into a soft pouch and carefully laid it in her trunk. "If I know you, even as we load up the carriage, you will still be throwing things into your trunk."

"You know me well. I promise I will be ready to depart when the first lark sings its morning song." Jane gave a little snort of disbelief and continued packing. "You doubt my word?"

Jane paused, a pair of earrings in her hand. "You continually open your trunk and take out something vital. Usually a book."

"Guilty as charged," Elizabeth said with a laugh. "Let me enjoy my walk, and I will see you at dinner." She made to leave Jane's room and threw over her shoulder before exiting the room. "Tomorrow, I will astonish you when I am waiting for you on the front drive, sitting on my well-packed trunk."

"I will not hold my breath, Lizzy Bennet," Jane called after her.

Elizabeth had just stepped through the front door, along with one of the duke's footmen, when her attention was caught by the fact Mr. Darcy was alighting from his carriage. She waited at the top of the stairs for the gentleman, who had smiled at her with no reserve, causing her heart to triple its rate of beats per minute.

"Miss Elizabeth, I have just come to ask if you would like to take a walk with me."

"Your timing is impeccable, sir. I was about to do that very thing."

"Excellent. Would you mind my company?"

She agreed and Mr. Darcy met her halfway down the steps, extended his elbow and she laid her gloved hand on his forearm. Together they crossed the road and upon gaining entry into the park directly across from the duke's residence, began to traverse the wide paths, the footman staying a polite distance behind them.

They walked in silence for about ten minutes before Mr. Darcy cleared his throat and said, "Did you enjoy the duke's ball?"

"I did. This is the first time Jane and I were able to attend. We have always spent the summer months at their country estate."

"Invitations to the duke's ball are coveted."

"And yet, this was the first one you attended."

She had learned this morsel of news when Susannah had dragged her into a private parlor after supper to question her with the finesse of a Spanish Inquisitor.

"I have had the desire to attend before. The added incentive of your company prompted me to change my mind."

"Me?"

He stopped walking and faced her.

"Yes."

She searched his eyes, looking for deceit and arrogance, finding none. Unsure of what to make of this man, she took his arm again and they continued to walk in silence. Eventually, the topic of books was introduced and although the conversation at first was halting, they soon revisited their former debate over Cowper and Byron and the remainder of the walk was pleasant. It was as they approached the exit gate, and his arm tensed beneath her hand, she knew he was searching for words. How she knew, she had no idea, but as sure as the sun would rise in the morning and set in the evening, she knew the gentleman was hesitant.

"Miss Elizabeth… I have enjoyed our walk."

"As did I."

"May I… that is, are you free to go for a ride tomorrow afternoon?"

His expression was hopeful and she felt terrible about what she had to say next.

"I am sorry. I must decline your gracious invitation."

An expression of dejection crossed his face so quickly, she almost thought she'd imagined it. Instantly, a familiar shade of hauteur overspread his features.

"Forgive me, madam, for taking up so much of your time."

He made to turn and leave but stopped when she impulsively took hold of his wrist, dropping it as soon as she'd realized what she'd done. Heat flushed her cheeks. She'd behaved no better than Lydia, but the need for him to not misunderstand had overwhelmed her normal reticence. Would the two of them never stop distrusting their words and motives?

"It is not because I dislike your company, Mr. Darcy. Jane is leaving for Hertfordshire tomorrow and I am off to Kent with my brothers."

"Where in Kent, if you do not mind me asking?"

"My friend, you knew her as Miss Lucas married our cousin and has invited me to stay with them at Hunsford. He is the newly appointed rector of the parish there and this will be the first time he conducts an Easter service. He is quite excited over the prospect."

She could not be certain, as the gentleman's habits and behaviors were still unknown to her, but his expression had lightened as she spoke of her upcoming visit with Charlotte.

"I will say my goodbyes then, Miss Elizabeth. Thank you for letting me join you on your walk."

"Truly, the pleasure was mine."

They parted ways and Elizabeth's brow furrowed as she entered the duke's house. What was Mr. Darcy doing? It was very plain he had purposefully sought her company today, as well as at the ball, but she had been told he was as good as engaged to his cousin. None of this made sense. She mentally shook the confusion from her mind. There was no reason to expect to see Mr. Darcy ever again. They did not travel in the same social circle and with Mr. Bingley giving up the lease to Netherfield Park, the man from Derbyshire had no reason to ever set foot in Meryton again.

The next morning, after Lord Holcomb along with Michael and Gabriel had arrived, Susannah and the marquess farewelled Jane and Elizabeth at the door. The duke and duchess having said their goodbyes earlier that morning.

"I shall miss you, oh so very much," Susannah said, tears forming in her eyes as she gave Jane a fierce hug. "One of you must marry Sebastian so I never have to lose you."

"I believe Jane is very much in love with Holcomb, dear sister," the marquess said as he bowed low over Jane's hand, ignoring the small glower exhibited by not only Lord Holcomb but also her ever-vigilant brothers. "And Elizabeth and I are too much alike to ever have a sedate marriage."

"Shall we make a pact, sir?" Elizabeth asked, her eyes sparkling with mischief. "If neither of us is married in ten years, we shall abscond to Gretna Green."

"If you are not married in less than one year, Elizabeth, I will eat my favorite beaver hat."

She outright laughed at this statement and replied, "My dear Lord Grenfell, my uncle has access to a vast array of exotic spices. I shall bring some to make your chapeau more edible."

Sebastian laughed out loud. "I stand by what I said. I do not think you will lack offers. Just make sure you choose a worthy husband. One who will put up with your lively mind, and enjoys engaging in debates over a multitude of subjects."

For some strange reason, Elizabeth's mind turned to Mr. Darcy. She mentally, and physically shook her head to disperse the gentleman from her thoughts. He was not for her; he was pledged to another. With many waves and goodbyes, Jane and Lord Holcomb left for Longbourn, while Elizabeth was off to Kent in the company of Michael and Gabriel. Her brothers took her as far as The Bell, a posting inn near Hunsford where Sir William Lucas and his daughter Maria had agreed to meet.

***

Upon her arrival at The Bell, Elizabeth was pleased to see Sir William Lucas already there, having arrived a scant ten minutes prior. She and her brothers joined them in partaking of a light lunch, then they each went their respective ways. Michael and Gabriel to Lord Ellery's estate near Ramsgate, with Elizabeth off to Hunsford with her longtime neighbors.

"We were very lucky, Miss Eliza, in that your brothers were traveling to Kent. It certainly saved Maria and me some time, not having to navigate the streets of London to pick you up at your uncle's house. Not that we would have minded."

"I agree, Sir William. Michael must return home in a few weeks to begin preparations for the spring planting. Gabriel has kindly offered to come by Hunsford and collect me at the end of the month. So much nicer than traveling by post."

"I was going to ask if your uncle was sending a man to meet you at The Bell, but I see my worries are unfounded. No better escort than a dedicated brother, or her mother."

Upon saying this, Sir William glanced down at his daughter, Maria, who only stared at her hands and added nothing to the conversation.

When they left the high road for the lane to Hunsford, all of them began craning their neck in hopes of being the first to spot the parsonage. Finally, Maria spied the house set prettily behind a laurel hedge. Mr. Collins and Charlotte appeared at the door, and the carriage stopped at a small gate, which revealed a short gravel walk to the house. Uncaring if it was thought indecorous, Elizabeth held her arms wide and Charlotte welcomed her with a warm hug. She then stepped aside and turned to greet her cousin.

"Mr. Collins," she said with a polite curtsy.

"Cousin Elizabeth, my wife, and I are exceedingly glad you were able to visit along with my illustrious father and sister. May I ask how your family is doing?"

"Papa's last letter spoke of everyone's continued good health. Jane returned to Longbourn as of today, and Michael and Gabriel kindly escorted me to The Bell, where I met up with Sir William and Maria."

She purposefully did not speak of Jane's engagement, wanting to tell Charlotte in private. Jane had asked Elizabeth and her brothers to say as little as possible so that she and Henry could enjoy their engagement without all the fuss Mamma would generate once she knew Henry was the Earl of Holcomb. At that thought, Elizabeth could not help but smile at the mental image of Mamma discovering his title. She might very well swoon.

Greetings finalized, Mr. Collins proudly began to show

them around the house and gardens. He would have continued at length if Charlotte had not reminded him their guests might require some refreshments after such a long carriage ride. Elizabeth admired the quiet way Charlotte stopped her husband's excessive posturing and took her sister and friend back to the house for a cup of tea without the enthusiastic company of her husband.

***

Elizabeth expected to meet the great lady Mr. Collins had spoken of so often at service on Sunday, but the day after her arrival at Hunsford, Miss Anne de Bourgh came by the parsonage in her phaeton and extended an invitation to dine at Rosings Park the following evening. To say Mr. Collins was beyond excited over the news would be like saying the sun was bright.

"I fully expected Lady Catherine to invite us to drink tea and spend the evening at Rosings after Sunday service, but I never could have foreseen such an honor as her Ladyship inviting all of us to dine at Rosings so soon after your arrival!"

"I am not surprised," Sir William said while puffing out his chest. "Good manners and elegant breeding are not uncommon among those who have been presented at Court. I myself have always been graciously received. I expect nothing less from Lady Catherine and rather suspect her invitation was issued so she could become acquainted with your extended family."

"You must realize, Cousin Elizabeth, while the meal itself will exceed anything you have seen or partaken in, this is an everyday occurrence for Lady Catherine and her daughter." Mr. Collins laced his fingers over his stomach and rocked back on his heels. "I, myself, have dined at Rosings Park at least six times now. I am almost as nonchalant about the dining experience as her Ladyship."

Elizabeth said nothing but ducked her head to hide a smile. While Lady Catherine very well could provide an elegant meal and grand settings, not much could compare to dining at the Duke of Belmont's house.

"Thank you for your thoughtfulness, Mr. Collins," Elizabeth managed to say without laughing.

Mr. Collins took this as an invitation to tell her what to wear and how to comport herself.

"Do not make yourself uneasy about the quality of your clothing. Lady Catherine is far from requiring that elegance of dress in us, which becomes herself and her daughter. I would advise you to wear the best dress you brought with you. Lady Catherine will not think any worse of you for being simply dressed. She likes to have the distinction of rank preserved."

When it came time to make their way to the great lady's house, Maria Lucas was so frightened, she trembled and held onto her father's hand the entirety of the walk across the park. Elizabeth saw much to be pleased with and anticipated exploring all the little paths she glimpsed on their way to Rosings Park. Her pleasure diminished somewhat when Mr. Collins went into raptures over the *façade* of the great house, enumerating the windows and how much money was spent glazing all of them.

Soon, they followed a servant to the room where Lady Catherine waited. For herself, Elizabeth thought the furniture dark and heavy, the decorations ostentatious and gaudy. Having visited several great homes over the past few months, including Henry's and the duke's, Rosings Park did not hold any appeal, whatsoever. She did not, of course, disabuse her cousin of his delight with all that Lady Catherine possessed. Not even the massive fieldstone fireplace, which apparently had cost over eight hundred pounds.

Lady Catherine, a tall woman with strong features, rose to

---

receive them. Her condescending manner and self-importance left them in no doubt she believed her visitors inferior to her in every way. Elizabeth almost expected her cousin to genuflect and kiss her ring. He did bow very low, but no ring kissing ensued. Sir William followed, and in spite of having been presented at St. James's, he was obviously awed by the grandeur surrounding him, barely managing a very low bow. He took his seat beside a frightened Maria, who sat on the edge of her chair, her hands clasped tight on her lap.

Mr. Collins bade Elizabeth to come forward and she gave Lady Catherine a very proper curtsy before greeting the grand lady's daughter and her companion. She then sat beside Charlotte and watched the scene unfold, often biting the inside of her cheek to keep from smiling. While Lady Catherine spoke decisively on any number of subjects, Elizabeth took the opportunity to study Mr. Darcy's affianced. Miss de Bourgh was not plain, she was actually quite pretty but appeared delicate and pale. When she spoke, her voice was so low, her companion, Mrs. Jenkinson, had to lean in and incline her ear.

Before long, Lady Catherine turned her attention to Elizabeth.

"My understanding is that your father's estate is entailed upon Mr. Collins," Lady Catherine announced as though she were talking about the weather. For a brief moment, Elizabeth was taken aback by such gross misinformation. "I think, for your sake Mrs. Collins—"

"Longbourn is not entailed." Elizabeth emerged from her surprised state to speak over Lady Catherine.

"Not entailed!" Lady Catherine jerked her head around at the unexpected interruption, and glared at Elizabeth, then turned her attention toward Mr. Collins, whose eyes widened and beads of sweat formed over his upper lip. "You told me you were to inherit your cousin's estate."

"I was misinformed by my father, Lady Catherine."

"And you did not see fit to inform me of these changes?"

"I… ahhh…"

"Lady Catherine, I must apologize for my husband," Charlotte said in her calm, steady manner. "His main focus, other than looking after the parishioners, has been to make easy my settling into our new home. I am certain if he had not been so conciliatory toward my comfort, he most assuredly would have remembered to apprise you of his news."

An uneasy silence settled over the room before Lady Catherine sniffed, and said, "I am pleased your husband is taking care of his new wife. I told Mr. Collins to marry a woman of good sense, and I see he followed my advice." Lady Catherine glanced at Elizabeth. "Who then inherits your father's estate?"

"My eldest brother, Michael."

"And your father did not enlighten Mr. Collins prior to his arrival?"

"Mr. Collins told us about the fire which took his father's life and which also destroyed all documents. Because of this sad fact, he was unaware of my brother's existence until he graced us with his visit this past autumn."

"Humph… highly irregular." Lady Catherine frowned, then fixed her attention once more on Elizabeth. "Do you play and sing, Miss Bennet?"

"I do, but only for my own pleasure."

"Then you will not mind entertaining us later. Tell me, do your sisters play and sing?"

"Sadly, no."

"No?"

"My eldest sister's gift is crafting her own perfumes and exquisite embroidery. I have several of her works hung in our room. Our youngest sister has yet to find her talent, although our mother wishes to teach her the piano. She, herself, is very proficient."

"That is good. A lady must have some accomplishment. Anne would have been a wonderful pianist, had her health allowed it." Lady Catherine tapped her finger on the arm of her chair, clearly in thought. "I am surprised your governess did not attempt to teach all of you to play the piano. That is most remiss on her part."

"We did not have a governess."

"No governess! Then, who taught you? Without a governess, you must have been neglected."

"I assure you, Ma'am, we were not. Our father encouraged us to read from an early age, and we enjoyed the tutelage of any masters deemed necessary. Our brothers went to Eton and then to Cambridge. My eldest sister and I attended Miss Tyler's Academy for Young Ladies."

Lady Catherine's eyebrows rose at the mention of the exclusive seminary.

"Your father can afford such luxury?"

"Yes, Ma'am," Elizabeth replied and fought to keep a grin from forming. She was highly amused by the imperious lady's interrogation. "My youngest sister will attend Miss Tyler's school when she turns sixteen."

It became obvious, to Elizabeth at least, Lady Catherine had no further questions to ask and after a respectable amount of time, they all adjourned to the dining room. The meal commenced in a slightly more decorous manner than the inquisition in the drawing room, filled with exquisite sighs from Mr. Collins, who rhapsodized over every aspect of the meal, echoed in large part by Sir William. Lady Catherine accepted all praise as if she herself had slaved over the hot oven and not her talented cook.

The gentlemen eschewed staying for port and Lady Catherine led them all back to the same drawing room where card tables had been set up as the evening's entertainment. Lady Catherine, Sir William, along with Mr. and Mrs. Collins sat down to quadrille. Miss de Bourgh chose to play at Cassino, so Elizabeth and Maria, and Mrs. Jenkinson joined in.

Elizabeth thought she would have been bored to tears, given the company around their table, but Miss de Bourgh kept a pleasant conversation flowing the whole time they played. She spoke of the grounds and the places she visited when out with her phaeton, and when she discovered Elizabeth enjoyed walking, told her which paths would give her the best exercise and which ones were more picturesque. Mrs. Jenkinson inquired every now and then if she was warm enough, to which Miss de Bourgh always answered in the affirmative. Poor Maria stayed silent, and the trembling of the cards in her hand showcased how nervous she remained, even after Miss de Bourgh tried to ease her suffering with kind words.

The evening finally drew to a close and after many low bows from Mr. Collins, always accompanied by a heartfelt thank-you, the five of them made their way back to the parsonage in one of Lady Catherine's carriages.

"You can have no doubt, Cousin Elizabeth, how our situation with regard to Lady Catherine's family is indeed the sort of extraordinary advantage and blessing which few can boast. You see how continually we are engaged there. Yes, my Charlotte and I have a good life here. She can have no cause to repine her decision to accept my hand."

"Indeed, Mr. Collins, she does not," Elizabeth said in all sincerity. "I am certain my friend is very content and in return, makes this a happy home."

"Yes, she does." Mr. Collins glanced toward the kitchen area where Charlotte had gone to leave instructions for the cook with regard to tomorrow's breakfast.

"I must bid you goodnight," Elizabeth said as she stifled a yawn. "I believe the day has finally caught up with me. Would you please wish your wife a good night for me?"

"Of course, it would be my pleasure. Goodnight, Cousin Elizabeth. May the Lord keep you safe while you sleep."

"Thank you."

She made her way upstairs, and almost as soon as her head hit the pillow, she fell asleep.

Sir William stayed a week complete and, having satisfied himself his daughter was quite content in her marriage, returned to Longbourn carrying letters from Elizabeth to her father and Jane. The next ten days were spent enjoying Charlotte's company, and hours were devoted to discovering the beauty of the park surrounding the main estate. They dined at Rosings twice, and still, Maria could not speak a full sentence. Lady Catherine pressed Elizabeth into playing the pianoforte each time, always saying she would be more proficient if she practiced, as would her daughter – if her health allowed it.

Elizabeth's enjoyment of staying with Charlotte came to a halt when Lady Catherine announced, on their fourth visit to Rosings Park, she would not be extending invitations any time soon, as her nephews, Mr. Darcy and Colonel Fitzwilliam were expected to arrive the following day, and her time would be fully consumed by them. Lady Catherine had then cast an imperious look at Miss de Bourgh, exclaiming she expected to announce her daughter's engagement to her nephew before the end of the month. Even though she had known of this fact for more than four months, Elizabeth's heart constricted at the news.

LONGBOURN'S ANGELS

Chapter Twenty-Two

Two carriages trundled up the long drive to Rosings Park. One held Darcy and his cousin, the second conveyed several trunks, along with Darcy's and Richard's manservants. Their personal horses were ridden by competent, heavily armed outriders.

Ever since the death of his father Darcy had made this annual trek to Kent, and he disliked it more and more with each passing year. The outrageous claims by Lady Catherine of his and Anne's betrothal would no longer be tolerated. He was determined to make it very clear he had no intention of marrying his sickly cousin, even if his lady aunt staged a compromise.

"We have arrived," Richard said, stating the obvious. "I know you plan on confronting our aunt with regard to Anne. I have but one request."

"And, what is it?"

"Can you wait until after you confer with the steward and look at the books? Once you lay down the law, so to speak, she will make our lives unbearable."

"I have no difficulty waiting a few days."

The carriage passed through the main grove which surrounded the manor, and his attention was arrested by the sight of Miss Elizabeth Bennet walking one of the paths. He could not help himself; he caught his breath. He hadn't expected to see her so soon.

"Darcy?" Richard asked. "You look as though you have seen a ghost."

"There was a woman I know, walking our aunt's grove."

"Ah… you have a little doxy here in Kent, eh?" Darcy glowered at Richard, who physically reared back in his seat, more by surprise than fear. "Pardon me. I did not know you had feelings for the lady."

"She is a gentleman's daughter." Darcy forced himself not to look back and gaze upon her again. "I met her while staying with Bingley in Hertfordshire."

"I wonder why she is here, of all places?" Richard mused out loud.

"She is visiting her newly married cousin, who is our aunt's rector."

Darcy did not reply because his mind, once again, revolved around a diminutive woman who continually filled his thoughts and dreams. His musings were cut short with their arrival at the manor house. Upon disembarking, he cast a practiced eye over their aunt's home.

"She did not repair the slate tiles from last year."

"How much damage do you think it might have caused?" Richard asked, also taking in the faded grandeur of a once elegant country estate.

"I fully expect the conservatory on the east wing to have significant water damage. I shall check it out after I have spoken with the steward, Mr. Chisholm. However, the attics will have taken the worst of it, which in turn will have carried down into the servant's quarters." Darcy shook his head. "What a mess."

"The fact she disregarded your advice about the repairs makes me wonder what monstrosity did she purchase in place of?"

"I heard rumors of a fireplace costing above eight hundred pounds."

"Eight hundred pounds for a fireplace!" Richard exclaimed. "Well, the lack of repairs has been fully accounted for. The earl will not be pleased. He is the one who makes up for any shortfalls Aunt Catherine has at year's end."

"After this year, your father can deal with his sister. Lady Catherine does not listen, nor take advice, and I am done wasting my breath and time. I will not return to clean up her continued mismanagement."

Darcy and his cousin mounted the front steps, unsurprised when the door swung open the minute their boots touched the top landing.

"Good afternoon, Colonel. Mr. Darcy," the butler said with a polite half-bow.

"Good afternoon, Rogers," both men replied before handing off their outerwear to waiting footmen.

"Lady Catherine awaits you in the main drawing room."

"I am surprised he does not refer to it as the throne room," Richard said under his breath.

"I am surprised she does not," Darcy teased. A rare occurrence that caused his cousin to choke back a laugh.

They followed the butler to where Lady Catherine waited. Also in the room were Anne and her companion, Mrs. Jenkinson. Her ladyship arose from her gilded chair to receive them.

"Ah, nephews, you have finally arrived," she began, her tone imperious. "Come, Darcy, sit by Anne. She is most desirous of speaking with you."

Darcy doubted the veracity of his aunt's statement. Anne barely raised her voice, let alone her eyes, whenever he was near.

"Thank you, aunt, but we only came to give you a brief greeting. Richard and I will return for refreshments after we have washed off the dust from our travels." He cocked his head at Richard, a silent signal for them to quit the room.

"Why the hurry?" Lady Catherine called out before they could make their escape. "Do I not deserve a warm hello or a familial kiss on the cheek?"

"Forgive us, aunt."

Darcy and Richard both went to the lady and dutifully touched their lips to her cheek. Darcy took a step back, surprised when his aunt clutched his wrist and held him in place.

"Give your betrothed a kiss as well, Darcy."

"I had hoped to leave this until I was ready to depart." He wrenched his arm from her grip. "But you have forced my hand early."

"What do you mean, forced your hand?"

Darcy took a step back and held his aunt's gaze.

"Anne and I are not betrothed. We will never marry not even if you arrange a compromise." Darcy turned and addressed his frail cousin. "You know I have affection for you, Anne – as a cousin, nothing more."

"I do not wish to marry you, Fitzwilliam"

Darcy did not know who was more shocked at Anne speaking up. Him or his aunt.

"What? You do not know what you speak of, Anne." Lady Catherine stood and began waving her arms about. "Mrs. Jenkinson, my daughter is obviously distraught and does not know her own mind. Take her to her room immediately."

Mrs. Jenkinson rose and began to help Anne to her feet, but once she stood, Darcy's youngest cousin glared at her mother.

"I know my own mind, Mother…"

Her eyes fluttered, then rolled back and she collapsed into Mrs. Jenkinson's arms. Richard rushed to her side and scooped her up into his arms.

"You have killed her!" Lady Catherine screamed at Darcy.

"Quiet, Madam. Your histrionics do not make the situation any better."

He called for the butler to send for the doctor, while Richard carried their cousin up to her bedchamber, Darcy right behind him. It was only when they turned at the top of the stairs, did she peek over Richard's shoulder, and winked. Darcy very nearly stopped in his tracks. What the deuce? He gathered his senses and entered the bedchamber, stepping aside to allow Mrs. Jenkinson to attend to Anne, whom Richard laid gently on the massive bed.

Lady Catherine, in the interim, could be heard bellowing to the servants. It escaped no one's attention she had not come upstairs to see how her only child fared. Anne rested on the bed for a few seconds, then she began to giggle like a schoolgirl. Darcy had not heard her laugh for so many years, he once again experienced a surreal sense of shock.

"You have not entered an alternate universe, Darcy," Anne managed to say when she finally stopped. She gave Mrs. Jenkinson a steady look, who nodded her head and left the room, closing the door behind her. "We do not have much time. Mother will come barging up here any minute to harangue you again."

"Do you wish for a glass of water?" Richard asked.

"No, thank you. 'Tis better if my lips appeared dry. We both know I must continue this charade a little longer."

"Then, you will be pleased to know that as of this Friday, I am no longer a colonel in His Majesty's army, I am simply The Honorable Richard Fitzwilliam of Matlock House. My release from the army came through prior to Darcy and I leaving London, and I have the license in my pocket."

Anne's light blue eyes shone with excitement and she clasped Richard's hand.

"Then, we can marry anytime we like?"

"Whenever your heart desires."

"Let us marry next week." Anne looked at Darcy and smiled at his shocked expression. "I would suggest you make yourself scarce over the next few days, cousin. I plan on languishing with some unknown illness to keep Mother off our scent."

"How long have you two been planning this?" he finally managed to ask.

His two cousins looked at each other, then shrugged their shoulders together in perfect synchronization. Although fascinating to watch, he needed answers.

"We first realized we wished to become more than cousins about, when was it Annie, in '09?"

"It was when Mother brought me to London at Christmas to have my portrait painted. You were on leave and we spent almost two months together."

"Could you not have informed me of your plans?" Darcy paced. "I have listened to your mother harp on our supposed betrothal for over five years now."

"Of course not," Anne took Richard's hand in hers. "You absolutely abhor deceit of any kind and would never have been able to fool Mother convincingly. There was nothing we could do until I reached my majority, and gained control of Rosings Park, which was this past February. The last detail of our plan was Richard's release from the army." She gazed up at the newly minted gentleman and smiled softly. "All that remains is for us to marry."

The door handle rattled and Anne quickly laid down, closing her eyes. All of them relaxed when Mrs. Jenkinson slipped into the room.

"Your mother is coming," she said in a soft voice.

Richard came to stand by Darcy, and Mrs. Jenkinson covered Anne with a duvet, then pulled up a chair to sit beside the bed.

Lady Catherine barged into the room, the door crashing against the wall.

"You will marry Anne!"

"Lady Catherine, lower your voice," Darcy could not even look at his aunt, his anger was so great. "Do you not even care for the wellbeing of your only daughter?"

His aunt gave a cursory glance toward the bed and sniffed. "Her doctor shall be here shortly and will attend to her needs."

"Madam, your behavior toward your own family member disgusts me." Darcy looked at Richard, who gave a slight nod. "I shall be in my chambers. Richard, please let me know how Anne fares after the doctor leaves."

Richard answered in the affirmative and Darcy quit the room. Once in the relative safety of his own bedchamber, he huffed out a relieved sigh. The boulder of responsibility which had sat heavily on his shoulders since his father's death was lifted, in a most extraordinary way. He shook his head in mild disbelief. Who would have thought Richard and Anne loved each other and had done so for years? It was unbelievable.

He barked out a laugh. It was fabulous. He was free to marry where he wanted without censure from anyone. His thought immediately flew to Miss Elizabeth Bennet. He could, in good conscience, follow his heart. The Matlocks might disapprove and could make their social life in town uncomfortable, which could, in turn, hurt Georgiana's chance of making a brilliant match of her own... however, he had a little over two years before she had her Come Out. Plenty of time to ride another wave of gossip. They were already battling the chaos Miss Bingley caused with that damning letter. What was one more minor disruption?

***

The next few days found Darcy either in his late uncle's study poring over the estate books or taking Arion for a ride to clear his head. Richard joined him a few times, but Darcy knew his cousin met with Anne frequently to solidify plans for their secret wedding. Of Aunt Catherine, he had no desire to speak further with her and tolerated her only at dinner. He refused to speak about an engagement with Anne, and his aunt no longer brought the subject up.

On his third day in Kent, he decided to walk the park. Not only to stretch his legs but with the hope of crossing paths with Miss Elizabeth. He knew she was an avid walker and from time to time, when out on Arion, he'd seen her traipsing through the groves. Because of this, he had a very good idea of which part of the park she preferred to ramble in. Within the hour, he met with success for seated on a log, facing the pretty brook which ran through the estate, sat Miss Elizabeth Bennet, her bonnet on the log beside her, a letter in her hand.

"Miss Bennet," he called out when he realized she had not heard him approach.

She startled and quickly folded the letter and snatched up her bonnet. While turning, she deftly tied the ribbon, securing the fetching hat on her mahogany curls. He did not know if he was disappointed that she'd hidden her glorious hair, or delighted because the bonnet framed her face in a most becoming manner.

"Mr. Darcy," she replied. "Pray, excuse me, I was about to return to my cousin's house."

"Lovely day, is it not?" he countered and was rewarded with a hint of a smile on her beautiful face. "There is nothing more refreshing than a spring afternoon in Kent."

"While I agree the day is refreshing, I do believe we can forego the opening salvo of discussing the weather."

"I would, by no means, suspend any pleasure of yours." He fully smiled at her this time. "Would you mind if I joined you? I had hoped to come across you once I knew you were a guest of my aunt's parson."

"You wished to be in my company again?" At his nod, she said, "Voluntarily?"

"Aye, unless you wish to check for marionette strings again," he said with a chuckle. "Ever since you and your siblings came to Darcy House, I have wanted to extend my heartfelt apology, not only for my manners but also for my words. I know not what made me say the things I did, other than abject fear of my sister's reputation."

"You made your disdain of our family abundantly clear when you were in Hertfordshire."

He ducked his head, knowing her words were true.

"I would have tendered my apologies at the duke's ball, but there were too many ears leaning in our direction."

"I do believe I heard a gasp or two as we took our places on the dance floor," she teased. "Apparently your abhorrence for dancing is not a secret, even amongst the elite of society."

"I do dance, but never the supper set."

"Oh…"

"There were mitigating factors which led me to hold myself apart that first evening in Meryton," – he raised his hand slightly when it looked like she might respond – "Still, vile words fell from my mouth in a most disgusting manner."

He struggled to continue. To verbally express Georgiana's terrible experience.

"This past summer, my sister was abused in a most heinous manner by Mr. Wickham. The rogue made her believe herself in love with him and had I not come across them by accident, he would have absconded with her to Scotland."

Elizabeth gasped and touched his forearm in a comforting manner. He was absolutely certain she had no idea that she had. It was in her nature to lend comfort. His arm tingled when she dropped her hand. He continued his long overdue explanation.

"I came to Hertfordshire because my aunt insisted Georgiana stay with her until a suitable companion could be found. Bingley had just purchased the lease and needed guidance with regard to estate management and so I accepted his invitation to visit. The very day I arrived was also the day of the Assembly, which I attended in one of the foulest moods I have ever experienced. As you know, you bore the brunt of my frustration."

"Mr. Darcy, I appreciate you giving me a glimpse of your anguish and find I must absolve you of any guilt with regard to the Assembly. However, your behavior in the weeks following cannot be set aside so easily. You, sir, were very haughty, and trust me when I tell you, the citizens of Meryton do not look upon you, or the rest of the Netherfield party with a kind eye."

He offered his arm and the world became a little brighter when she accepted and looped her arm through his.

"The recollection of my conduct and manners is now inexpressibly painful to me. This may surprise you, but I have been a selfish being all my life." He dared cut her a quick sideways glance to see if she smiled at his tongue-in-cheek tone, and was rewarded by a slight curving of her lip. "I will admit, as an only son, I was spoiled by my parents and thought myself above many people. These past few months, with all the gossip swirling around my sister, the blinders of arrogance have been torn from my eyes, and I have discovered who my true friends are, and who used me to gain access to areas they could not enter without my help."

"Harsh lessons, indeed," she murmured, then as an afterthought, asked, "How is your sister?"

He inherently knew she meant the incident with Wickham and not the gossip over the letter.

"Her tender heart was bruised, and she still cannot reconcile in her mind someone would lie so brazenly. When she found out he only wished to marry for her marriage portion, which is thirty thousand pounds, she declared through her tears she felt completely worthless as a person, and no one would marry such a foolish girl once they discovered her folly."

"Oh! – how awful. That poor girl, to be taken in by such a fiend."

"Yet, you were not. You made me very aware at Bingley's ball you knew exactly who and what Wickham was."

"I cannot take credit for such insight. If not for my brothers, I would have accepted Mr. Wickham at face value." She cut a quick glance at him and continued. "At one of my aunt's card parties, my eldest brother joined our conversation and pressed him on many untruths he had weaved into his tale of woe. Somehow, my brother knew exactly what Mr. Wickham was about, and sent him scurrying to a dark corner like the rat he is."

"I will admit, I would have loved to see good old George have his comeuppance. He has been a burr beneath my saddle for many years." At her quizzical expression, he explained. "He was my father's godson. Old Mr. Wickham was my father's steward, and a better man would be hard-pressed to find. My father also promised to give young Wickham a gentleman's education, in order for the son to have a better life than the father."

"It is plain Mr. Wickham did not take advantage of his education. Maybe if your father had left him a little something to aid him in furthering his career—"

"Father left Wickham a bequest of one thousand pounds. There was also an understanding that if he took orders, he would be given a valuable living in Kympton – when it came available. Wickham declared he was not one to make sermons and would rather study law. I heartily agreed with that assessment and gave him three thousand pounds in lieu of the living."

Elizabeth gasped when she heard how much money Wickham had received. "Such a sum. He had a veritable fortune at his fingertips."

"When the rector at Kympton retired three years later, Wickham wrote and claimed the position should be given to him. He said studying the law did not suit him, and he was in need of funds. I refused his request, and did not hear a whisper from him until the debacle with my sister."

"Wretched man! I am so glad my brother set him on his ear. I was so determined in my dislike of you, he could have told me you had blackened the moon and I would have nodded in agreement."

"You were that set against me, even after I apologized?"

"Well, apology aside, you had insulted me in a public venue, and then continued to stare at me whenever we were in the same room. I was certain you only looked to find more fault."

"Not true, I assure you. I was enthralled by your pleasing manners and the way you made everyone feel at ease around you. My cousin, Richard, has the same gift."

"Is this the cousin who has accompanied you to Rosings Park?"

"Yes, and when our aunt invites your party to dine at Rosings, you will have a chance to meet him."

"I would be delighted to meet another of your cousins. I have already been introduced to your betrothed."

Darcy abruptly stopped and Elizabeth let go of his arm.

"I am not betrothed to Anne," was all he could force through stiff lips.

"Forgive me. Your aunt has spoken of it so often, I assumed it was a done thing."

"What my aunt desires, and what she receives are two different things. Neither Anne nor myself wish to wed each other. Lady Catherine has deemed otherwise and will not hear any arguments against her decree."

He started walking toward the parsonage again and Elizabeth fell into step beside him.

"None of us ask for the family we are blessed with," she finally said, her tone light and airy. "It is good to know your family has its own blemishes to conceal."

"Touché, Miss Elizabeth." He decided to confront the other misunderstanding between them before it became too large to climb and conquer. "After much reflection, I realized I had no right to interfere, in any manner, with Bingley and your sister. It was badly done."

"What did it matter to you where Mr. Bingley found his happiness?"

Darcy blushed and struggled to put his thoughts into words that would not offend Elizabeth.

"Dare I suppose," Elizabeth continued, "you imagined my sister, who behaves as a proper lady at all times, did not feel anything but friendship toward your friend, and, if she had accepted his proposal, it would have been at the bidding of my mother, who made her wishes known to all who sat within ten feet of her at the ball?"

"Yes." His shoulders slumped in relief. She understood completely.

"You are not absolved simply because I understand your reasoning. It was not your place to determine who Mr. Bingley chooses as a wife."

"Bingley is one of my closest friends, I have often seen him in and out of love, and because of this proclivity of falling for the charms of beautiful women, I became his voice of reason." Elizabeth snorted rather indelicately and he smiled slightly. "When it became clear to me at Bingley's ball that expectations were rising, not only with your sister but also with the community at large, I began to watch her very carefully. At the end of the evening, I was convinced that while she received Bingley's attentions with pleasure, she did not invite them in any manner."

"I am perilously close to losing my temper."

He then noticed Elizabeth had clenched her hands, and wondered if a solid right hook was in his future.

"You are protective of your sister, which I admire and understand. I did not believe her to be indifferent because I wished it, I believed it because of what I witnessed. Her manners and the way she engaged with people did not change whether she was in Bingley's company or dancing with another gentleman. All of this lent credence to what I perceived."

"And what was that, Mr. Darcy?"

"While your sister liked Bingley, she did not love him, and I could not stand by and see my friend enter into a marriage of unequal affection."

"Of all the unmitigated gall. My sister hardly shows her true feelings to me!" Elizabeth exclaimed and stopped walking.

Darcy turned to face her.

"You have just proved my point," he replied with a calm he was far from feeling. At her continued look of astonishment, he continued. "If you, her most beloved sister, can barely read her feelings, how do you expect complete strangers to know what lies beneath her serene countenance?"

Elizabeth pivoted on her heel and began to pace back and forth on the pathway. He remained silent for a few minutes, allowing her time to gather her thoughts.

"Miss Elizabeth," he finally broke the silence, and she stopped pacing. "If I had seen only half of what you believe of your sister, I would never have interfered. Your sister is a gentleman's daughter, and marrying her would not only have made my friend exceedingly happy but would have raised his stature in society. I did not give my opinion to him lightly."

"It was not your place to make that decision," Elizabeth cried out in frustration, whirling on her heel to continue on the path to the parsonage. Her movement stayed by his hand on her elbow.

"I am well aware of that... now." At her questioning look, he continued. "Bingley and I discussed this at length when everything came to light, but it was too late for him to renew his addresses as your sister was betrothed to Lord Holcomb."

"They are well suited, and his daughter absolutely adores Jane."

Darcy could not help but feel a sense of relief at the news.

"I am glad," he rejoined. Miss Bennet was a gentle soul and Lord Holcomb a fine gentleman.

By this time, they had reached the fork in the path where they would depart from each other's company.

"Good day, Mr. Darcy."

"Good day, Miss Elizabeth," he replied. "I hope you do not mind if I happen to 'bump' into you tomorrow when you take your walk."

"I do not mind at all, sir."

For the next week, Darcy ambled with Miss Elizabeth through the grove, each gaining a better understanding of the other. As for Darcy, he became even more ardently in love with her and began plotting when and where he could propose marriage.

LONGBOURN'S ANGELS

SUE BARR

Chapter Twenty-Three

Elizabeth tore open the express, scanning the letter, her knees almost buckling at the words within. She staggered to a nearby log and practically fell onto it. Taking a deep breath, she read the letter again, taking the time to absorb each word.

The beginning of the letter held nothing unusual, other than the raptures of their mother over Jane's betrothal and the various parties and engagements they all attended so Mamma could brag about her daughter's good fortune. However, it was the latter half of the letter which brought Elizabeth to tears.

Since writing the above, dearest Lizzy, something has occurred of a most unexpected and serious nature. What I have to say relates to Lydia. Early this morning, it was discovered our sister has gone off to Scotland with Mr. Wickham!

She left a letter for Mamma, wherein she disclosed the sad truth she had been sneaking out of Longbourn to meet with Mr. Wickham, and from there they made plans to elope while the whole family was at a dinner party being held in my honor with regard to my betrothal. I knew Lydia was upset over not being allowed out, due to her age, but never would I have thought she would lower herself to run away.

Michael, of course, set off immediately to see if he could catch up with them, but they had a good twelve-hour head start, and the route they took is unknown. I have no hope he will find them until it is too late. So imprudent a match on both sides!

None of us can find a plausible reason for Mr. Wickham to have such an interest in Lydia other than the fact he must have learned her marriage portion is a little above ten thousand pounds, with a promise of another two thousand upon the death of our poor mother, who is sadly grieved and has taken to her bed. My father bears it better, but then he has hope Michael will be successful in his endeavor.

An express has been sent to Gabriel, begging his return and I know he will make haste to Hunsford in order to expedite your removal. We have asked the maid who discovered Lydia gone to refrain from speaking to anyone about it. Sally, bless her heart, has agreed. I shall continue to pray we have contained any gossip within the four walls of Longbourn.

To you, and you alone, dearest Lizzy, I am terrified this will cause Lord Holcomb to break our engagement. He must think of his daughter's future, and I could not bear it if my shame dragged his family's good name into the mud of gossip and derision.

I must conclude, for I cannot be long from my poor mother.

"Foolish, foolish girl!" Elizabeth cried out and jumped to her feet, folding the letter into her pocket.

Her anticipated walk with Mr. Darcy forgotten, she stopped in surprise when the man himself entered the glade. Her pale face and agitated manner made him start, and before he could speak one word, she hastily exclaimed, "I beg your pardon, Mr. Darcy, but I cannot walk today. I must hasten to the parsonage and begin packing. My brother is expected to arrive in a few hours, and I have not a moment to lose."

"You are leaving Kent today?" He strode quickly to her side, his presence strangely comforting.

"Yes, I received an express..." Elizabeth choked back a sob, thinking of the letter in her pocket.

"Good God, what is the matter?" he cried out. "Let me escort you back to the parsonage. You are very ill."

"There is nothing the matter with me," she replied and drew in a deep, cleansing breath. "I am quite well. I am only distressed by some dreadful news I have just received from Longbourn."

She burst into tears as she alluded to it, and for a few minutes could not speak another word, other than a mumbled thank you when Darcy pressed a handkerchief into her hand. At length, she spoke again.

"I have just had a letter from Jane, with contained such alarming news I can barely speak of it. My youngest sister has eloped. She has thrown herself into the power... of Mr. Wickham! You know him too well to doubt the rest. I fear she is lost forever."

"I am grieved," said Darcy. "Grieved and shocked. But it is certain, absolutely certain?"

"There can be no doubt. My foolish sister left a note, bragging of her cunning and deception."

"And what has been done to recover her?"

"My eldest brother has gone after them, but with such a head start and with no idea of what road they took..." She trailed off, then continued, her voice quiet. Defeated. "Even if Michael does come across them, how can a man such as Mr. Wickham be worked on? I have not the smallest hope."

Darcy made no answer, his expression reverting to one of stoic calm. Elizabeth observed his manner and instantly understood. Any esteem he may have felt for her was fading in the light of her sister's debauched behavior. It was at this moment she realized, too late, she could have loved him.

"Miss Elizabeth, I do not wish to add to your burden, but when your brother arrives, let him know Wickham will not make a run for Scotland. He will never marry a woman who cannot bring a small fortune with her."

"She has ten thousand pounds."

"He will want more. Your sister is but the carrot to dangle in front of the donkey."

"What are you trying to say?"

"I believe Wickham has learned the good fortune of your eldest sister and will take your youngest sister to London, where he can hide her quite effectively. After enough time has passed, when her reputation is ruined beyond repair, he will contact your family and demand a handsome ransom."

"But Jane and Lord Holcomb are not married! The earl cannot be expected to pay a fortune to a man he has never met."

"Wickham will not care. It is his way."

"You sound very sure of yourself in this."

"I have had years of dealing with that foul reprobate, and as you know, he attempted the same thing last summer."

"Then, I have most assuredly lost my sister forever."

Elizabeth was overcome with emotion and covered her face with her hands, and openly sobbed.

"I am afraid you have been long desiring my absence. I wish there was something more I could say or do to offer some consolation."

"Truly, Mr. Darcy, there is nothing you can say or do. This is a burden my family must bear alone."

"This unfortunate affair will, I fear, prevent the continued pleasure of your company at my aunt's dinner table this evening."

"Oh, yes. I know my cousin will extend apologies to your lady aunt, but would you be so kind as to express my regret to the good colonel? Might you say urgent business called me home? I would like to conceal the unhappy truth for as long as possible."

"You may be assured of my discretion. I have no desire to ruin your sister's, or your family's reputation. I bid you farewell, and safe journey, Miss Elizabeth."

With that, he turned on his heel and walked to the edge of the glade, turning only once to give her a somewhat serious look. Then, he was gone from her sight. Elizabeth watched him go with regret. In this early example of what Lydia's infamy might produce with regard to how society would treat their family, she began to mentally strengthen the foundation of her resolve, so the expected waves of anguish would not wash her out into a sea of despair.

She hurried to the parsonage and, fortunately, Mr. Collins was not at home. When she told Charlotte she had to leave for Hertfordshire, her friend followed her upstairs.

"Is there anything I can do for you, Eliza?"

"I am afraid not." Elizabeth dragged her trunk out from the small closet and heaved it onto her bed. She had no time to wait for Charlotte's man of all work to lug it around. Every second counted. "Gabriel should arrive early this afternoon and we shall depart immediately."

"Has something happened to your father?" Charlotte stood awkwardly near the door, wringing her hands. "Or to your mother? You are frightening me."

"I did not mean to frighten you, it is just... I cannot speak of it." Elizabeth turned her head away and fought the tears which threatened to spill again.

"Eliza!" Charlotte came near and wrapped her dearest friend in a warm hug. "You know I can be discreet. Please let me share this burden with you."

Elizabeth turned and sobbed openly into Charlotte's shoulder. After a few minutes, she calmed and stepped away, her cheeks flushed from emotion and embarrassment. She accepted a handkerchief from her friend and wiped her face and nose.

"This is the second time someone has lent me a handkerchief today. You must think me a complete ninny."

"No, I think you are shouldering a very heavy burden and I will once again offer to help you bear it."

Elizabeth sat on the edge of the bed and patted the empty place beside her. Once Charlotte was seated, she told her why Gabriel was on his way to pick her up, and how worried she was that Michael would not find Lydia in time.

"I remember Lydia making an acquaintance with Mr. Wickham that one time we all walked to Meryton with Mr. Collins, but I cannot comprehend how they established any sort of relationship." Elizabeth stared out the window, not seeing anything, so lost was she in thought, trying to understand her youngest sister's psyche. "She is not out in society. There would have been no opportunity."

"I have something I must share with you. It will not change what your sister has done, but it might shed some light on the genesis of how this event occurred."

"I would be most appreciative of any information."

"Please know what I am about to share could also ruin the reputation of my family. I am trusting your discretion as much as you have trusted mine."

Elizabeth's eyes widened, but she said nothing and only nodded in agreement.

"Maria came with Father to Hunsford, not because she wanted to see where her sister had settled, but because she and Lydia had been spotted in Meryton, flirting openly with the officers. When our father questioned Maria, it was learned the two of them went into town regularly. Lydia's favorite was Mr. Wickham, while Maria admired both Mr. Denny and Mr. Saunderson."

"Foolish girls!"

"Agreed. Needless to say, my sister was confined to Lucas Lodge unless accompanied by Mother, and she is to remain here in Hunsford until the militia decamps to Brighton." Charlotte stood and smoothed down her skirts. "My only regret is that Father did not speak with Mr. Bennet. I believe he stayed silent to protect my sister's reputation."

"I understand completely. I do not hold your family accountable in any way." She paused in thought. "Has Lydia written your sister whilst she is here?"

"She has... Do you think Lydia wrote about her plans?"

"Knowing how foolish she is... yes." A small surge of hope wiggled into her heart. "Would Maria mind bringing them to us, so we can read through them?"

"She might, but your sister's welfare supersedes any privacy Maria thinks they are entitled to." Charlotte moved toward the door. "I shall return shortly."

Elizabeth resumed packing her trunks and only stopped when Charlotte returned, two letters in hand. She gave them to Elizabeth, who skimmed through them quickly.

"Oh! thoughtless, thoughtless Lydia!" she exclaimed when finished. "When I see her next, I might be carried off to the Old Bailey, for I am going to wring her neck."

"What did she write?" Charlotte asked.

Elizabeth began reading the second letter aloud.

My dear Maria,

You will laugh when you know what I am planning, and I cannot help laughing myself at your surprise upon receiving this letter. In two weeks, I am going to Gretna Green, and if you cannot guess with who, I shall think you a simpleton, for there is but one man in the world I love, and he is an angel. I should never be happy without him, so think it is no harm to be off. You need not send them word at Longbourn of my going, I will leave a note myself.

Wish me all the best, and the next time I write, I will happily sign my name as Lydia Wickham. What a good joke it will be! I can hardly write for laughing.

"This is somewhat good news, is it not?" Charlotte asked. "An elopement is not the end of the world. The scandal will not be as severe as if she had run off and not got married."

"I wish it were that easy. Mr. Darcy believes Mr. Wickham has no intention of marrying her."

"Mr. Darcy! How is he aware of your news?"

"He came across me in the glade right after I finished reading Jane's letter. I was very distraught, and he behaved in such a conciliatory manner, everything tumbled out of me before I had gathered my senses."

Elizabeth gave the letters back to Charlotte, then finished packing her trunk. Mr. Collins' man of all work lugged it down to the door and the two ladies met again in the parlor to wait for Gabriel's arrival. Their quiet conversation was disrupted by the banging open of the front door and the almost comedic entrance of Mr. Collins.

"My dear Charlotte. There is such an uproar at Rosings!"

"What happened?"

"Lady Catherine's nephews are leaving Kent this very afternoon. She is very displeased over their abrupt departure and told them as much. Mr. Darcy was quite rude with his response, in my opinion. He told Lady Catherine his business was private and not in her purview to criticize. He left for his chambers to pack and the colonel chastised his aunt for attempting to interfere in Mr. Darcy's affairs." Mr. Collins stumbled to the closest chair and fell into it. He wiped his brow and took several deep breaths. "I have never seen Lady Catherine so angry. Normally, I bid my patroness a polite adieu, but given the circumstance, I left as quietly as I could and hurried home to you."

Elizabeth could barely contain her surprise at this turn of events. Could Mr. Darcy's hasty departure have anything to do with what he learned this afternoon with regard to Lydia's foolishness? Surely, he would not quit the area solely to avoid her company. Would he? Her heart sank. The whole Netherfield party had fled Meryton to avoid becoming embroiled with the Bennet family when their name had not been mired in scandal. What made her think the proud man would stick around when the mud of gossip was certain to be flung in their direction? For that matter, would Susannah maintain a friendship with the sister of a fallen woman? Tears, once again, threatened to spill at the thought of losing close friends, maybe even some family connections.

"You did the right thing, husband. I believe, in the future, I would not say anything about the disturbing sequence of events you witnessed. Lady Catherine is a proud woman and would not want anyone to know she and her nephews exchanged harsh words."

"Once again, my dear Charlotte, you are a fount of knowledge." Mr. Collins cast a frantic glance toward his cousin Elizabeth. "My dear cousin, I pray you will not speak of this."

"You may count on me not sharing this with anyone, Mr. Collins." His shoulders sagged in obvious relief. "As it so happens, I shall be leaving Kent as soon as my brother arrives."

It was then Mr. Collins took note of Elizabeth's trunk sitting by the front door.

"You are not scheduled to leave for another fortnight. Are you not happy with our company?"

"I received a letter from Jane, requesting my presence back at Longbourn."

"I hope it is not bad news. Your father has not taken ill, has he?"

"No, my family is in excellent health." Elizabeth hated to dissemble, but she had to keep Lydia's name out of people's mouths. "I would hazard to guess my mother is excited about Jane's good fortune and as such has demanded all her children home so she can parade us all about the neighborhood in celebration."

Elizabeth shot Charlotte a quick glance, who nodded in approval before adding her point of view to the story the two friends were weaving out of thin air.

"Do you recall, Mr. Collins, how Mrs. Bennet suffered from bouts of nervousness?" At his nod, she continued. "Jane has become betrothed to an earl, and—"

"An earl!" Mr. Collins exclaimed. "No wonder Mrs. Bennet is all nerves."

"You are quite right," Elizabeth said and looked out the bay window, wondering how long it would be before Gabriel arrived.

"I shall have our cook prepare some tea," Charlotte said. "I am sure your brother would appreciate some refreshments before you leave for London."

"Are you not for Hertfordshire?" Mr. Collins asked.

"It is too late in the day to reach Longbourn safely. We will stay with our aunt and uncle overnight, and proceed the next day."

Elizabeth had no intention of telling him they would likely stay in London. If Mr. Darcy's conjectures were correct, they would have to launch a search. The enormity of the situation was beyond anything she could imagine and her stomach rolled from apprehension and nerves. She now understood her mother's complaints of spasms in her stomach.

"I shall send a letter with you to my cousin Bennet, congratulating him on the successful betrothal of his daughter."

Wanting Mr. Collins distracted and out of her hair,

Charlotte agreed most heartily with his writing a letter and as soon as her husband quit the room, she sagged against the back of the settee.

"I have never stretched the truth so far in my life!" her friend whispered.

"Same here, however, all warfare is based on deception, and for my sister, I would do almost anything within reason." Elizabeth glanced at her friend and noticed she was chewing her lower lip, a sure sign of internal distress. "Am I correct in assuming your husband is not aware of the true reason Maria is here for such an extended visit?"

"My husband could not dissemble if his life depended on it. It is best for him to think she is here to learn how to run a small house and cook meals, as she most likely will not marry a wealthy man. Like myself, it is good to have some skills in the kitchen."

"Those skills have been put to good use. I still maintain you make the best mince meat pies in all of England."

"Even better than Longbourn's cook, Mrs. Pruitt?"

"Absolutely, although her roast chicken would put even the Prince Regent's chefs to shame."

"You cad, Eliza! Just the thought of her cooking has made me hungry."

The jangle of harness chains and rapid hoofbeats coming down the lane alerted the two ladies of Gabriel's arrival. They both rose to their feet and hurried to the front door. Elizabeth's surprise was great when she realized the equipage belonged to none other than the marquis, who jumped out of the carriage before his outrider could open the door. Gabriel followed immediately behind.

"Elizabeth!" Gabriel said and drew her into a familiar embrace. "Are you ready to leave? We cannot tarry long if we wish to reach London before nightfall." He looked over Elizabeth's shoulder and greeted Charlotte warmly.

"You should make some time for refreshments," Charlotte advised. "This would also give your horses a much-needed rest before continuing."

Even though her friend had not said anything out loud, Elizabeth knew Charlotte's curiosity was aroused by the presence of Sebastian and the prominent display of his crest on the carriage door.

"Charlotte, may I present to you the Marquis of Grenfell, Sebastian Harrington."

Charlotte dropped into a deep curtsy and murmured, "My Lord Grenfell."

Elizabeth continued the introduction. "Lord Grenfell, this is my oldest and dearest friend – next to your sister, of course – Mrs. Charlotte Collins. You will have heard Jane and me refer to her as Miss Charlotte Lucas."

"Mrs. Collins," Sebastian said and gave her a polite nod of the head. "I am delighted to finally meet the woman Jane and Elizabeth have praised for so many years." He glanced around the area and then caught Gabriel's eye. "Some light refreshment would not go amiss, as long as we can be on the road within the hour."

"Then, lead the way, Mrs. Collins," Gabriel said and further teased Charlotte with, "Dare I ask if you have any of that shortbread you used to make back home?"

"As a matter of fact, I do. Your sister made the same request yesterday. I am of the mind all you Bennets kept me as a friend to eat my baking."

"Alas!" Gabriel said in a very theatrical manner. "She has found us out, Lizzy."

Their party advanced into the parsonage and the marquis' men were tasked to load Elizabeth's trunk onto the carriage, then instructed to take care of the horses. Sebastian went ahead with Charlotte while Elizabeth looped her arm through Gabriel's.

"Charlotte is aware of why you are here." She said in a low voice and her brother's arm stiffened beneath hers. "Fear not. You know Charlotte too well to believe she will talk about Lydia's disgrace, and when I have a chance, I will fill you in on the reason why."

They entered the parsonage and not long after the tea was served, Mr. Collins emerged from his study to give Elizabeth the letter he'd written for her father. He stopped abruptly almost as soon as he entered the room, his attention immediately drawn to Sebastian.

"Cousin Elizabeth, here is the letter— Oh! I did not know we had company."

Mr. Collins's gaze flew to his wife who stood and with a nod of her head, invited her husband to stand beside her.

"Mr. Collins, I present to you, the Marquis of Grenfell?"

Mr. Collins's mouth dropped open and the letter fluttered to the floor. Elizabeth was afraid the man would swoon on the spot. Sebastian must have thought the same thing, because he said, "Please sit down, Mr. Collins. I am afraid you do not look well."

"You are a Marq...Marq...Marquis!" Collins finally sputtered out.

He then bowed so low, Elizabeth thought for sure his nose would touch the floor alongside the letter. When he straightened, his face bright red from exertion, Sebastian addressed him.

"Mr. Collins, I am flattered by your show of respect, however, I am not the King. A simple bow will suffice for my ego."

"I must inform my noble patroness, Lady Catherine de Bourgh of your esteemed presence in my humble abode. I am certain she will invite you to dine at Rosings Park while your carriage is being fixed. She is diligent in the preservation of rank, and if she were to discover you stopped here and not paid your respects, she would be most displeased."

"I have no intention of paying my respects to Lady Catherine as I have never met the woman, and why do you think my carriage has broken down?"

"There is no other reason to explain your presence." Mr. Collins's brow furrowed in confusion.

"Husband, the marquis is here with Gabriel to take Elizabeth home to Longbourn."

"My cousin Gabriel is on intimate terms with a marquis?" Mr. Collins swiveled his attention from Gabriel to Sebastian and back again. "I find that most unlikely."

Charlotte stooped down and picked up the letter, handing it to Elizabeth while saying, "The Marquis is actually Eliza's friend. Gabriel met him many years after she did."

By this time, Gabriel, Sebastian, and Elizabeth had seated themselves around the room. Mr. Collins fell into the closest chair and brought out his handkerchief for the second time that day to wipe his brow.

"I am very confused by all this."

"It is a long story, Mr. Collins, and I promise, once Eliza is on her way – she does not have a moment to spare – I will tell you all. I cannot add embellishments as my friend does, but I believe I can make it entertaining."

The trio enjoyed a brief tea, suffering the inanities and compliments of the portly rector, and were soon on their way, leaving behind a relieved Mrs. Collins, and a dazed Mr. Collins.

SUE BARR

Chapter Twenty-Four

"Now that we are beyond the exemplary hearing of our aunt, would you mind telling me what just happened?" Richard's tone was inquisitive, but it did not take a scholar to sense the undertone of anger threaded in his question. "You are aware Anne and I were supposed to wed in less than a week."

After leaving Elizabeth in the glade, Darcy had proceeded to Rosings Park and immediately sent his valet upstairs to pack, and ordered the carriages ready to depart within the hour. Richard, without any question, sent his man to pack their belongings and joined Darcy in breaking the news of impending departure to Aunt Catherine. Neither of them was surprised at her displeasure and ensuing anger.

"Those plans have not changed. I spoke with Anne briefly after I went upstairs to change and pack, and she is in agreement. Monday, our cousin will leave Rosings at first light and make her way to your father's house. Monday morning, at exactly ten o'clock, you will meet her at St. George's."

"I have not even spoken with the bishop. We shall have to marry from Father's house."

"You will be pleased to know that while you and Anne have been sneaking moments alone, I wrote family and filled them in on your little secret. Ashton immediately went out and booked the church, Aunt Lucinda sent out select invitations to those we can trust to keep silent, and Uncle

Robert took Sir Lewis's will to Anne's solicitor to ensure everything is legally tight. He also drew up a settlement for both of you and prior to the service, you and Anne will peruse the documents, sign them, and then marry."

Richard shook his head, then smiled. "My superiors at the War Office would give anything to have you in command. You have the precision and forethought of a general. I am quite impressed." He sat up with a start. "Aunt Catherine!"

"What of her?"

"How shall Anne explain her absence? You know our aunt checks on her each morning. She will sound the alarm and Anne will be hauled back before she makes the outer gates."

"Shame on you, Richard. Trust your cousin in this. On the days when Anne is 'indisposed by lady complaints,' her mother leaves her to sleep late."

"But she does not have them at this time." Richard's brow furrowed then, at the inquisitive look of his cousin shot in his direction, he flushed a dull red."

"And, how would you know this?" Darcy asked, having a good idea of the answer. He remained uncertain if he was happy for his cousins, or outraged at the risk they took.

"We… anticipated our vows, and do not dare to chastise me," Richard huffed out and sat up straighter on the carriage squabs. "I have waited two long years for Anne, and our passion for one another is just and natural."

Darcy could not imagine, in any way or form, his cousin Anne having a passion for anything beyond a warm blanket. Immediately, he felt guilt. Just because he felt nothing but familial fondness for his frail cousin did not negate Richard's seemingly unwavering affection.

"So, now that we have discussed my future felicity, why are we leaving in such a hurry?"

"Wickham."

"Wickham! What has that black dastard done now?"

"He took Miss Elizabeth's youngest sister to London. The chit thinks they are off to Gretna Green, but we all know that is just the lure he uses to catch an unsuspecting fish."

"The Bennets do not have enough money to tempt him. What angle is he trying to work here?"

"Miss Jane Bennet is betrothed to Lord Holcomb."

"I knew I should have run him through at Ramsgate!" A fearsome scowl creased his cousin's face. "That slimy piece of filth has never done an honest day's work in his life."

"We cannot change the past but we can direct our future. This is what we need to accomplish as soon as we arrive in town."

The remainder of their trip was spent strategizing and attempting to think like Wickham. It was the only way they could defeat him.

***

The ride to London was mostly quiet, with each passenger immersed in their own thoughts. Elizabeth did share some of the livelier events which had occurred during her three short weeks in Kent, which brought welcome relief to the tension that permeated the carriage. However, after they had refreshed themselves at The Bell, she brought up what Mr. Darcy had relayed with regard to Mr. Wickham's motive for absconding with Lydia.

"I am certain Mr. Darcy is congratulating himself on our family's misfortune," Gabriel muttered and stared out the window, his face a study of controlled anger.

"Indeed, he is not," Elizabeth said sharply and Gabe looked at her in surprise. "We have had several candid conversations since his arrival in Kent." At her brother's raised brow, she raised her own back in response, daring him to make a comment. When he shrugged and turned back to the window, she continued. "You will be pleased to know, he apologized for his conduct and explained why their party quit Meryton so abruptly. He cannot change what has been done, but he acknowledged all of them behaved badly."

"Did you believe his apology, Elizabeth?" Sebastian asked.

"I did. At first, I wanted to hold onto my anger, but his explanation was perfectly plausible and enlightened me as to why he was in such a foul mood the night of the assembly. Once I knew the details, I could not hold him at fault. From there, our friendship took a pleasant turn."

"He cannot say the same for the Bingleys."

"No, he cannot. Mr. Bingley may have been cautioned against pursuing our sister, but if he had truly loved her, nothing would have kept him away."

"Holcomb is extremely pleased Bingley pitched a daisy cutter. His loss is the earl's gain."

"No, Lord Grenfell," Elizabeth teased. "Mr. Bingley's poor performance is Jane's gain."

"Too true!" Sebastian declared and chuckled. "Will you and Mr. Darcy continue your friendship once he returns to town?"

"He and his cousin, Colonel Fitzwilliam, have already left Kent." She blinked back the tears which threatened to spill down her cheeks. "I am afraid our sister's reckless behavior will have more repercussions than expected."

"You have not lost my friendship," Sebastian said, his voice soft. "This is but a bump in the road."

"You are too good, Lord Grenfell, but your father might have an opinion on the matter."

Elizabeth brought out a handkerchief and dabbed her eyes. It was only when she went to fold and return it to her reticule, did she notice the initials *FD* stitched on the fine linen. Another wave of sorrow washed over her.

"My father is his own man and does not bow to the whims

and follies of le bon ton, and neither do I." Sebastian took her hand and squeezed lightly before letting go. "You will see."

"We should pay a visit to Mr. Darcy," Elizabeth said after staring out the window of the carriage for over an hour.

"Whatever for?"

"He knows Wickham better than any of us. He may have an insight into where they might hide."

"Your idea has merit," Sebastian said, rubbing his chin in a thoughtful manner. "It would narrow our search somewhat."

"What do you mean by our search?"

"Did you think I would abandon you once we reached London? You are family to me, my sister, and my parents." Sebastian leaned forward and held her gaze. "We could have at least twenty runners on the street before the day was done, looking for them. Just say the word, and I will make it happen."

"You are too good to us, Lord Grenfell!" Elizabeth exclaimed, completely overwhelmed by the marquis' generous offer.

"Elizabeth, you risked your life to save my sister. There is nothing the house of Belmont will not do for the house of Bennet. Our friendship transcends social parameters."

***

They arrived without incident to Gracechurch Street and Sebastian, as soon as their trunks were unloaded, took his leave but not without a promise to contact them once Bow Street Runners were hired and on the case. Early Monday morning, well before polite calling hours, Gabriel arrived at Darcy's home on Grosvenor Square. He did not have to wait long after presenting his card for the butler to escort him to the master's study.

"Mr. Bennet," Darcy said upon his entrance.

"Mr. Darcy," Gabe returned and flicked a quick glance at a second gentleman standing near the fireplace.

"Mr. Bennet, may I present to you my cousin, the Honorable Richard Fitzwilliam."

"Mr. Fitzwilliam," Gabe said with a nod of the head, realizing the gentleman must be the son of the Earl of Matlock. "Pardon my intrusion, Mr. Darcy, I am here to ask if you have any leads on where I can begin my search for Mr. Wickham."

"Unfortunately, I do not have time to discuss this. My cousin and I are about to attend to a personal matter."

"You do not have time to discuss the welfare of a fourteen-year-old child in the clutches of George Wickham! What, pray tell, is more important than that?"

"Richard is getting married in less than an hour and, although your sister is an urgent matter, we cannot postpone the ceremony."

"Oh!" Gabriel's surprise was evident. "Of course, you have other pressing matters."

"Darcy, you need to tell him our other news."

"Tell me what?"

Darcy and Fitzwilliam exchanged glances.

With a deep sigh, Darcy said, "We have a very good idea where Wickham is hiding."

"I am going with you."

"To the wedding?"

"Of course not, I intend to be there when you drag Wickham from his hole."

"I appreciate the offer, but this is something my cousin and I should do on our own."

"Are you related to Wickham?"

"Gads, no!"

"Are you related to Lydia?"

"Again, no."

"I have more at stake in this than you, Darcy, and you will not shake me off like a recalcitrant child. I will accompany you in the search for my sister, and the worthless cad who took her."

"I do not wish to expose you to the underbelly of London, Bennet, for it is the only place Wickham can hide. His stench of depravity helps him blend into the surroundings."

"Where do you think he took her?"

"If I were to make an educated guess, I would assume they are in Seven Dials. There are many twisting lanes and warrens he could hide in, as long as he has money."

"We know Lydia took money from Mother's tin. We think there may have been around twenty pounds saved, give, or take."

"They could remain hidden for weeks with such an amount, but not much longer. Knowing Wickham as I do, he will take a large portion of it, and try to raise capital by playing cards," Darcy grumbled, staring down at his feet.

"Given what I know of the man, he will be short in the pocket by night's end the first time out." Mr. Fitzwilliam bit out the words, clearly showing his frustration.

"If Wickham could make money using glib words, he would be richer than Prinny, but he has no luck in cards. He has always been a lousy player, yet he always thinks he can win. He ran through over four thousand pounds in five years – three thousand in these last two years alone," Darcy explained.

"Four thousand?" Gabriel's mouth threatened to drop open at the disclosure of such a staggering sum. "A family could live off that for years."

"Wickham has princely tastes on a pauper's wage."

Gabriel thought hard about Darcy's plan, knowing that as much as he wished to be at the forefront of their plans, his lack of intimate knowledge of the character of Wickham would be a hindrance in the long run.

"It goes against my very nature to allow you gentlemen to take up the banner for my sister, but I agree I would be a burden at this juncture of the plan. However, I must tell you the Duke of Belmont will not allow you to push him to one side and watch from the boxes."

"I know your family is acquainted with the duke," Mr. Fitzwilliam said, "but why would he get involved with something so tawdry?"

"Ever since my sister Elizabeth saved his daughter's life, he has been intimately involved in all aspects of her life, as well as Jane's. His son, Lord Grenfell, was with me in Kent when we received word of Lydia's elopement. Do not be surprised to find at least two dozen Bow Street Runners at your door sometime today with orders to lend aid."

Fitzwilliam and Darcy shared another look, reminiscent of Gabriel and his twin. It was very apparent the two cousins shared a deep and abiding bond.

"More boots on the ground might not be a bad thing," Fitzwilliam finally said.

"If Wickham even scents them at one hundred yards, he will disappear completely and we would never find him. Seven Dials is his stomping ground, not ours."

"You know the runners are discreet."

"Might we discuss this later?" Darcy pulled his pocket watch out of his waistcoat. "We must leave now or you will be late for your own wedding."

Gabriel immediately stood and held out his hand to the groom.

"We have only just met, Mr. Fitzwilliam, but I wish you joy. Please send word to my uncle's house on Gracechurch Street when you have run the mangy cur to ground."

"On that, you have my word," Darcy said while his cousin

shook Gabriel's hand. "Let us be off. We have not a moment to lose."

"Aye, we need to keep at least ten miles ahead of the dragon," Darcy's cousin quipped before smiling wide and Gabe wondered to whom they referred.

The three gentlemen made their way to the front door, separating at the bottom of the steps. Gabe to his uncle's carriage, Darcy, and his cousin to their own equipage.

***

Unable to concentrate on her needlework, Elizabeth put away her stitching and settled near the window, staring out onto the busy street. She had not been there long when a plain carriage pulled to a stop in front of her uncle's house. When a gentleman stepped out and came up the walk toward the house, she jumped to her feet and faced the door of the parlor. She did not wait long before Lambert announced the Marquis of Grenfell.

"Lord Grenfell," she said while dipping a polite curtsy. "Why are you here? Have you any news of Lydia? Have the runners found any leads?"

She was so anxious, the questions tumbled over themselves.

"No, I have no news from that quarter."

"For my family, I must extend my thanks for your involvement in a matter that is so grievous in nature." Elizabeth then realized they were both still standing, the butler remaining at the door. "Lambert, will you please advise my aunt we have company and have Mrs. Seggie bring some tea?"

"Yes, Miss Elizabeth," Lambert said and bowed out of the room.

"Please, Lord Grenfell, sit down. I am certain my aunt will

join us shortly." Elizabeth reclaimed the seat she'd abandoned earlier and Sebastian claimed the chair closest to hers. "I am pleased you would take time out of your busy day to see us."

"I have come with an ulterior motive and…" he took a deep breath, "what I have to say is very serious."

"Your manner is serious. Is this something about Susannah? Is she well?"

"Yes, she is and this is not about my sister, but about you and your family."

"I am not understanding you."

"If things become untenable. If rumors threaten the honor of your reputation, I want you to know you can always turn to me for help."

"I appreciate the offer; however, I must muddle through on my own."

"Let me make myself clear, Elizabeth, I will give you my name."

"I am…" Shock temporarily stole her breath away. "I am honored, but you are expected to marry a titled lady. Someone with connections on par with your own family."

"I can marry where I choose. Besides, my father loves you and your sister."

"Your father loves me as a friend to your sister, not as the future Duchess of Belmont."

"He would come around." At Elizabeth's delicately arched brow, he sighed. "No, he would not. At least not until he thought it through long and hard."

"While I appreciate the sacrifice you are willing to—"

"It is no sacrifice, Elizabeth. If I may be blunt about this whole business, there are times when I believe I am in love with you."

At this, Elizabeth laughed. Even more so at the marquis's look of outrage.

"My dear marquis," she said and reached over to take his

hand. "You believe you only love me sometimes, and if I may be blunt about this whole business, that is not the kind of love required for a good marriage."

"Is it not?" he asked, his tone displaying wounded pride, not one of a spurned lover.

She released his hand and sat back in her seat. "No, but it does give a hint to the fact you admire me and greatly esteem our friendship, which I find precious and welcome."

"You know, many of my peers marry for less. Some barely have a friendship."

"I will not marry you, Lord Grenfell, however, I thank you for the offer."

"You are welcome, I think." He rubbed his jaw and stared straight ahead. "Somehow, I never thought a marriage proposal from me would be rejected."

"Sebastian, regardless of how often I tease and torment you, I find your company absolutely delightful."

He turned to her and grinned, then his jaw dropped open in surprise.

"You called me Sebastian!"

"I did, indeed. I have been told, more than once, it is the name your parents blessed you with."

"Do you mean to tell me, after all these years, in order for you to call me by my name, all I had to do was propose?"

"It appears so." Elizabeth gave him a wide smile, her eyes twinkling.

"I truly should marry you. I would never be bored, that is for certain."

"You could never handle my outright impertinence."

"My dear Elizabeth, you would make an absolutely formidable duchess, and the denizens of the Ton would shake in their shoes in fear of offending you."

"I have no desire to make anyone fear my presence, we have a royal family for that role. All I require is a man to love me unconditionally, who does not mind if I play the piano ill, engages me in spirited debates, nor cares if I spend more time out of doors than partaking in ladylike activities near the hearth." She paused, thinking about a treasured memory. "The man who wins my heart will not think it dull if we only discuss the weather."

"I hope, my dear, you find this paragon. You deserve nothing less."

Their conversation naturally paused with the arrival of Aunt Madeline, and after a pleasant half hour, the marquis excused himself and took his leave.

"I have a feeling I interrupted something important," her aunt said once Sebastian had quit the house.

"Lord Grenfell wished me to know that he and his family stand with ours regardless of what happens with Lydia. He went so far as to offer marriage."

Her aunt's widening eyes delighted Elizabeth's love of all things imprudent. Hiding a smile, she lowered her gaze and fiddled with the handle of her teacup.

"Did you…? Did he…?"

"I refused him."

"Oh." Her aunt sat silent for a few long seconds. "Might I ask why? You would be the next Duchess of Belmont."

"Believe me, aunt, that is not the carrot this rabbit wishes to have dangled in front of her nose." Aunt Madeline shook her head and laughed lightly. "Jane and I swore we would marry only for the deepest of love."

"Be that as it may, offers from future dukes do not fall like ripe apples into a woman's lap."

"His sister is my good friend and I look upon Marquis Grenfell as another elder brother. We would not suit, and no amount of money or the promise of titles will ever sway my deepest held desire of loving someone and being loved in return."

"Whoever gains your love, my dearest Lizzy will never repine their choice, for when you fall for a man, you will fall very hard."

Elizabeth dared not tell her aunt she had already fallen and had a bruised heart to show for it. The man she wished to be with for the rest of her life would never make an offer of marriage. Not after the scandal her youngest sister created with the one man he loathed, with all his being.

The conversation was interrupted by another carriage pulling to a stop in front of twenty-three Gracechurch Street, and this time Elizabeth did not wait in the parlor but ran outside without even grabbing a shawl to run into the arms of her eldest brother Michael.

"I am so glad Gabriel's express rider found you!"

"As am I. Let us go inside, I am tired, hungry, and in need of my family."

Arms around each other, they turned and made their way into their uncle's house, where Elizabeth and her aunt explained what they knew of Lydia's escapade.

Chapter Twenty-Five

Darcy raised his fist and banged on a weathered door. Not long after, he heard the bolt of a lock sliding and the door opened a crack to reveal a young girl.

"What d'ya want?" she asked, revealing crooked teeth.

"I am here to speak with Mrs. Younge."

"She ain't home t'callers."

The girl made to close the door and Darcy stuck his scuffed boot in the way to keep the door ajar.

"She will be home to me."

"What's a scrub like you wantin' wif Mrs. Younge?"

"That is my business. Yours is to fetch your mistress and bring her to me."

"Well, she ain't here."

"I do not believe you."

Darcy had no time for prevarication and pushed past the girl to fully enter the house. Mrs. Young came into the front entrance and glared at him.

"I shall call the constable if you do not leave my home this instant."

Darcy turned to the man who had trailed in behind him.

"Constable Rossland, this lady would like to speak with you."

Mrs. Younge's eyes widened to the point where the whites of her eyes were completely exposed.

"Let us remove this discussion to another room," Darcy said and followed Mrs. Younge into a neat, but shabby parlor.

"You can make no demands of me. I am no longer in your employ."

"What you say is true, but I am of the belief you know where I can find Wickham, and you also know he has a gentleman's daughter, with him."

"Pffttt…, if that little strumpet is a gentleman's daughter, then I'm the Queen of England."

"Very well, can you tell us where we may find him, your Majesty?"

"What's in it for me?"

"A promise I will not call for your arrest and have you hanged."

"What!"

"You stole my mother's necklace from Georgiana. I retrieved it from a seedy little pawn shop in Ramsgate, and the owner of that fine place of business described the lady who brought it in, right down to the heart-shaped mole at the base of your ear." Darcy leaned into Mrs. Younge, bringing his face very close to hers, and said in a low voice. "That alone will see you hang, but I have the power to ensure your neck is not stretched by the hangman's noose."

Mrs. Younge's eyes rolled back and she began to swoon.

"I need to sit down," she sank down onto the couch.

"Where is Wickham?" Darcy asked bluntly.

Mrs. Younge nervously chewed her lip and when Darcy noticed her shoulders sag, he knew she would relinquish the much-needed information.

"He is on Great-White Lion Street, at the Pig & Whistle."

"Was he with a young girl?"

"You said she was a gentleman's daughter?"

"I did."

"She does not behave as one. She let him fondle and kiss

her with no regard for those who were in the room. It was disgusting."

"She is only fourteen years of age."

Mrs. Younge's shoulders slumped.

"I am not surprised. Wickham has become more depraved as time goes on."

"I need to find him before it is too late to do anything."

"You are far too late for the girl. If you like, you can bring her here. I can help her learn some kind of trade and, if she is with child, find the babe a good home."

"Her family hopes to broker a marriage with Wickham."

"Do not even attempt such an endeavor. If you make him marry, he will turn around and sell her to the highest bidder. No, it is better she learns now she has fallen from grace and must work for her supper – and not by lying on her back."

"We must leave now, Mr. Darcy," Rossland said.

Darcy silently agreed and they quit the house and climbed into the waiting carriage. The next afternoon, Richard joined him in his study.

"Already leaving your bride alone?" Darcy teased, even though he was glad to see his cousin's happy smile.

"She is busy gossiping with Georgiana upstairs. Annie knows what we are about and we will have the rest of our lives to drive each other to madness."

"Has Aunt Catherine made an appearance?"

"Anne left Lady Cat a note, wherein she detailed our wedding plans. She also informed her mother to direct any and all complaints toward the earl, as we intend to travel for at least three months before returning to Rosings."

"You have made your father aware you have brandished his name and title as a weapon?"

"Most assuredly," Richard said and grinned widely. "The earl is primed and ready to take on his sister. When I informed him how derelict she had become with regard to needed maintenance on the house, along with her tenant's care, I thought he would expire in an apoplectic fit."

"Thank goodness all that is in the past," Darcy said, then went on to fill Richard in on everything his agents had discovered about Wickham. Finishing with, "He knows about Holcomb. Even though the earl is standing by Miss Bennet, we shall tell Wickham the plump pheasant he expected to pluck is no longer part of the equation, then entice him with an offer he will not want to refuse."

"A reliable musket in his face would be an excellent offer."

"I do not want him killed. I want him gone."

"What is the difference?"

"Richard, I will not have the death of a man, no matter how vile a creature, on my conscience." Darcy thought further on the matter. "Are you still in contact with that navy captain?"

"Wentworth?"

"Do you think he would mind a new member in his crew?"

"Alas, the honorable Captain Wentworth retired earlier this year. Last I heard, he was in Bath." Richard scratched his cheek, covered with thick stubble. Darcy knew how he felt, his normally clean-shaven face was just as scrubby. "However, the good captain still has friends on the high seas, and his brother by marriage is an admiral. I am certain, between the two of them, they can provide us with a ship that requires men to man the cannons when they take on the French and Spaniards."

"Excellent. Send an express to Wentworth while I invite Grenfell to join us for a strategy session."

Later in the week, Darcy was ready to implement his plan. The duke's men still watched the inn where Wickham and Miss Lydia were staying and showed no signs of leaving. They had not yet heard from Captain Wentworth, but ever hopeful,

Darcy had his staff prepare a locked room in his wine cellar to house Wickham until he made his oceanic debut.

***

Darcy came alongside the burly man, who leaned against a grimy wall of one of the many taverns and gaming hells that lined either side of Great-White Lion Road.

"Anything new?"

"He entered The Admiral's Arms about twenty minutes ago." Upon hearing the name of the tavern, a feral smile creased Darcy's face. Quite apropos for what they had planned for the braggart. "I've not seen hide nor hair or the girl."

Darcy nodded at Richard, who took two men with him to guard the rear exit, while Darcy entered through the front. To look at him, one would never know he was one of the wealthiest men in all of England. He had not shaved for over a week and, while his beard was impressive, it was nothing to his cousin's. Darcy's knit cap was pulled low over his brow, and his clothes were ill-fitting and coarse. All in all, he looked as though he was a dock worker coming in for a pint of beer.

His two guards also dressed in a similar fashion, took up a position near the door, keeping their well-honed fighting senses alert for any sign of trouble. Darcy lumbered to a trestle table in the middle of the taproom and sat down across from Wickham, keeping his head down and his shoulders hunched.

"I don't recall asking for company, mate. Find your own space."

"I like this space. You shove off," Darcy grumbled, keeping his voice low and gravelly.

"Don't start a fight you can't win, boyo. Now, be off with you. I'd like to eat in peace."

"Already tired of your chatty paramour?" Wickham gave a start, his face paling to pasty white when Darcy raised his head to fully reveal himself. "Hello, George. Fancy meeting you here."

Wickham's frantic gaze darted about the room, and Darcy knew he'd spotted the two men stationed near the entrance. He slouched, turning slightly to his right. and threw his arm around the back of the chair, presenting a *façade* of having no care in the world. One would have to be stupendously unaware to not comprehend that Wickham planned on escaping out the back exit the first chance he got.

Such a ploy may have worked in the past because Darcy at all times behaved the gentleman. But, this time, Wickham had struck too close to home. This time, Darcy was protecting the reputation of a woman who meant more to him than life. There would be no escaping his wrath.

"It seems I must suffer your company for a brief moment in time," Wickham drawled, giving the appearance of being extremely bored. "Why are you here?"

"Where is Lydia Bennet?"

"The little soiled dove awaits me in my room."

"How much will it take to have you leave her family alone – forever?"

"Ah, Darcy, I don't think your pockets are deep enough to make that happen."

"Does the river Thames sound deep enough, *boyo*?"

Wickham jerked in surprise and would have bolted from the chair if the meaty hand of the former Colonel Fitzwilliam had not descended on his shoulder. Also, the battle-scarred tip of the seasoned warrior's blade at his throat urged him to reconsider his choices.

"Now, Dicky. No need to be testy 'bout all this. What stake do you have in the lives of the Bennet sisters? Are the both of you vying for sweet Miss Bennet's favors? She is the undisputed beauty of the family." Wickham's expression turned crafty. "Or do your tastes run in a different direction? Maybe the two of you would like a go at Miss Elizabeth. Loads of spirit, that one. She'd put up a good fight the first few times. I wouldn't mind having her beneath me every night – or day – for that matter."

"Button it, Wickham!"

"Who shoved a stick up your arse, Darcy? You abhor the Bennet family, and everyone in Meryton knows you think Miss Elizabeth is ugly and not handsome enough to tempt you. Why do you care so much about a family you disdain?"

Another gentleman slid into a chair beside Darcy. Wickham cut him a quick glance, no sign of recognition crossing his face.

"This is Wickham?" the gentleman asked.

"It is, Lord Grenfell."

"I thought he would be taller."

"If he were measured by the number of flattering lies dropped from his lips on a daily basis, he would be as tall as one of the Great Pyramids."

"He is not that handsome." Wickham frowned at Sebastian's taunt. "Are you certain this is the same gentleman you said could coax the petticoat off a nun?"

"Now, look here, Grenfell!" their quarry exclaimed with much indignation.

"That is Lord Grenfell to you, my dear chap," Sebastian said, his voice falsely cheery. "I have not given you leave to address me in such an informal manner. We are not friends in any way, shape, or form."

"I don't care if you're the son of the bloody King of England!"

This was the opening Darcy had been waiting for.

"Though not a prince, he is as close as you can get in our little corner of the world. Lord Grenfell is the eldest son of the Duke of Belmont. The marquis and his father are very, very, *very* good friends of Miss Elizabeth Bennet," Darcy explained and watched Wickham's eyes widen, in fear or surprise, he was not sure which. The Duke of Belmont was not a man anyone wished to cross. "For a somewhat intelligent man, Wickham, you have behaved in an extremely stupid manner."

Just as Wickham opened his mouth to speak, the front entrance of the pub crashed open and two large men stepped over the threshold. As one, they scanned the room, their angry gaze quickly settling on Wickham. In tandem, they began to cross the room, flexing their arms and hands as though preparing to fight. It seemed, to Darcy, the brothers grew in size with each step.

Wickham visibly paled again.

"Darcy, I beg you. Do not leave me alone with them."

"What bothers you? Are they not like all the other brothers whose sisters you defiled? What makes them different?"

"Look at them," he practically squealed. "They will show no mercy."

"Do you deserve mercy?"

"Yes!"

Before Michael and Gabriel reached the table, Sebastian stood and intercepted them. Gabriel stopped, but Michael made to move around him. Sebastian gripped his forearm and held firm.

"Let go of my arm, Lord Grenfell," Michael said between clenched teeth, his voice low. Dangerous.

"When Darcy asked me to tell you of our plans, I did not expect you to join us. Do not lose your head over this pathetic excuse of a man."

Michael speared Sebastian with a look full of righteous anger, then swiveled back toward Wickham.

"He defiled my sister, and I *will* have vengeance."

Sebastian tightened his grip but softened his voice.

"Wickham will pay for his misdeeds, on this you have my word, but you must let Darcy handle him. You do no good for your sister, or your family if you hang for murder."

Once again Michael looked at Sebastian and whispered, his voice tight with anguish. "What makes you think I wish to live when I could not protect my sister from such evil as this?"

"What of your other sisters? What of your mother? Your father? There is more to live for than to die for, Michael."

Darcy stood and faced the brothers, both registering surprise at his rough appearance.

"You must let me take care of this. It is my responsibility," he said.

"It was not your sister who was taken from her home."

"I understand your agony better than you know. It is because of me Wickham has continued unchecked in his behavior."

"You have no marker in this game."

"I also have a younger sister who fell prey to his charms this past summer in Ramsgate." Darcy paused briefly when Michael gave a visible start and cut him a sideways glance. "I, who knew what he was, allowed him to continue spreading his debauchery and lies unabated. If I had taken action then, none of this would have happened. Please allow me to correct my mistakes and make amends."

Michal paused for so long, Darcy wasn't sure if the man was too far gone in his anger. Finally, the eldest Bennet nodded in agreement and glared at Wickham, who had been watching their interchange, knowing his fate hung in the balance.

Michael put both fists on the table and leaned in toward the sniveling coward, who shrank as far away as he could in his chair.

"If for some reason the law does not see fit to judge you in a manner I deem as fitting, there is no place on this earth you could hide where I will not find you and give back seventy times sevenfold what you have done to our sister." He leaned in further. "On this, you have my solemn promise. My vengeance will be terrible and swift."

He then stood tall and upright, Gabriel by his side. Darcy could almost imagine them with flowing robes and swords of fire. He'd heard they were referred to as Longbourn's angels, and at this exact moment, the moniker was fitting. He approached Michael and began speaking in a low voice.

"We have a plan for Wickham which will see him removed from English soil. For now, we will take him to my townhouse and wait for the arrival of some naval friends."

Surprise flickered over the brother's faces.

"You are press-ganging him into the Navy?" Gabriel whispered.

"Aye. His life will be miserable."

"How so?" Michael asked.

"He becomes queasy simply crossing a puddle. The ocean will make him want to die."

Michael's smile was one of grim satisfaction, while Gabriel outright grinned.

"Has he told you where our sister is?" Gabe asked.

"Wickham will hold that information close to his chest as a bargaining chip. What he is not aware of is the fact I already have that information. The duke's men are very good at their job."

A half-hour later, after Richard and Lord Grenfell had 'escorted' Wickham to Darcy's townhouse, Darcy, and the Bennet brothers knocked on the door to the room where Lydia Bennet waited. Darcy was surprised when, without even asking who was at the door, the young girl flung open the door. She also did not look to see who stood on the other side, for she had turned and stomped toward a rickety table.

"I am starved, Wickham. You forgot to leave me money to buy food again."

"Wickham is not here, Lydia," Michael said, stepping into the room.

She whirled around, surprise clearly etched upon her face, although her face paled upon seeing her brother. When Gabriel and Darcy followed him into the room, she gave a small start.

"Where is Wickham?" she demanded, raising her chin in defiance.

"He is gone and will not come back for you," Michael said in a hard voice.

"I do not believe you. He loves me," Lydia declared, and with a flounce, retreated to the unmade bed and plopped herself down upon the wrinkled sheets.

"He lied."

"Why would he do that?"

"Because, sister, he wished to have relations with you which are meant solely for man and wife."

"We will be, as soon as some gentleman pays Wickham the money he is owed, we are off to Gretna Green."

"Miss Lydia, I have known George Wickham ever since we were young boys, and no one, I repeat, no one has ever owed him money. It has always been the other way around," Darcy tried to explain to the stubborn miss. "He has no intention of marrying you."

"Take that back! George has sworn everlasting love for me."

Darcy was an astute man and knew another Bennet sister needed to be shown how vile Wickham truly was. He partially turned his back to Lydia and spoke to Michael Bennet in low undertones.

"Your sister needs to learn the truth. I can arrange it so she hears a conversation between me and Wickham. Knowing George as I do, he will show his true colors." Darcy held the younger man's gaze. When he started to shake his head in disagreement, Darcy said, "Your sister is a stubborn Bennet," – Michael's lip tilted slightly at one corner – "and, as such, will not take our word in this matter."

"I agree with Darcy," Gabriel said. He sought his brother's gaze and held it. "She is safe now. Let us help her learn how vile that man truly is."

After a few long seconds, Michael nodded in agreement and Darcy turned to face the young girl, still seated on the unmade bed.

"Miss Lydia, if you knew what Wickham truly feels, would you rethink your position?" Darcy asked, keeping his voice soft.

Her head lifted, like a doe scenting the air. Just as quickly, a scowl marred her face and she hopped off the bed to look at herself in the badly chipped reflecting glass.

"You and my brothers cannot fool me, Mr. Darcy. I know Wickham loves me," she said and twisted an unruly curl around her finger.

"I can prove it, but first, you must come with me to my residence."

"I will wait for Wicky right here, thank you very much."

"Do you wish to see Wickham?"

"Of course." She snorted in a manner that told Darcy she thought his question foolish.

"As we speak, Wickham is at my house."

Miss Lydia narrowed her eyes and glared at the three of them through the mirror.

"You will not force me to stay if I wish to leave?"

"You have my word, as a gentleman."

She arched a brow at her brothers, waiting for an answer and Darcy almost smiled. She looked so much like her middle sister with that little quirk.

"If I had my way, I would have slung you over my shoulder and carted you out of this hell hole, uncaring if you screamed your lungs out. Mr. Darcy has convinced me you need to know what a snake in the grass Wickham truly is. For this reason, and this reason only, I give you my word I will not strongarm you back to Uncle's house."

"I shall hold you to your word, Michael."

She shrugged on a dirty pelisse and threw a few things into her reticule while Darcy told one of the men waiting to take a hackney to his townhouse with a message for Richard. He tasked the other man to make sure their carriage was ready to depart as soon as they exited the building. He turned to find Miss Lydia putting on her bonnet.

"Do you not have a valise or small trunk?" Darcy asked, not wishing to return to this hell hole.

"Wicky said I could buy new dresses once he received his money."

No wonder her dress was so wrinkled and filthy, after a week of wear it belonged in a rag bin. She dragged on her gloves, then declared with a frustrated huff of breath, "Well, are we going to stand about all day like nod cocks?"

When they reached his house, Darcy escorted the Bennet siblings to his library, which had hidden access to the study where Richard planned to escort Wickham. He cautioned her to remain quiet in order to hear what her lover had to say. With everyone in place, he stepped into the room, leaving the door slightly ajar. No more than two minutes passed before Richard entered with Wickham, who settled himself into a comfortable chair and crossed one leg over his knee in a manner of cocky confidence. It was clear he expected to exhort money out of them.

"Well, did you take the little lamb back to her uncle?"

"Are you speaking about your *fiancé*, Miss Lydia?"

"We are not and never will be engaged," George said. "As it is, I was overjoyed when you showed up to take the foolish little chit off my hands."

"Miss Lydia is convinced you are off to Scotland as soon as the money you are owed is received."

"What!" Richard scoffed at the notion. "No one has ever owed this piece of trash money."

"So, what was the plan, George? You know Mr. Bennet does not have funds to pay you off."

"Aye, but the toff engaged to his eldest daughter is loaded."

"The earl called off the wedding once he learned of his future sister's shame." Darcy hated to lie, but he could not stand the idea of Wickham getting any money from Lord Holcomb.

"I don't believe you," Wickham snarled, but when both Richard and Darcy stared at him without expression, he groaned and hung his head. "Damn."

"You dallied with a gentleman's daughter for this, Wickham. Have you no remorse?"

"The spoiled brat begged for my attention."

Darcy's fist curled and he longed to hit him. Was this how Wickham perceived his own sister, Georgiana? A spoiled young girl, begging for his attention? "You dare brag about seducing a child who is not yet fifteen?"

"There was not much seducing. The little slut practically threw herself at me. I easily lifted her skirts behind the haberdashery in Meryt——."

"You bastard!"

Lydia flew through the partially open door and launched herself at Wickham, fingers curled into claws like a feral cat. Wickham howled when she raked her nails down the right side of his face. Michael, who had followed, grabbed his sister around the waist and swung her away from Wickham, who started to stand but was shoved back into the chair by Richard

"Get that crazy woman away from me!" Wickham roared, lifting his hand to his bleeding face.

All this time, Lydia kicked and struggled, forever reaching for Wickham, screaming out curses Darcy had only ever heard from hardened men. Appalled as he was by her vulgar cant, Darcy had to hide a smile when Richard arched a brow at one of her more creative descriptions of Wickham's nether region.

"Stay with Wickham," Darcy said to Richard and followed Michael as he fought to carry Lydia back to the library. "Her brothers and I shall calm Miss Lydia."

"You shall not calm me. I will kill the bloody bast—"

Her curse was cut off when Michael covered her mouth with one hand. Upon entrance into the library, he tossed her onto the closest chair. Darcy closed the connecting door to stop her determined assault on Wickham. He did not expect the swift kick between his legs, and it was only because he was tall, and light on his feet, that he managed to twist enough so her booted foot barely grazed his thigh.

"Let me by, Mr. Darcy," she ground out between clenched teeth, her fists still curled in anger.

"He is not worth it, Miss Lydia."

Darcy did not move from his position in front of the door.

All of a sudden, Lydia crumpled into a sobbing heap on the floor. Moved by compassion, Darcy heaved a deep sigh. Once again, chaos and heartache followed in the wake of Wickham's ship of licentiousness. Gabriel bent down and lifted his sister in his arms and sat with her on one of the couches, letting her weep into his shoulder.

"Come, sister. Now that you know Wickham's true character, we will retreat to our uncle's house."

She pushed herself upright and with one hand shoved

unruly curls from her forehead, and with the back of her other hand, wiped her nose. Eyes, red-rimmed and swollen, told the tale of her anguish.

"I can't return to Uncle's house. Jane will hate me because Lord Holcomb called off the wedding. Elizabeth will hate me because I hurt Jane. You and Michael will wash your hands of me, and Papa will send me off to the Hebrides, or maybe even Iceland. I may as well throw myself in the Thames and be done with it."

"Lydia, you are our beloved sister. No matter what, we will stand with you." Michael held her tear-filled gaze. "It is time to come home."

***

With Wickham locked in the wine cellar, and Miss Lydia and her brothers returned to Gracechurch Street, Richard joined Darcy for a drink.

"As much as I wish to stay and see with my own eyes Wickham dragged off to his new career, my bride has barely seen me since we said our vows."

"I am sorry, Richard."

"The timing of this was not your fault, and Anne understands." Richard heaved himself out of the comfortable chair. "I bid you goodnight and will see you in the morning."

Darcy rested his head on the back of the chair and relished the silence of the room, broken only by the crackling fireplace. He thought of the last time he'd seen Elizabeth, crying in the grove at Rosings Park. He had planned on asking for a courtship once they left Kent and returned to London. Would she welcome his company now, or hate him forever for not having warned them of Wickham's black character?

The grand clock in the hall struck twelve before Darcy finally laid down to sleep, waking six hours later when Jenkins roused him, advising him the Marquess of Grenfell and some men had arrived. Burke had asked them to wait in the small parlor, away from the windows which graced the front of the house.

"By their uniform, I believe they are naval men."

"Tell them I shall be right down."

A short twenty minutes later Darcy entered the parlor, acknowledging Grenfell with a polite nod of the head, and then let his gaze move toward the five men standing together. The marquess quickly introduced naval lieutenant Sullivan, who asked if their newest recruit was ready for transport.

"He is, Lieutenant Sullivan, although he has not been made aware of his transfer to another branch of His Majesty's military service."

"He won't be the first one, nor the last." Sullivan turned to his men, every one of them burly sailors. "Come on lads, let us welcome our new brother in arms."

Burke escorted the men down to the wine cellar and once they cleared the room, the marquis finally spoke.

"I proposed to Elizabeth."

Darcy staggered back a step.

"You what?"

"I offered her my hand in order to protect her family's name and honor."

Darcy's blood turned to ice and he could not catch his breath. He had lost her. He hadn't even had a chance to tell her how much he loved her. He struggled to maintain his dignity and forced words from his lips, knowing he did not mean one single word.

"I wish you and Miss Elizabeth joy. She will make a wonderful wife and future duchess."

"She refused my offer," the marquess said, his intelligent gaze never leaving Darcy's face, whose legs gave out, and he fell heavily into the nearest chair. "She said, and forgive me if

I do not quote her verbatim, *she requires a man who loves her unconditionally, does not mind if she plays the piano ill."*

No more was said as the naval lieutenant and his men were heard in the foyer. Both Darcy and the marquess joined them. Wickham, bound and gagged, glared at Darcy with obvious hatred.

"I shall bid you a good day, Mr. Darcy," the marquess said with a polite half-bow. "Please give my regard to Miss Elizabeth and her family when next you see them." Grenfell paused and suddenly smiled before adding, "She also said the man who held her heart would not mind engaging in dull conversations about the weather."

Within minutes, Wickham was hustled into the waiting carriage. The marquess sauntered to his own conveyance and waved a farewell salute before hopping in and driving off. It was only when both carriages had rolled down the street and out of sight, did Darcy allow his butler to close the front door and wearily make his way to his study, ostensibly to write a note asking how Miss Lydia was this morning. However, his hand shook so hard, ink kept splattering onto the page, making the sloppy missive look like something Bingley would craft. He gave up the task in order to face the truth. The final words of the marquess gave him hope where he previously thought he had none.

Chapter Twenty-Six

Elizabeth sat near the window, recalling last night and Lydia's return with their brothers. They had received a poorly written express saying Wickham had been dealt with and Michael and Gabriel had gone with Mr. Darcy to retrieve Lydia. The hall clock had struck the ten bells when Uncle's carriage was heard coming down the street and, irrespective of the late hour, Elizabeth tore out the front door, flying down the steps as it came to a halt in front of the house.

"Lydia!" Elizabeth exclaimed when the carriage door opened and Michael stepped out, her sister right behind. Lydia, eyes rimmed red from crying, fell into her arms, and began to sob anew.

"Oh, Lizzy. I was so stupid."

"There is nothing we can do about that now." Elizabeth shifted to loop their arms together. Annoying as her younger sister could be, she never wanted to lose Lydia again. "Come, let us go inside and you can refresh yourself."

They made their way into the house, Michael and Gabriel closing rank behind them. Aunt Madeline met them in the front hall, her eyes widening at her niece's appearance.

"Lydia, I am so glad you are safe." Their aunt smoothed her expression into one of concern. "Have you had anything to eat?"

"I had two biscuits and an apple the other day." Lydia

bowed her head and stared at the floor. "I did not have anything today."

"The blackguard did not even feed you?" Michael almost shouted. "The navy is too good for the likes of him."

Gabriel's expression was as dark as his brother's

"The navy?" Lydia cried out and looked aghast at her brothers. "Who will marry me now?"

She burst into tears, and Aunt Madeline gathered her into her arms.

"Shhh… child. All will be well," their aunt murmured. "Lizzy, will you ask Mrs. Seggie if she can send up a tray for Lydia?"

"Of course," Elizabeth replied.

Aunt Maddie then turned the young girl around and with an arm around her waist, led her up the stairs. A heavy pall settled between the three remaining siblings.

"I want to go back to Darcy's, and kill him," Michael growled out.

"Slowly?"

"No other way. I want him to scream for mercy."

"And how will that help our sister?"

Michael and Gabriel gave a start and looked at Elizabeth like she had grown an extra head.

"It will make me feel a thousand times better than I do now," Gabriel said with a shrug.

"Will it? Taking the life of a man will edify your soul?" She stared her two brothers down. "Do not misunderstand me. I loathe that man." She refused to say his name. "But I will not allow myself to stoop to his level, for if I do, then he wins. Even without squeezing one penny from us, he wins. I will not give him such a victory."

Michael bit out a curse and turned his head to the side, his jaw clenched tight. When he spoke, it sounded as though each word was being torn from his throat.

"He defiled her, Elizabeth. How can I, her eldest brother, allow him to live after such a heinous act?"

"You defeat him by being the better man. By loving your sister and standing by her no matter what happens." Elizabeth cupped his cheek and forced him to look directly at her. "*Love your enemies, do good to those who hate you, bless those who curse you, pray for those who mistreat you.* That is how we rise above this."

Michael laid his hand over hers and pressed, his storm-colored eyes never wavering from hers.

"When you say your prayers tonight, sister, remember me in them. If I am to offer the other cheek, I need more strength of character than I possess right now because everything in me is dark and angry." He clamped his lips tight, dropped her hand, and drew air in through his nostrils. "Never have I felt so helpless."

Gabriel moved to stand close to his twin.

"I have the same anger swirling like a vortex in my soul, but Lizzy is right. If we cannot forgive Wickham, Lydia will forever believe we cannot forgive her, and we cannot do that to our sister. For her, we must let go."

The brothers bid Elizabeth a curt goodnight and strode down to Uncle's study where they would spend some quiet time together. She went upstairs to her room. There was nothing she could do at this point in time, other than pray. For what, she did not know, but this did not stop her from asking the Lord to heal her sister's broken heart and find a way to repair her damaged reputation and heal the hurting souls in their family.

***

"Papa, what news? Have you heard from Michael?"

"Yes, as a matter of fact, I have only just received a letter from him by express."

"Dare I ask, was the news good or bad?"

"Read it yourself."

Jane accepted the letter from her father's outstretched hand, and without even taking a seat, began reading by the desk.

Father,

At last, I am able to send word about Lydia. Soon after your rider caught up with me and told me the two of them had gone to London, I made my way to my uncle's house. Almost as soon as I arrived, I was fortunate enough to discover what part of the city she was staying in. I will relay the full particulars when we meet in person.

Jane glanced up a hopeful look in her eye. "Thank goodness, at least she is found."

"I suggest you continue, it does not get better," Papa said, settling back in his chair.

Jane frowned and read on:

By the time you receive this express, we expect our sister to be returned to our care. I must now tell you a disturbing fact. Lizzy has learned Wickham will not likely marry our youngest sister—

"Not marry her!" Jane lowered the letter again. "Do you think this was all for revenge because my brothers challenged Mr. Wickham and stopped him from spreading false stories about Mr. Darcy?"

"Maybe so, but this is all muddy water under a broken bridge. We still have to contend with the mess my youngest daughter has made. I suggest you continue reading the letter."

Jane skimmed the letter, muttering every now and then over salient points, her expression becoming more distressed by the minute.

...As far as we know, our Meryton neighbors remain unaware our sister has run off. Lizzy did mention Maria Lucas received a letter from our silliest sister while in Kent, boasting of her plans to elope in two weeks' time. However, Lizzy offered to write Mrs. Collins and put forward the story our sister had a change of heart and confessed all to Mother before the planned day. She will write that you, in turn, took Lydia to Uncle Gardiner's house to remove her from temptation. This should tie up any loose ends which may float in the direction of our cousin, Mr. Collins.

I would suggest, to facilitate this ruse, you make haste to London. No one needs to know Lydia is not in the carriage with you, and Mother can happily inform our neighbors how Lydia is off to London to be fitted for a new dress in time for Jane's wedding. This is our only recourse, Father, and I will give you more details upon your arrival.

Yours etc.,
Michael

Jane finally finished reading and sat in the chair across from her father; the letter clenched in her fist.

"Poor Lydia, she is completely ruined."

"I am of the same mind." Papa leaned back and rubbed his chin. "I wonder how much money Darcy spent on discovering them?"

"Mr. Darcy!" Jane openly gaped at her father. "What makes you think Mr. Darcy is involved?"

"I hired a man to start searching for Lydia the minute we learned she had run off. In one of his reports he wrote, a 'very tall, somber gentleman' had been making some inquiries of his own, and the streets were overrun with Bow Street Runners on the same quest. And, as you can see by the letter in your hand, Lydia has been found."

Jane held his father's gaze.

"I presume you are about to make a trip to London."

"I am." Mr. Bennet opened the bottom drawer of his sturdy desk and pulled out a thick leather bag. He withdrew a fistful of bank notes, and then some coins. "And I require my lovely daughter to join me."

"Me?"

"Absolutely. I need a delicate hand to wave a hanky at any neighbors we might come across when we slowly drive through Meryton. Every now and again, I expect you to giggle and exclaim, *La, I am off to London for a new dress*." He finished his sentence on a wobbly falsetto while waving his hand in the same manner as Mamma manifesting one of her nervous ailments.

"Papa!" Jane began to laugh. "You are outrageous!"

"I will gladly own that moniker until Lizzy returns home. Also, you may let your betrothed know you are also in town to shop for your trousseau."

"Bribery does not suit you, Father."

"You are turning down my offer?"

"I shall never say no to new dresses. When do we leave?"

Late in the afternoon that very same day, Mr. Bennet, and Jane arrived at Gracechurch Street. The express post had arrived several hours before them, so Mrs. Gardiner had had plenty of time to prepare rooms and advise the cook. The two of them, tired and dusty, met with everyone – save Lydia – in the parlor.

"Father!" Michael exclaimed and strode forward to hug his father.

Jane's eldest brother, while stout in stature and heart, felt things quite deeply and she knew this escapade of Lydia's hurt him deeply. Uncaring there were others in the room, Papa cupped Michael's head and touched their foreheads together, holding his son's somber gaze the entire time. "You have done well, Michael."

"I have not, Father."

Michael broke their connection and pulled away, tugging down his waistcoat. Papa turned his attention to the rest of the family.

"As much as I would like to freshen up, I must attend to my daughter." He looked toward Aunt Madeline. "Is she well enough to receive a visit from her Papa?"

"She is," Madeline said with a sad smile. "Come, I will take you to her."

They quit the room and Elizabeth tugged Jane down onto the closest settee.

"Oh, Jane, I am so glad you are here. I have needed your quiet confidence."

"Tell me what all happened?" Jane asked.

Elizabeth waited until everyone sat down, then told her portion of the story. Gabriel took over when she reached the part of them arriving in London and how Mr. Darcy helped them search and find Lydia.

"What of Mr. Wickham?" was the only question Jane asked after everything was said and done.

"As far as we know, he was press-ganged into the Navy."

"The Navy! What of Lydia?" Jane was quite distraught at the news. "What if she… what if there are repercussions?"

"Knowing they lived as man and wife for a number of days, we have to assume she will fall with child."

"Poor Lydia," Jane murmured. "If she does not? Fall with child, that is. Then what?"

"My dear, even if we are successful in quashing any or all rumors," Uncle Edward joined in. "Your sister made a serious mistake, and the consequence of her foolishness is she must marry. Child, or no child, she cannot go home to Longbourn."

"No, I refuse to believe Papa would sanction the marriage of a fourteen-year-old girl to a stranger." Jane stood and smoothed down her skirts. "I must speak with him immediately."

"Jane," Elizabeth said softly, "What of Henry? He may not wish such a scandal to tarnish his daughter's reputation. You may have no choice."

A flash of anger, quickly followed by the knowledge of such a reality spiked through Jane's body. Unknowingly, she straightened her spine and squared her shoulders, as though readying for battle.

"I will not see my sister forced to marry against her will, and if Lord Holcomb is unwilling to continue our engagement, then he is not the man I thought him to be. I pray he will not, but it is out of my hands."

All of their attention was diverted to the hall outside the parlor and the subsequent arrival of the very man they were speaking of. Lord Holcomb entered the room, scanned the occupants, and upon spying Jane, made his way directly to her, taking her hand in his.

"Jane!" Henry said as he raised her hand to his mouth and kissed her knuckles. "I must admit, I was in the hall, and overheard the last part of your conversation." He took both hands in his and held her gaze. "I will not break our engagement, and have no intention of turning my back on your family."

Upon her quiet sob, he looked about the room.

"For the record, if *my* sister does find herself with child, she can live with Jane and me on our estate in Buckinghamshire until the babe is born. No one need know, as we will tell everyone Jane wanted Lydia to spend time with us before she attends Miss Tyler's Academy."

Jane's heart melted a little further at the earl calling Lydia his sister and offering a compassionate solution. Still, there were more pressing issues that could arise from their showing support for what society deemed a fallen woman.

"But, what of your daughter? A scandal of this magnitude may prove an insurmountable hindrance, and ruin her chance of a good marriage." Jane would not let her sister's folly destroy Cassandra's future happiness.

"We have ten years before her curtsy and trust me, there will be other scandals that will take precedence before then." Henry guided Jane to the settee where Elizabeth sat, then took the chair nearest her. "You cannot run me off, Miss Bennet. We will marry as scheduled."

***

The next afternoon, before the polite hour for courtesy calls, Elizabeth and Jane were surprised when Lambert announced Mr. Darcy. The sisters shared a startled glance before the gentleman was admitted into their company. He made no move to claim a chair or a spot on one of the couches, although he did advance a few steps into the room.

"Forgive me for being intrusive, I have come to see how your sister is faring."

Elizabeth felt a sense of relief wash over her at this declaration. She worried this disaster with Lydia may have cooled the burgeoning affection Mr. Darcy displayed while the two of them were in Kent. It seemed, at the very least, she'd retained his friendship but would be very surprised if he took it further.

"Lydia is as well as can be expected," Jane answered in her calm manner. "She is to live with Lord Holcomb and me after we marry."

A nearly imperceptible tic at the corner of Mr. Darcy's eye was his only reaction to the news. Elizabeth silently commended him on such a subdued response. He, more than anyone, was well aware of the fragility of a woman's reputation, and she could only admire him for his restraint.

"I would presume you plan to reside on his estate in Buckinghamshire?"

"Yes, although we must spend some time in town when the House of Lords is in session. Lydia has decided she will remain on the estate during that time, for health reasons."

Mrs. Seggie entered the room with a tea tray and for the first time, Elizabeth spoke.

"Please, forgive our manners, Mr. Darcy. Have a seat and let me prepare you a cup of tea."

"I had not meant to stay long," he began.

"Nonsense. You are here now and Mrs. Seggie has added some of our cook's fresh strawberry tarts. She would be quite offended if you did not have any."

"I would never wish to offend your aunt's cook, Miss Elizabeth," Darcy said, and with a smile sat next to her.

She quickly poured him a cup of tea, with a touch of honey and handed it to him.

"You remember how I like my tea?"

He sounded surprised and Elizabeth felt a small measure of satisfaction over the fact. They engaged in polite conversation until Aunt Madeline joined them. Darcy immediately rose to his feet, as did Elizabeth.

"Good morning, Aunt. May I introduce to you Mr. Darcy of Pemberley?" Elizabeth asked and upon her nod, began their introductions. "Mr. Darcy, this is my aunt, Mrs. Gardiner."

Darcy gave a small start at her name.

"I am honored to meet you, Mrs. Gardiner," Darcy said with a polite bow and returned to his seat by Elizabeth. "Please excuse my curiosity, but is your husband Mr. Edward Gardiner?"

"Yes, he is. Have you met him?"

"Prior to Christmas, I invested with him and anticipate reaping a substantial return due to his business acuity."

"My husband mentioned he met with some gentlemen prior to our trip to Hertfordshire to spend the Yuletide with his sister, Mrs. Bennet. He is not one to bandy about the names of those who invest in his company, however, if he had, I would have been thrilled. I have fond memories of your home and of your parents."

"You knew my parents?" he exclaimed in surprise.

"I did, indeed. My father had a small estate just outside of Lambton, and my uncle is the rector there."

"Mr. Penfound is your uncle?" She replied in the affirmative and Darcy continued. "Then your father's estate is Hidden Hills."

"My mother often had tea with your mother when the family was at Pemberley, and your mother kindly returned her visits. Such a lovely woman. Always kind and genteel."

"She was, indeed. When you meet my sister, you will see a reflection of my mother."

Elizabeth almost gasped out loud when Mr. Darcy said, without any hesitation, *when you meet my sister*, not *if* you meet my sister. Could the affection she'd witnessed at Hunsford be genuine and not a figment of her imagination?

The parlor door opened and not only did Papa enter the room, but also Michael and Gabriel. Once again, Mr. Darcy surged to his feet, his face a moving canvas of both delight and dread.

"Mr. Darcy," Papa called out and strode forward to shake the man's hand. "My sons have told me the measures you took to find my daughter and I have no adequate words to express my thanks."

"I regret I did not expose Wickham when I was in Hertfordshire, then none of this would have happened."

"You must not shoulder all the blame, Mr. Darcy. My sons knew what a blackguard he was and warned the shopkeepers not to extend credit, and our friends to watch their daughters.

No one expected my youngest daughter to sneak off and meet with him. There is nothing you could have said or done to change her actions. She herself wrote the lines of her story and must now live with the consequence."

"It is a harsh sentence for one so young." Mr. Darcy's voice was filled with regret.

"Aye, but she will recover and likely faster than we wish. Now, my understanding is Wickham has unwillingly joined the Navy and, if what my sons tell me is true, he will be a miserable sod."

"He will, for several reasons. One is he suffers from sea sickness, and the other is he will not enjoy the chores of landsmen."

"Landsmen? Did you not say he was at sea?" Jane asked, her smooth brow furrowed from her confusion.

"Men of his ilk, who have been press-ganged into service are called landsmen because they have little or no naval experience. They are usually assigned to a watch."

"Am I to presume, because of his lack of experience, his watch will be at night?"

"Up in the tallest crow's nest of the ship, which will feed into his second fear."

"Which is?" Elizabeth asked, her eyes sparkling with mischief as she believed she knew the answer.

"Heights. His fear is so great, he will not even attempt to ride a horse. He has always taken a carriage."

"The poor man," Jane murmured.

"Your compassion is commendable, daughter, but it is wasted on one like Wickham. Many families have been ruined by this man, and it is right he does penance."

The clock struck the half hour and Darcy pulled his pocket watch out and glanced down.

"I must take my leave. I am expected at my aunts for tea."

He then stood and bowed at the assembled company.

"May I walk you out, Mr. Darcy?" Elizabeth asked.

"I would appreciate the company, Miss Elizabeth."

Ignoring the questioning looks from her family, she quickly rose and followed Mr. Darcy out and down to the foyer. She took this opportunity while waiting for the retrieval of his outerwear, to express her own thanks for his involvement in the recovery of Lydia.

"Let me thank you for the compassion you have shown, not just for my sister but for my family."

"If you will thank me," he replied, "let it be for yourself alone. You must know, surely, you must know, everything I did was for you." Darcy's face softened and with his thumb, he carefully wiped the tear which threatened to spill from her eye. "I thought only of you."

Elizabeth was bereft of words. To think, a little over a month ago, she thought she despised the man.

"What am I to do with you, Mr. Darcy? You save my sister, avenge the man who harmed her, and refuse my heartfelt thanks."

"I have a suggestion if you are willing to consider it."

"I am willing."

He took one of her hands in his. Was this to be their final farewell? He had done so much for their family, and Lydia's stain ran deep.

"Would you do me the honor of allowing me to call on you?"

"Call on me?" Her surprise was so great, she tried to extract her hand from his. "Even after… after what my sister has done?"

"Yes." The very hint of a smile touched the corner of his lips. "I would like to call on you. If that is acceptable."

"It is more than acceptable, it is—" He cupped her bare hand in his, turned it over, and kissed her palm, the unexpected intimacy sending shock waves up her arm. All coherent thought fled her mind at the touch of his firm lips caressing each gentle crease. "Oh…"

She felt his smile against the soft flesh and upon him releasing her hand back into her care, she curled her fingers, as though protecting that sacred place.

Where is your clever tongue now, Lizzy Bennet?

"When I arrive tomorrow, I will speak with your father."

So bemused was she, Elizabeth could only nod in agreement, blissfully unaware Lambert had arrived with the gentleman's outer coat, hat, and gloves. Taking her hand in his again, Mr. Darcy bowed over it and with a gentle squeeze said, "Until tomorrow, Miss Elizabeth."

She stood in the open door and watched him enter his waiting carriage and drive off. When Lambert gave a polite half-cough, she came to her senses and allowed him to close the door. Blushing profusely, she gave him a regal nod and returned to the parlor. Jane's questioning gaze had her blush again.

"Elizabeth," Papa said in a most congenial manner, "is there anything you wish to tell me?"

"Not at this time." She crossed the room and took her place on the settee.

Her father assessed her very carefully, then asked, "Did Mr. Darcy give you something?"

His attention had fallen on her clenched fist and she gave a small start. Knowing she should relax her fist was almost beyond her capabilities at this time. All she wanted to do was to press that newly kissed palm to her lips, wishing it were the man himself. She realized her father awaited an answer. Slowly, she unfurled her fingers and clasped her hands together. It was the best she could do until she had a modicum of privacy in such a busy household.

"No, Papa, he did not. However, Mr. Darcy has asked if he could speak with you privately tomorrow."

The room fell into silence, then Gabriel began to chuckle when Michael brought out his money clip and handed over a bank note.

"Might I ask what this is all about?" their father asked.

"I bet Michael one pound Elizabeth liked Mr. Darcy more than she let on."

"You know what I think of gambling."

"Now, Father, it is not gambling when you know it is a sure thing."

"What do you mean, a sure thing?" Elizabeth demanded. "I myself did not even like Mr. Darcy until we met again in Kent."

"Lizzy." Gabriel gave his sister a loving look, "You spent too much time disliking the man. If you truly did not hold him with any affection, you would have brushed him off, much like you did Sir Percival Milton."

"Sir Percy was an officious toad who would be better off marrying a mirror, as his image is the only thing which can stand his presence."

"I rest my case. You did not like Milton's manners, ignored him when he pranced around you, and set him on his ear when he dared ask to call on you. With Darcy, you spoke of him often, worried about what he would think of our family, and turned to him in your time of need. You cared for him even when you did not realize the fact."

Elizabeth opened her mouth to argue the fact but closed it just as fast when she saw even Jane's shoulders shaking in silent laughter. She raised her chin in defiance and drew herself as tall as she could while sitting, and gave her brother a familiar, but loving glare.

"You know my revenge will be swift and unexpected."

"I am not afraid of you, Lizzy Bennet."

Michael gathered her up in what she thought of as a 'big brother hug.'

"You know I did not like Mr. Darcy. I have since learned he is a man of honor. A bit prideful, but given what he has suffered these past few years, it is understandable, and I can forgive him some of his self-importance." Michael set her away from him and, with both hands on her shoulders, bent down to look her in the eye. "I like him, Elizabeth. If what we think might happen, happens, I will be glad to call him brother."

"I suppose we all must stay in town for at least another day, seeing as my Lizzy has decided to take on a suitor," Papa said to no one in particular. "One more day in London is not that long in the grander scheme of life."

"Gabriel and I will return to Longbourn as planned. Mother is there by herself and you know she does not handle stress well."

"I am sorry you have to change your plans, Papa." Elizabeth resumed her seat on the couch. "We can always leave for Hertfordshire as soon as Mr. Darcy has concluded his business with you tomorrow."

Her father smiled and leaned back in his chair. "For your Mr. Darcy, there is not much I would not do, my dear. He has gained my eternal gratitude and respect. I look forward to seeing more of him in the future."

Later, when Elizabeth was finally alone, she stared at her reflection. Light from the nearby candle highlighted the contours of her face and body. She turned slightly, wondering how she appeared to Mr. Darcy. She was not as tall as most women, but she was also not small. Yet, in the presence of Mr. Darcy, with his broad shoulders and athletic physique, she felt like a wood nymph. Diminutive. She smiled. She quite liked that he made her feel soft and feminine. How strange, as in the presence of her brothers, she'd never felt so… so delicate. Never did they intimidate her, rather the opposite. The more they blustered and growled, the more she stood toe to toe with them. She was fairly certain if Mr. Darcy growled at her… her thoughts skittered in a direction never traveled before and her tummy quivered. It was very plain to see that Mr. Darcy wished for more than a mere kiss on the hand. With these provocative thoughts chasing through her mind, Elizabeth Bennet took her first tentative step into womanhood.

The very next morning, as soon as the hour was deemed respectable to call, Mr. Darcy rang the bell of twenty-three Gracechurch Street and presented his card, asking if Mr. Bennet was available for a call.

LONGBOURN'S ANGELS

Chapter Twenty-Seven

A soft knock on the door had Darcy raise his head and bid his butler to enter.

"Mr. Bingley has arrived, sir."

"Very good. Please see that we are not disturbed."

"Yes, sir." Burke did not close the door completely, returning in less than a minute with Bingley.

"Darcy," Bingley said and went to shake his hand, then hesitated.

"Bingley." Darcy moved around the desk, his own hand extended, which Charles took with a firm grip and shook. "Would you like some tea, or something stronger?"

"It depends on why you asked for my presence," Bingley said as he took a seat near the window.

"A drink it is then." Darcy pulled out two tumblers and filled them three-quarters full with an excellent brandy. "Regardless of what has happened in the past, you remain my friend."

"Thank you," Bingley said and accepted the glass.

Darcy sat across from him in the matching comfortable chair and casually crossed his leg over his knee. He studied his friend, noting the dejected slope of his shoulders and subtle dark circles beneath his eyes.

"You do not look well, Bingley."

"I have not been sleeping well. Nothing brings me joy."

"For whatever part I may have played in this, I am truly sorry," Darcy said with complete sincerity, not having to reference the reason. They both knew of what he spoke. "Does your family depart for Scarborough soon?"

"We leave the day after tomorrow. I still have to sign some paperwork with my solicitor with regard to Netherfield."

"That is partly why I asked to speak with you." Darcy uncrossed his leg and leaned forward. "I wish to purchase the remainder of your lease."

"You what?" Bingley set his drink down on the side table. "For what reason?"

"I am courting Miss Elizabeth, and Netherfield is a convenient distance from Longbourn."

"You? You are courting Miss Bennet's sister?" Bingley rose to his feet and began to pace. "Unbelievable. The Bennets were too low born for me, but not for you."

"I never said they were low born. Those words came from your sister."

"You turned me from courting Miss Bennet!"

"I did, and I do not regret my opinion because at the time I was convinced she did not return your affection."

"It did not help that my sisters treated her with abject cruelty."

Bingley threw himself back into the chair and slouched into it, his chin nearly touching his chest.

"No, it did not," Darcy said in agreement. "I know you believe your happiness laid with Miss Bennet, but did you ever envision how your life would have unfolded if you had married her?" Bingley's eyes closed and a slight grimace crossed his face. "I see by your expression, that you have. Your sisters would have made both of your lives miserable. Miss Bennet is a gentle soul and tries to see the best in everyone, but you must admit, your sisters would have worn her down."

"I know." Bingley opened his eyes and finally looked at Darcy, his expression resolute. "I am releasing Caroline's dowry to her care after I drop her off in Scarborough before continuing on to Manchester."

"Manchester?"

"I have written my uncle and ordered him to open my father's house."

"What will you do while there?"

"I will resume running the family business and look for ways to diversify. I plan to invest in steam-powered engines. I think carriages will soon become a thing of the past. Buying an estate and becoming a gentleman will fall to any sons I may have."

"Bingley, you do not need an estate to be a gentleman. You already are one."

"Thank you, Darcy. I truly have appreciated your friendship all these years."

"We are still friends. Nothing has changed in that regard." Darcy raised his glass of brandy toward Bingley, who picked up his own drink. "To friendship," Darcy said.

"To friendship."

Two hours later, a slightly foxed Darcy and Bingley made their way to Bingley's solicitor, where Darcy signed a document taking over the remainder of the lease on Netherfield, and had the documents couriered to his own solicitor's office. It was on their return to Darcy's house that he shared a bit of news.

"Did you know Netherfield Park is owned by Gabriel Bennet?"

Bingley, who had rested his head against the back of the squab, jerked upright.

"What! I was paying rent to the Bennet family?" With a groan, he closed his eyes and dropped his head back onto the seat. "I truly did not think this whole debacle could get any worse. We were right prats, Darcy. Absolute and complete dunderheads."

"We were, indeed."

Bingley cracked open one eye and glared at him. "How did we not know this?"

"Mr. Bennet has been very careful to keep news of their wealth quiet, and because of that, he and his family live an elegant if not simple life. We should have known, given the dinners Mrs. Bennet hosted. The food and drink were always superlative." Darcy remembered the conversation he had with the Bennet patriarch when he requested permission to court Elizabeth. "Longbourn brings in more per annum than you, Bingley."

"Of course," Bingley groaned again. "I found the perfect woman only to have Caroline treat her worse than sheep dung on her shoe, and all along her family is well situated."

"You should inform your sister of this fact once you are on your way to Scarborough."

"Not a chance, for then I would then have to listen to her complaints the entire trip. I plan on revealing all after I release her dowry. Then, just before I step into my carriage to make my final farewell, I shall tell her of your courtship with Miss Elizabeth."

"You are cruel, Bingley."

"I am a helpless kitten when next to my sister." He stayed silent for a few minutes longer, then roused himself to sit upright. "I may forgive her... in five or ten years."

"You will forgive her the minute you find a woman to love and start your own family. You are not made to be resentful."

"You are correct. However, allow me to hold onto my bitterness for a while longer. I think I have earned the privilege."

Once Bingley's carriage reached Darcy's house, Darcy bid farewell to his friend and went inside the house. He had much to do before his departure for Hertfordshire and embarking on his courtship with Miss Elizabeth Bennet. He paused by his desk after setting down the documents for the lease of Netherfield Park and allowed his mind to roam freely in the direction of the impertinent woman who had captured his heart. He shook his head and smiled at his own folly. Nay, she had captured his soul.

***

For her part, Elizabeth was thinking, not only of Mr. Darcy but everything which had occurred over the past few months. She and Jane were traveling home with Papa. Michael and Gabriel had departed at first light, prior to Mr. Darcy's meeting with Papa. Lydia remained with the Gardiners and would return with them when they traveled to Longbourn for Jane's wedding. They all knew it was imperative for their friends and neighbors to see her before she was whisked away to Buckinghamshire.

Elizabeth's heart ached for Lydia. In her naivety, the youngest Bennet had made so many wrong choices and was now forced to take responsibility for her own actions, but at what cost? Could she really learn from her mistakes and make better decisions, or would she remain just as recklessly brazen as ever?

The carriage slowed, the movement of its wheels rumbling through the frame. The horses' hooves plodded down the main thoroughfare of Meryton. No one looked askance as their equipage passed by. No hands lifted to cover mouths so matrons could tittle behind fingers about Lydia's fall from grace. All in all, everything seemed normal. Everything was normal. The only thing that changed was their family. Irrevocably changed. Elizabeth lifted her worried gaze to meet Jane's tranquil one and saw a faint smile playing on her lips. Hope filtered into her heart when her sister's lips curved into a true smile that crinkled the corner of her eyes. Whatever the fallout from their sister's fall from grace, the Bennets would emerge from the other side stronger. Of that, she had no doubt.

When the carriage turned through the gates of Longbourn, no one was surprised to witness Mrs. Bennet hurry through the front doors before they had pulled to a complete stop. Her behavior was a mixture of giddy happiness and abject misery. One daughter had done very well with regard to her future while another one had courted disaster and paid a very heavy price. After a footman opened the carriage door and attached the small rail steps, Papa disembarked and instructed the footman to see to their trunks. He then helped Jane down the short steps before extending his hand, palm up, for Elizabeth's.

"Oh!" Mamma blushed when her husband greeted her with a kiss on the cheek. "I am glad you are returned safely. You have been sorely missed. Come inside. Hill has set up tea in the family parlor."

"I shall join you shortly, my dear. I must have a word with my steward before I indulge in the pleasant comforts of home," Papa said before striding off to his study. "If you see Michael, please ask him to attend me."

"Of course, Mr. Bennet."

Mamma's steps made little noise on the hardwood floor, but her breath came hard and fast the closer they came to the drawing room. It was obvious the mistress of Longbourn was in quite a dither, although at this juncture it was unclear what had her in such a frantic state. It was only when they were alone, and the door closed behind them, that Mamma launched into her news.

"You will hardly believe what I heard from my sister!" she exclaimed and dragged out a lace handkerchief to wave about.

"We await your pleasure in sharing the news," Jane murmured and settled into a comfortable chair.

"There is no pleasure in what I have to say. No pleasure at all."

Seeing as their mother had no intention of serving the tea, Elizabeth began preparing their beverages.

"Does this news involve Lydia in any form?" Jane asked and mouthed a 'thank you' when Elizabeth handed her a cup of tea.

"It does, indeed." Mamma stopped long enough to accept her own sweetened drink, then launched into her soliloquy. "Mrs. Philips had Colonel Forster's wife over for tea the other afternoon, along with Lady Lucas and Mrs. Goulding. Whilst there, the colonel's wife told everyone Mr. Wickham had deserted his post, the same night Lydia ran off."

"Has anyone connected Lydia to Mr. Wickham?"

"Not at all. Why would they? Lydia is not even out." Mrs. Bennet continued to twist her handkerchief between her fingers. "It is rumored he left behind debts of honor with his fellow officer and not only that, he stole a horse and carriage to make good his escape."

Elizabeth barely held back a smile upon remembering Mr. Darcy telling them how Wickham was deathly afraid of heights and always took a carriage instead of riding.

"And to think we had that man in our house for dinner and cards." Mamma released a shaky breath. "He could have stolen my good silverware. I can scarcely think of it without experiencing spasms in my side, pains in my head, and such beatings at heart, that I can get no rest by night nor by day."

"Mamma, calm yourself," Jane pleaded, setting aside her teacup to take hold of their mother's fluttering fingers. "Mr. Wickham did not steal your silverware, nor will he ever return to Longbourn, let alone Meryton."

"How can you be so certain?" Mamma asked, her tear-filled eyes fixed on her eldest daughter's face.

"I have it on good authority Mr. Wickham has transferred to the navy."

"The navy!"

Mamma's mouth dropped open in surprise.

"I believe Mr. Wickham was im-*pressed* with a surprising opportunity to earn great rewards and prize money."

Elizabeth choked on the bit of tea that had inadvertently gone down her airway when she gasped at Jane's deliberate twisting of the truth. Im-*pressed*, indeed.

"Are you well, Lizzy?" Mamma asked.

"Excuse me – *cough* – I will be," Elizabeth said and coughed a few more times before her throat settled down. "Mamma we are quite safe from the perfidy of Mr. Wickham."

"That is all well and fine, but what about Lydia?"

"She is recovering, that is all we know at this moment. Aunt Madeline has spent many hours with her, just listening, and talking. You know what a calming influence she is. They will all be coming to Longbourn for the wedding, and then you can see for yourself."

"I cannot believe my sons discovered where they were so quickly. London is large and dangerous."

"Our brothers were not the ones who discovered Lydia."

"Then who?" Mamma's brow furrowed.

"Mr. Darcy."

"Mr. Darcy! What does that gentleman have to do with all this?"

"It was Mr. Darcy who discovered them and brought Lydia to our uncle's house."

"That is all well and good, Lizzy, but it distresses me greatly to think proud Mr. Darcy has intimate knowledge of our family misfortunes."

"Mr. Darcy and I are courting, Mamma. He should be aware of what happens in our family."

Mamma caught her breath, then opened and closed her mouth as if to speak. She cast a glance at Jane, who smiled and nodded.

"Oh!" Mamma finally managed to say. "Oh my."

"Oh my, indeed," Elizabeth agreed with a smile.

"When did… that is to say, how did this all come about? We all know he did not find you handsome enough to tempt him last autumn."

"While it is true that was his first impression, he and I came to a better understanding in Kent."

"In Kent! I thought you were visiting Charlotte Collins. How did you come into Mr. Darcy's company?"

"It so happens, Mr. Collins' patroness, the great Lady Catherine de Bourgh is Mr. Darcy's aunt, and he visits her estate every Easter. As we had a previous acquaintance, whenever the parsonage was invited to dine, we naturally fell into conversation. I could not have asked for a better backdrop to appear elegant against."

Elizabeth gave her mother a very impertinent look, which elicited a smile from both her mother and Jane.

"Lady Catherine was that officious?"

"She is a woman who is not used to being gainsaid in her opinions and because of her great wealth and status, she has never been challenged."

"Until now." Mamma quipped, adding her own impertinence to the conversation.

"Until now," Elizabeth agreed. "I am not sure exactly what transpired between Mr. Darcy and his aunt, but it was quite evident they had a falling out. When Charlotte writes next, she may have more details. Everything was set aside when I received Papa's express requesting our return."

"Did Mr. Darcy ask for a courtship before you left Kent?"

"He did not. He asked for a courtship after he discovered Lydia."

"After! He was not frightened off by the scandal?"

"No, Mamma, he was not and I would be a fool to doubt the strength of his affection in light of that fact."

Chapter Twenty-Eight

London had never felt more desolate than the week following Elizabeth's removal to Hertfordshire. With every atom of his being, Darcy was impatient to see his beloved and start their courtship. He was well aware Elizabeth did not have the same strength of feeling for him as he did for her, but given her response to the unexpected kiss on her palm, the distance between like and love had shrunk. Truth in fact, he hadn't even realized he was in love until it had been too late to change course. Never had a man wished to be held so willingly captive. The thought of Elizabeth lifted his heart and filled it with joy.

His first order of business was to advise Mrs. Nicholls of his imminent tenancy of Netherfield. The housekeeper needed time to prepare the house for his arrival and rid it of Caroline Bingley's abhorrent decorating choices. Some people's taste in décor was truly nauseating. His second order of business was to invite Lord Holcomb and his daughter to stay at Netherfield before the wedding. There were no decent establishments in or near Meryton for them to stay any longer than one night, and he liked the gentleman. Hopefully, before the summer turned to autumn, he would call him brother. To that end, he invited the earl to meet with him at White's.

He was seated in his favorite corner of the room when Lord Holcomb entered. Henry canvassed the area and upon spotting him, smiled briefly. Darcy stood to greet him properly.

"Holcomb," he said with a nod of his head. "Thank you for accepting my invitation."

"I had no plans to attend the club until I received your cryptic note," Henry said as both men arranged themselves comfortably across from one another. "I have been trying to find a suitable situation for my daughter and me to stay near Meryton until the wedding. Jane told me her brother has an estate which abuts her father's, but it is leased to Mr. Bingley and I do not think he would appreciate me asking if I could spend a night or two in his home."

Darcy could not help himself, he chuckled at the earl's dry sense of humor. No, Bingley would not appreciate such a request. At least, not until his own bruised heart healed.

"This is where I have the happy task of giving you good news," Darcy said. "I bought out Bingley's lease and am removing myself to Netherfield Park later this week. You and your daughter are welcome to join me."

"I wondered how you would conduct your courtship from London," Henry said while accepting a drink from one of the footmen. "I accept your kind invitation and look forward to getting to know you better."

"The invitation stands for any of your family who wishes to attend the wedding. I was thinking of your wife's family. I am certain they would like to meet the lady who will become your daughter's mother."

Henry's eyebrows rose upon hearing Darcy's offer and he sat back in the chair, cradling his drink between his palms. He took some time before answering.

"I know Lord Sunderland and his wife worried about the speed of our courtship and having them meet Jane, with a chance to spend some time with her before the wedding, will ease their apprehension."

"Consider it a done thing." Darcy took a long drink from his glass, appreciating the warmth which spread throughout his body from the amber liquid. "I shall send Mrs. Nicholls an express, advising her to prepare a suite of apartments for your family." He paused in thought before continuing. "Is there anyone else? Cousins? Aunts and uncles, perchance?"

Henry chuckled. "Constance has a brother, Llewellyn, who may or may not attend. He did not take her death well as they were very close. I will invite him, but I may not know if he is attending until the morning of the very event."

"We shall keep a cupboard open for him then. Large enough to fit his hat, if nothing else."

At this, Henry laughed out loud.

"You understand completely, I see. Ah well, every family has someone whose actions they cannot predict." Henry set his glass down and leaned forward. "Jane and I have spoken candidly of her youngest sister's poor choices. We cannot express enough thanks for the manner in which you and your cousin dealt with that reprobate."

"Like you, Lord Holcomb, I look upon the Bennet family as my own. Even if Elizabeth ultimately chooses not to accept my proposal, I have come to care for them and to that end, they will always have my protection."

"I do not think she will say no," Henry teased. "After you received permission to court her, Jane wrote and said her sister spent an inordinate amount of time staring off into space, always with a smile gracing her face."

"Truly?" Darcy could not stop himself from asking.

"Truly," Henry replied, his expression one of smug satisfaction when the normally staid man stared off into space himself after receiving confirmation.

***

Like a child counting down the days to a birthday and the excitement of receiving presents, Darcy marked off each day on his mental calendar to his eventual removal to Hertfordshire and Elizabeth. Letters from Mrs. Nicholls informed him everything was ready, not only for Darcy but for his retinue of guests who would slowly filter in over the next week or so. He wondered what the denizens of Meryton would do when they realized that not only was an earl staying in their midst, but also a marquis and a duke. He knew the duke held the Bennet family in warm regard but nothing could have surprised him more when Lord Grenfell stopped by his house the previous day.

"Lord Grenfell, sir," Burke announced after knocking on his study door.

Surprised, Darcy bade his butler to show the gentleman in.

"Lord Grenfell," Darcy said and strode forward to shake the man's extended hand. He was very aware of the honor the marquis afforded him in this manner. "Would you care for a drink?"

"Thank you, but no. I have a meeting with my grandmother later this morning and must keep my wits about me. She is trying to find me a wife and if I am not at my best, she will have me before the archbishop before the end of next month." Grenfell sank into one of the comfortable leather chairs which bracketed the fireplace.

Darcy chuckled and sat across from his newest friend.

"Tell me then, what good deed have I done to bring you to my doorstep?"

"A mutual friend informed me you were taking over the lease of Netherfield Park."

"True," Darcy murmured, mildly amused at how well the duke's net of informants was. It made him rethink his own contacts and how much they were intertwined.

"I can hear the wheel cogs of your mind grinding from here," the marquis teased. "I have not set spies upon your house; I ran into Holcomb when I called upon the Gardiners to see how Miss Lydia was faring."

Darcy's eyebrows rose in surprise. He knew the marquis and his father had been instrumental in running down Wickham, but he thought their interest would have waned now that the elder Bennet sisters were no longer in danger.

"Pardon my errant thinking, I am but wondering at your extended concern for the young lady."

"Our family does not know Miss Lydia as well as Elizabeth and Jane, but that does not mean we do not wish for her health and happiness. The duke has written Mr. Bennet and offered one of our smaller estates and a suitable companion if what we fear might happen."

"That is very generous of your father, but he will find out soon enough that Holcomb and Miss Bennet already have things well in hand."

"Very good," Grenfell said with a heartfelt sigh. "I already offered for one Bennet daughter; I did not want to have to offer for another."

A very long silent pause stretched between the two gentlemen before Lord Grenfell started to laugh uproariously and slapped his knee.

"If you could see your face. When I wrote Elizabeth, at the bottom of one my sister's letters," he explained with haste when Darcy speared him with a jealous glare. "I would never write her myself; I told her I was going to lead you on a bit."

"I am pleased I could provide you some entertainment, my lord."

"When you marry Elizabeth, you will be part of our family."

"I have not proposed yet."

"But you will."

Darcy nodded in agreement, then brought the conversation back around to the original theme.

"You were asking about my leasing Netherfield Park?"

"I am here, hat in hand, asking if our family could infringe upon your celebrated skills as a host and stay at Netherfield Park in order to attend Jane's wedding."

Darcy noted he said Jane's wedding, not Holcomb's. Once again showing how much the duke's family valued the ladies of Longbourn.

"I would be deeply honored. Will your whole family attend?"

"Yes, even Frederick. Father granted him a week's reprieve from school in order for the occasion. I am not certain if Frederick is excited because he does not have to attend lessons, or because he cannot wait to see his secret love get married."

"Ah…" Darcy said with a soft laugh. "Miss Bennet has yet another admirer."

"There is much to be admired. She has grown into a lovely young lady. Even when we first met her at the age of eleven, we were all struck with her beauty and calm nature."

"I imagine your family has many stories of her and Elizabeth. I have been told they have spent every summer with your family at your country estate."

"They did. We will miss them, now that they are embarking on their own adventures with the men they have chosen."

"Things may naturally shift and change, but knowing the character of these two ladies, your family will never lose their friendship."

"True." Grenfell pushed himself out of the chair and stood, with Darcy following suit. "I must now be off to Grandmother's house. The Dowager is particular with regard to punctuality and I dare not be late. I shall send you a proper letter advising when to expect us in Hertfordshire."

"I look forward to it all, Lord Grenfell," Darcy said and pulled the lanyard to recall his butler. Burke quickly made an appearance and waited patiently by the half-opened door.

"If we are to be pseudo brothers, should you not call me Sebastian or just plain old Grenfell?"

"Until Elizabeth changes her name from Bennet to Darcy, I will not presume any further familiarity."

"The two of you are cut from the same cloth!" Grenfell made to exit the room, then tossed a roguish smile over his shoulder. "I would pay twenty pounds to see the two of you have a disagreement. Both of you have a keen intellect and perverse stubbornness. It would be highly entertaining."

On that note, Grenfell quit the room and Darcy heard his laughter echo down the hall.

***

Atop Arion, Darcy watched the diminutive woman weave her way up the only substantial rise in the ground, known to the locals as Mount Oakham. With a squeeze of his thighs and a quiet, 'hiya,' he urged the stallion to a gallop, anxious to spend time with his love. By the time he'd reached the base of the hill, she was at its crest, seated on a fallen log overlooking the valley and her father's manor. She had removed her bonnet and the morning sun glinted off her mahogany curls. By the tilt of her face, he knew she welcomed the warmth of that same sun on her face.

What would it be like to kiss her? Not that he had kissed many women, he hadn't. At least, not in the way a man and wife would kiss, but he had bussed the cheek of many a matron and had definitely kissed the back of many gloved hands. Only with Elizabeth had he kissed bare skin and upon feeling the soft flesh of her palm against his lips, he'd almost grabbed her by the shoulders and dragged her up for a good and proper kiss. Wouldn't that have shocked Gardiner's butler? It most assuredly would have shocked Elizabeth and knowing her fiery temperament, that solid right hook he feared very likely would have found purchase on his chin. He chuckled at the remembrance of her standing between him and her brothers that fateful night of the Meryton Assembly. His Elizabeth was not afraid to stand up to tall, brooding men.

His Elizabeth. He wanted to claim her more than he needed to draw breath.

By this time, he'd tethered Arion to a pretty hedge and was halfway up the hill. She must have heard him because her head cocked to one side and her body tilted in order to glance over her shoulder.

"Mr. Darcy," she said, not rising from her log, but he noted she shifted to make room for him beside her. On her lap lay a dainty handkerchief and a muffin she had torn into bite-sized pieces.

"Miss Elizabeth," he murmured in return and lowered himself next to her, stretching out his long legs in front of his body. "I had hoped you would come here this morning."

"This is my favorite spot to watch the sunrise, although I missed it today."

"Too many guests?"

"Too much Mamma. She is frantic with preparations for the wedding. Papa and my brothers have taken to hiding out in his study."

"And you?"

"I take long walks."

"Such as this morning."

"As you see."

"I, for one," he said. "Am very glad you embarked on one of your walks this morning. In fact, I had dearly hoped you would."

"Did you now," she asked, turning to face him, her smile lighting up her whole face. "Pray tell, what else did you hope for?"

He wanted to stay in this moment, just the two of them in this space for the rest of his life. He stopped twirling the grass and leaned toward her.

"I had hoped to steal…" His gaze fell to her lips and he noted with great satisfaction they had parted slightly. "The last piece of your muffin."

Before she could blink, he snatched the muffin off her lap and popped it into his mouth while hers dropped open in surprise before she burst out laughing. Not a dainty chuckle or a tittering giggle, much desired by the ladies of the ton, but an outright, body-shaking laugh, which he joined as soon as he'd swallowed his food.

"I am not certain if I should be offended or amused," she finally managed to say once their shared hilarity had subsided. "And here I thought you had climbed our vast mountain for my company. I have since discovered you were after Mrs. Pruitt's delicious muff—"

Darcy placed his index finger on her lips to shush her.

"I climbed your mountain, and would climb every single one on this earth if it meant I could be by your side."

When he slowly removed his finger, she tentatively licked her lips. He closed his eyes and drew in a deep breath through his nose. She was going to kill him. As surely as they sat on her bump in the ground, her innocent coquetry was going to absolutely devastate the small control he held over himself. When he re-opened his eyes, hers were staring directly into his.

"When you finally decide to speak flattering words, you do not waste time."

"I know what I want, Miss Elizabeth."

"Shall I tell you what I want?" She leaned toward him and

he was just as guilty as her, his mouth opening slightly with anticipation. Slowly her hand raised and cupped his cheek, drawing him closer. Her thumb caressed the sensitive edge of his top lip and a shudder of need rippled through his body. "I want…" He felt the soft exhale of her breath before she took the palm of her hand and wiped it fully across his mouth. Unexpectedly, she stood and began to run down the hill, her bonnet trailing behind her like a kite on silk ribbons. Over her shoulder, she gaily called back to him. "You had crumbs on your face, Mr. Darcy. You are a very messy eater."

Stupefied, he remained on the log, not moving before his brain finally engaged in rational thought. She had beaten him at his own game, the little minx. By the time he was in the saddle and tearing after her, delayed by the necessity of circumnavigating the base of the hill guarded by towering oaks, she had reached the gates of Longbourn and was daintily tying the bows of her bonnet to secure it on her head. He swung his leg over the saddle and slid down beside her. Elizabeth's eyes sparkled with mischief and something else he dared not name. Still holding Arion's reins, he gave her a polite half bow, very aware the matron of the house watched from a second-story window.

"Miss Elizabeth, good morning."

"Mr. Darcy," she replied and gave him a lovely curtsy, making it look as though they had only just met for the first time that day.

A lad from the stables joined them and Darcy handed off Arion. He extended his arm and Elizabeth willingly took it.

"You led me on a merry chase this morning," he said as they strolled toward the manor. He followed her inside and they paused just inside the entrance, whereupon the butler took his hat and gloves.

"I did."

Mrs. Bennet bustled down the stairs and into the hall,

clearly delighted to see him.

"Welcome, Mr. Darcy. I see you met up with Lizzy returning from her walk. Have you broken your fast yet this morning?"

"I had a small bite of something earlier, Mrs. Bennet, but nothing substantial," he replied, keeping his expression bland even when he distinctly heard Elizabeth gurgle a suppressed laugh.

"May I invite you to join our family for breakfast?"

"I was hoping you would extend an invitation. You are a gracious hostess."

"What a charming man you have become. Griggs, please let Mr. Bennet know Mr. Darcy is here." Mrs. Bennet gave the butler a small nod. "Well, Lizzy, let us not stand about in a stupid manner. Take Mr. Darcy through to the breakfast parlor."

"Yes, Mamma."

Elizabeth cocked her head slightly, a silent indication for them to make their way to the breakfast parlor. At first, he watched the gentle sway of her hips as she ascended the stairs, caught up in some very ungentlemanly thoughts. Her teasing looks over her shoulder in his direction broke the spell and motivated him to follow. An activity, God willing, he hoped to enjoy for the rest of their life.

LONGBOURN'S ANGELS

Chapter Twenty-Nine

The night before the final reading of the banns, a small group of gentlemen gathered in the billiard room at Netherfield Park for drinks and a few games. Assembled together were the Bennets, Lord Sunderland, Henry's previous father-in-law, the Duke of Belmont, Lord Grenfell, Darcy, and Richard, who had shown up unannounced two days prior, saying Anne loved weddings and Hertfordshire was the last place Aunt Catherine would think to look for them. Although nothing definitive had been said, they all tacitly knew it was a gentleman's night in honor of Henry's marriage. Bennet and the duke quickly commandeered the chess table while Lord Sunderland looked on, clearly enjoying the older gentlemen's company.

The clock had barely struck nine bells when Mr. Bennet took his leave, followed by his grace and Lord Sunderland, leaving the younger men and the groom to their own devices. Near midnight, the billiard table stood silent and everyone had claimed a comfortable chair. The fire was getting low, along with the very fine brandy Darcy had brought with him to Netherfield when Henry raised his near-empty glass in Darcy's direction.

"Have I told you how grateful I am you interfered with Bingley?"

Quite unprepared for the earl's segue, Darcy nearly choked on his drink.

"Pardon?"

"Bingley." Henry tilted his glass again and finished the drink in one gulp. "If you had not encouraged him to give up Jane, I would never have met that beautiful lady. The only reason she stopped at the park was to curb her anger before she returned to her uncle's house."

"I take it you met Miss Bennet in this park?"

"Aye. The one close to my home. She had just come from visiting Miss Bingley and her sister." Henry lifted the glass to his lips only to find it empty. "Where did my drink go?" he mused then chuckled. "She was in a righteous fury."

"I can scarcely believe Miss Bennet would ever be furious, with anyone or anything."

Both Michael and Gabriel, seated near the window, snorted at Darcy's comment.

"That is because you do not know her as I do," Henry sighed in contentment before he rested his head on the back of the chair and closed his eyes. Never had Darcy seen the earl so relaxed. "If my Jane could have spit nails that afternoon, she most assuredly would have aimed them in Miss Bingley's direction. However, she did not. Instead, I am told, she gave them a curtsy worthy of a courtier's praise and bid them a good day. She is a lady, from the top of her golden head to the tips of her little pink toes."

Darcy curbed the grin which threatened to emerge. It was plain to see the earl was deeply in love with his Miss Bennet.

"Who would have imagined Miss Bingley's rudeness would produce something good?" Grenfell murmured, more to himself than anyone else.

"Not I," Michael grumbled from his comfortable chair.

"Nor I," Gabe added before standing and twisting his body to stretch out his muscles. "We should leave while we are still able to ride our horses, Brother."

"I can always have Mrs. Nicholls prepare some rooms if you like," Darcy offered. "You can still make it back to Longbourn in the morning in time for church and the last reading of the banns."

"Tempting, but Mother would have our heads if we did not come home. Also, when Father arrived home earlier, he will have warned her in advance we may be in our cups and she will fret all night if she cannot see we are not injured or ill."

"Still worried about the future of Longbourn?" Darcy asked, not really expecting an answer.

"Always," Gabe said. "Although, with the advent of Jane's marriage, her fears have emolliated somewhat."

"If your other sister accepts my proposal, maybe we can fully put those fears to rest."

"Lizzy has always formed strong opinions." Michael rose from his chair and joined his brother. "But, once she has decided for you, nothing will move her from that decision."

"It is why I am allowing her to set the pace."

Even if it meant him climbing hills and chasing saucy maidens on his horse.

"Good strategy," Richard had roused himself enough to add to the conversation. "I have always told Darcy he was a good strategist. Damn shame he never offered those services to our military higher-ups. We might already have defeated the little Corsican if he had."

"Go back to sleep, Richard, or better yet, go up to your wife. Anne will thank me tomorrow for sending you to her."

Richard stood, and swaying slightly, approached the Bennet siblings.

"Egad, I forgot how tall you both are. No wonder Wickham wet himself upon your advance. You have my eternal gratitude for that happy memory." He gave them a sloppy bow, then straightened. "I shall bid you all adieu, gentlemen. As Darcy so politely pointed out, my wife awaits me upstairs."

With great aplomb, the former colonel pivoted crisply and marched through the door. Rather impressive, Darcy thought, then nearly laughed out loud when his cousin broke out singing an extremely bawdy song, which faded the further he was from the library and the closer he got to his suite of rooms.

"That is our cue to take our leave," Michael said. "Do not stand. We are all nearly family and I am not sure the earl is capable at this time."

All three of them looked over to Henry, who had fallen asleep in the chair, a contented smile gracing his face.

"Dreaming of Jane," Gabe said.

"Most assuredly," Michael agreed. "Good night, Darcy. We shall see you tomorrow at church."

Even though they had urged him to remain seated, Darcy rose and extended his hand to the eldest brother.

"On behalf of the earl, thank you for coming and giving him a gentleman's night out before he weds. He does not say anything, but at times like this, it is clearly evident he misses his father and brother."

"We cannot replace those he lost, but he is now part of our family and will gain two more brothers on Tuesday."

"God willing, he will become mine as well," Darcy said with great emotion.

"It is our hope as well." Darcy gave a start when Gabe slung an arm around his shoulder in a brotherly fashion. "Goodnight, Darcy. Michael and I will leave before all of us end up quoting poetry and sounding like Byron."

The brothers took their leave and Darcy returned to his chair. He leaned back, long legs stretched out before him and lost himself to thoughts about a future with Elizabeth.

"Your contentment is sickening."

A disgruntled voice from the other side of the room caused Darcy to crack open one eye and look in the direction of Lord Grenfell.

"I am content and will not apologize."

Grenfell straightened in his seat and, with a quick glance at Holcomb to ensure he remained asleep, leaned toward Darcy.

"I should have snapped up Elizabeth three years ago when she first came out."

"And yet, you did not, and I thank you for that, my Lord Grenfell. Your loss is my gain." Darcy wondered why the marquis had brought up the subject.

"She would not have accepted, even if I had."

"She has often said she looks upon you as a brother."

"Ugh... What man wishes to be thought of as a brother by a beautiful woman?" Darcy cleared his throat, not liking the thought of the marquis entertaining such thoughts of his Elizabeth. Grenfell noticed his disquiet and waved his hand in a dismissive motion. "Do not get your britches all twisted. I am not blind to the beauty of the Bennet sisters, it was a generalized statement to encompass any beautiful woman, your sister included."

Darcy cleared his throat again and arched a brow in the direction of the marquis, who shook his head and lifted his hands in surrender.

"I give up. I have one too many drinks and have become maudlin. I shall excuse myself and sleep off your fine brandy." Grenfell stood and crossed the room. "Goodnight, Darcy. I shall direct a footman to notify the earl's valet to attend to him. It would not be fair to saddle Holcomb with a stiff neck along with a sore head on the morrow."

The marquis quit the room and once Holcomb's valet arrived to escort the happy earl to his room, Darcy also made his way to his own chambers and was soon lost in a world inhabited by only himself and Elizabeth.

***

The next morning, six passengers crowded into the Bennet carriage to attend Sunday service at Longbourn's chapel. Mamma, normally garrulous to the point of exasperation, remained lost in thought, her fingers twisting and mangling her lace handkerchief. If Elizabeth had to guess, she would correctly surmise her mother was mentally reviewing every item on her exhaustive checklist for the marriage breakfast on Tuesday.

Jane remained serene as usual, and given the slight smile gracing her face, her thoughts were most likely centered on a handsome earl and their rapidly approaching wedding. Elizabeth directed her attention to her brothers. They had attempted to be quiet upon entering Longbourn last night after the clock had struck twelve bells, but given the amount of 'shushing' and missteps on the staircase leading to the family wing, she was fairly certain they had been in their cups and regretted that fact in the cold light of day. Her dear Papa caught her eye and winked. He also had been contemplating the family and she knew, later in the day, they would enjoy a quiet chuckle over their family's little quirks.

Strangely enough, during all this, Elizabeth missed Lydia. Yes, her sister was brash and thought only of herself, but she was a part of this family, and the rhythm of their daily lives was irrevocably altered by her absence. She released a deep sigh and focused her attention out the window. Tomorrow, Lydia would arrive with Aunt and Uncle Gardiner, and for once her worries were not how badly she might embarrass them, but of how she would keep her composure in the face of familiar faces as well as strangers at Jane's wedding.

Elizabeth knew Aunt Madeline would have spent the last few weeks counseling her youngest sibling and if anyone could reach the heart and mind of Lydia, it was their aunt.

Their carriage had arrived and Papa's chuckle was deep when he saw not one, but two gentlemen eagerly awaiting their arrival. Given his perverse nature, it surprised no one in the carriage that upon his exit, Papa took his time to extricate first his wife, then Jane – to the earl's waiting hand – followed by Elizabeth, who was tucked into Mr. Darcy's side the minute she had cleared the small stairs. The brothers departed the carriage from the other side and entered the church, choosing not to wait for their teasing father.

"Good morning, Miss Elizabeth," Darcy greeted her, his sonorous voice bathing her in a warm glow. "Will your father mind if we sat in the pew behind your family?"

"Neither he nor my mother will mind. They are quite distracted by Jane and her betrothed."

"Excellent. I had my cousin Richard and his wife hold spaces available for us. Shall we?" he asked and began to direct their steps toward the church.

"Lizzy, kindly remember to invite Mr. Darcy back to Longbourn after church," Mamma called out.

Elizabeth looked up at Mr. Darcy, noting the smile on his face.

"Mamma forgets you have ears to hear, sir."

"She is naturally excited over the whole wedding. I am not offended."

"She is also excited over my handsome beau."

"You think me handsome?"

Elizabeth pretended to gasp and brought her free hand up to touch her throat. "You dare seek compliments, sir? I am aghast at such forward behavior."

"Minx," he murmured, quite close to her ear.

She was thankful they had cleared the front entrance door

and were now in the vestibule and neither of her parents had seen him lean into her. Her only response was a quick squeeze of his arm as they had now entered the chapel and were on full display to her friends and neighbors. They quickly found their seat, and she whispered a good morning to Mr. Fitzwilliam and Mrs. Fitzwilliam. Elizabeth noted how well the former Miss de Bourgh looked. It seemed marriage suited her quite admirably.

Her parents, followed by Jane and Henry, slid into the pew in front of them, and soon after that, Mr. Ashcroft strode up into the pulpit and began the service. At its conclusion, he read the banns for Jane and Henry a third and final time, and everyone heard Mamma give a small cry of pleasure.

"Oh, Mr. Bennet. My heart is so full right now."

***

Dawn had just broken over the horizon when Elizabeth reached the top of Mount Oakham. In her pocket were two muffins, one for her and one for William – if he showed. Although they had met nearly every morning, weather permitting, she had no guarantee he could slip away. Especially as Netherfield Park was full of guests and his time was not his own, at least, not until after the wedding. Her mind was pleasantly engaged remembering the first time he had unexpectedly joined her when she clearly heard someone walking up the narrow path. Anticipating his arrival, she shifted on the log to make room and was not disappointed when he dropped down beside her.

"Good morning, Mr. Darcy," she began.

"I thought I asked you to call me William, or Darcy."

"Very well, good morning, William."

"Good morning, Elizabeth."

A rush of heat flooded her body when he picked up her

hand and twined their fingers together.

"I cannot wait to show you Pemberley. There is a rise, about a quarter mile from the house, very similar to this one, and if you like, I will have a bench built so you can greet the sunrise every morning."

"You need not go to so much trouble. A log or nice big rock will do."

"I will always strive to see to your comfort."

They both sat quietly, each to their own thoughts. Elizabeth pulled out the muffins and handed one to Darcy. Upon seeing the muffin, he grinned.

"Making sure I do not abscond with your breakfast?"

"Yes." She tore off a piece of the muffin and popped it into her mouth. Chewing slowly, she perused the spreading vista of the valley and, as always, her gaze fell to the roof of her childhood home. "Today is Jane's last day at Longbourn."

"Are you prepared for your sister to leave her family and cleave to another?"

"I am. Henry makes her so very happy, and she already loves Cassandra as a daughter." She inhaled deeply and released her breath with a great sigh. "I always knew this day would come, but now that it is upon us, I feel it has gone too fast. Less than four months ago, she and Henry had never met. This time last year, you and Mr. Bingley had not even looked over Netherfield Park to take up the lease, and now we are courting."

A single tear slid down her cheek.

"Elizabeth, what has upset you?"

"It is too fast! How can one know what their heart wants so quickly?"

She tried to turn her head away, but with one finger under her chin, Darcy turned her head back to face him.

"It may seem fast to you," he said softly, "because you have always lived in a society where you most likely expected to marry a local gentleman; you could dream of marrying him from the time you were a little girl. Whereas, for myself, marriages are brokered over one Season. By the ton standards, we are within normal parameters."

"You and I are so very different."

"I am a gentleman. You are a gentleman's daughter. In this we are equal."

"There are varying shades to the term 'gentleman,' and you know it, besides, I was speaking of our temperaments."

"Do you not see what has been happening these past few weeks and months? The more time we spend together, the more similar our minds seem to be. Yes, we have different temperaments, but I believe we fit together very well."

"How can you be so self-assured?"

"Because dearest, loveliest Elizabeth." He lifted their joined hands and kissed her knuckles. "Once we decided to mutually admire one another, our affection grew. Even a freshly planted kernel of wheat pushes through the fertile soil within weeks, and in a few short months is completely ready for harvest. Who are we to defy what nature thinks is natural?"

"Did you just compare our love to a stalk of wheat?"

"You love me?"

"I… that is, I have not…"

"You did! You said you love me."

He stood and pulled her to her feet, then wrapped his arms around her and executed a perfect spin. Almost as suddenly as he started, he stopped, both of them breathing rapidly. Achingly slow, he set her on her feet, his hands never leaving her body. Instead, they moved up her back to cup her face, whereupon he leaned down and kissed her. For Elizabeth, time stopped. The wonder of his mouth against hers momentarily suspended all thought, other than thinking that pressing the palm of her hand against her lips was a poor substitute for the real thing.

He broke the kiss and she dared to open her eyes, only to find him gazing into hers, his expression one of great tenderness.

"Why all this doubt when in your heart you know you love me?" he asked.

She tried to step out of his embrace, but he held firm.

"I never thought to marry."

He dropped his hands, surprise clearly etched on his face. "Never?"

"No, never. It has always been known Jane would marry, as will my brothers. All of us knew I was too opinionated, too rough and tumble to catch a man."

"But you did catch a man, and it was your opinions and reproofs which caught my attention."

"My reproofs?"

"That very first night we met, you reminded me we had not been properly introduced and threatened to let your brothers take me outside to teach me some manners. It was at that moment my heart was not my own."

She took a step back and assessed him carefully, then shook her head.

"You did not behave as a man who had lost his heart."

"When I agreed to help Bingley learn how to run an estate, never did I think I would find the woman who completed the other half of my soul." He captured her hand once more. "All my life I was taught what was right, but I was not taught to correct my temper. I was given good principles but left to follow them in pride and conceit. Then, a beautiful Hertfordshire maiden took me to task and showed me how contemptuous my pride had become. By you, I was properly humbled."

He pulled her back into his embrace. She lifted her face and looked upon his. Lowering his head, he kissed the sweet spot beneath her ear, along her jaw, and then the column of her neck. Her body grew weak with desire, pleasure spiraling out of control at the onslaught of his wandering lips.

"William," she whispered, loving how he lingered at the hollow of her throat, where her pulse fluttered like a hummingbird's wings. Did he have any idea how light-headed his kisses made her?

"Yes, my love?"

"I do love you."

Chapter Thirty

Later that day, it was a very subdued Lydia who arrived at Longbourn in the company of their aunt and uncle. Mrs. Bennet rushed toward the carriage and embraced her baby as soon as she had disembarked.

"My precious Lydia," she said soothingly, stroking her daughter's back. "If only you had confided in me that you had developed a strong affection for one of the officers—I would have explained how unrealistic such a notion was."

Mrs. Bennet led Lydia into the house while continuing to comfort her with gentle words. Elizabeth was struck by the thoughtful way her mother interacted with Lydia. Mamma might be flighty by nature, but she was a loving mother and this escapade with her youngest child obviously troubled her. Mindful of her own manners, Elizabeth properly greeted her aunt and uncle.

"You did not bring the children with you for the wedding?" she asked as they walked into the manor.

"It has become too difficult and expensive to travel with three children, especially when for such a short duration of time." At Elizabeth's quizzical look, Aunt Madeline continued. "It is not the same as traveling as a single woman. Children require their own retinue of servants. We will make it up to them later in the year. Your Mamma has agreed to watch them while the three of us tour the Lake District. That is if you are not otherwise 'engaged'…"

Aunt Madeline slid a sly glance at Elizabeth, who blushed.

"I have no plans, as of yet for this summer."

"What of Mr. Darcy's plans?" her aunt teased. "He did ask your father to court you. How is that coming along?"

"Mr. Darcy has taken over Mr. Bingley's lease of Netherfield Park and because of the close proximity, he has been a dedicated visitor to Longbourn."

"Has he now?"

Their conversation came to a natural close as the Gardiners wished to refresh themselves before they joined everyone in the parlor for tea and biscuits. Elizabeth was about to ascend the stairs, to see how Lydia was settling in when the front entrance bell was rung. A quick glance at the clock showed precisely two o'clock and her heart began its familiar tattoo against her ribs. There was no mistaking who would be on the other side of the door, for Mr. Darcy was known for his punctuality. She remained at the bottom of the staircase, waiting for her visitor to enter the house. As soon as Griggs opened the door, Mr. Darcy strode in and his gaze immediately settled on her, and the smile which graced his face almost made her faint with excitement.

Feeling suddenly shy, she dipped a polite curtsy as he approached.

"Mr. Darcy."

He returned the favor by taking her hand in his and bringing it to his lips, seemingly oblivious to the highly entertained butler watching their interaction.

"Miss Elizabeth," he murmured against her skin.

Shivers of anticipation rippled down her arm and through her body. She almost forgot to breathe and when he lifted an elegant brow, she realized she'd been staring at his mouth, remembering how those firm lips felt pressed against hers. She slid her fingers from his light grip and clasped her hands together. Suddenly, she realized he was looking at her, waiting for some form of response. Her cheeks heated and she knew they would be tinged a dull pink. She scrambled for something to say where she did not sound like a fool.

"My aunt and uncle have just arrived from London."

"Yes, I know. I noticed their carriage as I rode up."

Of course, he had, having arrived only minutes after them. Brush the cobwebs away, Lizzy Bennet.

"We are all meeting in the family parlor if you care to join us."

"It would be my pleasure." He handed off his hat and gloves to Griggs and a footman took his overcoat. "Shall we?" he asked and offered his arm to escort her to the parlor.

Elizabeth silently berated herself for her juvenile behavior. This silly blathering, all because her heart and mind were aflutter. In silence, they moved down the hall toward the parlor, the murmur of conversation from the room getting louder the closer they got.

"I am most distressed over this, Jane. How is it that the widow Jebson has not finished tatting the lace for your veil?"

"Her youngest son is not well, Mamma. Her child's health is a priority over an inch of lace."

"You are marrying an earl! That has priority!"

"Mamma!"

By this time, Elizabeth and Mr. Darcy had entered the room and all conversation stopped. Mamma, who appeared to have been pacing, whirled to face them, her face flushed in exasperation. Jane, implacable as ever, was seated by a small table near the window. It appeared she was attaching an intricate length of lace to the edge of her bridal veil. Elizabeth disengaged her arm from Mr. Darcy's and moved toward her sister.

"Is there anything I can do to help?"

"Thank you, but no. I am nearly finished."

"Finished! You are not finished. The lace does not extend the whole length of your veil." Mamma threw herself into the closest chair. "We are ruined!"

Both Jane and Elizabeth stared at their mother, aghast at her behavior in front of Mr. Darcy. Jane tied off her thread and began to fold up the delicate piece of tulle. As she busied herself with this task, Elizabeth made to approach her mother and settle her down. Her astonishment was great when Mr. Darcy seated himself on the small couch next to their mother and reached over for her hand.

"Mrs. Bennet, all is not lost."

"How can you say that? All my life I have dreamed of my daughter's marriage and now it will be ruined over a piece of lace."

Mr. Darcy chuckled and the soft laughter had Mrs. Bennet pluck her hand from his light grip and sit a little straighter.

"You think my distress humorous, Mr. Darcy?"

"No, Madam, but I will admit I am curious as to how you think this will ruin your daughter's wedding."

"Everything must be perfect," Mamma said her voice strained. "He is an earl."

Darcy leaned toward their mother and said, his voice earnest, "Do you truly believe Lord Holcomb will be looking at the bottom of his bride's veil when Miss Bennet walks down the aisle?"

"Oh." Mamma's eyes widened in tandem with her mouth. She cut a quick glance at her eldest daughter and a single tear made its way down her still-smooth cheek. "No, I daresay he will not."

"Then, you have nothing to worry about, for as long as your daughter pledges her troth to Lord Holcomb, the wedding will be spectacular."

Mamma turned her attention to Mr. Darcy and this time; she reached over and squeezed his large hand. Upon releasing it, she shifted in her chair and smoothed an imaginary wrinkle from her skirt.

"You are a good man, Mr. Darcy. You will do very well for my daughter. Very well indeed."

"I certainly intend to do my very best. That is if she accepts me."

Mamma's mouth dropped open and she stared at Mr. Darcy as though he had sprouted an extra head.

"Why would she not accept you?"

"She may not find my presence tolerable," he teased.

"That may be, Mr. Darcy," Elizabeth quipped and sat beside him on the couch. "However, you are handsome enough to tempt me."

"I assure you; the sentiment is reciprocated."

"I shall never understand you, Elizabeth Bennet," Mamma huffed out, still apparently dismayed over her daughter teasing a man who was as good as a Lord, with his ten thousand a year.

Any further discourse ceased as her aunt and uncle joined them in the parlor, followed quickly by Papa, Michael, and Gabe. Lydia kept to her room. Elizabeth did not know if it was because she was ashamed or exhausted after her ordeal. Either way, she had to admit she was rather glad her sister did not force everyone to pretend nothing had happened.

"Miss Bennet," William shifted to face Jane, who raised her head at him calling her name. "Lord Holcomb begged me to tell you that while he agreed the two of you would spend the day before your wedding with family, he dearly wished to be here, at Longbourn."

Jane's cheeks flushed a light pink and her smile was tender.

"You may tell Lord Holcomb I also wish he were here."

"Lord and Lady Sunderland also send their regard. They were most insistent I tell you they welcome you as an honorary daughter." Jane's eyes lit up at those words.

Elizabeth knew she had worried the parents of Henry's first wife might not accept her into the family fold. "I am certain they will reiterate these sentiments to you on the morrow. They are quite pleased and Lady Cassandra is beyond excited about her new mother."

"Thank you, Mr. Darcy. Her excitement is reciprocated."

"Will Lady Cassandra stay with her grandparents while you and Henry go on your wedding tour?" Aunt Madeline asked.

In response, Jane moved to sit beside her aunt and uncle and a quiet conversation began between them. Elizabeth took this opportunity to nudge William with her elbow. He looked down at her and smiled.

"Yes, Miss Elizabeth?"

"Mamma has said if we stay within the enclosed garden and within view of the drawing room, we may spend some time outdoors in relative privacy."

"No chaperone?" he asked as he stood and held out his hand, palm up. She placed her hand in his and also stood. Together, they moved to exit the room.

"She is most determined to have you propose and does not wish to scare you away."

By this time, they had made their way to the front entrance, and the two of them walked outside before turning right to enter the garden.

"I assume you have not made her aware that I have proposed at least five times during our short courtship."

"I dared not, for then she would chase you down and accept for me."

They paused while Darcy unlatched the gate and held it open for Elizabeth to proceed through.

"What will it take for me to finally chase you down?" he asked, his voice low and hoarse.

She turned, surprised to find him close. Mere inches

separated them, and her blood turned to liquid fire at the molten heat of his gaze. She bravely whispered, "There is no chase if I do not run."

She caught her breath, then outright gasped when he leaned impossibly closer and whispered just one word.

"*Run.*"

She darted off and had made it about five steps when a strong arm looped around her waist and she was lifted off the ground. Just as quick, she was turned in his arms and his lips were upon hers. His hot tongue slipped inside her mouth and at first, she was surprised by such an intimate act, but soon she relished in the activity and participated with vigor. On a ragged groan, he broke the kiss.

"Marry me, Elizabeth. I beg you to end my misery and agree to become my wife."

Passion had roughened his voice with need.

"Yes. I will marry you."

Suspended off the ground, his arms firmly wrapped around her, their faces level with one another, he smiled at her, a lazy, heart-melting smile. And then… he kissed her again.

***

Fanny Bennet had prayed daily for the safe return of Lydia. Her family thought her oblivious to what had actually happened to her baby, but she knew. Lydia had all the signs of a woman who had lain with a man, and it broke her heart. She had agreed with her husband in the manner of his and Jane's departure to London in such a public manner, hoping to fool their neighbors into thinking Lydia was with them in the carriage. A blatant falsehood when it was a truth, not universally known, she had already been gone four days by that time.

During those four long days, Mrs. Bennet became aware of a multitude of rumors. Her sister was so very good at ferreting out bits and pieces of odd gossip, and one of them was that the handsome Mr. Wickham had deserted his post the same night her daughter ran away. Of course, Fanny said nothing to her sister about Lydia. There was no reason to court disaster with a misplaced word in the wrong ear. Besides, that rumor was laid to rest with news of Mr. Wickham having transferred to the navy. Fanny snorted softly. As if anyone believed that snake in the grass had volunteered to join the navy.

Fanny also pondered on how her youngest daughter had come to meet the officer when she was not out to society. The only time she was allowed to leave the house unescorted was to visit Maria Lucas. Fanny finally concluded it was more than a coincidence Lydia and Mr. Wickham both disappeared the same night. The seemingly perfect timing of their departure suggested they had premeditated their getaway. There were no other plausible explanations, and sadly, given how lower-ranked officers could not afford to keep a wife, she believed the all too handsome Mr. Wickham did not have honorable intentions. Not for the first time, she regretted romanticizing the mild flirtation she'd had with an officer when she was around Lydia's age. No, it was not well done that her daughter had gotten caught up in the romance of an illicit flirtation.

And so, Fanny Bennet watched and prayed. Although her youngest daughter had not yet had her courses, it would be months before there was noticeable proof. It was vital Lydia be seen by their neighbors and friends in the pink of health. Any hint of rumor linking her to Mr. Wickham had to be squashed. It was why Fanny had demurely agreed to spread it about that her darling Lydia had been taken to London by her Papa, to have a dress made in time for Jane's wedding. Fanny also confided to Lady Lucas, knowing word would reach all and sundry within a week, that Jane's betrothed, the Earl of Holcomb, had graciously invited Lydia to come and stay with them at his estate until she attended Miss Tyler's Academy.

"What a good thing this will be for my youngest daughter," she'd told Mrs. Long, another of Meryton's notorious gossips. "If my Lydia does not marry a peer herself, I would be surprised."

Before Jane entered the church on her father's arm, Mrs. Bennet took this time to peruse the guests and nodded very politely to Mr. Bennet's older sister, Grace Harding. She had not seen her since the untimely passing of her beloved husband Josiah and her subsequent removal from Netherfield Park. Mrs. Bennet's smile in the direction of Mrs. Harding was warm and welcoming and she looked forward to having a nice cozy chat with her sister by marriage at the wedding breakfast.

She next saw four strangers seated behind her brother Edward. At first, given the cut and style of their clothing, she wondered why they were not seated on Henry's side of the chapel. There certainly was room for them. Then, as excited whispers began to circulate, she learned they were none other than the Duke of Belmont and his family. His daughter was the girl Lizzy had saved from drowning all those years ago. She knew both Jane and Lizzy spent their summers visiting them, and that the duke played chess with her husband by mail, but to have their presence in Meryton on the occasion of her daughter's wedding, was an honor.

On the groom's side of the chapel were the earl's former in-laws, Lord and Lady Sunderland, who sat with a very excited Lady Cassandra. Mrs. Bennet's heart swelled with love when she saw Lord Holcomb's daughter. She was such a polite and adorable child, yet filled with a nervous kind of energy.

In some ways, she resembled Elizabeth when she was younger; always questioning and curious. Mrs. Bennet couldn't count the number of times she wished for nightfall so she could find some peace from the endless questions like, 'why does a cricket's leg bend backward?' or 'how do clouds stay afloat?' Even when Mrs. Bennet checked on her children before bed, she often found Elizabeth in a tangle of sheets, still exploring in her sleep. The man who married her would need lots of patience to quell her curiosity. She blushed a little at the thought of how her husband had calmed her nerves when they first were married.

Fanny looked at Lord Holcomb – Henry – waiting patiently near the altar for his bride. At the time of Mr. Bingley's defection, she had despaired of her Jane ever finding happiness, but now that she'd met the earl, Fanny could not even begin to imagine her eldest daughter married to anyone else. Henry was faithful and true and valued Jane for more than her beauty, something Fanny had erroneously thought was the only valuable asset her daughter owned. Fortunately, the earl had seen beyond the physical and sought the woman beneath the skin.

Standing next to Henry was Mr. Darcy. Now, this was something Fanny had not expected. She knew the earl had lost almost all his immediate family to an influenza outbreak a few years ago, so there was no brother to stand with him. She reasoned, however, if Mr. Darcy's courtship with Elizabeth progressed further, the two men would become brothers through marriage, which created its own perfect symmetry.

Mrs. Bennet assessed the proud mien of Mr. Darcy. No one could deny the gentleman's attractive appearance, but his prideful bearing was, at times, difficult to overlook. Would he have the capacity and patience to handle Elizabeth's unparalleled enthusiasm for life? When she posed this question after being informed of their courtship, Mr. Bennet assured her if their daughter accepted a marriage proposal, she would have a very content life. Her husband explained Elizabeth's *joie de vivre* was exactly what the man from Derbyshire needed to soften his somber disposition. Fanny suddenly chuckled and hoped the fastidious man did not mind tangled bed cloths.

The church door opened and Elizabeth entered to begin the procession. Fanny happened to catch sight of Mr. Darcy's expression at seeing her second daughter walk down the aisle and sighed with satisfaction. He would not mind tangled sheets at all.

***

Happy was the day Mrs. Bennet saw her eldest daughter marry. Not only to a man she loved completely and wholeheartedly, but an earl! The various parlors and drawing room were filled with happy guests and Fanny had yet to greet them all. Finally, she entered a room where she noticed Elizabeth and Darcy speaking with the Duke of Belmont and his family. Elizabeth happened to glance up at that exact moment and hurried to her mother's side.

"Mamma, there is someone I would like you to meet."

She took Fanny's hand in hers and pulled her toward the convivial group.

"Mamma, may I present to you his Grace, the Duke of Belmont, his wife, the Duchess of Belmont, his son, the Marquis of Grenfell, his daughter, Lady Susannah Harrington, and their youngest son, Lord Frederick Harrington."

Fanny gave the best curtsy she could manage on wobbly knees.

"Your Grace, we are honored by your presence at our daughter's wedding."

"There are times, Mrs. Bennet when I feel like your girls are one of my own. We could not have stayed away on such a happy occasion."

"You are too kind." Fanny turned her attention to the duchess. "May I say, your Grace, your dress is beautiful. You almost outshone the bride."

The duchess smiled and said, "No one could outshine dear Jane. She was absolutely transcendent. Lord Holcomb is a lucky man."

Fanny was about to reply when Mr. Bennet joined them.

"Your Grace, I thought I might show you my next move rather than write. Would you care to join me for a few minutes in my study?"

"I wondered how long it would take for you to challenge me in person. You know you will face defeat in three moves?"

"I will not give up the field until I am forced to tip my king."

"Well then, let us get this over with." The duke cut a quick glance to his wife. "We shall not be long, my dear."

"Do not let me keep you from the game. You have been gloating over this win for the last two weeks."

She offered her cheek, which the duke kissed lightly and both men took their leave and made off to the study.

"Mrs. Bennet," the duchess said and looped her arm around Fanny's, leading the two of them to two empty chairs. "How do you put up with your husband's obsession with chess?"

They arranged themselves quite prettily on the chairs and continued to talk as though they had been friends for years.

***

"Mr. Bennet," Darcy began after coming alongside Elizabeth's father when he and the duke rejoined everyone in the crowded parlor. "Might I have a quick moment of your time?"

"Now?"

"I had planned on waiting until tomorrow, but my guests will be here for another two or three days and I think this is something we should discuss sooner rather than later."

"I can spare you, at minimum, fifteen minutes. I have already wasted enough time today, only to lose a game of chess to his grace. I do not want to miss a minute of my last day with my eldest daughter before she leaves with her shiny new husband."

"I will take what you offer, sir. Finer details can be discussed later."

Bennet turned and left the room, Darcy closely following. Once they were in his study, he settled behind his desk and Darcy sat in the comfortable leather chair across from him. Bennet shook his head and stifled a chuckle. Not too long ago, another young man had sat in that very chair and now his daughter was married to him. It seemed as though history was repeating itself, but this time with a different hopeful groom and with an entirely different bride.

***

Elizabeth, happy to see her mother behave with such decorum, felt light of heart and she, along with Darcy, who had mysteriously disappeared for close to twenty minutes, conversed at length with many of the guests, stopping only when it was time to bid Jane and Henry farewell. This also signaled to their guests it was time for them to take their leave and soon all that remained were the Bennets, Gardiners, and Darcy.

"Elizabeth, would you see me out?" Darcy asked. "I cannot in good conscience allow my guests to return to

Netherfield Park and not be there myself. As much as I am loathed to depart your company, I must."

"Of course, I understand."

She accompanied him to the front entrance and waited with him while Griggs retrieved his outerwear and a footman was dispatched to call up his horse. Darcy took this time to speak with her privately.

"Given the fact I shall still have a house full of guests, I cannot come to Longbourn until this Thursday."

"I am not going anywhere, William, except for my morning walk. You are always welcome to join me if you can manage time away."

"If I can, I will be there." He took her hand in his and lifted it to his lips. "In the church, I whispered the vows in my heart to you. For richer, for poorer, in sickness and in health, I will always cleave to you, my Elizabeth."

Her eyes shimmered with tears.

"I, too, whispered those vows in my heart. To love, to cherish, to sometimes obey..." she giggled at his soft snort. "I will always cleave to you, my Fitzwilliam."

"How I love you." He traced the pad of his thumb over her full bottom lip. "And how I wish I could kiss you, but I hear your man approach with my coat."

They stepped apart just as Griggs appeared and all too soon, she was standing on the front sweep, waving goodbye. About to turn back into the house, her attention was caught when Darcy wheeled his horse around and cantered back up to the house. He positioned Arion near the sweep, swung down to the ground, and with a crook of his finger, beckoned her to come. As soon as she reached his side, he swept her up into his arms and kissed her. When he finally set her down, her eyes were hazy, her lips moist and plump from kissing.

"William, my father might see us!"

"It is too late; he has consented for us to be married."

"What?"

"I bearded the lion in his den and we have his blessing. We will marry as soon as the banns are read. By this time next month, you shall be Mrs. Fitzwilliam Darcy."

"Oh, my darling!"

She laughed as he twirled her around, causing his horse to shy away from her flying feet. Suddenly, she stopped laughing.

"We cannot marry until March."

William set her down – hard.

"Elizabeth, that is nearly ten months away! Do you take pleasure in torturing me?" His voice was strained, and his hands were clenched into tight balls.

"There is a reason, which you may or may not like."

"Dare I ask why you wish to prolong my agony?"

She smiled, her eyes twinkling with a mixture of mischief and impertinence, and carefully unclenched one of his fists, loosely holding his fingers in hers.

"On the last day of this past February, Lord Grenfell said if I was not married within the year, he would eat his favorite beaver hat. I do so wish to win this bet and see him humbled, which means I must wait until the first day of March to become your wife."

Darcy lowered his head and beneath hooded eyes, watched her intently.

"Let me understand this correctly. You wish to remain separate from me – body and soul – in order to watch the Marquess of Grenfell eat a hat."

"Yes," she blushed and lowered her gaze. It sounded so silly when he said it like that. "I fear you think me foolish."

"I think of you as lively and vivacious, but in this? Yes, you are frivolous. You would put off the beginning of our life together for a glib wager you made with a brother of your friend. How would you feel if I said we could not marry until next Christmas, of next year, because Richard declared he would swim in Pemberley Lake on the first day of the new year if I were not married to you by then?"

"Did he really say that?"

Darcy inhaled deeply and closed his eyes for one brief moment.

"Elizabeth, whether he did or did not is moot. I would never put such folly ahead of you."

The words hung between them, suspended on a gossamer strand of desperate need. Mesmerized, Elizabeth watched his eyes darken with desire and a shiver ran through her body. This man, this glorious, handsome man loved her. She softly bit her lower lip, and his gaze dropped from her eyes to her mouth.

"Woman, you will be the death of me," he finally managed to breathe out.

"Fitzwilliam," she said with a sigh, wanting only to please him. "What is it you wish?"

"You know full well what I wish. Please do not tease me in this manner."

He took her hand in his big, warm one to entwine their fingers, bringing them up to his chest. His heartbeat was a reassuring steady thump. With his other hand, he cupped her cheek and kissed her tenderly.

"Lord Grenfell will be very happy his hat was spared," she murmured against his lips.

"Enough of Sebastian Harrington," Darcy practically growled out the name. "I desire you kiss me, Miss Bennet, so that I may kiss you back."

"With pleasure, Mr. Darcy."

…and she did, for the next forty-plus years.

THE END

Made in the USA
Coppell, TX
08 December 2023

25387464R00225

TRANSACTIONS OF THE
ROYAL HISTORICAL SOCIETY

FIFTH SERIES

VOLUME 23

LONDON

OFFICES OF THE ROYAL HISTORICAL SOCIETY

UNIVERSITY COLLEGE LONDON, GOWER ST., W.C.I

1973

ISBN 0 901050 19 9

Made and Printed in Great Britain by Butler & Tanner Ltd, Frome and London

CONTENTS

PAGE

The King's Affinity in the Polity of Yorkist England. By
D. A. L. MORGAN, M.A.   1

The French Origins of the 'Right'. By J. M. ROBERTS,
M.A., D.Phil., F.R.Hist.S.   27

Age at Marriage in England from the late seventeenth to
the nineteenth century. By R. B. OUTHWAITE,
B.A., Ph.D., F.R.Hist.S.   55

Southern Irish Unionism: A Study of Cork Unionists,
1884–1914 (*The Alexander Prize Essay*). By IAN
D'ALTON, B.A.   71

The Ecclesiastical Patronage of the Lord Keeper, 1558–
1642 (*proxime accessit for the Alexander Prize*). By
ROSEMARY O'DAY, B.A.   89

The Emergence of an Urban Ideology at Florence,
c. 1250–1450. By GEORGE HOLMES, M.A., Ph.D.
F.R.Hist.S.   111

Patrician Culture: Venice and Amsterdam in the
Seventeenth Century. By PETER BURKE, M.A.,
F.R.Hist.S.   135

The Role of Religion in the Cultural Structure of the later
Victorian City. By Revd. J. H. S. KENT, M.A.,
Ph.D., F.R.Hist.S.   153

The Pursuit of Happiness in the City: Changing Oppor-
tunities and Options in America (*The Prothero
Lecture*). By Professor ERIC E. LAMPARD, B.Sc.,
Ph.D.   175

The New History and the Sense of Social Purpose in
American Historical Writing. By J. R. POLE,
M.A., Ph.D., F.R.Hist.S.   221

Presidential Address: Aspects of the European Tradition
of Historical Writing: 4. The Sense of the Past. By
R. W. SOUTHERN, M.A., D.Litt., F.B.A.   243

Report of Council, Session 1971–2.   265

Alexander Prize   273

David Berry Prize   276

Officers and Council 1972   277

List of Fellows   280
List of Associates   313
List of Corresponding Fellows   318
List of Publications   320

TRANSACTIONS OF THE

ROYAL HISTORICAL SOCIETY

THE KING'S AFFINITY IN THE POLITY OF YORKIST ENGLAND

By D. A. L. Morgan, M.A.

READ 4 FEBRUARY 1972

THE rise and fall of the house of York is a story which sits uneasily towards both revolutionary and evolutionary interpretations of fifteenth-century England. Indeed, in general, attempts to tidy away the political process of Lancastrian and Yorkist times into the displacement of one type of régime by another always fail to convince. They do so because as a régime neither Lancaster nor York kept still long enough to be impaled on a categorical definition. The political life and death of both dynasties composes the pattern, changing yet constant, of a set of variations on the theme of an aristocratic society predominantly kingship-focused and centripetal rather than locality-focused and centrifugal. In so far as the political process conformed to the social order, the households of the great were the nodal connections in which relationships of mutual dependence cohered. Those retinues, fellowships, affinities (for the vocabulary of the time was rich in terms overlapping but with nuances of descriptive emphasis) have now been studied both in their general conformation and in several particular instances; I have here attempted for the central affinity of the king over one generation not a formal group portrait but a sketch focused on the middle distance of figures in a landscape.[1] The meagreness of household records in the strict sense is a problem we must learn to live with. But it would seem sensible to make a virtue of necessity and follow the life-line of what evidence there is to the conclusion that if an understanding of the household is only possible by attending to its wider context, so an understanding of that wider political scene requires some attention to the household.

For the household was in its nature a political institution. It is true that the sociological punditry of the time categorized separately

[1] My primary debt is to the conversation and writing of K. B. McFarlane. I am also overdrawn on the critical kindness of Dr R. R. Davies. Since I hope to treat the subject more at length elsewhere, I offer here only a selective annotation.

things public and things private, and allocated the household not to politics but to economics, the science of the management of the family and its property. The pseudo-Aristotelian *Economics*, in the opening words of Leonardo Bruni's version, is magesterially definitive: 'Res familiaris et res publica inter se differunt', differing, as the Old Latin version more widespread in northern Europe continues, 'non solum tantum quantum domus et civitas . . . verum etiam quod politica quidem ex multis principalibus est, oeconomica vero monarchia.' Such formulae were not meaningless: they offered one way for expressing dissatisfaction at the equivocal continuum of private and public. Yet what gave them a point of reference was a system of personal kingship which put one household at least in the centre of public life.[2] Of the king's servants those whose functions entailed the exercise of a formally impersonal public authority were a minority. All told, the staffs of those stationary metropolitan agencies of the crown—Common Pleas, King's Bench, Exchequer, Chancery, Privy Seal—cannot have numbered much more than two hundred. Those *domestici, famuli, familiares* who were the staff of the king's household, even at moments of the most stringent retrenchment, were more than twice as many.

Its numbers notwithstanding, the household was seen as a coherent unit, not merely as an abstract grouping of disparate agencies. But its description, then as now, did involve emphasizing its elaborate structural articulation. The most obtrusive line of sub-division was indicated by the phrase 'household and chamber', a discrimination which corresponded in terms of domestic economy to 'below stairs' provision (the household as *domus providencie*) and 'above stairs' consumption (the chamber as *domus magnificencie*). The household in this narrower sense of the domestic offices was staffed by about half

---

[2] Josef Soudek, 'Leonardo Bruni and his Public: a statistical and interpretative study of his annotated Latin version of the (pseudo-) Aristotelian *Economics*', *Studies in Medieval and Renaissance History*, ed. W. M. Bowsky, v (Nebraska, 1968); A. D. Menut, 'Maistre Nicole Oresme: Le Livre de Yconomique d'Aristote', *Transactions of the American Philosophical Society*, new series, vol. 47, pt 5 (1967). On an example of the genre which shows particularly well the relationship to the 'mirror of princes' type of writing on the one hand, and to the household ordinance and etiquette book on the other, see A. Pelzer and Th. Kaeppli, 'L'*Oeconomica* de Conrad de Megenberg retrouvé', *Revue d'histoire ecclésiastique*, 45 (1950), and Sabine Krüger, 'Zum Verständnis der Oeconomica Konrads von Megenberg: Griechische Ursprünge der spätmittelalterlichen Lehre vom Hause', *Deutsches Archiv für Erforschung des Mittelalters*, 20 (1964). Cf. A. R. Myers, *The Household of Edward IV; the Black Book and the Ordinance of 1478* (Manchester, 1959), pp. 76 *et seq.*, for the introduction to the Black Book. In its general aspects the whole topic is illuminatingly treated in various writings of Otto Brunner, *e.g.* 'Das "ganze Haus" und die alteuropäische Ökonomik', now available in his *Neue Wege der Verfassungs- und Sozialgeschichte* (Göttingen, 1968).

of the total personnel of some 550, and in administrative structure it formed a specialist, centralized agency controlled by 'the bourd of dome' in which the steward presided, acting with the marshal as the court of marshalsea, and with the treasurer, comptroller, cofferer and their three clerks as the counting-house.[3] In its latter capacity the board acted as the pivot of the whole mechanism, whose governing procedures were geared to the Exchequer's 'order of account'.[4] Socially, apart from these head officers of the board and some thirty clerks and serjeants and master cooks who ranked as esquires, this 'below stairs' world was only exceptionally a place for careerists and gentlemen. Both organizationally and socially it stood in marked contrast to the 'above stairs' *domus magnificencie*. Here such centralized ordering as there was related to ceremonial not accountancy. Several of its constituents—the heralds, the minstrels, the chapel—were largely autonomous groups each with its own corporate existence. Others—the signet office, the jewel-house, the wardrobes of beds and robes—in their different degrees possessed departmental separateness. But the central corps—the knights and esquires of the king's body, the gentlemen, yeomen, grooms and pages of the chamber, some of them also describable as carvers, cupbearers, sewers, ushers, physicians and surgeons—belonged more immediately to the staff headed by the chamberlain and directed in its courtly duties by the gentlemen ushers.[5] Less integral to the routine of the court was a

[3] I use here the terminology of the Black Book, in A. R. Myers, *op. cit.*

[4] P.R.O., Exchequer, King's Remembrancer Memoranda Rolls, E.159/239, Brevia Directa, Hilary m. 28, gives the privy seal writ of 3 December 1462 for the hearing of the treasurer of the household's account 'as reason conscience and the order of accompte requiren'. *Cf.* P.R.O., Chancery, French Rolls, C.76/148 m. 1 for the formality of Geoffrey Garnet's surrender of 'totum ius suum statum et titulum' as serjeant of the chandlery.

[5] Supplementary to both the general household and specifically chamber ordinances was a less formal instructional literature, whose key text would seem to be the 'Ryalle Book' of those things 'whiche bene necessary to be had in the remembrance of the Kings Chambrelayne and to his Usehers off the Chambre and appertenyn unto the offices', printed in F. Grose and T. Astle, *The Antiquarian Repertory*, 1 (1807–9 edn), pp. 296–341. This includes the note: 'The Book whiche all thes things bene enactid in was wont allwey to be in ye houshold. Of the last man yt I undirstand that had it was Hampton squyere for the body in all thes offices and maters' (this referring to John Hampton temp. Henry VI). There are several variant sixteenth- and seventeenth-century copies, *e.g.* Magdalene College Cambridge MS. Pepys 2516, Bodleian MS. Ashmole 804, MS. Ashmole 1116 fos 83–93, MS. Rawlinson B.47. Some of the contemporary etiquette-books are in effect manuals of 'above stairs' service, *e.g. A Fifteenth-century Courtesy Book*, ed. R. W. Chambers (Early English Text Society, o.s. 148, 1914), corresponding to 'the booke of vrbanitie' used by the master of the king's henchmen (A.R. Myers, *op. cit.*, p. 127).

further group of king's knights and esquires of the household associated formally with the hall rather than the chamber.[6] In the aggregate these men of chapel, hall and chamber comprised the remaining half of total household personnel, and socially presented a mirror-image of the domestic offices group in being very largely gentle in status.

The functional relation of these two structural divisions was clearly one in which the 'below stairs' group was secondary: it existed to perform the technical and specialist supporting rôle of providing the rest with food and lodging and transport. In consequence the relation of the household to politics also requires discriminations. The politics of the household as *domus providencie* was tantamount to the single issue of purveyance, recurrently a cause of court–country antagonism over the long period which includes at least the two centuries before and the two centuries after the fifteenth, occasionally obtruding in parliamentary and other complaints, but usually remaining an under-current which might swell a wider surge of protest.[7] That apart, what made the household a political institution was the group of some 250–300 knights, esquires, gentlemen and clerks whose function was not technical and official but personal and variable. In number they amounted to as large a proportion of the political community as the parliamentary Commons or the justices of the peace, among both of whom they could expect to sit. In standing they ranged from the lords who served as steward and chamberlain, to the neophyte gentle-men (some more urban than rural in origin) who ranked as grooms of the chamber, to the clerks who spanned the gamut from bishop-confessor to briefly unbeneficed chaplain. They wore the king's liveries of cloth or collar; they pocketed his fees and wages and rewards and gifts; they divided their time between his court and their own countries in a seasonal interchange which was not their least important feature. As individuals they would accumulate a further increment of involvement in central and local patronage and service. As a group they would show the manner in which kingship acted as a centripetal focus. And as kings varied so would their style.

*　　*　　*

In its generalities such a description might suit more than one point of time. But the numbers mentioned so far (some 550 household

---

[6] The term 'esquire of the household' was applied to categories of servant even more loosely attached to the court, *e.g.* serjeants-at-arms and members of the 'offices outward' of the Great Wardrobe and Works. 'Aula' and 'Camera' seem to have been amalgamated into a single office for purposes of household accounting in the 1360s.

[7] Although after 1445 the spate of anti-purveyance statutes stops, the issue was still live: *e.g.* the London proclamations of March–April 1469 and November 1481 in *Calendar of Letter-Books of the City of London: Letter-*

servants of all kinds, of whom some 250–300 formed an entourage rather than a commissariat) describe more particularly the situation of the early 1460s.[8] They are, even as numbers, politically descriptive. Edward IV's reign began after a decade in which the size of the household was a contentious issue. By 1454, when an attempt was made to scale down the household which by 1450–51 had soared to over 800,[9] the demand for a numerical reduction had become linked with the demand for a readjustment of the household's place in the overall political structure. In 1454–56 such household reform proved illusory when unaccompanied by a resolution of political faction, and the resulting collapse of central authority precipitated the household's refashioning as a Lancastrian affinity in open conflict with a coalition of dissident magnate affinities. The victory in 1460–61 of that dissident syndicate produced both a new king and a household whose rôle changed yet again. Its recruitment, in terms both of overall size and of individual selection, was part of the wider issue of how the king's 'good lordship' should be exercised and what should replace the politics of exclusion. Edward IV's first parliament, through its Speaker, advised him that in his appointments to office he should think first of those who had fought for his title, but also of 'other persones in such wise and prudent trust and affection as accorde with th'assured prosperite of your high estate'.[10] Such a course had obvious attractions, given the fluidity of alignments throughout the troubles of the 1450s: anything like mutually exclusive followings of York and Lancaster were of only the most recent standing, and if the further unsettlement of the climacteric phase of those troubles had intensified factional bitterness it had also made a policy of inclusive flexibility easier to envisage. For the victorious syndicate of the spring of 1461 was no longer the same in political balance as that of six months earlier. Most obviously it had acquired a new leader whose personal success at Mortimer's Cross had provided a hope of recovery from the reverses suffered by his seniors at Wakefield and St Albans. This in no way changed the fact that Edward's election and inauguration as king on 3–4 March 1461 was an assertion that the parliamentary declaration of Yorkist right of the previous October should not lapse

---

Book K. ed. R. R. Sharpe (London, 1911), pp. 84, 188; the manifesto of 1469 (below, note 23); the preamble to the 1483 Household assignment in Rotuli Parliamentorum, vi (London, 1783), p. 198.

[8] The figure is calculated from the treasurer of the household's account book for 1463–64, P.R.O., Exchequer, Accounts Various, E.101/411/13, making allowance for categories of servant not there included.

[9] This figure is calculated in the same way as the preceding from E.101/410/6. For the intervening years the household records do not permit such computation.

[10] Rot. Parl., v. 462–63.

with the death of the man who had then forced it through: the change of dynasty was the work of the nobility, however reluctant, however divided, and however over-persuaded in a struggle to survive. Nor did it mean that the army with which Edward bore out that assertion in his crowning victory at Towton was more narrowly based than the army whose victory at Northampton had given Duke Richard his chance. But it did mean that the new eighteen-year-old king despite his age had contributed powerfully to his own creation, and because of his age stood heir to the political process of the 1450s without inheriting that factional identity which had brought his father to his death.

In the creation of his own political identity Edward naturally began at home. Although it accommodated many old Yorkists, his household was at no stage the same as his father's affinity. In part this was the straightforward consequence of a change of generations. Duke Richard died old if violently, and even apart from those who died with him many of his prominent servants died in the natural course of things at much the same time. Of those surviving most were found a suitable niche in the outer circle of the new affinity as king's knights (William Herbert, Walter Skull), several combining this with service to the duke's widow (John Clay as her chamberlain, Walter Devereux as steward of her lands in Herefordshire). Nor did Edward's household start life as the direct continuation of the household set up for Henry VI in 1460. Whereas in the case of the 'out of court' offices of Chancellor, Treasurer and Keeper of the Privy Seal Edward simply renewed the appointments made after the battle of Northampton, in the household he made changes. William lord Fauconberg, who replaced John lord Beauchamp as steward, and John Fogge, who replaced John Clay as treasurer, with John Scott as comptroller, were very much men of the 1460 coalition—Fauconberg as a Neville, Fogge and Scott as the leaders of the Kentish gentry. But the chamber appointments had a different look. As chamberlain John Neville lord Montague[11] gave place to William Hastings whose father, a long-serving but unremarkable retainer of Duke Richard, had successfully commended him to the duke at his death in 1455; in blood and land William had no standing of his own but owed his advancement to being attached to Edward when earl of March. William Port, the musician Fellow of New College who had gone on to matrimony and a Hampshire estate through service to Cardinal Beaufort and Henry VI,[12] now replaced Humphrey Bourchier lord Cromwell as treasurer

---

[11] Jean de Waurin, *Recueil des Croniques* . . ., ed. W. and E. L. C. P. Hardy, v. (Rolls Series, 1891), p. 318; *State Papers and Manuscripts existing in the Archives Collection of Milan*, ed. A. B. Hinds (London, 1913), nos 64, 65.

[12] A. B. Emden, *A Biographical Dictionary of the University of Oxford to A.D. 1500*, iii (Oxford, 1959), pp. 1501–2; F. Ll. Harrison, *Music in Medieval*

of the chamber.[13] His antecedents are not out of keeping with those of the four knights of the body, one of whom (William Peche) came from the same Kentish set as Fogge and Scott, the rest (William Stanley, John Howard, Thomas Montgomery) from the pre-1460 household of Henry VI with little hiatus thanks to the individual safety-nets formed by their other connexions. In this eclectic manner Edward persisted. The most unpredictable extension of the affinity waited until his marriage in 1464, but the Woodvilles were already at court in the first months of the reign, while by 1462 Queen Margaret's ex-chancellor Laurence Bothe bishop of Durham had become the king's confessor and John Bothe the king's secretary.[14] Accumulating additions increased both the diversity and the size of the group. By 1466 there were ten instead of four knights of the body, three of the extra six (Thomas Burgh, Thomas Bourchier, John Fiennes) coming as promotions from within the 1461 chamber, three (William Norris, Gilbert Debenham, Robert Chamberlain) coming from earlier service to Mowbray and Lancaster. Initially the household had conformed to the numerical desiderata of 1454. By 1466–67, leaving aside the new household of the queen, the 1463–64 total of 550 had risen to over 630, the increase occurring mainly 'above stairs'.[15]

All this indicates a search for personal loyalty as an escape from the insecurity of faction. Hence too the complementary device of pardon for the recalcitrants of 1460–61. Sometimes, at least, their earlier attitude was held publicly to their credit. Sir Thomas Tresham, attainted in 1461 as against the king at Towton and singled out as one of the eight for whose death a reward of £100 would be paid, was pardoned his life in 1464 and in 1467 allowed to recover his lands specifically because 'at the felde besides Tawton [he] stode menyall servaunt unto Kyng Henry, and Counteroller of his House, and by hym preferred to divers other notable Offices, and in his service brought up of a childe, and so as his menyall servaunt of Houshold was there by his commaundement'.[16] Sir Richard Tunstall, chamberlain to Henry in 1459–60 after years in his household, loyal even after Henry's capture in 1465, attainted as against Edward at Wakefield and Towton and holding Harlech against him until August 1468, was pardoned in October 1468 and after resuming his place as Henry's

---

Britain (London, 2nd edn, 1963), p. 159. The evidence for his identification with the treasurer of the chamber, though not conclusive, is stronger than Emden indicates.

[13] E.159/243, Brevia Directa, Mich. m. 1ᵈ.

[14] P.R.O., Exchequer, Enrolled Accounts (Wardrobe and Household), E.361/6, m. 54ᵈ.

[15] E.101/412/2.

[16] *Rot. Parl.*, v. 616–17. In his case continuing attachment to Lancaster proved fatal in 1471.

chamberlain in 1470–71 was again immediately pardoned and promptly recruited to Edward's affinity as a king's knight.[17] To recruit such loyalists must have seemed the most desirable political investment. It certainly seemed so to the Croyland Chronicler who deplored Henry VII's insistence in 1485 on attainting those loyal to Richard III: 'Oh God! what assurance from this time forth are our kings to have that in the day of battle they will not be deprived of the assistance of even their own subjects when summoned at the dread mandate of their sovereign.'[18] Perhaps he had the satisfaction of seeing Henry VII come round to his point of view by enacting in 1497 'that noe person going with the Kinge to the warres shalbe attaynt of treason'.[19]

Nonetheless the political chemistry of the 1460s produced a mixture rather than a compound. If it was an experiment in anything it was surely not government. That the gambit of diversified recruitment was deliberate, or at least deliberately whimsical, seems likely. That it was the carefully thought out means towards the end of kicking over the traces of 1461 seems much less likely. That it was an effective extension of the king's centripetal control is not likely at all. The tragi-comedy of Henry Beaufort's brief rôle as a Yorkist courtier might be written off as a spectacle worth staging in the interests of reconcili-ation. The confiscation of Bishop Bothe's palatinate so soon after his welcome as the king's confessor was a farce which just might be seen as exemplary. But haphazard adaptation did not induce a sense of stability. In patronage matters the king had to compete with others. In 1463 Lord Clinton, when trying to get his brother-in-law made Prior of Folkestone in preference to a chaplain of the king's mother, thought it useful to claim that although the king and the duchess were against him, lords Ferrers and Herbert and other lords of the king's council were for him.[20] In 1465, when recruiting William Norris as a knight of the body, the king proposed to give him a wardship and the stewardship of Cookham and Bray which his father had held before 1461 as an esquire of Henry VI's body. The stewardship he got, because the king managed to cajole a surrender of his previous grant to Piers Beaupie, chief clerk comptroller of the household and like others of his Welsh marches family in Yorkist service before 1461;

17 *Calendar of Patent Rolls 1467–1477* (London, 1900), pp. 97, 271. He went on to be knight of the body to both Richard III and Henry VII.

18 W. Fulman, *Rerum Anglicarum Scriptorum Veterum Tom. I* (Oxford, 1684), p. 581. I borrow the translation but not the interpretation of H. T. Riley, *Ingulph's Chronicle of the Abbey of Croyland* (London, 1854), pp. 511–512.

19 *Statutes of the Realm*, ii (London, 1811), p. 568.

20 Historical Manuscripts Commission, *Fifth Report* (London, 1876), pp. 590–92.

but the wardship he did not get, because the king found the Treasurer had already given it to an Exchequer colleague.[21]

Such incidents were the small change of politics, but then those whose prime distinction was to be 'great about the king's person',[22] cut little figure in affairs at large. The household, which despite some numerical increase was still only of moderate size, was neither sufficiently inclusive nor sufficiently cohesive to act as a controlling force. And in 1469 its political nullity became apparent. In the manifesto of 12 July 1469 which heralded the struggle for mastery the Nevilles singled out the Woodvilles, William Herbert, Humphrey Stafford of Southwick, John Audley and John Fogge as the cabal estranging the king from 'the true lords of his blood'.[23] As part of the indictment they threw in the matter of non-payment for household provisions, with much point since the household under Fogge's treasurership had fallen into long arrears of account and had run up mounting expenses and debts.[24] But in essentials the attack was aimed neither at the household 'below stairs' nor at the chamber staff of the king's close dependents but at that wider diffusion of the outer circle of the affinity. In 1468 Fogge had relinquished his household office; though still a king's knight and councillor he now figured more as what he had been already in 1461, a ruling power in Kent.[25] Herbert and Stafford were king's knights whose activity was concentrated on turning their power in Wales and the south west respectively, already formidable in 1461, into local monopolies. The Woodvilles, though obviously much at court, preferred the Exchequer to the king's household as their hold on patronage.[26] To see these as primarily the king's men would not be

[21] P.R.O., Privy Seal Office, Warrants for the Privy Seal, P.S.O.1/27/1403, 1434; P.R.O., Exchequer, Warrants for Issue, E.404/73/1/101.

[22] *Paston Letters and Papers of the Fifteenth Century*, ed. N. Davis, i (Oxford, 1971), no. 320, letter of 11 December 1462 from John Paston III to John Paston II: 'I am well aqueyntyd wyth my Lord Hastyngys and my Lord Dakarys whyche be now gretest a-bowt the Kyngys person.'

[23] John Warkworth, *A Chronicle of the First Thirteen Years of the Reign of King Edward the Fourth*, ed. J. O. Halliwell (Camden Society, 1839), pp. 46–51.

[24] Fogge did not account at all during his period of office, his accounts for 1461–63 being heard in 1469–70 and those for 1463–68 in 1472. E.101/412/4, a roll of 34 membranes, is the accumulated list of 'creditores diversorum officiorum hospicii' outstanding from his time as treasurer, compiled seemingly in 1472.

[25] *Les Reports des Cases en Ley en le Cinque An Du Roy Edward le Quart* (London, 1680), pp. 127–29, shows Fogge and Scott acting as spokesmen of the shire community in 1465 when, backed by twenty esquires, they challenged the earl of Warwick's jurisdiction as constable of Dover. *Cf. Calendar of Patent Rolls 1467–1477*, pp. 42–43.

[26] The reasons for John lord Audley being singled out for mention are not altogether clear. Indeed, this is not the only moment of puzzlement in a long

useful: for them the king's favour was permissive rather than formative. Accordingly the affray at Edgecote was a settling of differences
not altogether unlike the fight at St Albans in 1455. As in that earlier
episode the king was affected, but only at a political remove. The
chronicle of Jean de Waurin describes an Edward on the eve of the
collision, caught unawares by the convergence of local warbands,
accepting the advice of his retainers that if he sent away the Woodvilles he would have no need himself to take the field.[27] In the event
the Nevilles' failure to control in their own country the local turmoil
they had stirred up thwarted their hope of a general ascendancy, and
instead left the chance (which was also the necessity) of turning survival into mastery to a king whose competitive instinct was no doubt
aroused by the humiliation of helplessness and constraint.

It was Edward's return to London in October 1469 which brought
a new momentum to Yorkist politics. John Paston caught the note of
change. 'The Kyng hym-selffe hathe good langage of the lordys of
Claraunce, of Warwyk, and of my lordys of York, of Oxenfford, seyng
they be hys best frendys. But hys howsolde men pave other langage,
so what schall hastily falle I cannot seye.'[28] What consolidation the
Yorkist régime achieved it achieved in 1469–71 by a simplifying and
concentrating drive which replaced the earlier, looser affinity by a
more compact group whose activity stemmed from the king's personal
initiative. In the autumn of 1469 household men moved to the fore in
appointments and commissions. In the spring of 1470 the king's commitment to them was made manifest when he accepted as his own
quarrel the troubles of his knight of the body Thomas Burgh,[29]
taking the field against the Lincolnshire insurgents, forcing their
magnate promoters into exile. The exiles' return six months later
found him unprepared: not all his retainers were with him when the
urgent warning of the serjeant of his minstrels and the sub-almoner
convinced him of the need for immediate flight.[30] Of those stranded,
Thomas Saintleger tried to rally support in Salisbury,[31] while Thomas

---

and complicated political career which seems to begin with his indenture of
retainer with James earl of Wiltshire at 20 marks a year for life on 18 March
1457 (E.159/257, Recorda, Easter m. 2b) and to culminate with some odd behaviour in 1483–84 (*Calandar of Close Rolls 1476–1485* (London, 1954), no. 1218,
Calandar of Patent Rolls 1476–1485 (London, 1901), pp. 415, 488, 558–77).

[27] Jean de Waurin, *op. cit.*, v, p. 581.

[28] *Paston Letters* . . . (*ut sup.*), no. 245.

[29] John Warkworth, *op. cit.*, p. 8; *Chronicle of the Rebellion in Lincolnshire,
1470*, ed. J. G. Nichols (Camden Society Miscellany, I, 1847), p. 22.

[30] T. Hearne, *Thomae Sprotti Chronica* . . . *et Alia Quaedam Opuscula*
(Oxford, 1719), p. 306.

[31] Historical Manuscripts Commission, *Various Collections*, iv (London,
1907), pp. 207–8.

Howard took sanctuary in Colchester.[32] But even those imprisoned survived,[33] and Edward's return drew the group together. The *Historie of the Arrivall* (borne out by the complementary memorial of Exchequer warrants) makes the march south, from a Yorkshire heavy with popular hostility only slightly offset by magnate inaction, sound like the roll-call of a household assembling as a war-band, knights of the body, esquires and chaplains each bringing his contingent and swelling the initial three ship-loads of 1,000 refugees to fighting proportions. 'At Leycestar came to the Kynge ryght-a-fayre felawshipe of folks to the nomber of 3000 men well habyled for the wers, suche as were veryly to be trustyd as thos that wowlde uttarly imparte with hym at beste and worste in his qwarell withe alle theyr force and myght to do hym theyr trew service. And in substaunce they were suche as were towards the Lorde Hastings the Kyngs Chambarlayne, and for that entent above sayd came to hym stiryd by his messages sent unto them and by his servaunts frinds and lovars suche as were in the contrie.'[34] It was as master of such an affinity that at Barnet and Tewkesbury King Edward won a wider mastery.

*   *   *

To say that the concentrated affinity which emerged from the events of 1469–71 retained its style in the later phase of Yorkist rule would be an assessment easier to qualify than to quantify. In the longer term the court expanded: by the early seventeenth century household personnel totaled some 1,500, the increase occurring mainly 'above stairs' and being accompanied by an elaboration of structure. Whereas the organization of the *domus providencie* scarcely changed between its settling into definition in the fourteenth century and 1782, the *domus magnificencie* was reshaped both organizationally and architecturally in a process still under way in the seventeenth century but notably lively in the earlier sixteenth century.[35] Culminating on

---

[32] J. Weever, *Ancient Funeral Monuments* (London, 1631), pp. 834–40.

[33] *Paston Letters* . . . (*ut sup.*), no. 345, letter of 12 October 1470 from John Paston III to his mother: 'John Pylkyngton [esquire of the body], Mastyr W. Attclyff [king's physician and secretary], and Fowler [probably Thomas], usher of the chamber] ar takyn and in the castyll of Pomfrett, and ar lyek to dye hastyly, wyth-owte they be ded. Syr T. Mongomeré [knight of the body] and Jon Done [esquire of the body] be takyn; what shall falle of hem I can not sey.'

[34] *Historie of the Arrivall of Edward IV in England*, ed. J. Bruce (Camden Society, 1838), pp. 9–10. The 100 men with whom Henry Pierrepoint served at Barnet and Tewkesbury were no doubt the sort of contingent making up the Leicester influx (E.404/75/1/60).

[35] G. E. Aylmer, *The King's Servants the Civil Service of Charles I, 1625–1642* (London, 1961), pp. 26–27, etc.; J. M. Beattie, *The English Court in the Reign of George I* (Cambridge, 1967); H. M. Baillie, 'Etiquette and the Planning of the State Apartments in Baroque Palaces', *Archaeologia*, ci (1967).

the eve of the seventeenth-century civil war, how near in date to the fifteenth-century civil war did this process begin? The answer has to remain doubtful because of the disobliging behaviour of the evidence. Although as between the 1460s and the 1470s household records have survived in roughly equal bulk, in the later phase they change in one respect which rules out even such an approximate calculation of total household personnel as is possible for the earlier phase. The section of the treasurer of the household's book of particulars of account entitled *Feoda et Robe* (listing the members of most categories of household servants) is now omitted, the last such extant list relating to 1466–67; not until after 1509 is the loss offset by 'establishment lists'. The omission is deliberate but unexplained. The date at which the change becomes apparent is 1474–75,[36] and this raises the possibility that it should be understood as part of a series of household reforms aimed at 'certayne enormytees and myssguydinges'[37] in expenditure and accounting, beginning with the enactment in the parliamentary session of October–December 1473 of the king's promise to settle his household debts,[38] producing in 1478 'certain ordinaunces for the stablysshing of oure howshold', and ending in the next parliament of January–February 1483 with the assignment of an annual revenue to cover household costs. If the elimination of *Feoda et Robe* should be seen as the product of a thrifty concern for marginal cost-benefit efficiency, that might tell us something about how the king viewed his relationship to his servants.[39] But since the

---

[36] E.361/7, mm. 71–74. John Lord Howard's accounts as treasurer of the household 1468–74 were never rendered: he was allowed exemption from them in pardons of 1 April 1473 and 20 May 1475 (*Calendar of Patent Rolls 1467–1477*, pp. 387, 516; P.S.O.1/37/1941).

[37] Preamble to the 1478 household ordinance, A. R. Myers, *op. cit.*, pp. 211–212.

[38] *Rot. Parl.*, vi. 71–72, the preamble to the Act of Resumption. P.R.O., Exchequer, Exchequer of Receipt Miscellanea, E.407/6/136, a fragmentary bundle of 49 documents mentioning the list of household creditors (above, note 24), shows the process of settlement under way in 1474–75, although the general warrant to the Exchequer in pursuance of the 1473 Act 'for the more nere and shortere contentacon of oure detts' only issued on 20 July 1478 (P.R.O., Exchequer, Treasury of Receipt, Council and Privy Seal Records, E.28/91/72).

[39] Other sections which disappear from the household accounts at the same time are *Vadia falconariorum* and *Empciones equorum*, and it may be that the change should be seen merely as administrative streamlining, restricting the treasurer of the household's expenses almost exclusively to the wages and provisions grouped under *Diete*. On the other hand, it is not clear that *Feoda et Robe* payments were transferred to any other source, and the *Oblaciones et Elemosina* section shows streamlining of a straightforwardly enconomizing kind. In 1466–67 *Feoda et Robe* payments amounted to £727. 4s. out of a total expense of £12,247. 11s. 3¾d.

saving was absorbed by a rise in the total spent on daily wages and provisions we might deduce that there was some increase in numbers.

That the increase was not large and tailed away after 1478 is suggested on such general grounds by the household accounts for 1474–80 and by the level of the household assignment of 1483.[40] The same impression is given by a cofferer's ledger which includes wage-lists for several categories of servants over the eleven months November 1473–September 1474.[41] In structure too there is little sign of change. The chamber regulations of 1471, though perhaps in presentation influenced by recent acquaintance with the Burgundian court, mark no new departure organizationally.[42] However, they do show that the complement of knights and esquires of the body was larger than before. As with the matter of overall size, the number of such servants has to remain imprecise. From various sources it is possible to list the names of 38 who were knights of the body at some stage of the reign; in 1468 there were ten,[43] in 1471 probably twenty, in 1483 probably thirty. For the most part the increase came by promotion from within the existing chamber staff, notably with the knightings of the king's followers at Tewkesbury. The esquires of the body (totalling about 50 for the whole reign, between 30 and 40 in 1483) tell a similar story. After 1471 as before there were some piecemeal additions often from other affinities, as with the recruitment of Humphrey Talbot (a Mowbray retainer) as knight of the body, or Henry Vernon (a Clarence retainer) as esquire of the body, in both cases before the disappearance of their ducal patrons.[44] In converse to such increases the category of king's knights not belonging to the chamber staff dwindled with the failure of newcomers to keep pace with the death-rate of those already relatively senior men so described in the 1460s: in the 1470s the outer circle of the affinity was neither as numerous nor as prominent as the chamber staff, and it seems clear that there was

[40] The matter is discussed by A. R. Myers, *op. cit.*, pp. 44–45. By 1482 the Stable had been assigned an annual income of £500 (P.R.O., Exchequer, Tellers Rolls, E.405/70, mm. 1, 7).

[41] E.101/412/5, fos 25–34ᵛ.

[42] A. R. Myers, *op. cit.*, pp. 199–202. Such occasional ordinances were a feature of the Burgundian court, *e.g.* those printed in *Mélanges d'histoire offerts à Henri Pirenne* (Bruxelles, 1926), pp. 267–70. But Olivier de la Marche's exposition of the Burgundian household, though occasioned by English interest in the early 1470s, makes clear the structural differences of the two households (*Mémoires d'Olivier de la Marche*, ed. H. Beaune and J. D'Arbaumont, iv (Société de l'Histoire de France, 1888), pp. 1–94).

[43] E.361/7, m. 70 shows that the 1466–67 list remained unchanged in 1467–68.

[44] These relate to the territorial re-ordering of 1473–78, which I adumbrate below, but which needs examining in a closer family and local focus.

no appreciable extra set of royal annuitants outside these household categories. At the top of the household's official hierarchy a few new-comers were drafted in; the most important politically was Thomas lord Stanley, appointed steward in 1471–72; but perhaps the most memorable was Jaquet Blondell, a Norman who in 1450 was both avenar to Queen Margaret and in the service of the duke of Suffolk, and who in 1461 was alleged to have declared that 'he had noon othere soverain lord ne never wold have whiles he lyved but king Henry and to him he was sworn and to Quene Margaret'. He survived that out-burst and adapted himself by the thoroughly respectable means of continued service to those de la Poles who were now King Edward's relatives and supporters, in 1466–67 surfacing as Queen Elizabeth's avenar and in 1479 becoming the king's cofferer. When in 1492 this well-established East Anglian esquire came to write his will he looked back with impartial satisfaction to these varied patrons whom 'I sum tyme servid in household and had of theim my living according to the degre that hir grace called me to and better thenne I coude deserve god quite it theim in hevin'.[45]

A few such exotics notwithstanding, the style of this affinity seems set by an employer whose preferences are close and settled. When in the last weeks of the reign an Act of Apparel prescribed the clothing differentials appropriate to the gradations of society, eleven exemp-tions were allowed.[46] All were men of the household. Three clearly were exempt as holders of a specified position: Sir John Elrington as treasurer of the king's household, Master John Gunthorp as dean of his chapel, Master Oliver King as his secretary. King and Gunthorp, both Cambridge graduates of the 1450s, had achieved their positions fairly recently—King after some time studying civil law at Orléans and serving Edward of Lancaster as secretary, working his way after 1471 as a clerk in the signet office to the French secretaryship in 1476 and the chief secretaryship in 1480; Gunthorp, whose higher faculty was theology, spending some years of wandering scholarship in Ferrara and Rome, entering the queen's service as chaplain and secretary and the king's as almoner in 1468 and dean of the chapel in 1476. In Elrington's case the path to glory went through the kitchen. Belonging to a Northumbrian family several of whom followed the

---

45 *Calendar of Patent Rolls 1467–1477*, p. 297; British Museum, Egerton Charter 8779; P.R.O., P.S.O.1/18/920, P.S.O.1/22/1176A, E.36/207, p. 39, C.67/48, m. 20, C. 67/51, mm. 20, 33, Prerogative Court of Canterbury, Probate 11/11 (Register Horne).

46 *Rot. Parl.*, vi. 220–21. There are also more general provisos, such as the stipulation that esquires of the body enjoy some of the show appropriate to knights, which relate to the various contemporary attempts to conflate into a precedence code the different hierarchies of rank, *e.g.* those transcribed in Bodleian MS., Ashmole 857, pp. 139–43.

trail of business to Hackney and Shoreditch, his father and elder brother being London lawyers, he found an opening after 1461 as sub-clerk of the king's kitchen, rising in 1464 to chief clerk of the kitchen, in 1471 (after sharing the king's exile) to cofferer, and in 1474 to treasurer.[47] The remaining eight of the 1483 exemptions, though not so called in the Act, were knights of the body. It may be that one of them, William Parr, was listed here because he also held the position of comptroller of the household, for he was exceptional in this partic-ular set in having been in the 1460s a retainer not of the king but of the earl of Warwick: in 1470 the king had personally persuaded him over,[48] in 1471 he had shown a convert's zeal, and in 1481 he was made comptroller. His younger brother John, however, had been of the king's chamber from 1461, in 1469 becoming master of the horse and from 1471 until his death in 1475 William's fellow as knight of the body. And this was the career-pattern common to the other seven singled out in 1483 (Thomas Montgomery, Thomas Burgh, Thomas Vaughan, John Donne, Thomas Saintleger, Thomas Bour-chier, and Thomas Gray), all of whom were members of the original chamber staff of 1461 and some years older than the king. As a group these seven have no peculiar coherence; in origins they were widely diverse and reached Edward's service in quite individual ways; they differed from their fellows only in the degree to which they possessed the features characteristic of their type. Their sartorial exemption was clearly the personal choice of the king from among those whose service to him was for life.

In function the affinity's general characteristic was its combination of this permanent, life-long membership of a group which as a group performed the central fixed routine of court ceremonial, with an essentially occasional, individual performance of any task of concern to the king. Two matters, both political, were pre-eminently standing concerns in which all were to some degree involved: the 'outward causes' of diplomacy and war, and the inward compulsions of land and lordship. Diplomacy, so largely an interchange between courts, saw men of the household eclipse men of Chancery and Privy Seal. The secretaries were here much occupied; others developed personal specialisms—William Parr and Master Alexander Lee[49] in Scottish

[47] A classic case of the obscurity which lies in wait for social mobility which combines geographical migration with later failure to maintain a family iden-tity, his derivation perhaps comes out best from P.R.O., Probate 11/7 (Register Logge) f. 59, Probate 11/9 (Register Dogett) f. 193, C. 71/105, m. 8, C. 67/48, m. 32, S.C.6/1140/25, 26, 27; Historical Manuscripts Commission, *Third Report*, p. 109.

[48] *Chronicle of the Rebellion in Lincolnshire (ut sup.)*, pp. 14–16.

[49] After 1476, when William Dudley (dean of the chapel) became bishop of Durham, Lee (clerk of the closet by 1466, sub-almoner by 1469) became, in

transactions, Louis de Brutailhs and his brother-in-arms Bartolet de Ribeyre in Breton and Italian missions respectively, Bernard de la Force (a third Gascon refugee and king's esquire) in Castilian marriage negotiations,[50] a succession of chaplains as proctors at Rome; while many more were called on for the main business of French and Burgundian missions. After 1471 Calais occupied an even more focal position for these purposes than before, its personnel making it almost an 'outward office' of the chamber administered by several household men, with the chamberlain himself at their head as lieutenant, handling the bulk of French and Burgundian business[51] and organizing the secret service.[52] The Calais garrison was also the perpetuation of the *familia regis* as a war-band.[53] The great military occasion of the French expedition of 1475 was an expansion of this standing force (within the established framework of war as the enterprise of Parliament, Exchequer and nobility) into a general household levy, whose commissariat was provided by the domestic offices headed by John Elrington as treasurer of the king's war with Thomas Thwaytes, treasurer of Calais and esquire of the body, seconded as temporary treasurer of the chamber to repeat his 1471 performance as clerk of the king's war.[54] In the king's intention 1471 had been the household's last occasion as a war-band within England, 'sith it is and must be to the displesure of gode and also contrary to all good polyce infynitely to procede in such quarelles'.[55] But 1473 brought the threat of an

---

addition to his direct involvement in the king's affairs, a key man in the secular administration of his native diocese (University of Durham, Dept. of Palaeography, Church Commission Deposit 18983o, 189761, 221161).

[50] A. Peyrègne, 'Les emigrés gascons en Angleterre, 1453–1485', *Annales du Midi*, lxvi (1954).

[51] A fragment of his correspondence survives among the Hastings MSS in the Huntington Library, San Marino California (HA 13879, headed 'Copies de plusieurs lettres envoyees au Roy Loys et a ladmiral de France a Calais lan' 1477).

[52] P.S.O. 1/45/2337, 5 July 1478: ' . . . Lord Hastyngs oure Chambreleyne by oure comaundement at divers seasons late sente certeyne secrete persounes into the parties beyonde the see to bringe us knowlege of certeyne matieres suche as they were sente thider for, wherof we have the perfytenes to oure grete pleasir.'

[53] Immediately after the English battles of 1471 Hastings took up his Calais post with 1500 men retained with the king and wearing royal livery (E. 405/55, m. 6ᵛ).

[54] E. 159/253, Brevia Directa, Trinity m. 10; E. 405/53, m. 1. Predictably, Thwaites's rôle in the 1475 French expedition was in the 1482 Scottish expedition taken by Alexander Lee, again as part of a household commissariat headed by Elrington.

[55] Proclamation of 27 April 1471, entered on the Close Roll (*Foedera*, ed. T. Rymer, xi (London, 1710), p. 709) and also—with a few verbal differences,

invasion by the recalcitrant earl of Oxford, steward of the household during Henry VI's Readeption.[56] On 5 June the king sent a letter under his signet and sign-manual to John Cheyne sheriff of Devon to quell rumours that the earl had landed: the sheriff was straitly charged 'that ye ne assemble ne suffre to be assembled eny people with eny manner of persone or persones what so evir he or thei be for no manner of cause, but that ye sit stil and be quiet'.[57] And when the earl did land at St Michael's Mount on 30 September it was not a local worthy such as John Cheyne of Pynne but the king's Devonshire esquire of the body John Fortescue who was entrusted with the siege, in the conduct of which he relied on his household colleagues John Wode as master of the ordnance and for naval supplies John Sturgeon and Edward Brampton (the Portuguese Jew now emerged from the Domus Conversorum as the king's godson and usher of the chamber).[58] The siege over, the captive earl was taken to Calais where he spent his time in the charge of James Blount, keeper of the castle of Hammes and another esquire of the body.[59]

How to make things 'sit stil and be quiet' was a predominant concern of the king in 1473. During that 'gret hote somere', while many of his household men were in Bruges and Utrecht and Edinburgh on his outward matters, the king moved to and fro across the midlands from Fotheringhay to Ludlow, mindful of his promise of 'sana et solida gubernatio' made in parliament the previous November in response to the Speaker's request for action against disorder especially in the Welsh marches.[60] The request had hinted that a good place to start would be the misdeeds of the 'famulier servauntez' of the king and other magnates, and in June he at last took action to end the ten-year-old Stanley–Harrington feud in Lancashire, whose protagonists were now the steward of his household and a knight of the body.[61] But his approach to the problem both in this case and generally showed an intention to deal with disorder and feud as epiphenomena

---

and a delay in transmitting it to the sheriff of Durham for publication until 13 May when the political trend was clearer—on the Durham patent roll (P.R.O., Palatinate of Durham 3/49, mm. 4, 5).

[56] P.R.O., King's Bench, Coram Rege Rolls, K.B. 27/839, m. 82.

[57] British Museum, Additional Charter 56425.

[58] E. 405/57, m. 5; E. 404/75/3/69, 70; Cecil Roth, 'Sir Edward Brampton, alias Duarte Brandão: governor of Guernsey, 1482–1485', *Transactions of La Société Guernesiaise* (1956).

[59] P.S.O. 1/43/2204.

[60] *Rot. Parl.*, vi. 8; E. 404/75/3/52 for the payment to the Speaker of 40 marks for his attendance during the summer's progress.

[61] *Calendar of Close Rolls 1468–1476* (London, 1953), nos 136, 278, 900, 1155; *Calendar of Patent Rolls 1467–1477*, pp. 241, 426–27; P.R.O., Duchy of Lancaster Chancery Rolls, D.L. 37/48, no. 12, D.L. 37/49, no. 36; E. 28/89/22.

for which the cure was a territorial re-ordering. The politics of the 1470s were the politics of land, and 1473–74 saw the shaping of a land policy which combined family endowment with a tidy-minded regionalism. A later stage of its development was the creation of an apanage for the king's second son Richard, born at Shrewsbury in the course of the 1473 progress. By 1475 the plan was to endow him with a collection of lands in the east midlands—Fotheringhay, Stamford, Grantham and the other Duchy of York lands in Northamptonshire, Rutland and Lincolnshire; the Duchy of Lancaster honours of Bolingbroke and Higham Ferrers in the same counties; and the former Welles-Willoughby estates in Lincolnshire. In 1476 the prospect opened of a marriage which would bring in the geographically apt increment of the Mowbray estates, and although the heiress's death in 1481 threatened to spoil the tidiness of the scheme the king showed himself determined not to let the rights of collateral heirs stand in the way.[62] By then he had invested heavily in the policy of which this was the extension and the progress of 1473 the start. He had then bent his efforts to making his elder son's household at Ludlow the governing power in Wales and the west midlands, grounded on the Mortimer lands as well as the principality, and similarly to establishing his brother Gloucester as heir to the Neville lands and ruler of the north. In both cases the enterprise was politically fraught. In 1469–70 the king in a position of need had recognized the established order of landed society by recalling the Percies and the Staffords to their accustomed importance. In 1473–74 the Percies were accommodated in the new scheme, Gloucester and the earl of Northumberland agreeing with the king on a carefully constructed co-operation in the north.[63] But in the west the Staffords were not so accommodated, and the duke of Buckingham, who was allowed to enter on his inheritance at the beginning of 1473, was a year later relegated to political limbo.[64]

---

[62] S. Bentley, *Excerpta Historica* (London, 1831), pp. 370–72; *Calendar of Patent Rolls 1467–1477*, p. 508; *Rot. Parl.*, vi. 168–70, 205–07; B.M., Additional MS 6113, fos 72ᵛ–73.

[63] I have not seen the original, but I assume the correct date for the 'appointment' reached by the king between Gloucester and Northumberland (on which their indenture of 28 July 1474 was based) is 12 May 1473, as given in *Percy Bailiffs Rolls of the Fifteenth Century*, ed. J. C. Hodgson (Surtees Society, 1912), p. 106, and in Historical Manuscripts Commission, *Sixth Report* (London, 1877), pp. 223–24, not 12 May 1474 as given in the transcript in W. H. Dunham, *Lord Hastings' Indentured Retainers 1461–1483* (New Haven, 1955), p. 140. The central and local interlock of the resulting northern situation is best shown by *Plumpton Correspondence*, ed. T. Stapleton (Camden Society, 1839), pp. 31–33.

[64] His exclusion from the commissions of the peace in all shires except Stafford is the most obvious sign, and calls to mind the date of the heraldic decree allowing him the undifferenced arms of Thomas of Woodstock, since

1474 saw the scheme pushed forward with the last and most severe of the reign's Acts of Resumption and the beginning of an apanage endowment for the king's step-son Thomas Grey in the south-west.[65] The momentum builds up to the 1478 elimination of the unassimilable duke of Clarence. Thereafter until the king's death, with some further tightening, it was in this territorial strait-jacket that politics were made to 'sit stil and be quiet'.

Where in this scheme was the place of the household? The two leading household men were fitted in as the heads of further regional blocs. Lord Stanley, whose appointment as steward followed from events in 1469–71 which may well have convinced the king of the need to combine family endowment with a clear territorial demarcation,[66] was made undoubted ruler of Lancashire: the king's solution to the feud with the Harringtons was to back Lord Stanley firmly and thereafter it was he who was regarded as the arbiter of local feuds. In Cheshire and north-east Wales also Stanley power was extended, Lord Stanley's younger brother William (knight of the body from 1461) building an ascendancy on grants both of land and office.[67] The chamberlain similarly emerged in 1474 as ruler of the north midlands from Rockingham to the Peak, though in contrast with the Stanleys the aggrandizement of Hastings and his younger brothers was less the recognition of a family's local rise to supremacy than the invention of a hegemony which presumably would be only for life: his hereditary endowment was effectively in his native Leicestershire and otherwise his influence rested on office.[68] For the rest a place in

he has 'ascended to a coate neire to the king and of his royall bloude' (Bodleian MS., Ashmole 857, fos 50–51, 18 February 1474). Thereafter the only favour that came his way coincided with his involvement as Steward of England in the trial of Clarence: the 7 February 1478 conversion of his 4 March 1477 lease of the manor of Ebbw in Newport into a grant in tail male (D.L. 37/46, no. 20, D.L.36/57, no. 27); and the king's baptismal sponsorship of his son born on 3 February 1478, bringing with it a gold cup worth £42. 15s. (E. 405/65, m. 1).

[65] This was intricately linked with the 1473–74 re-grouping in the midlands (*Rot. Parl.*, vi. 106–08, 215–17; E. 404/75/4/32; *Calendar of Patent Rolls 1467–1477*, p. 460).

[66] Behind Stanley's ambivalent political behaviour in 1470–71 lay a quarrel resulting from the way Edward brought forward Gloucester in 1469, and further involving John Pilkington, a retainer of both Edward and Gloucester (*Foedera* xi. 654; P.S.O. 1/36/1893A).

[67] The only land grant—Chirk and Chirkland in tail male—came to him in lieu of the lordship of Skipton in Craven, which was transferred to Gloucester, 5 March and 12 June 1475 (B.M., Cotton MS. Julius B. XII, fos 246–52. The greater part of this volume, fos 108–316, apart from some later additions consists of Gloucester's 1469–83 evidences).

[68] The key appointment was the stewardship of Tutbury for life on 30 March 1474, coinciding with the conclusion of his first large batch of indentures of retainer with esquires and gentlemen of the area (W. H. Dunham, *op. cit.*, p. 119).

the landed establishment was not created. Yorkist England saw no inflation of honours, and after 1471 peerage creations were no part of patronage. From 1471 to 1483, though almost no commoners except household men were considered for election as knights of the Garter, only two (William Parr and Thomas Montgomery) were actually elected.[69] Of those eight knights of the body exempt from the 1483 Act of Apparel five were certainly younger sons, and Thomas Vaughan of such obscure derivation that the question of inheritance was not material.[70] Some of them were the king's relatives—Thomas Bourchier and Thomas Gray his cousins, Thomas Saintleger his brother-in-law, Thomas Montgomery the son of his godmother. Several of them married into baronial families, and the king was quite willing to use his influence with others on his servants' behalf,[71] and to stand godfather to their children.[72] But so far as he endowed them permanently it was mainly from forfeitures and not on a lavish scale, perhaps on the premise that those with constant access to the king's grace also had constant access to other people's favour.[73] Thomas Burgh was allowed to build up something of an ascendancy in Lincoln-shire by accumulated grants of office both royal and magnate, but of grants of land he got little to increase his inheritance from his mother. In the king's family scheme his retainers existed to serve two purposes. One was to act as a network linking the court to the outlying regions— Thomas Vaughan for instance as chamberlain to the prince of Wales, William Parr as sheriff of Westmorland for life and the duke of Gloucester's deputy in Carlisle and the west march, Thomas Gray as chamberlain to Richard of Shrewsbury[74] (had that household ever

[69] J. Anstis, The Register of the Most Noble Order of the Garter, ii (London, 1724), pp. 187–212.

[70] E. D. Jones, 'The Parentage of Sir Thomas Vaughan (d. 1483)', National Library of Wales Journal, viii (1954). The exceptions were Thomas Burgh and William Parr.

[71] E.g. J. Hunter, South Yorkshire: the history and topography of the deanery of Doncaster in the diocese and county of York, ii (London, 1831), p. 54; Historical Manuscripts Commission, Eleventh Report, vii (London, 1888), pp. 93–94.

[72] Calendar of Patent Rolls 1476–1485 (London, 1901), p. 37. It seems likely that the large crop of Edwards produced by household men were similarly sponsored.

[73] E.g. Historical Manuscripts Commission, Ninth Report, i (London, 1883), pp. 106, 116, for Christ Church Canterbury's fulfilment of a promise to give Thomas Saintleger, in return for his advocacy at court of their claim to a manor, the stewardship of it.

[74] Harley MS. 4780, f. 44ᵛ. A contemporary pedigree was drawn up to demonstrate his multiple relationship to his ducal charge (Visitations of the North, Part III: a Visitation of the North of England circa 1480–1500, ed. C. H. Hunter Blair (Surtees Society, 1930), pp. 53–54)—entirely consistent with his life-long exploitation of his genealogy for patronage, beginning in

been locally established). The second purpose was to act as a network of closer mesh within that region reserved for the king's more personal control; to hold together the concerns of the *res publica* as sheriffs and justices of the peace and commissioners, and the concerns as stewards and receivers and auditors of that *res familiaris* which was the king's landed property. How personal that control was is suggested by a signet letter of 1479, addressed 'to our trustie and welbeloved squier John Harcourte one of our ushers of our Chamber and of our Receivors', rebuking him for slowness in providing money for the serjeant of the catery from the lands in his charge, and concluding with the king's autograph post-script: 'John we pray you faile not this oure writinge to be accomplisshed'.[75] That sounds the convincing note of authoritative familiarity.

*   *   *

In what longer vista of development does this form of authority best fall into perspective? To Dr Harriss the 'household system' of administration was a détour from the prevailing direction of governmental advance;[76] and surely he is right. To Mr Keen 'if one is looking for signs of development in the middle ages one will not get very far by comparing different kinds of close personal connexions', for it was 'not the development of new kinds of relation between man and man' which induced social change;[77] and surely he too is right. In subscribing to these views I would add only one corollary. Our understanding of constitutional and social changes would be limited unless we saw them as involved in a continuing political process and a developing political consciousness. In this the rise and fall of the house of York had its place. If the Yorkists were participants in a general monarchical recovery in later fifteenth-century Europe, they stood aloof from the development of monarchical ideology. Although the women of the dynasty showed awareness of new forms of religious sensibility,[78] the political style of their menfolk was atavistic. Edward

---

the 1450s with the duke of York and the bishop of Ely (P.R.O., Ancient Correspondence, S.C. 1/51, no. 92; Cambridge University Library, Ely Diocesan Records, Register Gray, fos 7ᵛ–8, 75ᵛ, 77ᵛ).

[75] P.R.O., Duchy of Lancaster Miscellanea, D. L. 41/42/4. *Cf.* the general commentary of the Croyland Chronicle, on the 1473 Resumption as the beginning of Edward's attempt to ground his kingship 'de propria substantia propriaque industria sua', and on the post-1478 phase in which his authority rested on the local estate network of his 'fiducialiores servitores' (W. Fulman, *op. cit.*, pp. 559, 564).

[76] G. L. Harriss, 'Medieval Government and Statecraft', *Past and Present*, 25 (1963), 31 (1965).

[77] M. H. Keen, 'Brotherhood in Arms', *History*, xlvii (1962).

[78] C. A. J. Armstrong, 'The Piety of Cicely, Duchess of York: a study in late mediaeval culture', *For Hilaire Belloc*, ed. D. Woodruff (London, 1942).

IV's preferred public image was the king as Old Testament war-lord, as depicted in a poster-sized rendering of his advent in 1459–61 juxtaposing scenes of his military exploits with biblical correspondences,[79] or in the 1471 proclamation, issued between the fights at Barnet and Tewkesbury, emphasizing 'victorye in the battailles' as the decisive vindication of right to 'the high souerayne pouer Ryall'.[80] His courtiers, though, contributed their mite towards a more critical awareness. They certainly produced no overt political thinking of the calibre of *The Meroure of Wyssdome* written by that Scottish academic turned courtier, their contemporary John Ireland.[81] And it may be that the outlook of most of them tallied with that flat poem ascribed to the 1470s, *The Assembly of Ladies*, with its externalized description of the rituals of etiquette and petitioning at the court of Lady Loyalty, whose clients may permit themselves the passing thought that 'long to sue it is a wery thing', but who nonetheless soldier on,

> 'Submyttyng us lowly til hir servise,
> For as us thought we had our travel spent
> 'In suche wise as we hielde us content.'[82]

But a few at least were open to self-criticism. James Goldwell, king's chaplain and well acquainted with courtly petitioning as the king's master of requests and then as proctor at Rome, bought a translation of the *Hiero* or *De Vita Tirannica et Privata Liber*.[83] James Friis, who made a career as the king's physician while retaining contacts with his native Low Countries, owned a copy of one of the two key works of the anti-courtier literature of the time, Aeneas Sylvius's *De Curialium Miseriis Epistola*.[84] And no doubt from the same milieu

[79] B.M., Harley MS. 7353. *Cf.* Lancashire Record Office, Crosse of Shaw Hill papers, D D Sh. 15/2, a long illuminated roll, datable 1461–64 and showing a strong Bourchier interest, relating Edward IV backward to the kings of Judah by a skeletal 'polychronicon' which turns into a family tree.

[80] Above, note 55.

[81] J. H. Burns, 'John Ireland and *The Meroure of Wyssdome*', *Innes Review*, 6 (1955). I retail one sentence: 'And gif you spere at me . . . quhat thing is polite, I ansuer that it is a congregacioun of men or persounis in this mortal lif that are ordenit togidder be law or commandiment and obedience ressonable to live togeddir in pes and sufficience ether in temporalite or in spiritualite.'

[82] *The Floure and the Leafe and The Assembly of Ladies*, ed. D. A. Pearsall (London and Edinburgh, 1962), pp. 19, 117, 126.

[83] Bodleian MS., Rawlinson G. 47. His brother and executor left a copy of that pre-eminent treatise 'de nugiscurialium', the *Policraticus* (A. B. Emden, *A Biographical Dictionary of the University of Oxford to A.D. 1500*, ii (Oxford, 1958), pp. 783–86).

[84] Bodleian MS. Arch. Selden B. 25; this was subsequently owned by Friis's colleague William Hobbes (surgeon successively to Richard duke of York, Edward IV and Richard III, as in 1488 he insisted should be recorded on his

came the copy of its companion-piece, the French version of Alain
Chartier's *De Vita Curiali* which Caxton Englished as *The Curial*,
contrasting the corrupt artificiality of the court with the country
dweller's 'true and ryghtful lyf' of natural liberty.[85] Literary convention though it was, it finds an echo in that cryptic injunction which
John Blount lord Mountjoy addressed in his will to his sons: 'to leve
right wisely and never to take the state of Baron upon them if they
may leye it from them, nor desire to be grete about princes, for it is
dangeros'. We may think it a household man's *cri-de-cœur*, for John
Blount, baron though he became, was by personal career and family
background a man of the household. His father was the last of a long
line to serve the house of Lancaster, changing in 1453–54 from the
household of Henry VI to that of Richard of York, in 1465 attaining
that rare prize a Yorkist peerage; and John himself, even when a lord
a retainer of the king's chamberlain, was—like his elder brother who
died for Edward IV at Barnet and his younger brother who fought for
Henry VII at Bosworth—an esquire of the body.[86]

His disenchantment may have been recent. Both the writing of his
will and the printing of Caxton's *Curial* (like the printing of that
other work apposite to the politics of affinity, Malory's *Le Morte
Darthur*)[87] coincided with the political collapse of 1483–85. And on
the fall of the house of York the household men perforce offered their
commentary, in deeds if not in writing. Between 9 and 20 April 1483
they performed their last group function, as the funeral escort of the
king's two bodies of cadaver and effigy.[88] The household's dissolution

---

tomb, P.R.O., Probate 11/8 (Register Milles), fos 136–37); *c.* 1514
the work was Englished by Alexander Barclay. To the brief account of
Friis in A. B. Emden, *A Biographical Register of the University of Cambridge
to 1500* (Cambridge, 1963), p. 243 should also be added the interesting 'forma
indenturae inter duos fratres conjuratos'—a close civilian equivalent of a
brotherhood-in-arms pact—which he concluded with an Oxford apothecary in
1447 (*Munimenta Academica*, ed. H. Anstey (Rolls Series, 1868), pp. 554–55).

[85] *The Curial made by maystere Alain Charretier*, ed. F. J. Furnivall (Early
English Text Society, 1888). It would be worth knowing more about the provenance of British Museum, Harley MS. 1883, a late fifteenth-century Low
Countries collection which includes the *Hiero*, the *De Curialium Miseriis*, and
the *De Vita Curiali*. On the genre in general see Pauline M. Smith, *The
Anti-Courtier Trend in Sixteenth-century French Literature* (Geneva, 1966),
pp. 13–54.

[86] *Cf.* the conclusion to K. B. McFarlane, 'The Wars of the Roses', *Proceedings of the British Academy*, i (1965).

[87] For one of several recent attempts at a 'political' reading of Malory see
Elizabeth T. Pochoda, *Arthurian Propaganda 'Le Morte Darthur' as an
historical ideal of life* (Chapel Hill, 1971).

[88] W. H. St John Hope, 'On the Funeral Effigies of the Kings and Queens
of England', *Archaeologia*, lx (1907), p. 538; College of Arms, Arundel MS.
51, fos 14–17[v]. The latter necessitates more correction to Ernst H.

at the last stage of that ceremony left them (in the words of the ceremonial valediction), as 'men without a master and out of their offices', with the problem of survival. Careerists that they were, the problem was built into their lives. Sir Robert Wingfield, whose career included service to the dukes of Norfolk and Suffolk, to Clarence as general surveyor of his lands, and to Edward IV as comptroller of the household, used a signet seal with the device of a mole-trap and the legend 'gardez vous destre prins'.[89] For him death in 1481 avoided the problem of 1483 but his fellows were left to make good their escape from the consequences of their master's scheme of land and lordship. That scheme, by rewarding them in the main through grants of office and annuity, and so keeping them primarily men of the court rather than independent powers in the country, made them unavoidably a party to the succession struggle whatever their wish to contract out of its dangers. For a while it also gave them an interest in supporting Edward V, once his household as prince had been removed; and the renewal of Hastings's appointment as chamberlain held out a tenuous hope of largely intact group survival at the centre. But even as a group they carried insufficient weight in a situation dominated by a resurgence of the power of the lords of the land and the sway of aristocratic hierarchy. The report immediately after Hastings's fall, that 'all the lord Chamberleyne mene be come my lordys of Bokeynghame menne',[90] was perhaps an intelligent if premature deduction from the prevailing drift of events. In fact his fall and the concomitant change of king precipitated that regrouping from which a new dynasty emerged. For Richard III rose at the head of an already formed and sizeable affinity, and if some of his brother's men managed to survive by adoption into it, others were driven to turn first to Henry Stafford and then to Henry Tudor. The regrouping of 1483 prevented Richard from fully extricating himself from his place in his brother's scheme of things: he remained the leader of a predominantly local, northern affinity, and in 1485 many of his recent recruits felt sufficiently marginal to offer their services elsewhere. One way or

---

Kantorowicz, *The King's Two Bodies: a study in mediaeval political theory* (Princeton, 1957), pp. 411–12, than is suggested by Ralph E. Giesey, *The Royal Funeral Ceremony in Renaissance France* (Geneva, 1960), p. 140. The fact that the public acts of Edward V's reign begin on 21 April, the day after the burial, seems relevant to Giesey's interesting theory of the 'ceremonial interregnum', *ibid.*, pp. 125, 183, 188 etc.

[89] C. Spencer Perceval, 'Notes on a selection of ancient charters, letters and other documents from the muniment room of Sir John Lawson of Brough Hall near Catterick, in Richmondshire, Baronet', *Archaeologia*, xlvii (1882), p. 189.

[90] *The Stonor Letters and Papers, 1290–1483*, ed. C. L. Kingsford (Camden Series, 1919), no. 331.

another their survival rate was high: Sir Robert Wingfield would have approved. But as a political process it was the compulsive drive of men in search of a master, men who as individuals had more will than power to control their lives.

University College, London

THE FRENCH ORIGINS OF THE 'RIGHT'

By J. M. Roberts, M.A., D.Phil., F.R.Hist.S.

READ 10 MARCH 1972

MODERN political history begins with the French Revolution. This is not merely because the Revolution began a diffusion of institutional innovations—universal suffrage, rights of association and publication, and so forth—which have been the political shibboleths of advanced societies ever since. It is also that there then appears the modern vision of politics. The term 'vision' is deliberately chosen, because it does not imply any necessary or objective correlation with the facts of political life. It is a name for a chosen way of seeing things, a persuasive account of the facts, not the facts themselves. Intransigent opponents have been able to agree on this vision and in finding it inspiring or clarifying. Its essence is a presentation of politics as a struggle between two enduring forces or principles. Sometimes these forces are sharply contrasted, sometimes they are only the opposite ends of a spectrum whose middle ground makes precise distinctions hard (though never impossible). Such modifications of the model do not matter; it is the enduring conflict which is crucial. Whatever names they bear—progress and reaction, liberalism and conservatism, movement and order, Left and Right—in this vision these principles are always at war, and that is what politics is about.

This point of departure is so familiar that we usually take it for granted and do not notice its astonishing implications. Just in that fact lies the justification for dwelling on it a moment longer. It has been found so persuasive that it has even been read into the politics of other ages and societies; the struggles of Greek city states, the trumpetings of medieval barons and the aspirations of the Levellers have all at one time or another been said to exemplify it. It is so comprehensive that it sometimes seems to be claimed that all particular political questions or standpoints may be subsumed in it and restated as expressions of the fundamental antithesis. Furthermore, this vision is exclusive: questions which cannot be stated in terms of its antithesis are not thought to be political questions (though, it may be remarked, the tendency inherent in this way of looking at things is that more and more things shall be engulfed in the political). Yet this vision has never fitted all the facts and was, indeed, always resisted by some people and in some places.[1]

---

[1] Especially, of course, in this country and the United States of America. It is interesting here to note that the word 'Right' in its political sense appears

Nonetheless, it has enjoyed sweeping success. It is only now beginning to lose its seductive power in Europe and a success which has lasted since the age of the French Revolution is certainly one more registration of the fact that the Revolution created modern politics. The Revolution formulated and made urgent the issues which made the two-pole model of political life specious and effective. The aim of this paper is to initiate an examination of the way in which this model came to be accepted by one group of men, the early European Right. Such a model is integral to the notion of being on 'Right' or 'Left' at all, because what pre-defines such an attitude is just the acceptance of the view that politics is fundamentally an either/or business, a conflict of fundamental principle whatever the particular circumstances in which the principle may be embodied. It is, in short, the reintroduction of ideology to politics. It is still unclear how men first came to think of themselves as being on the Right, as being, that is to say, committed not merely to the defence of particular interests or traditions, but to participating in some sort of cosmic struggle. It seems to have been assumed that there is no problem, that such an evolution is not of great consequence except to publicists and political theorists; if, indeed, this process is part of the definition of the whole scope of modern politics, this is implausible. But the subject cannot be exhausted and can hardly even be broached in a brief paper. What follow are only some very preliminary reflexions based on well-known and long-available public evidence about the ways in which the definition of the Right can be made clearer.

France seems the right place to start, but this is not because French politics and reflexions upon them were the only sources from which the European Right was to draw important ideas and inspirations.[2] Nonethe less, France was the primal source. This was of great importance. The ideas of the European Right were from the first much stained by French assumptions, experience and associations, and those who later voiced these ideas elsewhere were not always aware of their partial, local, special origins, nor of the limitations and incoherences this might impose. It is tempting to risk a further hypothesis: that, in large measure, the acceptability or inacceptability of the ideas of the Right is a function of the extent to which the receiving society shares French

---

in the *O.E.D.*, viii (1910), only with reference to continental practice, citing an American magazine of 1887. The *O.E.D. Supplement* (1933) does not add to this. Neither volume contains 'right-wing' in its political sense.

[2] Germany, where there are special features in Right-wing thought arising from exaggerated political fragmentation and a multi-confessional culture (to remark only the most important), is obviously crucial. The study by K. Epstein, *The Genesis of German Conservatism* (Princeton, 1965), is the best starting-point for its exploration.

experience. The lack of this sort of ideology in British experience no doubt has many other empirical explanations, but it is at least worth remarking that this country had, in the most striking sense of that word, no Enlightenment, nor, above all, a French Revolution; its *ancien régime* had crumbled away a hundred and fifty years before.

It is not hard to get so far as this. But when we try to discern the Frenchmen who need to be studied, difficulties soon begin. The first thing is to be sure what we are looking for and what distinguishes it from other political stances with which it may be confused. Here it is necessary to be summary and schematic, because there is no space to convey the full richness of the attitudes of thinkers such as Bonald or De Maistre. It has to be said, simply, that the centre of such attitudes as theirs was a judgment about the meaning of the Revolution. Like many of the future Left, the men of the Right characterized that enormously complicated event with deliberate simplicity; they saw it as a *bloc*, to use Clemenceau's word. The Revolution expressed coherent and unified principle, and it was the Enemy. Moreover, it was the Enemy on every front; the Revolution was not just about the political arrangements which should prevail in France. Again like the later Left, the Right saw in it implications of all sorts, moral, social, religious, metaphysical. This comprehensive assessment was later to be reflected in the way 'revolution' changed its meaning between the eighteenth and nineteenth centuries and eventually came to stand for an abstract force, with no particular embodiment; men came to speak of 'The Revolution' as something at work in every age. From being a term denoting striking, but limited and possibly cyclical change, it acquired the connotations of cataclysm. It came to be seen as a complete and almost certainly violent overthrow of the entire social structure. So the word began a course of ever wider and more ludicrous application until it runs out of power in the journalistic shallows of our own day.

In opposing such a danger, the Right saw itself as defending much more than privilege. In their articulated form, its convictions are rooted in an order divinely authorized; a new religious consciousness is, indeed, the clearest break between the the mature Right and the French ruling elites of the *ancien régime*. Respect for prescription and tradition was thought to be the best safeguard of a divinely sanctioned order. This, it should be noted, does not imply historical relativism. It is, rather, the fetish of the past. It implies no sense of development, far less of progress: the past is ideal, the present corrupt. Property is respected for this reason as well as for its own sake: it is part of a whole complex of inherited traditional institutions.[3] Property, moreover,

---

[3] Revealing differences between men who defend the same institution can

illustrates that it is the nature of the inherited order to be a collective trust: the Right is anti-individualist. Besides exacting respect for hierarchy, it emphatically rejects the social and economic institutions of the new age.[4]

Finally, a corollary to this schematic discussion which may at first seem somewhat surprising: men of the Right do not necessarily uphold things as they are. Nor do they necessarily obey established, or even rightful, authority. That authority may compromise its own principles, that *status quo* may embody immorality, and social order is not worth purchase at that price.

Such ideas are distillations of very complex and specific experiences. To trace them exhaustively here is impossible. There is, too, a grave difficulty even in identifying them in their early history. It is hard to know where to start looking for them. Ideas are held by people. Right-wing ideas are the ideas of the men of the Right. It might seem, therefore, to be easy to seek the mentality of the Right by simply looking at the behaviour of those whom we know to be on the Right. Unfortunately, it is not quite as simple as that; 'being on the Right' is a confused idea. There has been plenty of study of the evolution of opposition to the French Revolution, but it reveals, by and large, an entity delineated by a moving frontier. The exercise becomes a matter of expounding the way in which a series of political crises and a set of continuing pressures led men to co-operate in and out of the National Assembly. This tends to produce a picture of the Right as a kind of layer cake, or multi-decker sandwich, some new flavour being added at each juncture of the Revolution, a compilation of discrete factions, not a compound. This process is, of course, not endless. A line can be drawn round it which enables one to say that beyond it, however conservative the temperament and social consciousness of some politicians, they are not men of the Right. (In this sense, presumably, membership of the Convention is a decisive, if remote boundary: whatever a man of the Right was, he was surely for the monarchy, and a *conventionnel* could not say he was that, though he might be very unsympathetic to extreme democracy.) But this throws us back on the word 'monarchist', a classification so comprehensive as to conceal great fissures. It is a commonplace that monarchist disunity long worsened the prospects for conservatism. The gravest example is the most notorious: the disjunction between the aims of the court and those of many of the *emigrés*. But when we look

---

too easily be overlooked in the Revolution. No one could have respected property more than, say, Sieyes, but to call him a man of the Right on this basis and leave the matter there would be ludicrous.

[4] In this connexion, see D. K. Cohen, 'The Vicomte de Bonald's Critique of Individualism', *Journal of Modern History*, xli (1969).

for the idea of the Right, which faction is to be the touchstone of orthodoxy?[5]

Nor is the 'Counter-Revolution' a very helpful term. Clearly it flows into and influences the history which we have to consider in this paper. But mixed up in it can be found outraged constitutionalists, even those who could later be called liberals. Agreement among counter-revolutionaries was sometimes simplified by tactical needs which blurred distinctions of principle, even if only temporarily. Nor did its opponents always see it as did its adherents. And, finally, there are all the confusions created by the positive forces which flow into the counter-revolution and make it so much more than just the mentality of the Right: popular dislike of revolutionary change, divisions of clan and locality, antagonisms between townmen and peasant, the legacy of old religious hatreds and the steady pressure of hard times.[6]

It may be that there is an irremovable difficulty here, posed by the very nature of conservative politics. 'Conservatism' is, after all, a relative term; it is a matter of specific response, rather than doctrine. It is a temperament, not an ideology. Conservatives take their stand on things as they are, and therefore may accept even liberal innovation once it is decisively there. Men as different as Ferrières, Malouet, Mounier and Sieyes are all reasonably called conservatives.[7] Moreover

[5] A sense of the *nuances* which must be taken into account is easily obtained by consulting the lists of party names provided by F. Brunot (*Histoire de la langue française des origines à nos jours*, ix, *La Révolution et l'Empire*, new edn Paris, 1967, pp. 835–7). A recent and important study of some of the oppositions inside the royalist camp is by Mlle J. Chaumié, *Le réseau d'Antraigues et la Contre-Révolution 1791–93* (Paris, 1965); Antraigues' group looked to the exiled princes for leadership. After excluding the constitutional monarchists from classification as counter-revolutionaries, Mlle Chaumié points out that the 'royalistes' of 1789–92 'ne forment pas un bloc monolithique' (p. 19). Further light has been thrown on the well-known divergences between the aims of Louis XVI and those of his brothers in a recent article by H. A. Barton, 'The Origins of the Brunswick Manifesto', *French Historical Studies*, v (1967). Evidently Louis XVI was not a man of the Right; Marie Antoinette's position is harder to assess.

[6] It is worth noting that this subject and its great variety have not only been illuminated recently by such French scholars as Mlle Chaumié (*op. cit.*) and Paul Bois (*Paysans de l'Ouest*, Le Mans, 1960) but also by Englishmen and Americans. The publications of Professors Goodwin and Cobb, Dr Gwynn Lewis, Mr Hutt and Professor Tilly spring to mind; there is much work still moving through the pipelines of research, too.

[7] The marquis de Ferrières, member of a distinguished *épée* family, navigated the whole crisis of privilege as a member of the Constituent and belonged to the *société populaire* and the revolutionary administration of his village (see his *Correspondence inédite*, ed. H. Carré, Paris, 1932, pp. 1–16). He thought that Mounier, spokesman for the constitutional innovators, was already beginning to calm down and reveal a conservative concern in early

Conservatism tends to relate to particularity and the national setting. The Right is altogether more abstract, more doctrinal, more a matter of principle; it is, in short, an ideology.

This point has been obscured in the two most considerable and helpful recent attempts to deal with the area in which this topic falls.[8] The most striking feature of the pictures provided by both Professor Beik and Professor Godechot is their variety and lack of coherence. Each presents to us an extraordinary diversity of views. The panorama of conservatives they survey spreads far beyond the Right in any firm sense; it stretches from visionaries like Bonald to moderate constitutionalists like Montlosier—and of course, since Professor Godechot is dealing with the counter-revolutionary movement, he legitimately includes foreigners like Burke and Mallet du Pan. Among so many reactionaries it is impossible to discern doctrinal unity. This is because of the clear but broad principle on which these two authors have selected their examples: they are thinkers and politicians whose shared characteristic is a positive one, not a principle, but a stance, that of being against the Revolution.[9] The grounds of this stance are not relevant to their inclusion. Although this provides a reasonable definition of an area of study, a finer discrimination within it is necessary for our purpose. The distinguishing mark of the mature Right is an overall view characterized by a certain depth and perspective, an ideology, with all that means of distinctive metaphysical assumptions; it is what is presupposed by a bipolar, Left–Right vision of politics. It is the grounds, not the fact, of opposition, which identifies it. Not all of those who took part in counter-revolutionary activity shared them, far less all who were socially conservative. The attitude of the Right may, of course, from time to time be found in men who behave on specific questions much as do many conservatives; in practical politics they may be indistinguishable. Nonetheless, their

---

August 1789 (*ibid.*, pp. 118–19). Malouet tells us (*Mémoires de Malouet*, Paris, 1874, i, pp. 271, 301) that Mounier saw the error of his ways after the Tennis-Court oath. But Sieyes, detested by the Right, is perhaps the most striking example of a man whose fundamental conservatism only appears as events unroll. Yet the kernel of his ideas is already clear in the idea of a *régime censitaire* adumbrated in his most famous book—and in some of its fears: 'en France, en Hollande, et partout, on a des terribles examples de la coalition naturelle entre la dernière classe de la société et les ordres privilègiés'; *Qu'est-ce-que le Tiers Etat?*, ed. R. Zapperi (Geneva, 1970), p. 14.

[8] P. H. Beik, *The French Revolution seen from the Right. Social Theories in Motion* (Philadelphia, 1956); G. Godechot, *La Contre-Révolution. Doctrine et Action 1789–1904* (Paris, 1961).

[9] Professor Beik narrows his field so much as to include 'only those whose opinions would not stretch beyond the point of incorporating the Estates General on a regular basis into the political life of the nation' (p. 3), but this is already to include great diversity.

attitude is not mere conservatism, but, rather, a marker from which
we can read off the strength of individual examples of conservatives.
Since Right-wing attitudes are a clarifying focus and always offer a
rallying-point for conservatives in an inflamed situation, they may
attract support from them at one time though not at another. The true
man of the Right is constant in his stand.

Confused though distinctions in this area are, it is nonetheless
worth while considering one other possible approach which rests on
classification. Any historian must be tempted to see a prospect of
success (in arriving at a working definition of the idea of the Right)
in the evidence of the emergence of the word and an associated
terminology. The creation of a new political vocabulary in the revolutionary era is some of the best evidence of the appearance of a new
politics. In the Restoration it is well-established: 'Red', 'White',
'Liberal', 'Conservative', 'Ultra', 'Constitutional', are all there.
Usage can be a useful guide in questions of this sort though there is
always a danger of anachronistic deformation of the history of a
period if we are not very cautious. But one cannot jump from a proper
caution in this matter to an intransigent assertion that something does
not exist until it has been recognized and named by contemporaries.
There is a moment when a historical reality is coming to birth, is perhaps born, when it is not yet named but when an awareness that there
is something that needs to be named is spreading.

The words '*droite*' and '*gauche*' do not seem to be established until
1791, the year to which Brunot gives his earliest references.[10] They do
not arise from the vituperative identification of partisan opponents,
but from what has been called the '*géographie de l'Assemblée*', a
phrase found, says Brunot, in Mirabeau as early as September 1789.
It obviously implies a certain consistency in the way members of the
Assembly distributed themselves along its benches, though not, at
that stage, a consistency rooted in ideological affiliation, but in
arrangements surviving from the original meeting of the Estates-
General.[11] The first seating-plan had been consciously modified by
a rearrangement of the furniture in July at the suggestion of Dr
Guillotin, who thus made another of his helpful practical contributions
to the regeneration of his country, since it permitted the president of
the Assembly for the first time to observe all the deputies at once and
not to have his back to some of them. But it was not until the removal
to Paris in October that an analysis of the Assembly as a spectrum of
opinion became possible even in principle. On the eve of that removal,
one deputy proposed that the Assembly should no longer maintain

[10] See Brunot, *op. cit.*, pp. 769–71.
[11] On this subject, see G. Rouanet, 'Les débuts de parlementarisme français', *Annales Révolutionnaires*, viii (1916), pp. 173–211.

distinctions of station or precedence among its members, nor have such distinctions recognized by special costume or reserved seating.[12]

Such a request shows that like-minded men might still at this time find themselves separated from one another and sitting among those who did not share their views. The discussion of business or concerting of tactics with their friends would be difficult. At such a moment, therefore, *droite* and *gauche* cannot have had much ideological import, even if the states of mind they were later to designate already existed. They were certainly in use in a ideological sense in 1791 (and perhaps in 1790), but they cannot have been coined until the Assembly moved to Paris and probably not until it was finally settled in the *Manège*. That is about all we can gather from this usage.

Yet there are other indications which certainly suggest the presence of components of the mentality of the later Right in the early Revolution. One word which usually covers them, but bundled up with other ideas, is the familiar word '*aristocrate*'. Like the associated '*aristocratie*', it confuses matters still further. In the first place they are too vague and often indicate only a disapproval of the way things are going, real or suspected. More important, they also have complex pre-revolutionary associations. They had well-established anti-monarchical overtones which they did not lose suddenly on the day the Estates-General met; Fersen was presumably thinking of some of them when he said 'ce sont les aristocrates qui ont commencé cette Révolution'.[13]

These words had a long history and it is not clear when they became common polemical currency. Interestingly, one monarchist journalist under the Constituent blamed Lamoignon for introducing this group of ideas into political debate. Certainly *aristocrate* and its derivatives were used by pamphleteers in 1788.[14] The word with which they were usually contrasted, *patriote*, was a party word as early as 1770, though not with quite the meaning it had in 1789, when it dissolves into a label for a general endorsement of the Revolution. There were many other words, too, which expressed this sense, but did not catch on so

---

[12] *Archives parlementaires*, ix, p. 454 (15 October 1789).

[13] Chaumié, p. 23. The idea that the privileged started the Revolution is now, of course, a commonplace, though the idea still remains in need of further exploration and definition. I do not know who first suggested it; Professor Godechot finds the earliest statement to be by Sénac de Meilhan (whom he quotes in *La Contre-Révolution*, pp. 45–46).

[14] Montjoie, the author of *L'Ami du Roi*, said in his first number (i, p. 12) that Lamoignon 'rappela (au Parlement) que la France était une monarchie, et non une aristocratie. C'est la première fois que ce funeste mot, qui a produit tant de crimes a été prononcé.' For a pamphlet title embodying an idea similar to Lamoignon's see *Le gouvernement sénati-clerico-aristocratique*, said to be of October 1788 (*Archives parlementaires*, i, p. 56).

successfully. *Aristocrate* is an antonym for all of them and any specific motion of the Right is lost to sight in polemical crudities.[15]

Though usage can give helpful hints, therefore, it does not seem that it can do more than this in uncovering the emergence of a mentality. When people adapt terms which are already current, we can never be quite sure how fast or far they are going and how much of the past they are retaining. Another weakness of usage as an indicator is more serious; the progress of the Revolution was such that its clarifying effect on ideology did not quickly emerge in language. For a long time while a new political idiom was emerging the central issue was privilege, which helped to keep alive among the nascent Right an awareness of social distinctions which would only slowly lose its weight as it was balanced by a growing sense of ideological cohesion. From a variety of conservative responses, all expressed in the language of the past, there only slowly emerges a new attitude, that of the Right.

Nonetheless, in this variety lie essential elements of later ideology. To discern them is not easy and the necessary preliminary to doing so is to understand that their context is not the Revolution but the politics of late eighteenth-century France. The ideas of the Right are not historically comprehensible against the background of 1789 alone. They are rooted in apprehensions and judgments going well back into the *ancien régime* and plausible long before the Estates-General met. Men were then already feeling their way towards later ideas. They did so because they found an established political idiom and vision of politics increasingly inadequate.

The rest of this paper is a tentative discussion of this fact, but in relation to an almost antithetical suggestion, for while the roots of modern ideology may be sought before 1789, they have a hard struggle then to get nourishment. The institutions and practices of the *ancien régime* are unrewarding, unwelcome soil for ideology; they are very resistant to interpretation in Left–Right terms, though attempts to impose on them this anachronistic strait-jacket have often been made. An almost traditional false emphasis must be resisted. It is even worth considering whether our picture of the eighteenth century in France has not too long been distorted by a myth created by the Revolution and embodied nowhere more decisively than in the attitude of the Right.

This is to go too fast. The starting point must be the positive setting.

---

[15] An ironical use of the antithesis of *aristocratie* and *democratie* is to be found in the first number of the *Actes des Apôtres* (p. 4), together with some teasing of Robespierre for producing another version in *aristocracie*, but the antithesis can be found earlier than this (e.g. B. A. de Barruel, *Le patriote véridique*, 1789).

We still lack a political history of the reign of Louis XVI written with the closeness of texture and the insight to which we have become accustomed in English history.[16] The reign (and the better part of that of Louis XV) is still most easily narrated as a succession of crises, scandals and disjunct *causes célèbres*. The context and conditions of the political struggle, rather than its content, is what we know most about. In part this reflects contemporary difficulties. After the uproar in the second third of the century over the Jansenist–Jesuit issue, Frenchmen could not easily agree on a simplification which would make sense of their political struggles. In part this was shown by attempts to use the language of an earlier period after it had lost its vitality and meaning—by applying, for example, the word 'Jansenist' in a purely non-religious sense, sometimes even ludicrously, as in its application to Mme Doublet's sceptical little 'parish'.[17] To a considerable extent, therefore, French politics in the last two decades of the *ancien régime* fell back on an interpretative language and conceptual framework which was a function of French institutions. Just as the content and concepts of the politics of any society are shaped by the political idiom available for their discussion and by the nature of the issues at stake, so they are delimited and biassed by the institutional forms available as the setting of political debate. Under the *ancien régime* these forms tended always to press debate towards something rather like accusatory procedure in a court of law. Political argument was predominately forensic in tone. Its statements almost always took the form of an argument by one of the participants in a two-sided exchange. These participants were usually the ministry and the sovereign courts (though other corporations joined in from time to time) and their arguments almost always related positive acts to vested interests or to constitutional principles alleged to be acceptable to all Frenchmen. Even the forms of legislative utterance and procedure helped to accentuate the impression of confrontation in an imaginary court. The business of registration, the *lits de justice*, the *arrêtés*, decrees and remonstrances all emphasized the resemblance to the dialogue of pleaders.[18] The problem was that there was no acknowledged judge.

[16] An obvious obstacle to providing one is, of course, the lack of any personal and institutional focus so dominating as the House of Commons, though it seems fair to remark that even when (in the Revolution) such a focus appears, French historians do not seem to favour political history; the Convention awaits its Namier. It is the economic and social historians who have provided the sustaining continuities of French eighteenth-century history.

[17] On y était janséniste, ou du moins très parlementaire, mais on n'y était pas chrétien'; *Correspondance littéraire, philosophique et critique par Grimm, Diderot, etc.*, ed. M. Tourneaux (Paris, 1877), ix, pp. 317–18.

[18] And, of course, many of these were published so that the assumptions

Of the two disputants in this model, it was of the very nature of government under the *ancien régime* that the ministry should on the whole sustain an innovatory, sometimes a radical role. After all, it almost always had the initiative. Its opponents tended to respond to initiatives rather than to take them. Neither of these statements is absolute—the skill with which the *parlements* could exploit opportunities in a positive way was, for example, shown in the attack on the Jesuits—nonetheless, the tendency runs clearly enough. Yet it would be misleading to move (as some have done) from this view to a categorization of the *parlements* as 'conservative' in any except a very limited and historical sense. Still less would it be proper to say that the *parlements* represent a future 'Right' while their opponents do not. Among those opponents were the reforming ministers, not one of whom did not see his work as essentially conservative—of the monarchy, the state, their greatness and true interests. It was Calonne, a quarry pursued by the Parlement of Paris even after he had gone into exile, who was to be the future minister of the counter-revolution. The terms of the quarrel of the end of the *ancien régime* have to be transcended before the categories of a new politics can become meaningful.

The favourite theme of the *parlementaires* in these years when their polemics sought for continuing realities was a real one, a debate over the actual nature of the French state. It found its usual expression in the old warhorse which they always let out for a canter when tempers ran high, the cry of *despotisme ministériel*. In principle, it was what almost everyone in France who thought about these things was in favour of attacking in 1789, because it was the antithesis of constitutional, limited government. But although agreement that ministerial responsibility would be a good thing was general in 1789, that was where agreement stopped. And this was mainly because 'ministerial despotism' had become a catchphrase which had obstructed thought on the real problem which lay behind it, the nature of the French constitution and the problem of sovereignty.

Both aspects of the problem, the positive impact of arbitrary government and the fundamental deadlock over sovereignty can be

---

of this model were widely diffused. R. W. Greenlaw pointed out that *arrêtés* and other official declarations or statements by *parlements* or similar bodies made up almost one-third of the publications he considered: 'Pamphlet Literature in France during the period of the aristocratic revolt (1787–1788)', *Journal of Modern History* (1957), xxix, p. 351. The proportion (of a lower absolute total) would probably have been higher at earlier periods when restrictions on publication were more effective. The Crown often published its replies to the assertions of corporate bodies, thus tending to accentuate the impression of a dialogue.

seen clearly in the great political crisis which began the last phase of the *ancien régime*—the 'Maupeou revolution'.[19]

Its essence was Maupeou's response to a strike begun by the Paris *parlement* in December 1770. This had been provoked by the violent language of a royal decree warning *parlementaires* of the consequences of indiscipline: a registration had been imposed by a *lit de justice*. This quarrel was seemingly on the mend when a dramatic move by the Chancellor detonated a much more serious explosion. Early in the morning of 20 January 1771 each magistrate of the Paris *parlement* was woken by an officer with a file of soldiers who ordered him to say at once whether or not he would resume his duties. Those who refused were exiled the same day. This angered their colleagues who had agreed to resume work; they too now withdrew their acquiescence and in due course also left for exile. A large area of France was now a judicial void; the creation in April of a new reformed judicial structure to fill the gap, and the consequential abolition of other institutions (among them venality of office) were the core of the 'revolution' and provoked a further furious outburst of pamphleteering. In 1772 the turmoil subsided; the new arrangements got under way and lasted until 1774, when they were swept away at Maupeou's fall from office and the *parlementaires* were recalled.

This was clearly *despotisme ministériel* in its most outrageous form, thought the *parlementaires*. Maupeou's musketeers were still being cited twenty years later.[20] Some critics saw in the coup the ultimate degradation of the state, a relapse into the practices of the Sultan: 'il s'agit de force ouverte, de main armée, pour renverser les loix de l'Etat, détruire la Monarchie Française, et fonder en France le despotisme Oriental'.[21] Ministerial despotism had shown its teeth and

---

[19] About which debate continues. See, for example, W. Doyle, 'The Parlements of France and the Breakdown of the Old Regime 1771–1788', *French Historical Studies*, vi (1970) and J. Egret, *Louis XV et l'opposition parlementaire* (Paris, 1970), for two recent attempts to explain it. The fullest study and point of departure is the old book by J. Flammermont, *Le Chancelier Maupeou et les parlements* (Paris, 1883). M. Antoine's recent study *Le Conseil du roi sous le règne de Louis XV* (Geneva, 1970) illuminates the crisis in passing from the point of view of government, and another relevant recent article is by J. F. Bosher, 'The French Crisis of 1770', *History*, vii (1972).

[20] 'Ces disgraces, ces efforts, que l'on fait sous différentes formes pour empêcher la verité de parvenir jusqu'au trone, n'annoncent que trop le changement du constitution que les ennemis de la magistrature avaient tenté dès 1771' said the premier president of the Parlement of Paris at the sitting of 8 May 1788; *Archives parlementaires*, i, p. 316.

[21] *Réflexions générales sur le Système projetté par le Maire du Palais, pour changer la Constitution de l'Etat* (Paris, 1771), p. 52. On 24 June 1772 Malesherbes used the same comparison in a letter to Mme Douet: 'L'administration établie en France depuis quelque tems et à laquelle on a donné le

its opponents ever after suspected the worst; in 1787, rumour said that Calonne had 33 *lettres de cachet* ready for signature in order to purge the Assembly of Notables.[22]

Now Calonne, too, was a conservative, somewhat in the style of a more polished Strafford. To apply the anachronistic antithesis of liberal–conservative or Left–Right to such conflicts is only to make them harder to understand. The interpretative scheme chosen by the participants in them was very different. Eighteenth-century Frenchmen on both sides turned for guidance (as had Englishmen a hundred and fifty years before) to the fundamental laws of the kingdom: *despotisme ministériel* could be checked—or shown not to be *despotisme*—by reference to the constitution. Unfortunately, as in England, there was no court of appeal, though the lawyers might seek to constitute themselves one.

The great set-to over Maupeou's coup provoked a mass of polemical literature embodying arguments almost all of which fell into this constitutional pattern. The *Protestations* to the king published by the princes of the blood provide an example; they stuck throughout to specific charges of constitutional innovation, pointing out that they had already written without success to the king 'pour lui faire connaître les surprises faites à sa Religion, la porter à établir l'ordre légal et public'.[23] The Chancellor, they assert, is attempting to subvert an existing and known constitution. The enemy they struggle against is the despotism which the lawyers always feared and detected lurking behind the acknowledged propriety of absolutism, and it seems to have been in this new crisis of an old debate that *patriote* acquired its new and commendatory overtones; it was applied to the pamphleteers who attacked the edict.[24] Their argument preserved the classical form of *parlementaire* argument throughout the century; it was never to be abandoned, but only to disappear with the sovereign courts themselves.[25] Similarly, the declarations of the government and its

dernier degré de perfection depuis . . . la destruction des cours, nous conduisoit au veritable despotisme oriental et non pas à celuy de Prusse ou d'Autriche'; P. Grosclaude, *Malesherbes et son temps. Nouveaux documents inédits* (Paris, 1964), pp. 75–76.

[22] *Mémoires secrets pour servir à l'histoire de la république des lettres en France depuis MDCCLXII jusqu'à nos jours* (London, 1774–89), xxx, pp. 13–14 (entry for 22 April 1787).

[23] *Protestations des Princes du sang, Contre l'Edit de Décembre 1770* (Paris, 1771), p. 6. It is interesting that this pamphlet speaks of 'citoyens'.

[24] *Mémoires secrets*, xxi, p. 20.

[25] Even the wittiest of attacks on the chancellor only goes in one respect beyond the constitutional argument, and does so only by accusing the minister of personal financial corruption (*Maupeouana, ou Correspondance secrètte et familière du Chancelier Maupeou avec son cœur Sorhouet*, Paris, 1773, pp. 22 ff).

pamphleteers concentrated on the argument that the *parlements* are arrogating powers which are not theirs. Both sides agree on the form of the argument: a constitution exists and what is in question is what it means. This acceptance of the terms of debate was pervasive; it seems wilfully and anachronistically misunderstanding to say, as one writer has done, that 'the immense and unshakeable popularity of the parlements suggest how little rational political discussion there was in eighteenth-century France'.[26] There was a great deal and the *parlements'* popularity rested in some measure on it, but it was not, of course, in the idiom of the next century.

The constitution about which debate took place was envisaged as a mass of particular and known laws, liberties, customs and, above all, privileges which regulated the king's rule of his subjects. Historic practice and the judicial protection of specific rights sustained it. Some laws were thought especially sacred: they were fundamental to the constitution of the kingdom and could not be changed even by the acknowledged absolute power of the monarchy. The Salic law was the classical example on which everyone could agree, but there were others. The Princes of the Blood spoke of the 'heureuse impuissance où sont les Rois de France de changer . . . les Institutions primordiales et sacrées qui tiennent à la constitution de l'Etat'.[27] Even the crown's undoubted right to make laws for the good of Frenchmen could not extend so far. On the title-page of one of the anti-Maupeou pamphlets of 1771 appears a quotation from Bossuet which expresses this very clearly: 'il est de Loix fondamentales qu'on ne peut changer . . . Le gouvernement arbitraire où il n'y a de Loi que la volonté du Prince, ne se trouve pas dans les Etats parfaitement policés, il n'a pas lieu parmi nous, il est visiblement opposé au gouvernement légitime'.[28]

In 1789, it is well known, such a view no longer appealed to all Frenchmen. 'Songez avant tout que vous n'avez pas eu de constitution, que vous devez en établir une', wrote one pamphleteer in 1789; this was to pose the question of national sovereignty.[29] 'Avant de créer une Constitution, examinez s'il n'en existe pas une qui ne demande qu'à être rétablie dans toute sa pureté' was a conservative reply, but hardly one which met the case.[30] It was precisely the difficulty of deciding what was such a constitution that led to a cry for a new one. Maupeou had had plenty of time to reflect on these matters; doubtless

[26] P. Gay, *Voltaire's Politics, The Poet as Realist* (Princeton, 1959), p. 323.
[27] *Protestations*, p. 5.
[28] *Réflexions générales.* Eighteen years before, the Parlement of Paris quoted just the same passage from Bossuet in a remonstrance (printed in *Remonstrances du Parlement de Paris au xviiie siècle,* ed J. Flammermont, i (Paris, 1888), p. 526).
[29] *A la nation française,* cited in *Archives parlementaires,* i, p. 572.
[30] *Journal Général de France,* pp. 193–96 (23 Apr. 1789).

he put it in too narrowly polemical a manner, but nevertheless he hit the real target when he looked back on the events of his chancellorship for the benefit of Louis XVI: 'avions-nous un seul souverain, ou la France était-elle soumise à douze aristocraties?'[31] By 1789 a few more people had probably come to see things in this way and this is one of the evolutions which French political thinking goes through in the last twenty years or so of the *ancien régime*, the dark age which sees the crystallization of many of the elements from which later Right-wing views were to be assembled. They were already beginning to help to prise apart the old sequences of constitutional debate; the assembly of the Estates-General exploded them. It was bound to do so, for few people dared to sustain the proposition that the Estates-General did not embody a legislative power superior to that of the Crown and to the validating power of the sovereign courts.[32] But the question of sovereignty was still not clear; how far could the Estates-General go? Not dangerously far, thought some. The *parlements* began the campaign for the Estates-General thinking it fitted their view of the constitution and the assembly of the clergy also asked for them.[33] Misgivings were not slow to appear, nonetheless. At the heart of them was the key-question of the early revolution—privilege. But that was still not enough for the language of debate yet to transcend the old terms in most instances.[34] The outstanding example of its beginning to do so before 1789 is the *mémoire* from the princes to the king after the second Assembly of Notables.[35]

One important development, nonetheless, had been taken in political thinking, and taken almost unawares. Both sides of the old *ancien régime* political battle had drifted almost unaware into a shared

[31] Flammermont, *Le chancelier Manpeou et les parlements*, p. 623.

[32] A point appreciated by the party of progress but not overlooked by all conservatives. It appears to have been only in 1771 that a parlement (Rouen), for the first time in the eighteenth century asked for the summoning of the Estates-General (R. Bickart, *Les Parlements et la notion de souveraineté nationale au xviiie siècle*, Paris, 1932, p. 249). No doubt the idea had been maturing well before this. M. Antoine reveals (*Le Conseil du roi*, p. 428) that the idea was being canvassed on the other side of the political fence by quoting Bourgeois de Boynes: 'on ne voit rien qui puisse opérer cet effect (of curbing the parlements) plus efficacement que l'assemblée des états généraux, par ce qu'il est bien certain que la force des parlements a pour base le principe qu'ils cherchent à établir qu'ils représentent les états, du Royaume.' But, he went on to say, 'est-on sûr que l'assembléedes états généraux, après avoir réduit à justes bornes l'autorité des parlements, ne s'occuperait pas des moyens de tempérer aussi la trop grande autorité du Roi?'.

[33] *Ibid.*, pp. 385–86. Mr Doyle has noted that the clergy had been opposed to the recall of the *parlements* fifteen years before (*op. cit.*, p. 441).

[34] See the language of a conservative case set out by a minister to the royal council, 27 December 1788; *Archives parlementaires*, i, p. 489.

[35] *Ibid.*, pp. 487–89.

assumption that there lay at the heart of French political life some kind of appeal to the people. Later, conservatives were to see in this a grave mistake. It was said already in 1788: 'dans une Monarchie, il ne faut pas accoutumer le peuple à juger les matières d'Etat'.[36] Incoherences soon began to appear in the conservative camp as the pamphlet debate on the forms and powers of the Estates-General got under way, but an example of the slow evolution of the ideas even of people whose interests were obviously 'conservative' is provided by the king's speech in the *séance royale* of 23 June 1789.[37] This was the last attempt of the monarchy to impose its political will through the forms of the *ancien régime* before turning to force and it is interesting to see in what narrow terms the royal policy was still at this late date conceived. Many reforms were offered, in the best tradition of enlightened despotism. Yet the monarchy still shied at the fence of sovereignty to which it was urged by its wisest counsellors; the Tennis Court oath was to be nullified and the National Assembly was to resume its debates with the system of three orders intact. The monarchy, that is to say, still could not disentangle its own interests from privilege, from the very institutional setting which had prejudiced them. Given this conservative reluctance to recognize a clear legislative supremacy in Crown and Assembly together, the practical reforms conceded (eventual abolition of fiscal privilege, abolition of *lettres de cachet* and so on) were beside the point. But the failure which was embodied in this programme was not merely a failure of political imagination, but of political intellect. Old conservatism could not yet accept the idea of legislative sovereignty.[38]

When that happened and when the particular questions of *ancien régime* politics had been transcended, then the modern Right would exist. But this evolution must not be anticipated. On the eve of Revolution, notable though the evolution of political thought since 1771 might be, it had not gone so far as to overcome divisions which had to be overcome if politics were to be realigned on a Left/Right basis. Many people still found the received political idiom adequate

[36] J. P. Papon, *Histoire du gouvernement françois, depuis l'assemblée des Notables* . . . (London, 1788), p. 78, a work strongly condemning the first Assembly of Notables and another candidate for the distinction of being the earliest expression of the thesis that the nobles started the Revolution.

[37] *Archives parlementaires*, viii, pp. 143–46.

[38] It is fair to say that the Right always found it difficult to overcome its distrust of an unrestricted sovereignty which might, after all, be misused. Much of the next century was to be spent seeking a principle of authority which would control and validate the operation of unrestricted law-making power. In the long run, the Right usually plumped for Legitimism and/or Rome. But difficulties were likely to arise in a crisis—when, for example, a king conceded a constitutional charter or when, as in 1871, a legitimist pretender did not come up to scratch.

for their thinking on these issues. However accelerated the process, the final clarification had not occurred by 1789. It could only come with the great institutional and theoretical upsets of 1789–91, the terrible simplifications which the Revolution imposed on French political thought. Soon, Frenchmen who did not find a plausible reading of the national life in terms of antithetical opposites were nonetheless to be driven to doing so by opponents who did. From two stances about the Revolution, Left and Right were suddenly and finally born.

When that happened, not only the meaning of the present, but that of the past was suddenly clarified. Frenchmen looked back and thought they could see in the past the adumbration of what they now knew to be true. The Revolution made explicit a politics which the Right would say had been really going on for twenty years and more. The struggles of the *ancien régime* were then seen as prefigurations of those of 1789–91; no doubt they were somewhat clumsy prefigurations, for the actors moved stiffly in the gothick trappings of traditional practice and constitutional theory, but they were real prefigurations, nonetheless, to those who were ready to believe. Men remembered things seen and felt; their true meaning was now revealed.

This makes it important to distinguish precisely what it was that had happened before 1789 which went to the making of Right-wing mentality at the end of the day, how it was that the elements in this mentality evolved towards the later synthesis. The core of that synthesis was a pessimistic belief that what was at stake in the Revolution was much more than forms, interests or privilege. What was at stake was the whole social order. It was during the closing years of the *ancien régime* that some men began to accumulate the basic materials which would eventually sustain this idea, and as they did so, they felt they were discerning behind the comings and goings of French politics a consistent theme giving a meaning to those events concealed from those who simply accepted them at their face-values. Like their opponents, the men of the Right took a selective view of the *ancien régime*, thus achieving a new view of the past, built round themes and emphases which gave it consistency. New patterns were discerned in familiar facts. This was a part of the process by which elements central to the mentality of the Right when it at last became clearly discernible were picked up from the years before 1789 and gradually combined into a new whole.

There is one particularly striking example: the *philosophe* bugbear. It was to have a long and respectable life and it, too, may be conveniently approached by way of the Maupeou revolution. This is a good place to begin because very little of that episode in fact touched on this bugbear: it is one of the revealing cases when the dog did nothing in the night. In the storm aroused by that coup, we can discern few traces, and at most only fugitive ones, of a willingness to extend the debate beyond the traditional area and into more general questions of ideology. In so far as the debate did broaden, it appears to be the Chancellor who in an aside, introduced these wider themes. In the edict of December 1770, he referred to an 'esprit de système' which he detected in the attitude of the *parlements*, and attributed to it 'funestes atteintes' against religion and morals.[39] The *parlements*, that is to say, were tarred with the brush of *philosophie* in his eyes. Or so he said; the assertion did not appeal to his opponents. 'Des personnes qui connaissent particulièrement m. René-Nicolas-Charles-Augustin de Maupeou', wrote one pamphleteer, 'le voyant, dès l'entrée dans sa funeste carrière, s'ajuster la masque du zèle pour la Religion et pour les mœurs, se sont écriés, *Ah l'hip . . . ! Oh le scel . . . ! Il ne croit pas en Dieu*. Qui ignore, en effet, ses liaisons avec Voltaire et autres ennemis de la Religion et des mœurs; la protection qu'il a accordée a l'Encylopédie et autres mauvais livres; les obstacles qu'il a mis à la publication des écrits faits pour les combattre?' He went on then to turn the charge of 'esprit de système' against Maupeou himself by using the phrase in a slightly different sense to cover the Chancellor's dogmatic vanity which (he said) would make all things new without regard for tradition or consequence.[40]

The significance of such an exchange surely lies not in the truth or falsity of the charge, but that it should be thought telling. Nonetheless, it was unusual for constitutional debate to enter this territory and this appears with striking clarity in Voltaire's own contribution to the argument on behalf of the Chancellor. In 1771 appeared his short and tendentious work, *Les peuples aux parlements*. He chose as his opening theme a simple assertion of constitutional law: that the *parlements* were not *Etats*, but subordinate tribunals. This was a conclusion which might be contested, but it was irreproachably within the traditional framework of French juridico-historical debate. From this point he proceeded, it is true, with a pragmatic argument, invoking the memory of Calas as evidence that such tribunals could not dispense with a controlling and correcting authority; the new arrangements were, therefore, desirable on practical grounds, and should not be resisted. This, too, was basically a conservative argument: it evoked the traditional duty of the crown to act for the public good. But at bottom Voltaire's case rests on two propositions of history and law; that the *parlements* were not sovereign legislative bodies, and that a superior constitutional authority belonged to the king's council, the *conseil d' état*. Besides prompting the reflexion that it is interesting to find Voltaire on this side at all if Maupeou's assertions in the

---

[39] Flammermont, *op. cit.*, p. 116.
[40] *Réflexions générales . . .*, pp. 4–5.

edict are meaningful, the pamphlet's lack of ideological content is striking.[41]

Twenty years later, the contrast is evident. In 1790 a monarchist journalist launched a new newspaper, the *Ami du Roi*. Announced as an attempt to provide a continuous narrative of the political events of the Revolution, its parts were republished the following year preceded by a historical account bringing its readers down to the moment of publication and continued until 1792. At the very beginning of the work, the theme of a *philosophe* conspiracy is prominent. Picking up the trail in the second half of the reign of Louis XV, with the suppression of the Jesuits, the author puts it in a striking way, 'alors se forme cette ligue', he says, 'cette conspiration contre l'auteur même du notre religion'.[42] It is an important point: the hated enemy who is triumphing in the Revolution is identified in the first place not as anti-monarchical, but as anti-Christian. The charge of insurrection against royal authority only comes a little later in this account. There is even denunciation of one monarch—unnamed, but presumably Frederick the Great—for his acquiesence in the *philosophe* conspiracy; it seems clear that the political threat in the *philosophe* ascendancy is seen as less threatening than the pagan. We have already reached the point where conservatism is sloughing off the scepticism of the *beau monde* of the *ancien régime*.

This idea embodied a view of recent French history which had been formulated over several decades and whose elements had, at the beginning, even been supplied by the 'enlightened' themselves. It was their correspondance which provided the ammunition their critics used. At the very beginning of Bachaumont's *Mémoires secrets* can be found a statement embodying the essence of what some enemies of the *philosophes* dreaded long before the Revolution provided them with justification.[43]

'L'Invasion de la Philosophie dans la République des lettres en France', says the *Avvertissement des editeurs*, 'est une époque mémorable par la Révolution qu'elle a operée dans les Esprits. Tout le monde en connaît aujourd'hui les suites et les effets. L'auteur des *Lettres Persannes* et celui des *Lettres Philosophiques*, en avaient jetté le germe; mais trois sortes d'Ecrivains ont surtout contribué à

---

[41] It may have something to do with the fact that Voltaire appears to have been writing specifically in reply to the *Protestations* of the princes. Diderot chided Voltaire for not going far enough and for showing too much restraint; *Œuvres complètes de Diderot*, vi (Paris, 1875), pp. 402–3.

[42] *L'ami du roi, des françois, de l'ordre et surtout de la vérité, ou Histoire de la Révolution de France et de L'Assemblée nationale* (Paris, 1791–92), i, p. 2. The author was Galart de Montjoie.

[43] *Mémoires secrets . . .* i, pp. iii–iv.

le développer. D'abord les *Encyclopédistes*, en perfectionnant la Métaphysique, en y portant la clarté, moyen le plus propre à dissiper les ténèbres dont la Théologie l'avait enveloppé, ont détruit le Fanatisme et la Superstition. A ceux-ci ont succedé les *Economistes*, s'occupant essentiellement de la morale de la Politique Pratique, ils ont cherché à rendre les Peuples plus heureux, en resserrant les liens de la société par une communication de services et d'échanges mieux entendus, en appliquant l'homme à l'étude de la Nature, mère des vraies jouissances. Enfin des tems de trouble et d'oppression ont enfanté les *Patriotes*, qui remontant à la source des Loix et de la Constitution des Gouvernements, ont démontré les obligations réciproques des Sujets et des Souverains, ont approfondi l'Histoire et ses monumens, et ont fixé les grands principes de l'Administration. Cette foule de Philosophes qui se sont placées comme à la tête des diverses parties de la Littérature, a principalement paru apres la Destruction des Jésuites: veritable point où la Révolution a éclaté.'

This is an almost classical formulation (though some would have antedated the *philosophe* success), remarkable on many grounds, but noteworthy here because it summarizes approvingly just such a view of the recent past as made sense of it to the bitterest opponents of the *philosophes*. 'Cette secte, depuis quarante ans acharnée à saper dans les ténèbres les fondemens du temple', as the *Journal Ecclésiastique* later put it, was for many men of the Right the very core of the danger they faced.[44] It was a danger which, as had been asserted before the Estates-General met, extended beyond religious to secular institutions, too.[45]

It is, of course, a particular version of the conspiracy view of history, a view, as is well known, which was not confined to the Right nor to the anti-*philosophe* thesis.[46] The heart of this idea is a belief in

[44] *Journal Ecclésiastique*, i (Paris, 1790), p. 3.

[45] 'Plaise à Dieu de conserver toujours à la France cette antique constitution qui, par la force de son esprit, supérieure à la révolution des temps et à la licence des opinions, a porté le royaume au plus haut degré de splendeur! S'il en pouvoit déchoir, ce serait par les illusions de cette philosophie téméraire qui depuis longtemps semble avoir entrepris de vouloir donner de nouvelles lois aux monde; qui voudrait tout détruire dans l'ordre politique, comme dans celui de la religion, sous prétexte de tout réformer, et qui professe hautement l'opposition à toutes les anciennes maximes.' From the remonstrance of the Clergy of France, 15 June 1788; *Archives parlementaires*, i, p. 379.

[46] I ignore here the masonic and protestant conspiracy hypotheses, which were certainly very important to men of the Right, because they are dealt with elsewhere. See my book on *The Mythology of the Secret Societies* (London, 1972), esp. pp. 146–202, and an article 'The Origins of a Mythology; Freemasons, Protestants and the French Revolution', *Bulletin of the Institute of*

conscious agency; very little consideration (if any) was given by its holders to the possibility that the *philosophes* might be fundamentally well-intentioned men whose mistaken views happened to have had unfortunate but unanticipated effects. A case might be made for saying that the first people to take up the conspiracy idea systematically were the *philosophes* themselves, with their talk of *l'infâme*, and they were equally relentless. The most celebrated and successful statement of the plot hypothesis, the *abbé* Barruel's famous work, too, did not say in it that the *philosophes* were guilty of the worst crimes against God and man, but gave them a subordinate role in his drama.[47] Yet long before the Revolution he had detected in the *philosophes* the great danger of the age. His first major work had been an exposure of the 'secte' and a refutation of its errors.[48] He brought especial keenness to the task of denunciation because he thought that the efforts of the *philosophes* to use their influence to silence him had begun some years before.[49]

The idea that there was a 'sect' or conscious subversive party did not first occur to Barruel and was very important. Its roots have already been alluded to: the assertions of the *philosophes* themselves. Their great triumph, in their own eyes and those of their critics, was the overthrow of the Jesuits. This had also had an important practical consequence in that many former Jesuits (Barruel was one) took to polemical journalism or attacked the victorious 'sect' from other refuges as preachers or teachers. Another cause of alarm was the worldly success of the *philosophes*. The extent of their assimilation by the establishment, culminating in their capture of the Academy in the 1770s has recently been pointed out.[50] Naturally, clerical

---

Historical Research, xliv (1971). It is worth noting that in each case, as in that of the *philosophe* scare, the elements from which the hard dogmas of the post-Revolution Right are fashioned are traceable well before 1789.

[47] A. Barruel, *Mémoires pour servir à l'histoire du Jacobinisme* (4 vols, London, 1797), of which only the first volume is devoted to the *philosophes*.

[48] *Les Helviennes, ou lettres provençales philosophiques* (Amsterdam, 1784–88).

[49] This was in controversy with another priest Soulavie, whose views on creation provoked Barruel to an angry rebuttal, *La Génèse selon M. Soulavie* in 1784. But, claimed Barruel, all copies had disappeared because their destruction had been ordered by the *Garde des Sceaux*; he therefore reprinted it in *Les Helviennes*, a law-suit followed and one can see how easily a suspicious man might couple to the idea that he was personally the object of persecution the idea that subversive influences were at work in high places. On the whole episode see A. Mazon, *Histoire de Soulavie* (Paris, 1893), i, pp. 31–35. Jean Louis Soulavie wrote a number of historical books and during the revolution had a brief and unfortunate career as a French diplomatic agent.

[50] By Mr R. Darnton in 'The High Enlightenment and the Low-Life of Literature in pre-Revolutionary France', *Past and Present*, li (1971).

opponents saw this as the fruit of backstairs influence and intrigue—as it sometimes was. They were the more alarmed because they did not make fine distinctions: the scurrilous *libelliste* and cultivated sceptic were all one to them. In an age when public opinion was becoming more important—'qui peuvent l'or et les soldats contre l'opinion?' asked a royalist journalist in 1790[51]—they saw the nefarious influence seeping downwards through society. One of the last Assemblies of the Clergy asked for stronger censorship on the grounds that 'les leçons de la nouvelle philosophie retentissent jusque dans les ateliers des artisans et sous l'humble toit du cultivateur'.[52] The danger seemed very real, given the rising tide of publication in the last years of the *ancien régime*. The audience of the new literature still awaits exploration, and historians, being clerks, may overestimate the power of the written word, but the arguments set out in the numerous political books and pamphlets which appeared especially frequently after the American war show that people thought it worth while to debate in this way and may even show to what extent people thought it worth while. They help to make understandable the alarm of conservative writers. The language of these publications, too, reveals something about the way in which Frenchmen categorized and analysed their affairs. It is a language which does not remain static, but changes, and one of the most striking changes is a growing tendency to involve the 'natural law' terminology associated with the *philosophes*.

By 1789 many Frenchmen certainly felt that they were in the presence of a genuine public opinion, the sounding board and court of appeal taken for granted in the modern political style. It flourished in print, thrived in the *salon* and the *café*. This favoured the emergence of a new idiom of debate which was able, given a coincidence of economic bad times and an acute attack of the chronic and rumbling financial and administrative ills of the *ancien régime*, to provide Frenchmen with an accepted and intelligible political outlook. It did not happen overnight, but within a very few months in the early Revolution the language of one political era was beginning to be replaced by that of a new, which revealed a new political world's existence. It was a world characterized by the either/or view of politics of which the Left/Right division has become the supreme expression. At that moment, the work of a few conservatives who had long urged that more than was apparent was going forward in the political events of the reign of Louis XV seemed suddenly justified. The great years of Fréron's anti-*philosophe* journal, the *Année*

---

[51] *L'Ami du Roi, loc. cit.*

[52] Q. M. Perronet, 'Les Assemblées du clergé de France sous le règne de Louis XVI (1775–1788)', *Annales Historiques de la Révolution Française*, xxxiv (1962), p. 14.

littéraire, had been the 1760s. As 1789 approached, his successors looked back to him more and more with reverence as the pioneer champion of religion and a discerning prophet. They flattered themselves that under them the paper was still, as it had been in his day, the object of a special persecution. 'Quels efforts pour l'anéantir', wrote one contributor in 1788; 'son existence, au centre de la philosophie moderne, scandalise autant les servans de la secte, qu'une église au milieu des mosquées choqueroit les regards des bons Musulmans'.[53] When it finally went under in 1789, the paper's director promptly started a newspaper which proclaimed just the same distrust and hatred of *la secte* and began by invoking Fréron's memory as an inspiration.[54]

The black legend of the *philosophes* had soon settled into a conventional, even canonical form. The prehistory was usually the Protestant Reformation. Then came the open proclamation of first enlightened and then atheistical principles in the eighteenth century. The publication of the *Encyclopédie* and the victory over the Jesuits were the two great events; they were followed by sustained subversive influence in government under Choiseul, a favourite target of anti-*philosophe* writers. Next in the demonological succession were the *économistes*; at the end of the procession was the renegade prelate, Loménie de Brienne, whose alleged suicide was dwelt upon with mingled dismay and satisfaction, the first possibly less sincere than the second. Just before the Revolution, the edict conferring civil status on the French Protestants was taken as a final and particularly flagrant instance of the improper influence of the *philosophes*.[55]

With the Revolutionary enlargement of the area of debate as more and more legislation affected the standing of religion and the interests of the Church, the continuation of this scenario was only too easy. Soon Antraigues was able to attack a declaration by the French bishops in the debate over the standing of Catholicism as an established religion, for not going far enough, for not revealing 'dans toute son étendue, le plan des destructeurs de la religion catholique; et se bornant à défendre les principes de l'église contre les attaques de l'assemblée nationale, il n'a pas développé dans sa totalité, le plan longtemps médité par les impies, les protestans, les philosophes, et

---

[53] *Année Littéraire*, 1788, i, p. 20. Elie Catherine Fréron (1718–76) had founded the journal in 1714; it was sometimes suspended by the censor, misfortunes usually attributed by the editor to the influence of his enemies. See on him the eulogistic but informative book of F. Cornou, *Elie Fréron (1718–1776)*, (Paris and Quimper, 1922).

[54] This was another paper called *L'Ami du Roi*.

[55] For a typical account see *L'Ami du Roi* (Montjoie's), i, pp. 1–11 and, on the last point references in Roberts, in *Bulletin of the Institute of Historical Research*, xliv (1971), already cited.

qui l'assemblée nationale tente d'exécuter, en renversant l'édifice de la religion de nos pères, sur les débris sanglantes de la monarchie française'.[56] The culmination was, of course, the Civil Constitution of the Clergy and laws against non-juring priests.

By this time the legend emerging during the decades before the Revolution, whose centre was the *philosophe* bugbear, had reached maturity. The announced intentions of some *philosophes* had provided the clue that a larger significance could be given to historical events than the mere registration of success or failure by traditional contestants seeking to uphold their own interest. Yet though the idea of a *philosophe* plot provided the point of departure for an historical scenario later approved by the Right, it was the danger of total subversion which in the end provided its metaphysic. The final clarification and acceptance of this historical view came only with the Revolution but the groundwork was being done long before by lonely, untypical men, preaching against the prevailing currents. They provided, in the end, the fundamental ideas which are a part of the explanation of the leap of French political consciousness; between 1771 and 1791 France went in a bound from the politics of the early Stuart parliaments to those of the Great Reform Bill.[57] This was something shared by both sides, for (to reiterate) the emergence of a new politics is precisely this, the emergence of the two-pole, Left–Right view of politics. The Right-wing vision of this scheme, long only the concern of a few churchmen divided from other conservatives by their defiance of the prevalent scepticism of French society, was embodied in the ideology which became the stamp of the *bien pensant*. An attitude rooted in a specific and ancient dread of irreligion had grown gradually into a terror of the general and universal calling in question to which philosophy had led. The social integration of the *philosophes* with *le monde* and their pretty general vested interest in it counted for nothing against what were conceived as the objective results and significance of what they did. They had shaken confidence in everything; nothing was sacred any more.[58] When the Left more and more

---

[56] H. A. Audainel (pseud.), *Dénonciation aux Français catholiques des moyens employés par l'Assemblée nationale, pour détruire en France, la religion catholique* (London and Paris, 1791), p. 2.

[57] The parallel has a little more than illustrative significance, for many Frenchmen in the revolutionary crisis showed their awareness of similarities between their situation and that of Englishmen in the seventeenth century. There is no space to pursue this here, but I hope to write about it elsewhere. These conscious similarities operated in many ways, among them by contributing to the later anglophobia of the French Right and, of course, to its obsession with Protestantism.

[58] In the light of subsequent revolutionary changes which were to do much to substantiate these fears, it is interesting to see how even secondary revolu-

after 1789 stressed the international and universal significance of what was happening in France, this vision seemed all the more persuasive. Perhaps such an emphasis had always been implicit in the idea of a *philosophe* plot: the target of much practical and theoretical criticism by men of the enlightenment was, after all, the Church, a universal institution. There are also some signs that a consciousness of the whole social fabric being at stake was prompted by other reflexions, too. It would be interesting to see how far back these can be traced, though there is no space to do this here. Misgivings multiplied during the pre-revolutionary crisis. An anonymous pamphleteer from the Dauphiné undoubtedly expressed views not held only by the legally privileged when he wrote in December 1788 that 'en politique, comme en moral, rien n'est plus dangereux que de vouloir tout détruire pour réedifier et qu'en portant ainsi la cognée à l'aveugle, on s'expose à retomber dans l'anarchie'.[59]

Startling, even cataclysmic and therefore truly innovatory as the Revolution may have been in the matter of political thinking, therefore, it did not create a new politics out of nothing. Some of the components of what was to become classical Right-wing mentality are to be discerned well before 1789. What the Revolution provided was the spur of painful change and whole sets of new facts. These were soon to be regarded as conclusive evidence for what had been asserted only in a disjointed, individual, particular way under the *ancien régime*, and for a long time, too, only by relatively few people. The new facts were suddenly understood as a demonstration of what was implicit in the politics of the *ancien régime*. The result was a quite new sense of the scope and importance of what was at stake in the debates of the Constituent Assembly. In looking at one facet of the process by which modern politics came into being we find ourselves considering a conflict of ideologies whose roots cannot be explained, therefore, if we confine ourselves to the Revolution itself.[60] One consequence is that we must once more blur the old line which divided *ancien régime* and Revolution and which has been blurred by so many historians in other ways. It has been, and of course remains, important to recognize

---

tionary manifestations could be anticipated. In January 1788 the *Journal Ecclésiastique* (pp. 110–11) reported that proposals to modernize the calendar were under consideration. There was talk, it said, of 'l'an premier de la règne de raison', of holidays named 'fête de l'Amour' or 'de la Reconnaissance et de l'Amitié.'

[59] J. Egret, *Les derniers Etats de Dauphiné* (Grenoble, 1924), pp. 92–93. The more spectacular example of concern of the *Mémoire* of the princes of the blood has already been referred to.

[60] Professor Beik makes the point with special reference to the continuing preoccupation of many conservatives with safeguards against absolutism; *The French Revolution seen from the Right*, p. 4.

that if we do want to choose a date for the beginning of modern history, 1789 has better claims than any other year. But it will be necessary also to remember that to understand the politics of the nineteenth century we have to try to understand the different politics of the eighteenth—and not merely because those politics provided the setting of the Revolutionary crisis.

Nevertheless, it is in France even more true than in Germany or England that the Revolution is the great crystallizing and creative force. When men consciously accept the bipolar, Left–Right mythology, we have reached (in terms of political culture) the nineteenth century: whichever of its elements can be detected before 1789, they are only elements. A secondary aim of this short set of reflexions has been to insist that it is anachronistic and misleading to use words like 'liberal' or 'conservative' of the politics of the *ancien régime* in any but the most specific sense, in one, that is to say, which is defined by recognition of the necessary relativity of such notions to the political forms, institutional and intellectual, of the day.[61] Before 1789 there were certainly people advocating humanitarian and national goals which would later be sought just as eagerly by nineteenth-century admirers who saw in them forerunners; there were also men tenaciously defending the *status quo* as they saw it. But this does not mean that confusion will not result from seeking 'liberalism' in the resistance of the sovereign courts to *despotisme ministériel* or from struggling to allocate between them and their ministerial opponents the label 'conservative'; both of them are entitled to it. 'Liberal' and 'conservative' principles could be combined in an age when these two alternatives did not exhaust all the possibilities of politics. We have to deal with men of the eighteenth century and must not be misled by the fact that we still use much of their terminology into thinking that we understand it in the same way.

Since the whole conventional literature is soaked in this anachronistic assumption this point is of great importance.[62] Historians have, by and large, been until recently too ready to accept

---

[61] Anachronism creeps in even when an attempt is made to use such words restrictively. A useful account suddenly remarks that 'on sait, en effet, que sous les dehors libéraux, les parlementaires déguisaient le plus étroit conservatisme social, le plus âpre égoisme politique' (R. Bickart, *Les Parlements et la notion de souveraineté nationale*, pp. 278–79).

[62] Many examples could be given but one to be cited with respect (both because of the range of information it compresses and because of the stimulus it has given to scholarship and teaching) is Professor R. R. Palmer's *The Age of the Democratic Revolution* (Princeton, 1964). The notion of a bipolar system of politics essentially continuous from 1760 to 1800 is fundamental to this work. A more specific and common example is the interpretation of the *parlements'* behaviour (along the lines indicated in the passage from Bickart just cited) by those in the tradition of Flammermont.

the mythology which only won acceptance as a result of the French Revolution—that liberals and conservatives had been consciously locked in combat before 1789. So they had, of course, but the unspoken presumption that this implies anything of the generality or clarity of such terms in the nineteenth century, or that people could not be 'liberal' or 'conservative' on one issue but not on another, is not true. Moreover, besides carrying with it the danger of deforming historical actuality, such terminology also forces us to leave out much in politics which can only be described in different terms.[63] An anachronistic extension backwards of the myth has for too long saved us the labour of trying to understand the eighteenth century in terms of its own categories, and should now be given up. The very totality of the change implied by the eventual restoration of ideology to European politics makes it clear how far beyond eighteenth-century assumptions such a change goes. In 1789, the process by which different conservative interests were to consolidate had still hardly started along the road to anything like a general acceptance of such views as those of De Maistre on the Right. But when this process was completed, ideology would find a place for everything in its condemnation: steam-engines, gaslights, *laissez-faire*, Lancastrian schools, juries, freedom of the press, Kantian philosophy, bible societies—the list is endless. Its comprehensiveness reminds us how different is the ideal of the true Right from that of the differing conservatisms of the eighteenth century—or, indeed, from that conservatism with which, mercifully, we are more familiar in our own historical tradition.

Merton College, Oxford

[63] A point which may also be thought worth making about the history of the Revolutionary era itself. This is not only a matter of the growing complexity revealed by social historians to lie behind such simplifying abstractions as *peuple* and *sans-culotte*; there is also the detail of faction to account for. An example is the curious association of Pétion and Antraigues touched on by Mlle Chaumié (*Le reseau d' Antraigues*, p. 12).

AGE AT MARRIAGE IN ENGLAND FROM THE LATE SEVENTEENTH TO THE NINETEENTH CENTURY

By R. B. Outhwaite, B.A., Ph.D., F.R.Hist.S.

READ 12 MAY 1972

IN the two centuries after 1700 there occurred upwards of twenty million marriages in England and Wales.[1] It is perhaps forgivable, therefore, that this paper has about it the air of an interim report. It might be thought doubly foolish for an individual, and in this field a professedly amateur investigator, to embark upon any enquiry into past demographic behaviour when there exists that formidable, professional task force, the Cambridge Group for the History of Population and Social Structure. At the last count it had within its lockers, for example, 'aggregate analyses' of over 550 English parishes.[2] To provide information about the ages at which people married, however, the Cambridge Group appears to be relying primarily upon 'family reconstitution' techniques. It is not necessary to explain these techniques or to describe the remarkable light they have shed on the vital events of the past. With such tools the Cambridge Group have not only crept literally between the sheets of history; its individual members have not been abashed at publishing their preliminary findings.[3] Yet obscurity remains and with it the thought that family reconstitution may not prove entirely adequate to the insistent demands for more information on when and why people married. For the undertaking of full family reconstitution both registration and record survival have to be good, and the method is undermined where there is a great deal of migration, albeit temporary or permanent. Unfortunately many of the most interesting demographic questions revolve around urban behaviour, and town

[1] I wish to thank Mr Gareth Rees for this calculation and to express my gratitude also to the Research Board of the University of Leicester for the financial help extended to me.

[2] 'News from the Cambridge Group', *Local Population Studies*, v (1970), p. 7.

[3] See, for example, P. Laslett, *The World We Have Lost* (London, 2nd edn, 1971); E. A. Wrigley, *Population and History* (London, 1969); and R. S. Schofield, 'Historical Demography: Some Possibilities and Some Limitations', *Transactions of the Royal Historical Society*, 5th series, xxi (1971), pp. 119–32. 'Aggregate Analysis' and 'Family Reconstitution' are described at length in *An Introduction to English Historical Demography*, ed. D. E. C. Eversley, P. Laslett and E. A. Wrigley (London, 1966).

records may be deficient on many of these counts, especially in that vital and perplexing period from about 1780 to 1840. To secure an adequate sample the parish to be reconstituted has to be fairly large, and this adds to the laboriousness of the exercise. It is perhaps not insignificant that so far only one complete reconstitution study has been published by the Cambridge Group.[4] Moreover, if, as Wrigley suggests in that study, 'Societies are unwilling to allow matters to reach a Malthusian extreme', it is still not altogether clear why the marriage age of both men and women at Colyton should have *fallen* before the advent of the plague of 1645–46, and why the marriage age of women especially should have climbed so abruptly thereafter.[5] To test possible explanations more information is required about such things as the occupational structure, employment opportunities, the movement of real wages, and the pattern of migration. Unfortunately parish registers are often deficient in one crucial respect: they rarely consistently provide information about occupations. If this deficiency is remedied by using other documents in association with the registers, then obvious problems of occupational mobility within the lifetime of the persons examined begin to arise. The recent reconstitution study of three Lancashire parishes by D. J. Loschky and D. F. Krier relies partly upon wills.[6] But a man who died a farmer need not necessarily have been married as one. All this tends also to reduce the size of the sample. Loschky and Krier, for example, undertake an elaborate analysis of marital behaviour within particular social and occupational groups, and indeed extend their conclusions to English population experience generally, but four of the eight male groups appear to be based on the experiences of seven gentlemen, seven tradesmen, three clergymen, and a solitary pair of labourers.[7]

Whether agricultural groups married earlier or later than non-agricultural ones and how age at marriage has responded to modern economic growth are questions upon which opinion is divided. Conflict exists, not surprisingly, on the highest plane of generality—in general demography and the sociology of the family[8]—and it is, of course,

[4] E. A. Wrigley, 'Family Limitation in Pre-Industrial England', *Economic History Review*, 2nd series, xix (1966), pp. 82–109, and 'Mortality in Pre-Industrial England: The Example of Colyton, Devon, Over Three Centuries', *Daedalus* (Spring 1968), pp. 546–80.

[5] Wrigley, 'Family Limitation . . .', pp. 109 and 87.

[6] D. J. Loschky and D. F. Krier, 'Income and Family Size in Three Eighteenth-Century Lancashire Parishes: A Reconstitution Study', *Journal of Economic History*, xxix (1969), pp. 429–48.

[7] *Ibid.*, p. 436.

[8] See, for example, the statements on these themes in K. Davis and J. Blake, 'Social Structure and Fertility: An Analytical Framework', *Economic Development and Cultural Change*, iv (1955–56), pp. 211–35; K. Davis, 'Statistical

a part of that larger division of opinion about the effects of economic development upon fertility.[9] If attention is turned from the general to the particular—to the case of England in the eighteenth and nineteenth centuries—no unanimity emerges. There are those who have argued that there occurred at some time during this period a general decline in marriage ages. This group would include Habakkuk, Langer, and the most enthusiastic proponent of such views, J. T. Krause, who has argued that the fall was most pronounced *circa* 1780–1820.[10] Ranged with varying degrees of firmness in opposition are McKeown and Brown, Goode, Eversley, Razzell and Drake.[11] The reconstitution studies of Wrigley have clearly been influential in persuading Habakkuk recently to restate his beliefs.[12]

Despite the volume of opinion upon this subject, however, there are precious few references to the mean[13] age at marriage of English bachelors and spinsters from the late seventeenth century onwards, and what exists is extremely difficult to interpret. For the nineteenth century we have the Registrar General's national returns of mean age at first marriage. These exist for the years 1839–41, 1851, 1857–60,

---

Perspective on Marriage and Divorce' and J. Hajnal, 'The Marriage Boom', in *Demographic Analysis*, ed. J. J. Spengler and O. D. Duncan (Glencoe, 1956), pp. 243–55 and 220–42; W. J. Goode, *World Revolution and Family Patterns* (New York, 1963), chapter 2; E. van de Walle, 'Marriage and Marital Fertility', *Daedalus* (Spring 1968), pp. 486–501.

[9] D. M. Heer, 'Economic Development and Fertility', *Demography*, iii (1966), pp. 423–44, and 'Economic Development and the Fertility Transition', *Daedalus* (Spring 1968), pp. 447–62.

[10] H. J. Habakkuk, 'English Population in the Eighteenth Century', *Economic History Review*, 2nd series, vi (1953), pp. 117–33; W. M. Langer, 'Europe's Initial Population Explosion', *American Historical Review*, lxix (1963), pp. 1–17; and J. T. Krause, 'Some Neglected Factors in the English Industrial Revolution', *Journal of Economic History*, xix (1959), 528–40.

[11] T. McKeown and R. G. Brown, 'Medical Evidence Related to English Population Changes in the Eighteenth Century', *Population Studies*, ix (1955–56), pp. 119–41; Goode, *op. cit.*, p. 43; D. E. C. Eversley, 'Population, Economy and Society', in *Population in History*, ed. D. V. Glass and D. E. C. Eversley (London, 1965), pp. 40–45; P. E. Razzell, 'Population Change in Eighteenth Century England. A Reinterpretation', *Economic History Review*, 2nd series, xviii (1965), pp. 312–32; and 'Population Growth and Economic Change in Eighteenth- and Early-Nineteenth-Century England and Ireland', in *Land, Labour and Population in the Industrial Revolution*, ed. E. L. Jones and G. E. Mingay (London, 1967), pp. 260–81; M. Drake, 'Age at Marriage in the Pre-Industrial West', in *Population Growth and the Brain Drain*, ed. F. Bechofer (Edinburgh, 1969), pp. 196–208.

[12] H. J. Habakkuk, *Population Growth and Economic Development since 1750* (Leicester, 1971), pp. 35–46.

[13] All references to 'average' ages at marriage hereafter refer to the arithmetic mean. Although it may not always be the most appropriate measure of central tendency it is the one encountered most frequently in the literature.

and become continuous from 1867.[14] The series for both sexes show a remarkable small range of variation. The lowest figure we have for bachelors is that for 1839–41, 25·5 years, the highest figure that for 1899, 26·6; over the same period the average for spinsters rose only from 24·3 to 25·2 years. The earliest figures, however, were based on a very small sample, for in only about six per cent of all marriages did both parties return their age. By 1867, however, the return had risen to two-thirds. In 1897 the Registrar General looking back in time found it difficult to reconcile the slight reported rises of under one-third of a year between 1839–41 and 1867 with the rising proportions of marriages of minors over the same period, and he argued that in reality a fall in the age at marriage had occurred. The small early sample, he suggested, was biassed in the direction of the young, elderly couples being less likely to render their actual ages.[15] If the earliest figures are too low, however, the real ones were unlikely to have been substantially above the 25·8 for males and 24·6 for females based on the 37 per cent return for the year 1851.[16] Over half a century of profound structural change in both the economy and society appears, therefore, to have affected age at first marriage only slightly.

Longer-run comparisons are made difficult by the fact that before 1839 there are no national figures; there exist only figures for a few localities and these are produced by a variety of means. If attention is first confined to the few averages produced by family reconstitution then a number of features are immediately apparent.[17] There is no doubt that ages at first marriage of both males and females tended to vary over time, though the degree of variation observed depends both on the number of observations made in each time period and the length of the periods chosen for comparison.[18] Secondly, the direction

[14] These figures are to be found in the Fourth, Twentieth and the Thirtieth to the Sixty-Second Annual Reports of the Registrar General of Births, Deaths and Marriages in England.

[15] *Fifty-Ninth Annual Report of the Registrar General* (H[ouse of] C[ommons], 1897, xxi, p. 735), pp. ix–xiii.

[16] *Thirty-Fourth Annual Report of the Registrar General* (H.C. 1873, xx, p. 1), p. xii.

[17] The following discussion draws on the figures to be found in Wrigley, 'Family Limitation . . .', pp. 86–87; N. L. Tranter, 'Population and Social Structure in a Bedfordshire Parish: The Cardington Listing of Inhabitants, 1782', *Population Studies*, xxi (1967), pp. 275–76; C. F. Kuchemann, A. J. Boyce and G. A. Harrison, 'A Demographic and Genetic Study of a Group of Oxfordshire Villages', *Human Biology*, xxxix (1967), pp. 255–56; R. E. Jones, 'Population and agrarian change in an eighteenth century Shropshire parish', *Local Population Studies*, i (1968), p. 16; J. A. Johnston, 'Family Reconstitution and the Local Historian', *The Local Historian*, ix (1970), p. 11.

[18] Compare, for example, tables 2 and 3 in Wrigley, 'Family Limitation . . .', pp. 86–87, and see also P. E. Razzell's 'Note' in *Local Population Studies*, ii (1969), pp. 40–43.

of change appears to have varied, not only between localities but, more interestingly, between the sexes in the same locality. As a result there were, thirdly, considerable differences in marriage ages between communities at any one moment of time. For example, in the mid-eighteenth century, bachelors at Powick, Worcestershire, married at 22·4 years but at Charlton-on-Otmoor, Oxfordshire, at about 28 years. In the late eighteenth century spinsters at Charlton married at about 22, their counterparts at Moreton-Say, Shropshire, at 27·8 years.

Fortunately, we have rather more information about spinsters if the net is thrown to take in ages gathered by means other than family reconstitution. Krause, for example, cites some averages culled from the marriage registers of nine communities *circa* 1770–90.[19] The range of variation is again great, extending from 20·9 to 27·0 years, but seven of the nine fall in the range of 24–25 years. There are also a number of averages derived from whole collections of marriage bonds and allegations. These figures stretch over periods from the early seventeenth to the mid-eighteenth centuries. Rarely do they drop below 24, never do they rise above 26.[20] The use of marriage licence materials clearly raises questions of comparability with the other data, but it must also be asked whether such materials can be used in isolation to make comparisons over time.[21]

The temptation to generalize from this scanty and assorted collection ought to be resisted. Most past generalizations have been based, however, on a fraction of that scrutinized here. Those renewing the argument for a long-run decline in marriage ages will have to find many more pre-1750 examples of communities where men married for the first time at average ages above 27, and where women married above the age of 25. Even then there remains the problem that there must always have been local variations about the national mean. It is surprising that there are no local average ages in the Registrar General's reports. There were, however, noticeable differences between regions with respect to the numbers of marriages of minors as a proportion of all marriages occurring. In the years 1838–41, for example, in the Metropolitan division only 1½ per cent of all male marriages involved minors, while in Bedfordshire the figure was nearly 12 per cent. On the female side the figures were 8 per cent and 25 per cent respectively.[22]

[19] J. T. Krause, 'Some Aspects of Population Change, 1690–1790', in Jones and Mingay, *op. cit.*, p. 205.

[20] Razzell, 'Population Change in Eighteenth Century England . . .', p. 315; Laslett, *op. cit.*, p. 86.

[21] In the ways deployed by Razzell (note 20 above) and by Habakkuk, *Population Growth and Economic Development*, pp. 36–37.

[22] *Fourth Annual Report of the Registrar General* (H.C. 1842, xix, p. 441), p. 7.

Instead of attempting chronological comparisons of much that may not be comparable, perhaps more attention should be paid to the reasons why marriage ages varied between English communities at the same moment of time. The most favoured explanations of such variations appear to revolve essentially around the consequences for marriage of occupational differences. It is here that we enter another contentious area. There are major disagreements, for example, about whether significant relationships exist between the occupations men pursued, the ages at which they married, and the ages of their brides.[23] Several features have characterized the debate: in some cases an absence of empirical evidence, but where such evidence is produced a heavy reliance on ages culled from marriage licence documents. The methods of analysis adopted are so varied, however, as to make impossible anything other than rather impressionistic comparisons between such studies.

To test these impressions, and to discover generally what marriage licence documents can tell us about age at marriage, a large number of bonds and allegations have been examined for three different periods of time. Examined in the first period, the late seventeenth and early eighteenth centuries, were over 600 Suffolk licences for the years 1684–1723, over 2,500 Yorkshire ones for the years 1691–1710, and over 1,100 Nottinghamshire licences 1701–10, all of them stating an age for at least one of the marriage partners. For the mid-eighteenth century over 1,800 Nottinghamshire licences were looked at, over 500 Suffolk cases, and over 1,400 Surrey ones, all for the decade 1751–60. Finally, over 700 Sussex licences and over 2,300 Leicestershire ones were scrutinized for the decade 1801–10.[24] These

[23] Those appearing to argue that the occupational structure had some real significance for marriage ages would include: R. H. Tawney, *The Agrarian Problem of the Sixteenth Century* (London, 1912), pp. 104–6, n. 3; J. D. Chambers, *The Vale of Trent 1670–1800* (Economic History Review, Supplement no. 3, 1957), pp. 51–53; Habakkuk, *Population Growth and Economic Development since 1750*, pp. 35–46; Krause, 'Some Neglected Factors . . .', pp. 530–31; Loschky and Krier, *op. cit.*, pp. 429–48. These arguments are denied at one or a number of points in the chain of reasoning by McKeown and Brown, Razzell and Drake (see above, note 11).

[24] The Leicestershire cases were taken from the card index to the marriage bonds and allegations of the Archdeaconry of Leicester, the Archives Department, Leicester Museum. The other cases are from: *Allegations for Marriage Licences in the Archdeaconry of Sudbury*, ed. W. B. Bannerman (Harleian Soc. Publications, lxix and lxx, London, 1918–19); vol. iii of *Paver's Marriage Licences*, ed. J. W. Clay (Yorkshire Archaeological Soc., xlvi, 1912); *Abstracts of Nottinghamshire Marriage Licences*, ed. T. M. Blagg and F. A. Wadsworth (British Record Soc., lviii and lx, 1930 and 1935); *Abstracts of the Bonds and Allegations for Marriage Licences in the Archdeaconry Court of Nottingham, 1754–1770*, ed. T. M. Blagg (Thoroton Soc. Record Series, x, 1947); *Allegations for Marriage Licences issued by the Commissary Court of Surrey,*

10,000 cases were chosen on no other grounds than suitability and convenience; they come, with the exception of the Leicestershire marriages, from those printed marriage bonds and allegations which are best endowed with the relevant information. Bachelors in each of these eight samples were separated, where this was possible, into a number of social and occupational groups. One was the gentry, another the farmers, a third was labourers, a fourth servants. It was sometimes possible to constitute a fifth group of clothiers and hosiers, which one would like to think of as a textile employer class, though one cannot be sure of course that it is really differentiable from the sixth group, other textile workers. Finally into a seventh group went the consistently large numbers of other artisans and tradesmen—butchers, bakers and candlestick makers—who are to be found marrying in this fashion. Spinsters marrying into these groups were also analysed.

On the male side, one finds almost everywhere farmers marrying latest, certainly later than labourers where they can be measured, with the gentry occupying a rather shifting position usually somewhere between the two. Nearly everywhere also one finds the textile workers, whether employers or employees, and the other artisans and tradesmen marrying earliest of all. There are exceptions, of course, to all these generalizations. It is on the female side, however, that the results are most interesting. Amongst the rural groups gentry wives

---

ed. A. R. Bax (Norwich, 1907); *Calendar of Sussex Marriage Licences*, ed. E. W. D. Penfold (Sussex Record Society, xxv and xxvi, 1917 and 1919). The mean ages at marriage of bachelors and spinsters in each of these samples are given below. In the Yorkshire sample widowers were not always differentiated.

	Bachelors	Spinsters
Suffolk, 1684–1723	26·3	24·5
Yorkshire, 1691–1710	—	23·1
Notts. 1701–10	26·5	24·2
Notts. 1751–60	25·9	24·2
Suffolk, 1751–60	26·6	25·5
Surrey, 1751–60	26·5	24·4
Sussex, 1801–10	24·5	22·3
Leicestershire, 1801–10	25·6	23·8

On the male side, ignoring (for reasons explained below, p. 68) the two early-nineteenth-century samples, the closeness of the figures is immediately apparent, not only to each other, but also to Laslett's average of 26·9 for some Canterbury licences, 1619–60, and indeed to the Registrar General's national averages. The averages on the female side, again disregarding the early-nineteenth-century figures, support the conclusion reached earlier that such figures rarely drop below 24 and rarely rise above 26. Again the similarity with the Registrar General's returns might be noted. But see below, p. 68.

were almost invariably younger than farmers' wives, but not in mid-eighteenth-century Nottinghamshire. In the two Nottinghamshire samples, moreover, labourers' wives married later than those marrying farmers, but in Surrey and Sussex the reverse was the case. In Leicestershire labourers' wives married latest of all groups, in Sussex earliest of all. In fact, the results, on the female side, are much more varied than on the male side. One important reason for this is that in nearly all these county samples the gap between the spinster group marrying earliest and that marrying latest was inconsiderable: the three earliest samples yield differences of 1·9, 1·0 and 1·2 years; the three mid-eighteenth century ones, 1·8, 1·4 and 1·7 years; and the last two, 2·6 and 1·5 years. Only in early-nineteenth-century Sussex was there a difference greater than two years, the result primarily of a low age at marriage (20·9 years) of some 90 labourers' wives.

To what extent are any of these findings vitiated by the nature of the evidence and the methods of analysis adopted? In particular, what reliance can one place on any findings based on marriage licence documents? Although irregular ceremonies loom large in the marriage literature of the eighteenth century most marriages were regular ones, preceded either by the formality of thrice-called banns or by the acquisition of an ecclesiastical licence which allowed the parties to dispense with that formality.[25] The most notable characteristic of licences, therefore, is that they offered greater privacy. This was true of licences throughout in that the notification of intention to marry was avoided, but probably down to Hardwicke's Act of 1753 licences also offered, in practice though not in theory, greater latitude to those wishing to marry in a parish other than that in which one of the parties resided. Licences also offered speed. A couple could, in theory, marry within minutes of obtaining the licence, providing of course that the church named within it lay near at hand. Privacy and speed had, however, to be paid for. In his report for the year 1845 the Registrar General put the normal cost of a licence at £2 12s. 6d., 12s. 6d. of which was then stamp duty. Minors paid an extra 10s. 6d. however.[26] In 1864 the cost of a marriage with banns was put at around 12s. and one by licence at about £3 4s.[27] A tax of 5s. was first imposed on marriage licences in 1694[28] and there seems little doubt that this, and

[25] Attention is here confined to the ordinary ecclesiastical licence and not to the Archbishop of Canterbury's special licence. On the distinctions between them see *Twentieth Annual Report of the Registrar General* (H.C. 1859, session 2, xii, p. 1), p. iv.

[26] *Eighth Annual Report of the Registrar General* (H.C. 1847–48, xxv, p. 1), pp. xxvi–xxvii.

[27] *Twenty-Seventh Annual Report of the Registrar General* (H.C. 1866, xix, p. 1), p. x.

[28] By 5 & 6 Wm & M, c. 21.

subsequent tax increases, tended to widen the gap in cost between the two forms of matrimony.[29]

There is no doubt that the licence system was popular, however, though at the moment this can be measured accurately only from the onset of general registration. In the years 1838–41 there were nationally 19 or 20 marriages by licence for every 100 marriages by banns. The range of variation in the major registration areas ran from about 16 to 28 per cent, with the whole of the North, the North Midlands, Monmouthshire and Wales, experiencing above-average rates, and the South and East below-average rates.[30] It is impossible to make comparisons with earlier periods because the only precise published figures relate to particular churches, like St Nicholas's, Rochester, and Holy Trinity, Stratford-upon-Avon, and although the numbers marrying by licence in both are in excess of those marrying with banns, both churches lay in close proximity to an issuing authority, which probably accounts for the high proportions.[31] Frith has tentatively suggested, however, that in seventeenth-century Gloucestershire the proportion of licences to banns may have been as high as one to three.[32] The number of licences taken out annually in Leicestershire 1801–10 was greater than the number of marriages by licence occurring there each year in the early years of general registration. Although there must have been some licences wasted, the possibility exists that in Leicestershire also the proportion marrying by licence may have declined before the onset of general registration.

The licence system undoubtedly appealed to a sizeable minority of the population. The social composition of this minority varied, probably between regions and certainly over time,[33] although it is difficult to measure these variations accurately if only because in every collection of licence documents there are large numbers for which no occupations are given. Wealthier groups are always better represented, however, than the poorer ones. Labourers and servants are clearly

[29] A certain amount of information on the fees charged before the nineteenth century can be found in R. Burn, *Ecclesiastical Law* (2nd edn, London, 1767), i, pp. 223, 226; *A Cavalier's Note Book*, ed. T. E. Gibson (London, 1880), p. 263; *Hampshire Allegations for Marriage Licences*, ed. W. J. C. Moens (London, 1893), p. viii; W. E. Tate, *The Parish Chest* (3rd edn, Cambridge, 1969), pp. 130–32.

[30] See, for example, *Fourth Annual Report of the Registrar General* (H.C. 1842, xix, p. 441), p. 17.

[31] *National Index of Parish Registers*, ed. D. J. Steel (London, 1968), i, pp. 227–28.

[32] *Gloucestershire Marriage Allegations 1637–1680*, ed. B. Frith (Publications of the Bristol and Gloucestershire Archaeological Soc., ii, 1954), p. xvi.

[33] L. Stone, 'Literacy and Education in England, 1640–1900', *Past and Present*, xlii (1969), pp. 103–12.

under-represented. Indeed this must have been part of the licence system's attraction. The most important reason for this social bias was undoubtedly the higher cost of a licence. Obviously an outlay of several pounds was well within the capacities of most gentlemen, farmers and tradesmen, but it would represent a considerable slice of the annual income of an agricultural labourer or domestic servant. Yet these latter groups are never absent and the proportion of licences issued to them was higher in the eighteenth and nineteenth centuries than previously.[34] The nature of the records probably leads also to some misrepresentation of the real presence of wage-earners. In 2,113 Leicestershire licences issued 1801–10 there were 200 specified labourers and servants but there were also 281 instances in which no occupations were given, and some labourers must also have been lurking among the 552 artisans and tradesmen. As there were, in addition, 194 textile workers, the wage-earners are clearly not neglected. Yet bias towards the wealthy there was, and it continued well into the nineteenth century, when the Registrar General could report, 'High prices of wheat depress marriage among the classes (five out of six) who marry by banns, to a greater extent than they depress marriage among the remaining sixth of the people marrying by licence.'[35]

Speed and privacy, argued Blagg, the editor of the Nottinghamshire bonds and allegations, 'doubtless explain the abnormal number of widows and widowers who took advantage of this method and also the large proportion of minors'.[36] Comparisons with the proportions remarrying in the early years of general registration do not suggest 'abnormal' proportions, however, especially if allowance is made for the generally higher remarriage rates which must have prevailed before the late eighteenth century fall in mortality. Nor is there any real evidence that the proportion of minors marrying by licence was in any way extraordinary. Indeed, there is more evidence of an appeal to the older bachelor and spinster—those aged 40 and above —than there is of any special appeal to minors. Marriages of the very young—14 to 16-year-olds—are rarely encountered in these documents. It may be that, far from exercising a special appeal to any particular age-group, marriage by licence was preferred where there were marked disparities of age between couples. This could occur, of course, at any level of ages. When James Clark of Sudbury took out a licence in 1752 his age was returned at 53; Jane, his bride-to-be, was 17. In 1801, the 21-year-old Charlotte Loton, of East Langton, Leicestershire, was linked in a licence with the 16-year-old William

[34] L. Stone, 'Literacy and Education in England, 1640–1900', Past and Present, xlii (1969), p. 106.
[35] Eighteenth Annual Report of the Registrar General (H.C. 1857, session 2, xxii, p. 279), p. iii.   [36] Blagg, op. cit., p. vii.

Cooper.[37] One does not have to over-indulge the historical imagination to discern why couples such as these might prefer to avoid banns. The Registrar General once cited a private correspondent who told him how in Cumberland there was 'a disinclination to publication of banns, on account of the notoriety it gives to the intended marriage, at which in many country parishes, idle lads congregate, and often annoy the parties'.[38] No doubt the fun would be even greater where one party was markedly older than the other. A dangerous moment in the ceremony itself was when the officiating clergyman asked, 'If any man can show any just cause why they may not lawfully be joined together. . . .' A parish clerk recounted how on one occasion 'an unwelcome visitor . . . a noted character . . . under the influence of drink' used the opportunity to remark audibly, 'I've no objection.'[39] The Registrar General's correspondent thought that the rowdyism on which he remarked 'caused many to prefer going to the expense of a licence, and when several do a thing of that kind it becomes a kind of fashion which others follow'.[40] Snobbery no doubt speeded the process of social emulation, for marriage by licence was the resort of the upper classes, who, we have been frequently told, married this way to avoid their affairs being publicized before all and sundry.[41] Foreigners, like Misson, declared as much: 'To proclaim banns is a thing nobody cares to have done'—nobody who mattered that is.[42] So also did Horace Walpole, outraged by Hardwicke's Act, when writing to Seymour Conway: 'It is well that you are married. How would my lady A. have liked to be asked in a parish-church for three Sundays running? I really believe she would have worn her weeds forever, rather than have passed through so impudent a ceremony.'[43] It is very reminiscent of Lydia Languish's despair, at the collapse of her plans for elopement and a 'Scotch parson', that she might 'perhaps be cried three times in a country-church and have an unmannerly fat clerk ask the consent of every butcher in the parish to join John Absolute and Lydia Languish, Spinster!'[44] The desire for privacy might also be joined, before Hardwicke's Act, with the intention of marrying in a distant, perhaps fashionable, church. Many gentry couples in the Yorkshire licences, for example, intended to marry

[37] Bannerman, *op. cit.*, p. 215; Card Index to Archdeaconry of Leicester marriage bonds, Leicester Museum.
[38] *Twenty-Seventh Annual Report of the Registrar General* (H.C. 1866, xix, p. 1), p. viii.   [39] Anon., *Cupid's Pupils* (London, 1899), p. 132.
[40] See above, note 38.
[41] G. Hamilton-Edwards, *In Search of Ancestry* (London, 1966), p. 65.
[42] Cited in J. C. Jeaffreson, *Brides and Bridals* (London, 1872), ii, p. 179.
[43] Cited in G. E. Howard, *A History of Matrimonial Institutions* (Chicago and London, 1904), i, p. 457.
[44] R. B. Sheridan, *The Rivals*, Act 5, scene 1.

at York Minster. Once we have a peer group behaving in this way the practice could spread by simple emulation. The cost of a licence acted as a deterrent to complete social debasement of the system, but it was always possible, of course, for the less wealthy to offset the price of a licence against the lower costs of a quiet, more private wedding. There were also, it must be said, cheap licences to be had in some places. The great rise after 1730 in the number of marriages in the tiny Nottinghamshire parish of Fledborough is less likely to be explained, as Professor Chambers romantically hoped, by the magic of the incumbent's name—the Rev. Amos Sweetaple—than by cheap licences offered by that notorious parson.[45]

It is difficult to exhaust the personal reasons why privacy might be desired. A late Elizabethan defence of the licence system justified it because it provided facilities for the bashful; it was of benefit in those cases where there were marked disparities of class as well as age; it allowed young people, once presumably they had reached the age of 21, to follow their own hearts rather than the dictates of their parents; and it enabled some bachelors—in decent privacy— to make honest women of their mistresses.[46] One could extend the list. Thrice-called banns might be a public torment, for example, for those cursed with unfortunate names. Was it this which persuaded Miss Pleasant Love to marry by licence in Nottinghamshire in 1710, or Avis Urine to seek a licence in Sudbury in 1712?[47] It is noticeable that in the index of names to the volume of Suffolk licences from which the last example was taken two of the largest entries relate to the families of Prick and Balls.[48] It is also noticeable that they were conspicuously successful in avoiding each other in the matrimonial market. Oddities of appearance were of sufficient interest to persuade one nineteenth-century parish clerk, recounting in print his long career, to include a chapter on 'Anomalous Couples', including one 'whose proportions outraged all the rules of symmetry . . . The bride- groom was a poor little weak stripling of a man, quite insignificant in appearance. The bride was six feet three, and had a brother who was seven feet six inches, and weighed thirty-four stone. His indi- viduality was so remarkable that he was presented to her Majesty at Buckingham Palace, and had the honour of receiving from the Queen a valuable souvenir of the interview.'[49] With love, as with monarchs, there is no accounting for taste.

---

[45] Chambers, *op. cit.*, p. 50; Blagg, *op. cit.*, p. vii.
[46] 'Reasons for licences to marry', printed in P. McGrath, 'Notes on the History of Marriage Licences', in Frith, *op. cit.*, pp. xxiv–xxvi.
[47] Blagg and Wadsworth, *op. cit.*, p. xii; Bannerman, *op. cit.*, p. 65.
[48] Bannerman, *op. cit.*, pp. 392, 439. See also 'Cock' (p. 402).
[49] *Cupid's Pupils*, p. 145.

Speed may have been an attribute of the licence system which influenced the character of its clientele. Some have seen signs of its influence in numbers of sailors and soldiers resorting, at certain times and places, to marriage in this fashion. More important, however, is whether a system offering speed would have special appeal to the pregnant. If haste was necessary such girls would, of course, have to be in an advanced state of pregnancy for a few weeks to make much difference. The same is arguably true if it was privacy, rather than haste, which was required. Also, if by the end of the eighteenth century one-third of all first pregnancies were conceived out of wedlock, one wonders seriously whether girls were so embarrassed by their condition as to make them marginally prefer licences to banns. If they were, the question arises of whether girls conceiving out of wedlock were likely to be younger than virginal brides. Hair, however, has discounted that bridal pregnancy was due to teenage innocence.[50]

A number of other possibilities suggest themselves. Before Hardwicke's Act a church marriage was desirable, if only to establish property and hereditary rights, but it was not necessary for validity in the eyes of the church; after the Act marriage in an Anglican church of the parish of residence of one of the parties became a legal necessity for all except Quakers and Jews. The licence system may take on significance in the light of these facts. Did it, for example, appeal to those indifferent to religion, the non-churchgoers, more likely to be found among the industrial and commercial classes than amongst the agricultural ones? The social composition of the licensees may be significant in this respect. Did it offer some appeal to non-Anglicans, especially after 1753 when they were compelled to go through an Anglican ceremony? Here the geography of the licence system in the mid-nineteenth century is interesting, especially the above-average proportions in the North and in Wales. In a period also when physical mobility was increasing did the system offer a marginal appeal to relative newcomers to both rural and urban parishes? In all these cases it is possible that the licence system could have minimized both contacts with the parish clergy and any embarrassment this was likely to have caused.

Before considering the consequences of all this for the conclusions previously arrived at, we must consider the greatest deficiency of these documents—the accuracy of the ages returned in them. The editors of printed bonds and allegations have tended to deprecate their accuracy; those who wish to use these documents for sociological

[50] P. E. H. Hair, 'Bridal Pregnancy in Rural England in Earlier Centuries', *Population Studies*, xx (1966–67), pp. 233–43; 'Bridal Pregnancy in Earlier Rural England further Examined', *Population Studies*, xxiv (1970), pp. 59–70.

enquiry, not surprisingly, are less pessimistic.[51] The precise degree of accuracy overall is impossible to establish, and exceedingly laborious to establish in individual cases, but the ages are probably less accurate than those volunteered ones that successive Registrar Generals relied on. A vicar drew attention in 1872 to some of the defects of those: 'both parties to the contract shy of telling, perhaps for the first time to each other, their exact ages, both also, in country parishes often apparently woefully ignorant of their own ages'.[52] Everywhere in the eighteenth-century licences one finds evidence of rounding: usually at 30, 40 and 50, but not in the Yorkshire licences where the ages bunch at 29, 39 and 49—an interesting example of Yorkshire tact. A more serious failing lies in those cases where age was returned as '21 and above'. Some of these at any time were formalistic entries, denoting 'of mature age', but the proportions of such entries tended to rise in the eighteenth century. In the Leicestershire and Sussex licences of the early nineteenth century over one-third of all the entries were of this type. The proportions were much lower in the three earliest samples: 5–6 per cent for bachelors, 12–15 per cent for spinsters. The higher proportions for females may mean they had a greater propensity to lie about their ages, but they also reflect the fact that 21 lay nearer the modal age at marriage for women than it did for men.

Thus there was at any moment of time some under-reporting of age and this tended to become much more serious as the eighteenth century progressed. This fact, allied with the social composition of the licensees and its tendency to vary, means that average ages calculated from whole collections of licences should not be compared with each other, certainly not over periods embracing the beginning and end of the eighteenth century. Nor, for all these reasons, should averages calculated from whole collections of licences be compared with reconstituted ones. The thought also occurs that in comparing averages derived from licences with the Registrar General's age returns we may simply be comparing the efficacy with which different generations lied about their age.

What is much more difficult to establish is whether the character of both licences and licensees seriously invalidates any of the conclusions about social differentials, especially among females. One reason for the narrowness of female differentials may be the narrowness of

[51] Compare, for example, Blagg, *op. cit.*, p. vii, and P. E. Razzell, 'Statistics and English Historical Sociology', in *The Industrial Revolution*, ed. R. M. Hartwell (Oxford, 1970), pp. 108–9. (There appears to be an error in the relevant Razzell passage: 'seven' should read sixteen.) The pessimism of editors may be explained by the fact that most could foresee their value only to genealogists.

[52] Cited in Steel, *op. cit.*, p. 58.

male ones. In the eight area samples explored here, the differences between the average ages of those bachelor groups marrying earliest and those marrying latest were 2·1, 1·5, 2·8, 3·5, 2·3, 2·6, 2·0 and 3·4 years. It is difficult to see how anything so far stated could greatly extend the age difference between the group marrying latest, usually the farmers, and those marrying earliest, the textile workers, artisans and tradesmen, and, in early-nineteenth-century Sussex, the labourers. Indeed, the differences may already be exaggerated by a number of characteristics, such as the tendency for wage-earners marrying by licence to be wealthier than those marrying with banns, and the tendency in the documents for there to be fewer than average formalistic (age 21) entries among the farmers and a more than average number among the early marrying groups.

That these age-differentials are not entirely the product of the sources used may be seen by comparing them with those produced for nine occupational groups by William Ogle from the marriage registers of 1884–85.[53] The age-spread between groups was, paradoxically, much greater. Among the bachelors it was 6·16 years, among the spinsters 4·45 years. One reason for this appears to be that the intervening period does seem to have witnessed some marriage postponement among those males marrying latest—the 'professional and independent' group and the farmers, and these groups were choosing older brides than they had done in the eighteenth century. Another reason is that at the other end of the male age-spectrum we have the miners, a group not represented in the licences. Their brides also were a clear year younger than those of textile workers, the group otherwise marrying earliest. But from at least the mid-nineteenth century miners had displayed a fondness for young brides, and also for high fertility, a propensity Brownlee put down to the large coal fires they kept blazing in their tiny houses.[54] The interesting fact, however, is that the differences among the remaining six groups—textile hands, shoemakers and tailors, artisans, labourers, commercial clerks, shop-

[53] *Forty-Ninth Annual Report of the Registrar General* (H.C. 1887, xxiii, p. 1), pp. vii viii; W. Ogle, 'On Marriage-Rates and Marriage-Ages, with Special Reference to the Growth of Population', *Journal of the Royal Statistical Society*, liii (1890), pp. 253–80. Ogle's groups and ages for bachelors and spinsters were (bachelors' ages first): Professional and Independent classes—31·22 and 26·40; Farmers and sons—29·23 and 26·91; Shopkeepers and Shopmen—26·67 and 24·22; Commercial Clerks—26·25 and 24·43; Labourers—25·56 and 23·66; Artisans—25·35 and 23·70; Shoemakers and Tailors—24·92 and 24·31; Textile hands—24·38 and 23·43; Miners—24·06 and 22·46.

[54] T. H. C. Stevenson, 'The Fertility of Various Social Classes in England and Wales from the Middle of the Nineteenth Century to 1911', *Journal of the Royal Statistical Society*, lxxxiii (1920), pp. 401–32 and 'Discussion', p. 433.

keepers and shopmen—were 2·29 years for males and 1·0 year for females.

It is possible, of course, that the differentials are not greater in all these cases because of the deficiencies of the occupational descriptions. All users of such materials are familiar with them: the mixture of status and occupational description; and the impossibility of establishing the degrees of wealth or independence lurking behind nominally similar labels. A 'farmer' could be operating on 100 acres or on ten. A 'baker' might be either a master or an employee. Even people describing themselves as 'labourers' must in reality have varied a great deal. In so far, therefore, as it is difficult to isolate groups enjoying common employment characteristics it is impossible to test precisely the influence of male employments upon age at marriage.

Even if we could isolate groups with more precision, however, we would have also to acknowledge that the nature of a man's employment was only one influence on age at marriage. That decision was probably moulded by a whole host of other influences: sibling order, patterns of inheritance, custom, the sex balance within the eligible age group within communities,[55] the power-structure within the parish,[56] the availablity of housing—of vital importance if the prevalence of the 'nuclear or conjugal' household is insisted upon,[57] the nature and availability of female employments,[58] and so on. Intensive economic and social studies of particular communities have much to tell us about the factors influencing marriage arrangements, and age at marriage is a subject which should not be left exclusively in the hands of the parish register demographers.

University of Leicester

[55] If, for example, Gregory King's enumeration of the ages of the population of Lichfield in 1695 is correct, there were 108 bachelors aged 20–39 to 244 spinsters of the same age. See D. V. Glass, 'Gregory King and the Population of England and Wales at the end of the Seventeenth Century', in Glass and Eversley, *op. cit.*, p. 181.

[56] This might determine *inter alia* whether the parish was 'open' or 'closed', the ease of obtaining a 'settlement', attitudes to squatters, the nature and general administration of poor relief, and the availability of cottages, commons and allotments.

[57] Laslett, *op. cit.*, p. xiii, and 'Size and Structure of the Household in England over Three Centuries', *Population Studies*, xxiii (1969), pp. 199–224.

[58] Ogle, *op. cit.*, p. 269; *Twenty-Ninth Annual Report of the Registrar General* (H.C. 1867–68, xix, p. 1), pp. v–vi.

SOUTHERN IRISH UNIONISM: A STUDY OF CORK UNIONISTS, 1884–1914[1]

The Alexander Prize Essay

By Ian d'Alton, B.A.

READ 9 JUNE 1972

AUGUST THE FIFTH, 1914, was a cool, windy day at Mitchelstown, County Cork: but the guests at the houseparty in the Castle were not really conscious of the chilly breeze that whisked the clouds over the tops of the Galtee mountains that stood towering behind the Castle. Here during the afternoon the guests moved about the sunny, gusty terraces and talked, in little low groups, of the War. In retrospect, however, both this garden-party and those who attended it have a significance, dramatic and historical. August the fifth was the day after the War broke out; the garden-party was one of the last ever held in the Castle; and it was not a very ordinary group of people who talked of the War, and of whether its coming would avert the calamity of Home Rule.

> For miles around, each isolated Big House had disgorged its talker, this first day of the War. . . . Braced against the gale from the mountains, licking dust from their lips, these were the unmartialled loyalists from the South. . . .[2]

So Elizabeth Bowen, herself a participant in the scene, records the attitude of mind of the Southern Irish Unionists, in August 1914.

To Miss Bowen's eyes, the garden-party at Mitchelstown Castle symbolized the end of an age, the end of a life-style. Within seven years, almost all that the Anglo-Irish gentry stood for had been swept away: there were new forces in the land: and even Mitchelstown Castle itself was no more.[3] The Great War and its aftermath provided the final *coup-de-grâce* to a type of existence which had been in decline for many years. The purpose of this paper is to provide, in a more prosaic form than Elizabeth Bowen's, an analysis of the social,

---

[1] I would like to express my thanks to Professor Oliver MacDonagh, without whose encouragement this paper would never have been written.

[2] Elizabeth Bowen, *Bowen's Court* (London, 1942), p. 323. Another account of the garden-party at Mitchelstown Castle is given in the *Journal of the Cork Archaeological and Historical Society*, new series, lxiv, p. 63.

[3] The Castle itself, home of the Dowager Lady Kingston's second husband, William Downes Webber, was burnt by Irish rebels in 1922.

economic and political framework within which this philosophy of existence was formed. 1885 has been chosen as the date of commencement of the study, since it was in this year that the fundamental basis of the Anglo-Irish *raison d'être*—the Union—was first directly threatened, from within Ireland by Parnell's phalanx, from outside by Gladstone's conversion to Home Rule. Cork city and county have been chosen as suitable areas of examination for four main reasons. First, the city and the county provide the material for studying in close juxtaposition the two broad streams of southern Irish Unionism —the landed and the commercial. Second, in areal terms, Cork county is big enough (1,800,000 acres) to allow statistical generalizations to be made about social background and political behaviour. Third, Cork city boasted of two vigorous newspapers, one Unionist the other Nationalist, which provide an almost unique balance of comment and events.[4] Fourth, a strong *esprit de corps* is found amongst Cork county Unionists: there is an antipathy against the city Unionists, which throws a spotlight on many interesting facets of the Unionist mentality at the end of the century.

As a broad generalization, it is true to say that the county Unionist was Protestant, a landowner and a sportsman.[5] It is equally true to describe the city Unionist as a Protestant, a merchant and comparatively wealthy. These, however, are not universal descriptions. Not all Protestants were rich, not all Unionists were Protestants, and not all landowners and merchants were Unionists or Protestants.[6] The very fact, for instance, that 90 per cent of the Protestant community was Unionist in political behaviour made the action of a group of Protestant Home Rulers in 1885–86 all the more interesting.[7] The small band of Catholic Unionist merchants was a moderating influence on the

[4] The *Cork Constitution* (Unionist) and the *Cork Examiner* (Nationalist) were the two newspapers; there was a third organ: *Cork Daily Herald* (Nationalist).

[5] The diaries of Daniel Conner of Dunmanway (those surviving, 1871 and 1877) show that the main preoccupations of a country gentleman were his estate, his sport, his family, his health and his involvement in local government. (See Conner Papers, Manch House, Ballineen, Co. Cork, Bundle 'Personal Papers'.) Similarly, the papers of Savage French of Queenstown show how much paperwork a conscientious landlord had to undertake (French Papers, Cuskinny, Co. Cork).

[6] It is interesting to note that many of the 'neutrals' and Protestant Home Rulers were non-conformists; it seemed axiomatic that members of the disestablished church were always Unionists, though it must be remarked that the leader of the Protestant Home Rulers in Cork city in 1886 was a member of the Church of Ireland; Diocesan Records, Cork: Vestry reports, Easter 1886.

[7] This group was quite active in the period 1886–93, when it contested several municipal elections: by 1899, the group had more or less ceased to exist (various newspaper reports, November each year, 1886–95).

Unionist side during the politico-religious squabbles of the 1890s. These 'misfits'—the Catholic Unionists, the Protestant Nationalists, the neutrals, provided the points of contact between the two essentially inert bodies of Catholic Nationalists and Protestant Unionists. What was the relationship between the Unionists' economic and political power in the years around 1885? In 1881 the Unionists were entrenched in the wealthiest sectors of the occupational structure.[8] In Cork city this can be measured by examining Unionist representation on the Town Council. The Council, elected on a high-rating franchise, gave more indication of wealth than of numbers.[9] A similar economic franchise in Cork county not only gave the landed classes a representation disproportionate to their numbers on Boards of Guardians, Grand Juries and Dispensary Committees, but also gave the Protestant merchant class in the towns (Bandon, Kinsale, Mallow, Fermoy, etc.) a large say in the municipal government of those towns before 1898. In town and county the proportion of local taxation paid by the Unionists was very high:[10] this fact produced a dichotomy of views difficult to reconcile. On the one hand, the landed class increasingly based their claims to control of local government on their taxable capacity: on the other, they frequently called for a diminution of those taxes.[11]

[8] The Unionists were represented as follows, in the following occupations in Cork city:

Insurance	100%	Bank officials	45%
Jewellery and bullion	75%	Clergy	40%
Medical profession	48%	Legal profession	29%
Engineers	48%		

(*Census of Ireland*, 1881, Province of Munster, County and City of Cork, part 1, vol. ii, no. 2) .

[9] Of the 36 Unionist Aldermen, Councillors and candidates in the period 1891–96, at least 19 were either merchants, large shopkeepers or involved in company management. There was also a railway secretary, a rate collector and a hotel proprietor: conspicuous by their absence were the doctors and solicitors. Although there had been three solicitors of the party on the Council in 1886, by 1891 this element had entirely disappeared. The leader of the Unionists in the city during this period was Alderman (late Sir) John Scott, managing director of a coal-importing and ship-owning concern in the city (F. Guy, *Directory of Cork* (Cork, various dates, 1890–98); R. A. Hodges, *Cork in the Twentieth Century* (Brighton, 1911), pp. 145–315).

[10] It was frequently asserted that the Protestants of Cork city, for instance, paid over half the city rates. See Sir John Scott's remarks at a meeting of Cork Unionist Hundred, 23 November 1892, and again at a meeting of Cork Corporation, 2 December 1894; *Cork Examiner*, 25 November 1892; 3 December 1894.

[11] The agitation against the overtaxing of Ireland as a result of the Financial Relations Commission was started in Cork in September 1897 by a prominent group of Nationalists and Unionists, led by the Earl of Bandon, the Lord Lieutenant for the county. See also the Cork Constitution, 21 November 1898, for a report of a meeting of the Irish Landowners' Convention (Cork) at which the tithes problem was discussed.

In Cork city, the dominant group within the Unionist ranks were the merchant-shopowning classes, who formed about 20 per cent of the Protestant male working population.[12] The leaders of the Unionist Party in the city throughout the period 1884–1914 were, with few exceptions, from this class, while the rank-and-file Unionist members of Cork Corporation were frequently shop-owners and grocers. All this would suggest that Unionist representation on Cork Corporation was largely a matter of economics, not politics. Rising rates and the extension of municipal activities made representation on the local rating body imperative for such merchants. A narrowly based municipal franchise meant that on the Catholic and Nationalist side the same conditions applied: on the Corporation before 1899 economic differences between the two sides were minimal, and this meant that Unionists on the Corporation tended to be more politically aggressive before the passing of the Local Government Act in 1899. The Parnellite split exacerbated this between 1891 and 1899, and for many years the Unionists on the Corporation held the balance of power between the Parnellites and the anti-Parnellites.[13] The influx of a new, organized group of labour representatives in 1899 was responsible for the creation of a Commercial Party, comprising many Unionist and Nationalist ratepayers now banding together for the protection of their mutual economic interests.[14] If, within the Unionist group in the city, the economic dominance of one class was obvious, this same dominance amongst the county Unionists was

[12] As has been noted above (note 9), the leader of the city Unionists during this period was of this class. The second-in-commands—E. J. Julian and W. T. Hungerford—were, respectively, a rate-collector and local businessman, and a prosperous retail merchant and bicycle-dealer. Edwin Hall and Joseph Pike, the two city Unionists most prominently connected with 'parliamentary Unionism' in the borough, were both company directors, and Pike owned extensive properties in the City (Local Government Board enquiry in Cork, 10 March 1899; F. Guy, *Directory of Munster* (Cork 1886); Hodges, *Cork in the Twentieth Century*, pp. 228, 271).

[13] The numbers on the Corporation between 1891 and 1898 reflect the position of the Unionists during the split. In 1895 the parties were represented as follows: Unionists 18 seats, Parnellites 22, anti-Parnellites 16. The real value of the split to the Unionists can be seen in the municipal election results in 1891 and 1892: in those years they *gained* three seats and four seats respectively (*Cork Constitution*, 26 November 1891; 26 November 1892). In 1894 a Unionist Mayor was elected by a combination of Unionist and anti-Parnellite groups: and during the period 1891–98 the High Sheriff (elected by the Corporation each year) was always a Unionist (save in 1894). (For a report of the Mayoral election of 1895 see *Cork Examiner*, 3 December 1895.)

[14] As a result of the municipal elections of January 1899, held under the Local Government Act, a strong body of labour delegates, nine in number, made their way into the Corporation; *Cork Constitution*, 7 January 1899.

even more marked. In the county areas, save for the small towns, the Unionist political creed was dominated by, and operated in the interests of, the larger landowners. In 1878, this class consisted of some 700 persons, owners of 500 acres or upwards each.[15] This small, elitist and compact corpus provided the 'traditional' background to the Unionist political philosophy in the county.[16] The towns provided a professional and merchant element within the county structure:[17] but at no time in this period was there any attempt, or possibility of an attempt, by this element to usurp the gentry's leadership. This is not to say that the two elements had little contact with each other: on the contrary, the average Cork landowner, overburdened with mortgages, leases, tenancies, Land Acts, agents, bailiffs and ailing relatives, always had to lean on a host of solicitors, land agents and doctors.[18]

No discussion of the social and political activities of the Unionists in either Cork city or county is possible without an explanatory note on the distribution of the Protestant / Unionist population within these areas. According to the 1881 Census there were in that year 34,239 Protestants in county Cork, representing 8·3 per cent of the total population.[19] Of this number 10,051 (29 per cent of the Protestant population) were resident in the various county towns.[20] Two points

[15] The statistic of 700 is taken from U. H. de Burgh, *Landowners of Ireland* (Dublin, n.d., but probably 1878).

[16] Using De Burgh's figures it would appear that well over half the landlords were resident in Cork (556); 115 were resident in other parts of Ireland, and 60 were resident in other parts of the United Kingdom, or abroad. Twenty-one landowners owned over 10,000 acres, while a distribution graph shows that 552 landowners owned estates between 500 and 3,000 acres in size.

[17] Lists of Town Commissioners for Bandon, Clonakilty, Fermoy, Kinsale, Mallow, Midleton, Queenstown, Skibbereen, and Youghal; Guy, *Directory for Munster* (1886).

[18] The Conner Papers, for instance, contain a voluminous correspondence between Daniel Conner and his solicitor, Thomas Downes of Skibbereen on all sorts of subjects; James Penrose-Fitzgerald, agent to the absentee Earl of Midleton, was in a similar position; Public Record Office, Midleton Estate Papers, Letter Books.

[19] *Census of Ireland*, 1881, Province of Munster, County and City of Cork, part i, vol. ii, no. 2.

[20] *Ibid.*, Table xxix. The percentage of Protestants in each of the towns was as follows:

Bandon	33%	Midleton	12%
Fermoy	26%	Skibbereen	12%
Kinsale	23%	Bantry	12%
Queenstown	18%	Youghal	10%
Passage West	16%	Mallow	8%
Dunmanway	14%	Macroom	1·6%
Clonakilty	14%		

arise from these statistics. Firstly, there is a distinction to be drawn between 'town' and 'county' Unionism in the county: and secondly,

> The nearest of our neighbours lived a couple of hundred yards away, but as they were in a cottage that did not count—in fact, nothing counted for about three miles on any side of us because there were no Protestants until then.[21]

Lionel Fleming's description of Protestant isolation around the small village of Timoleague highlights the second point to be made from these statistics. Although the statistical generalization for the county tells us that 8·3 per cent of the total population were Protestant, this gives us no clue to their distribution within the county: and for any understanding of the social and political activities of the county Unionists, some knowledge of this distribution is essential.

Working on the basis of the civil parish divisions in the county, and the percentage that were Protestant in each, we find that the Unionists were not at all spread evenly throughout the area.[22] There are certain areas (e.g. in the west and south-west of the county, and around certain towns such as Bandon and Kinsale) in which the proportion of Protestants is much greater than the average for the county as a whole.[23] Equally, there are large areas, such as the extreme north-west of the county, which come below the average. The position of the gentry on local Boards of Guardians also gives some indication, within any particular Poor Law Union, of the relative thickness of the gentry on the ground. Thus, where the *ex-officio* element on any Board was strong, this was an indication of an active and numerous local gentry. The fact that the *ex-officio* Guardians on the Boards of Kinsale, Bandon and Mallow were able to control these Boards until 1898, reinforces the conclusions drawn from a study of the parishes.[24] In general, then, it can be said that distribution played a very large part in the determination of the social and political behaviour of the county Unionists: a closely knit group meant an active political role and a boosting of corporate morale.

---

[21] Lionel Fleming, *Head or Harp* (London, 1965), p. 36.

[22] The percentage of Protestants ranged from 29·4% in Templebreedy parish (which included a military establishment at Crosshaven) to 0·04% in Nohovaldaly (in the extreme north-west of the county). The range was very great (*Census*, 1881, Table xxviii).

[23] In the west and south-west of the county was a relatively large number of Protestant tenant farmers—Hawkes, Goods, Kingstons, Damerys, Batemans and Hobbses. See Fleming, *Head or Harp*, p. 22; Cork, Cloyne and Ross Diocesan Records, Baptism Register; personal information; Catherine Shannon, 'The Kingston Family in West Cork', *The Diocesan Magazine of Cork, Cloyne and Ross*, 1893.

[24] Minutes of various Boards of Guardians, Cork Courthouse.

Increasingly, as the last years of Queen Victoria's reign went by, the Anglo-Irish gentry became less concerned with economic problems, more concerned with a 'crisis of identification'. Successive Acts of Parliament, coupled with that upsurge of Celtic nationalism known as the 'rise of an Irish Ireland' began to remove the mainstream of Irish life further and further away from the doors of the gentry. In economic terms, the links were broken by the Land Acts, which removed a direct bond between landlord and tenant; in political terms, by the severing of the connexion by the gentry with local government in 1898; and in cultural terms, with the rise of the Gaelic and direct anti-British movement.

The survival of landed Unionism–Anglo-Irish society is central to any study of the Unionist position in this period. The uniqueness of that society's position, in economic and political terms, meant that on its survival rested the maintenance of an active political life amongst the Unionist population. Commercial or city Unionism was suspect: its greater integration, and its lesser economic friction with groups around it, meant that defections could, and did, take place more frequently from its ranks. Only in landed Unionism was there a strong elitist conception, an unique economic position, and an important imperial tradition. With a weakening of morale from within the ranks, a dismantling of their economic position, and an imperial tradition growing almost too grand for itself, the southern Unionist position began to crumble.[25] The remainder of this paper will largely be concerned with discussing the social and political framework within which this crumbling position was contained.

In Cork county, the Unionists were spread in a thin, uneven film over the entire area: this dispersal was the major determinant in the type of their social activities and the form of their political behaviour. The Big Houses have been referred to as islands: and as islands one can examine the relationships between them, and the relations between the individuals on them.[26] The necessity for 'a bit of company' was the main determining factor governing the type of social activity enjoyed by the gentry. Sports and physical activities of all types were avidly engaged in by even the most slothful of county Unionists;[27] and while tradition played a large part in the choice of

---

[25] On a national scale, this 'crumbling of morale' is demonstrated by the reaction to the Financial Relations Commission, the Devolution scheme, and the split in the Irish Unionist Alliance in 1912–13.

[26] Bowen, *Bowen's Court*, p. 13; Fleming, *Head or Harp*, p. 22.

[27] One only has to read Edith Somerville's books (especially the 'Irish R.M.' stories) in order to realize this. See also the Conner Papers, Diaries, 1871 and 1877.

such activities, county Unionists were not slow in taking to new and unusual pursuits.[28]

There is little evidence to show that the gentry in the county were ever bored: if *ennui* finally crept over them by 1914, it was not readily apparent in the 1880s and 1890s.[29] Precisely because the Big Houses were big, there was never a lack of anything to do. Each was a little realm of its own, generally full, not only of immediate family, but also of aunts, uncles, brothers- and sisters-in-law, grandparents, nephews and nieces. Each was a hive of industry—Edith Somerville's fight to keep Drishane (the Somerville home at Castletownshend) clean and relatively tidy was indicative of the activities of many women in the Big Houses around the county.

What were the features of Unionist social activity in Cork county? Such activities were nearly always rigidly exclusive. The rigidity and stagnation of Anglo-Irish society only began to be broken up at the end of the century and even then, it was a very gradual process, frequently resented by the gentry themselves. This exclusiveness was not only manifested on religious/political lines: the division was also one of breeding and money, which could only be surmounted with the greatest difficulty (or by the greatest wealth).[30] Generally, this exclusiveness worked both ways; if the tennis club in Timoleague was exclusive to Protestants ('and not to all of these'),[31] it was equally unusual to find the gentry participating in the gatherings of a Nationalist or Catholic character. Within the Unionist community itself, the divisions were deep: the nearest social point of contact between the Protestant gentry and the Protestant farmers and shopkeepers was at the parish church on Sundays.[32]

The county gentry took part in these social and physical activities for two main reasons. Firstly, tradition expected them to; and it was difficult to avoid such an hereditary commitment, even if one wished

[28] At the turn of the century, the city and county gentry were quick to take up golf and motoring. See Guy, *Directory of Cork* (1913), pp. 178–81, for a list of motor owners. About 134 out of 254 owners were Protestants. For a description of how jealously the gentry guarded their golf courses, Brian Inglis, *West Briton* (London, 1964), pp. 18–19.

[29] For those lucky to live near the garrison towns—Fermoy, Cork, Crosshaven, Buttevant, Charleville—there was always a changing nucleus of young officers ready to supply the raw material for a spinster-ridden gentry.

[30] For example, Augustine Roche, leader of the Parnellites in Cork, three times Lord Mayor, rich merchant and collector of antiques, Nationalist M.P. for Cork city in 1905, could mix easily with the gentry. He was one of the few Catholics invited to the wedding of Sir John Arnott's daughter in 1898; *Cork Examiner*, 17 September 1896; also Hodges, *Cork in the Twentieth Century*, p. 278.

[31] Fleming, *Head or Harp*, p. 36.

[32] Private information.

to. Secondly, they had to: the lack of any alternative company meant that they had to band together, they had to meet on each other's islands. In such a way, then, the gentry's uniqueness was at once its downfall and its saving grace.

The picture of the Unionists in Cork city is very different. Here, the conception of the Unionist as the 'huntin', shootin', and fishin' ' type is totally out of place. Two outstanding features differentiate the city Unionist from his counterpart in the county. First, the difference in density was quite considerable: in 1881, an average of one Protestant to every eight acres in the city, compared with one to every eighty acres in the county.[33] The Unionists in Cork city were in a large, closely knit community; and in a pre-telephone, pre-motor age, this closeness gave them a group solidarity that was lacking amongst the county gentry. Psychologically and physically, the city Protestant was less isolated, more integrated, and more capable of being less hidebound than traditional Anglo-Irish society. The second factor was, that at every level of city society, the Unionist/Protestant had his Nationalist/Catholic counterpart. All along the economic and social line, from the railway director to the agricultural labourer, from the university professor to the milling hand, there were Protestants and Catholics. There was not any unique stratum of society on either side. The result of the interaction of these two factors was the production of a more integrated, more open-ended society on both sides: a world where neither the Catholic Unionist nor the Protestant Home Ruler was really out of place: in fact, a society in which the conditions for the flourishing of such persons were particularly favourable. The social atmosphere in the city was mutually less exclusive, but the very existence in close proximity of two antagonistic groups meant that conflict—often political, frequently religious—could more easily break out. During times of exceptional political activity, and stimulated by the Orange Order in the city,[34] religious quarrels were never much below the surface: when such outbreaks occurred, the real casualties were the Liberal Unionists, the Catholic Unionists, and the moderate Nationalists.[35]

---

[33] There were 11,464 Protestants in Cork in 1881: their percentage numbers in the various city wards were as follows:

North East Ward	35%	West Ward	12%
South Centre Ward	25%	North Centre Ward	10%
Centre Ward	24%	North West Ward	5·7%
South Ward	13%		

(*Census*, 1881, Table xxix).

[34] The records of the Cork Orange Lodges no longer exist.

[35] The Parnell split exacerbated religious differences in the city. The Unionists were quick to raise the cry of 'priestly dictation' (*Cork Constitution*, 14 June 1892; 25 June 1892; 4 November 1893; 20 May 1898).

The importance of organized religion in the city during this period cannot be overemphasized. Most social, cultural and charitable organizations were arranged on a religious basis;[36] and it is to be noted that the two main cultural societies in the city (Cork Archaeological and Historical Society, and Cork Literary and Scientific Society) were only able to operate successfully at the expense of a rigorous system of rules controlling the discussion of religious and political questions.[37] Thus, in the absence of any common forum, political dialogue was made virtually impossible, and the opposing groups were left to shout at each other in the Corporation, the Board of Guardians, and other local bodies. Although religion and politics were divisive factors, there is evidence to suggest that with the gradual rise of a prosperous Catholic middle-class in the city, the real division within city society came to be economic as the new century approached. The close co-operation between the Catholic and Protestant business ascendancy at the time of the Cork Exhibition (1902–3) is evidence of this, as is the formation of a Ratepayers' Association in 1898.

To an extent, an analysis of the social and economic background of the county and city Unionists can be divided, in areal terms, since the two life-styles tended to be so different (and on diverging courses). However, an examination of the political structure of Unionism cannot be so conveniently subdivided: while, in political terms, the city Unionists found themselves virtually unable to exert any influence over the gentry,[38] the county Unionists, through the medium of the County Club, had little difficulty in asserting their supremacy in the city whenever it was necessary.[39]

The question of a philosophical basis for Unionism has already been mentioned. How did the southern Irish Unionist regard himself, and his political purpose? It is evident that, by and large, the deeper implications of a 'dying ascendancy' were very little realized by the great mass of the Anglo-Irish gentry.[40] Edith Somerville to the end of her long life certainly did not believe this. The realization that the

[36] Guy, *Directory for Munster* (1886), pp. 340–42.

[37] See correspondence in the *Cork Constitution*, November 1898.

[38] Except during some poor-law elections in electoral divisions near the city; see *Cork Constitution*, 5 March 1892.

[39] The classic example of this occurred in 1891 when Parnell's death caused a by-election to be held in Cork. Scott, the leader of the city Unionists, was passed over by the County Club and Captain D. R. Sarsfield, a county Orangeman, was chosen as Unionist candidate; see *Cork Examiner*, 10 October 1891; 24 October 1891. Even Balfour, the Chief Secretary, was against the local Unionists fielding a candidate; L. P. Curtis, Jnr, *Coercion and Concilia-tion in Ireland, 1880–1892* (Princeton, 1965), p. 321.

[40] For a further discussion of this point, see L. P. Curtis, Jnr, 'The Anglo-Irish Predicament', *Twentieth Century Studies*, iv (November 1970).

gentry were being forced slowly out of the life of the community was a retrospective idea, mulled out of a massive collective inferiority complex that seemed to attack articulate ex-Unionists when the Union finally had been destroyed. There was little evidence of this sort of attitude in the 1880s and the 1890s: disestablishment, virtual elimination from parliamentary politics, the Land Acts—all these were looked on as acts of a malignant government, not as the outward signs of the decline of a ruling caste. Not until the cataclysmic revolution of 1898 was there any serious doubt about Unionist morale.

County and city Unionists, consciously or unconsciously, tended to project two different images of themselves. Firstly, there was the pragmatic and practical Unionist:

> He held it to be a narrow and circumscribed sense, in which 'Unionist' simply meant anti-Home Ruler. But the Unionism which he and his associates had always in public life tried to preach and practice had been the principle that when any question arose involving the mutual welfare and prosperity of the country, as to the administration of the poor law, or as to the relief of suffering distress, then the true meaning of the word 'Unionist' was that every true-hearted Irishman should join together and work together harmoniously, or, if they liked, agreeing to differ where they must differ, but working harmoniously for the common good.[41]

Such was one liberal Unionist's definition of his political credo. There is no mention of cultural and traditional values, no mention of the civilizing and educational standards that, in general, the gentry set. It is an exposition of utilitarian Unionism, much like that given later by Sir Horace Plunkett, with its emphasis on, and commitment to economic prosperity, and the standard of living.[42] This is probably how the Unionist saw himself in local terms: a paternalistic view of his role in the community.[43] However, on a wider, national scale, the Unionist saw his role as a defender of monarchy and religion, and the custodian of an Imperial tradition—this last is clearly evidenced by local support for the Boer War. When the local Unionists got together in the Orange Lodges, the Primrose League and the Registration Associations, such sentiments were freely expressed.

[41] Sir George Colthurst at Blarney, addressing a mainly Unionist audience during the county council elections of 1899 on 25 March 1899; report in the *Cork Constitution,* 26 March 1899.

[42] Sir Horace Plunkett, *Ireland in the New Century* (London 1904), especially Part II ('Practical').

[43] Daniel Conner's Diaries shows this emphasis on a duty to local administration; his entries relate (for December 1877) his driving five miles alone through snow and wind in order to attend Petty Sessions in Dunmanway; this was when he was in his late seventies.

'Public' Unionism was channelled into two distinct spheres of activity—the expression of Unionist political opinion in specifically Unionist groups, and Unionist participation in local bodies, such as Grand Juries, Boards of Guardians, Town Commissioners and Petty Sessions courts. Unionist activity in Cork in the period 1885 to 1895 shows quite clearly that political *rigor mortis* had not yet set in. In these years, both in city and county, new Unionist organizations were being formed, and old ones were being revamped and updated. Two main influences account for this. The Land War in the 1880s, together with the Plan of Campaign on certain estates, provided an economic impetus; while the triumph of Parnellism in 1885–86, and its collapse in 1891 provided the political catalyst.

The landlords of Cork county were the first in the county to take up the challenge of the Land League. At a meeting in September 1885, the gentry of the county met in Cork to found Cork Defence Union, a body equipped to combat the League on the Plan of Campaign Estates in Cork county (principally the Kingston Estate near Mitchelstown, and the Ponsonby Estate at Youghal).[44] The Union's activities were widespread and effective. In its first year of existence, money was raised in large quantities by public subscription in Ireland and England, evicted farms were taken over, boycotted farmers were assisted with men and machines, cattle and sheep were bought and sold, landlords and their families were supplied with the necessities of life, and in general fairly successful attempts were made to frustrate the Land League and its efforts to keep the pot boiling.[45] In a notable conflict with the Nationalist Cork Cattle Traders' Association in the winter of 1885–86 (when the Association refused to ship cattle in the same boats as the Defence Union), the local shipping company was nearly ruined, many labourers were made redundant, and a lot of bitterness was engendered. But the Union, as soon as its value was seen by other landlords, was quickly imitated throughout the country. The movement culminated in the formation of a central organization, the Irish Defence Union, which was the direct precursor of such bodies as the Land Corporation, and the Irish Landowners' Convention.[46]

Cork Defence Union provided two services to Unionism in Cork. In the shape of material help to beleaguered landlords and boycotted tenants, the Union came to the immediate rescue.[47] Secondly, the

[44] The movement was led principally by A. H. Smith-Barry, owner of 27,000 acres in Ireland, Liberal M.P. for County Cork 1867–74, Unionist M.P. for South Huntingdonshire, 1886–1900, created Baron Barrymore, 1902, chairman of the Irish Unionist Alliance, 1911–13, died 1925.

[45] First Annual Report of Cork Defence Union, published in the *Cork Constitution*, 16 November 1886.

[46] Curtis, 'The Anglo-Irish Predicament'.

[47] George Pellew, *In Castle and Cabin* (New York, 1887), p. 83.

success of the Union's activities provided a much-needed boost of morale for Cork Unionists: and the Union's propaganda efforts on the other side of the Irish Sea were attended with no little success, and can be considered as one more factor in the Unionist electoral victory of 1886 in Britain. Cork Defence Union stayed in existence until 1918: but after the brief land agitation of 1900-3, the virtual settlement of the land question by 1909 made the Union redundant.

Political activity was revived in the late 1880s and early 1890s. There are two aspects of such activity. First, there was the necessity to 'show the flag', to uphold the Throne and the Constitution, and to glorify the Empire. Since these ideals were in a sense purely political, with no overt social undertones, they were open to subscription by every Unionist. At this point, however, Unionist politics must be tempered with the second aspect—the social effect of such activity. This meant that although such organizations as the Primrose League were in theory open to all classes and creeds, in practice the gentry and upper professional strata began to monopolize the League; and with a widely separated, mutually isolated group such as the gentry, Primrose League meetings very soon began to take on the aspect of genteel tea-parties.[48]

Thus, while the public objectives of such Unionist organizations were fiery and active, the real aims (although never expressed) were geared to upholding Unionist morale in the county. In view of the tiny percentage of Unionists in the county, and their wide dissemination, the objectives could hardly be otherwise. Much talk was often expended on questions of registration, of canvassing and of converting —but very little was ever done, for the simple reason that such work would have been useless.[49] Only in the city, where the high money qualification for the municipal franchise meant that the Unionists were in a strong position, was such political work taken seriously. In the county, it was necessary to keep up a level of enthusiasm for politics: and the evidence suggests that there were small numbers of political activists always prepared to stir up the flagging enthusiasm of the county Unionists.[50] Contrary to contemporary nationalist opinion, not every landowner was an *agent provocateur* for whatever govern-

[48] See the description of one such tea-party meeting of the Primrose League, in *Cork Examiner* 18 August 1971, described by Patrick Madden.

[49] See Lord Castleton's remarks ('Organize! Orangize!') at a meeting in Cork, 26 March 1886 (*Cork Constitution*, 27 March 1886); also, A. H. Smith-Barry at a Primrose League meeting in Cork ('we must fight the registration and attempt conversions') on 1 October 1890 (*Cork Constitution*, 3 October 1890).

[50] Such men as Colonel William Johnson of Fermoy, who was active in the Primrose League, the Unionist Clubs, and local government; A. H. Smith-Barry; and (Sir) Robert Penrose-Fitzgerald, Bart, M.P. for Cambridge, 1885-1905, were all important in the Unionist political sphere in Cork.

ment happened to be in power, and not every Big House was an active centre for political Unionism. Many so-called Unionists were quite happy to have their Unionism decently hung up in mothballs only to be shaken out at times of exceptional crisis, if at all.[51]

Two organizations in Cork county demonstrate the problems of the political versus the social—the Primrose League, and the Unionist Clubs. The League, founded in 1883, was an organization dedicated to the advancement of Conservatism,

> to bring Conservatives together in friendly and united work, for the advancement and maintenance of those constitutional principles which have made Great Britain what she is, also to maintain the cause of religion and monarchical government as against atheism and republicanism.[52]

The League came to Ireland in 1883, and there were Habitations (as local branches were called) in counties Cork, Dublin and Waterford by 1884.[53] By 1891, St Patrick's Habitation in Cork had over 4,000 members, and the Habitation was split into four based on Mallow, Fermoy, Bandon and Kinsale.[54] The League's pseudo-Imperial trappings, with its Knights and Dames, its Ruling Councillors and silver insignia, did not detract from its morale-boosting function amongst county Unionists. While the League was, from the first, almost entirely the preserve of the gentry, there is evidence to show that it went some way towards attracting, and accepting, the Conservatives and Liberal Unionists from the towns of Mallow, Fermoy, Mitchelstown and Kinsale.[55] Two further points of interest concerning the League can be discussed. These concern the involvement of the Protestant clergy, and the participation of women in the Primrose League. It has been suggested that these two groups showed a parallel development with the power of the Roman Catholic clergy in the National League, and the Women's Land League, started by Anna Parnell and Michael Davitt in 1881. Whatever the superficial similarities might suggest, here the resemblances cease. The Ladies' Land League was an all-female organization: the Primrose League

---

[51] For instance, during the Home Rule crisis of 1893, when much money was subscribed to an anti-Home Rule fund, and during the Boer War, when an even larger amount was forthcoming.

[52] Lady Mary Aldworth (aunt to the Earl of Bandon) on 21 July 1898, at the annual meeting of the Blackwater Vale (Co. Waterford) Habitation; *Cork Constitution*, 27 July 1898.

[53] P(ublic) R(ecord) O(ffice), N(orthern) I(reland), D989A/7/2; annual report of the Irish Unionist Alliance, 1898.

[54] *Cork Constitution*, 20 April 1891, editorial.

[55] For example, see the report of the annual meeting of Mitchelstown, Fermoy and Castlelyons Habitation; *Cork Constitution*, 16 May 1898.

was not.[56] The Nationalist women's activities were political and economic in tone: the role of the women in the Primrose League was essentially a social one, acting as complements to the men. On the other hand, there seems to be more justification for parallels to be drawn between the clergy in the different groups. Both groups of clergy were politically minded: but while the priest frequently led in political matters, the Protestant clergy rarely attempted to challenge the supremacy of the gentry in the Primrose League.

The pattern at meetings of the League was always the same: there would be a speaker from outside the county, and an articulate Unionist from within it. The former would deal with some national or Imperial topics, while the latter would talk about some local topics affecting Cork Unionists.[57] The activity of the League was greatest in the period 1891–93, at the beginnings of the Parnellite split. Nationalists, especially during the hey-day of the Land War, were wont to accuse the League of being a 'boycotting and electioneering agency';[58] but the existence of other Unionist organizations devoted to such objects would have made the League's existence superfluous.

If the Primrose League was an attempt at 'tea and cakes' politics, the Unionist Clubs movement was sterner and more aggressive in conception. Founded by Viscount Templetown in Belfast in early 1893, it was one of the first attempts to organize the Ulster Unionists on a separate footing, and its organization was mainly due to the threat of a Home Rule Bill becoming law. It is not clear from whom came the initial suggestion to start clubs in the southern provinces, but at the inaugural meeting of the Unionist Clubs' Council (U.C.C.) in Belfast on 13 March 1893, twenty-nine delegates from the south attended: these included nine from Cork.[59] The motives for the organization of the clubs in Cork seem to be varied. The prospect of Home Rule appears to have been the most important, and protection of Unionists' homes and families in that event. Dissatisfaction with the over-socializing tendencies of the Primrose League was certainly a factor.[60] There was some initial friction with the Irish Unionist

[56] One of the accusations brought against the Cork Habitations by the nationalist press was that the League was run entirely by women; there is no doubt that they provided the vast majority of the active members.

[57] *Cork Constitution*, 29 January 1891; 20 April 1891; 4 June 1892; 9 September 1892; 23 May 1895. Guest speakers at meetings during this period included Sir William Marriott, M.P., Sir John Columb, M.P., Lord Ernest Hamilton, Lord Templetown, Lord Castletown and Hon. John De Grey.

[58] *Cork Examiner*, 30 June 1891, editorial.

[59] P.R.O., N.I., D1327/1/2; Unionist Clubs' Council, minute book of the Executive Committee, 3 October 1893.

[60] See Sir Augustus Warren's speech at the Unionist Clubs' Council meeting, 13 March 1893; P.R.O., N.I., D1327/1/1; minute book of the Executive Committee.

Alliance, technically the 'governing body' for Irish Unionists, over which a group was to control the southern branches.[61] Eventually, the southern clubs were taken under the Alliance's wing as 'divisional branches'.[62] Twenty-three branches were organized in County Cork in 1893, of which the majority merely existed on paper.[63] With the lessening of the threat of Home Rule after 1894, the need for the U.C.C. virtually disappeared: and with it died the last effort to organize political Unionism in the county on a grand scale. However, during the Home Rule crisis of 1893, the clubs were instrumental in organizing lists of Unionists and petitions, holding meetings, and raising money for the Irish Unionist Alliance.[64]

The activities of the Primrose League and the Unionist Clubs were mainly confined to the county. Unionist political activity in Cork city was concerned principally with Unionist representation on the Corporation and other local boards, and reaction to parliamentary elections and Home Rule Bills. Unlike the county, the emphasis was firmly placed on the political aspect, not the social. Two catalysts, one a depressant, the other a stimulant, changed the face of Unionist organization in the city in the 1880s and 1890s. The first was the extension of the parliamentary franchise in 1885; this finally killed any chance the Unionists may have had of winning even one of the two city seats.[65] The second was the Parnell split in 1891, after the

[61] See correspondence with the secretary of the Irish Unionist Alliance read at the executive committee meetings of the Alliance; P.R.O., N.I., D989A/1/5; and minute book of the Unionist Clubs' Council, 24 August 1893; P.R.O., N.I., D1327/1/1.

[62] A Cork delegate, E. F. Sanders, put the relationship between the clubs and the Alliance thus: 'The Unionist Clubs outside of Ulster are an integral part of the Unionist Club organization of Ulster. They will work in perfect harmony with the Irish Unionist Alliance, and will assist that body in every way possible but will only take orders from the Unionist Clubs' Council and its Executive.' (P.R.O., N.I., D1327/1/1, 13 March 1892, minute book of the Unionist Clubs' Council.)

[63] From an undated list in longhand, P.R.O., N.I., D989A/5/1. This list is similar (except for one club) to that given in the *Annual Report* of the Irish Unionist Alliance, 1897, p. 16 *et seq.*

[64] See various reports in the Cork Constitution, March–April 1893. The clubs also raised money for the Alliance General Election fund in July, 1895; see *Cork Examiner,* 8 July 1895; *Cork Constitution,* 13, 17 July 1895. A special report of the executive committee of the Unionist Clubs' Council stated that eight southern clubs (six of which were in Cork) contributed £367 to the joint Unionist Clubs' Council–Irish Unionist Alliance Fund.

[65] A hotch-potch of Unionist candidates contested the six divisions of County Cork in 1885; in Cork city, the two seats were challenged in that year. Cork was, however, one of the few places where the Unionists could put up a decent fight; it was the only place outside Ulster and Dublin in which the Irish Loyal and Patriotic Union (the forerunner of the Irish

O'Shea divorce. This stimulated Unionist activity on the parliamentary and municipal fronts, and in April 1892 the city conservative association was reorganized on a broader basis, under the title of 'Unionist Hundred'.[66] The Hundred exercised some control over the selection of candidates for municipal elections, and arranged registration and property votes when necessary.[67] Like the county organizations, it too was involved in morale- and money-raising during the Home Rule crisis of 1893, and also during the Boer War. Like the local nationalists to some extent, the city Unionist association found itself almost totally independent of the central organization in Dublin.[68]

The decline of Unionism to 1898 in the county and city of Cork was, in some degree, masked by their continued involvement in local government. With its 'democratization' by the Act of 1898, however, the Unionists rapidly found themselves as onlookers, not participators, in the new structures. Some managed, through a spirit of deference, 'because of some lingering respect for the family, for the sake of "the old Colonel" or "the old General"' to remain involved.[69] For the rest, the vast majority of the county gentry and the city merchants, it was a tremendous blow to their collective confidence: this is the real significance of the 1898 Act. To come to terms with Home Rule or not, this was the question; it was their tragedy that most could not. Even as late as 1898, they could still have had the leadership, locally and nationally, of Ireland; but they forbore to take up on the option.[70]

Unionist Alliance) suggested a contest in 1886; P.R.O., N.I., D989A/1/2; Minute Book of the Organizing Sub-Committee of the Irish Loyal and Patriotic Union, 21 May 1886; also 3 June, special meeting.

[66] *Cork Constitution*, April–June 1892, various dates.

[67] *Ibid.*, 2 November 1893; 29 March 1898.

[68] In April 1892 the Unionist organization in Cork city was reorganized; however, not until February 1893 was any attempt made to communicate this to the Irish Unionist Alliance in Dublin; P.R.O., N.I., D989A/8/2, letter file, Irish Unionist Alliance papers, Sir John Scott to R. G. Cox (secretary of the Irish Unionist Alliance), 28 February 1893, detailing lists of officers.

[69] On a national scale there were the examples of Lord Dunraven and Sir Horace Plunkett; on a local scale, Sir John Scott (who headed the poll at the 1899 municipal elections in Cork city), and the Earl of Bandon, who was returned unopposed in April 1899 to a seat on Bandon Urban District Council; *Cork Constitution*, 18 January 1899; 8 April 1899; see also Lennox Robinson, *Bryan Cooper* (London, 1931), p. 44.

[70] The Nationalist support given to the Unionists R. M. D. Sanders and J. R. B. Newman during the county council elections (Cork) of 1899 is evidence of this; Catherine Shannon, 'Local government in Ireland, the politics and administration' (unpub. M.A. thesis, National University of Ireland, 1963), pp. 191–94.

The decline of southern Unionism was more marked between 1900 and 1914; this is evidenced by the meek acceptance of the 1903 Land Act, the withdrawal from local affairs,[71] and the watery opposition to the 1912 Home Rule Bill. Thus, with a tradition of service to their country cut off, the southern Unionists to some extent became bewildered, rootless. The outbreak of War restored their collective feeling of 'belonging'. In this sense, then, 1914 can be considered as their finest hour; it was also their swan song.

University College Cork

[71] At the first Cork county council election in 1899, nine Unionists offered themselves for election, for the first and last time. No Unionists stood in 1902, 1905, 1908, 1911 and 1914; *Cork Examiner*, 7–10 April (annually) 1899–1914.

THE ECCLESIASTICAL PATRONAGE
OF THE LORD KEEPER, 1558–1642

By Rosemary O'Day, B.A.
(Proxime accessit for the Alexander Prize, 1972)

IT is perhaps surprising that no systematic study of the lord keeper's or chancellor's ecclesiastical patronage has been produced.[1] In 1927 Jean Wilson dealt with the office of lord chancellor in the early seventeenth century but devoted a very few pages only to the exercise of his patronage.[2] Professor Jones scarcely touched upon the matter.[3] Yet at the very least there is a need to establish how the lord keeper administered his ecclesiastical patronage and to assess its importance.[4] Did the various lord keepers adopt a policy? What influenced their distribution of patronage? The sources available have imposed limitations of their own: central records of presentations exist in overlapping blocks for the years 1559 to 1603; 1596 to 1616/17; and 1627 to 1640 alone. These papers are not of uniform format and the information which they can be made to yield varies in type.[5] The papers of lord keeper Coventry, for example, are not lists of presentations but loose docquets of presentation, and these make no mention of petitioners or commenders other than the presentee. Wherever possible, however, the somewhat barren nature of the formal documentation has been supplemented by the use of diocesan and private papers.

By the reign of Elizabeth the patronage of the lord keeper was very much institutionalized. This seems inevitable when the extent of the

---

[1] The titles 'Lord Keeper' and 'Lord Chancellor' have been used interchangeably although not everyone fulfilling the office was given the superior title of Lord Chancellor, e.g. Nicholas Bacon.

[2] Jean Strachan Wilson, 'The Administrative Work of the Lord Chancellor in the Early Seventeenth Century' (unpublished London Ph.D. thesis, 1927).

[3] W. J. Jones, *The Elizabethan Court of Chancery* (Oxford, 1967), p. 165.

[4] See D. M. Barratt, 'Conditions of the Parish Clergy from the Reformation to 1660 in the Dioceses of Oxford, Worcester and Gloucester' (unpublished Oxford D.Phil. thesis, 1950); and H. G. Owen, 'The London Parish Clergy in the Reign of Elizabeth I' (unpublished London Ph.D. thesis, 1957), for some perceptive comments on the patronage of the lord keeper as it affected their own areas of study.

[5] British Museum, Lansdowne MSS 443–45; Bodleian Library, Tanner MS. 179; B[irmingham] R[eference] L[ibrary], Croome Court Collection, vols 901, 902. As all three collections are chronologically arranged, folio numbers have not been provided in the footnotes. Full dates have been included to facilitate location of specific instances.

patronage in his hands is remembered.[6] The lord keeper customarily held in his gift all crown livings below twenty pounds in value: this constituted the bulk of crown patronage and the crown *was* the single largest advowson holder in England and Wales. A flood of royal acquisitions at the Reformation reinforced his position further. He also had the right to present to many other livings: for example, he claimed the right to present to livings under twenty pounds in value in the gift of crown wards, and he was entitled to present to livings which had been in lapse for twelve months or longer.[7] Nicholas Bacon could expect in normal years to present to an average of 113 benefices —a number which was spread geographically throughout the kingdom.[8] The average had dropped slightly to 108 presentations per annum during Egerton's chancellorship.[9] It fell yet again to 98 for 1627 to 1640.[10] The difference in the number of presentations made in individual years could be startling: in 1558/59 the keeper presented on 223 occasions; in 1579/80 on 248; whereas in 1562/63 he provided to livings on 76 occasions only. Although annual numbers fluctuated under Egerton the chart does not reflect the sharp peaks and troughs of the earlier period. Discrepancies can sometimes be explained in simple terms: the lord keeper did not always present to a living immediately it fell vacant and low numbers of presentations for one year and inflated ones for the next might well be due to this.[11] 1558/9 itself obviously represents an extraordinary year—one would like to know what proportion of the vacancies had occurred because of deprivations and resignations stemming from the change of regime; Professors Fisher and Hoskins have suggested that an unusually high death rate prevailed in 1558, due to an influenza epidemic,[12] and this may have accounted for large numbers of the vacancies. This suggestion is supported by an examination of the Lichfield records for

[6] See Wilson, *op. sit.*, p. 45. Working from the Patent Rolls alone, she estimated that the lord keeper presented to an average of 15 livings per annum.

[7] The patron of a living had six months in which to fill a vacancy; if he failed to do so the right to present fell to the bishop of that diocese for a further six months; at the end of this time the living fell in lapse to the archbishop for six months and then to the Crown.

[8] This figure is based upon British Museum, Lansdowne MS. 443, for the years 1560 to 1580. The lord keeper also sealed an average of 34 crown presentations per annum.

[9] Bodleian Library, Tanner MS. 179.

[10] B.R.L., Croome Court Collection. This drop may be attributable to the fact that these are loose docquets and not necessarily a full listing.

[11] The bishops could not present to crown livings in lapse.

[12] F. J. Fisher, 'Influenza and Inflation in Tudor England', *Economic History Review*, 2nd ser., xviii (1965), pp. 120–29; W. G. Hoskins, 'Harvest Fluctuations and English Economic History, 1480–1619', *Essays in Agrarian History*, ed. W. E. Minchinton, vol. i (London, 1968), p. 105.

the relevant years, and it may also be extended to the year 1580.[13] Included in the average, however, are those livings which fell into his hands for other extraordinary causes: simony, lapse, deprivation, minority. Quite large numbers fell to his patronage because of lapse, for example, causing one to wonder why the bishops, normally portrayed as starved of patronage opportunities, had not seized upon these. An examination of the records for 1596 to 1617 suggests that there can be no monocausal explanation for this. Some of the livings in question were so impoverished that probably neither patron nor diocesan could find persons willing to take them; still others were reasonably wealthy and one must speculate that circulation of information about vacancies was in some cases so poor that the bishops were unaware of the existence of patronage opportunities. When Edward Bennet, M.A., was presented to Cubley rectory, Derbyshire, on 5 February 1612/13, after the living had fallen by lapse to the lord keeper, it was, in fact, the bishop of Coventry and Lichfield who commended him. Here it appears that the bishop either could not find a candidate for the living immediately, despite the fact that it was worth thirteen pounds in the King's Books; or he was not informed of the 'lapse' until too late; or that he was forced for some reason to wait on Bennet in order to present. This is but one isolated instance and demonstrates a rare occasion when the bishop even if he acted belatedly did act: for the most part the records provide no further clue to the bishops' strange inactivity.

The keeper came by little patronage through wardship and was probably little disturbed in the 1620s when he was denied the right to present to wardship livings assessed at below twenty pounds.[14] The number of livings falling to him by simony was somewhat larger and was apparently growing throughout the period—this is probably an illusory growth in the actual incidence of simony, due to more stringent attempts to suppress it—but the method by which the reasons for vacancy were recorded makes any definite estimate unreliable.[15] The task of providing to all these livings—both those traditionally the property of the crown and those falling to it for extraordinary reasons —was difficult to perform and required a degree of organization.

As early as 1558 the presence of the bureaucracy is evident. Nicholas Bacon, Elizabeth's first lord keeper (1558/59–1579), appears to have

---

[13] For example, of 33 vacancies occurring in the archdeaconry of Coventry from 1557 to 1559, 29 were caused by death. Even when one considers that death was necessarily the chief factor in causing vacancies this seems too high a proportion to be normal. Lichfield Joint Record Office, B/A/2ii/1.

[14] *Calendar of State Papers Domestic, James I, 1623–25*, pp. 96–97, letter of Robert Tanfield to Lord Zouch, 16 October 1623.

[15] See appendix 3.

employed a staff of at least two who were exclusively concerned with ecclesiastical patronage: Bartholemew Kempe, 'head of the department', and 'Master Hawfylde'. On 22 December 1558 Bartholemew Kemp, gent., was appointed registrar of all benefices and other ecclesiastical promotions; in 1558/59 Mr Hawfylde is described as 'presentacionium clerici'.[16] Professor Aylmer has estimated that the office of clerk of presentations was worth perhaps £300 to the holder in the reign of Charles I.[17] Bartholemew Kempe continued in his position as registrar until at least 1594;[18] he was part of the permanent bureaucracy and not a personal employee of the lord keeper, and his duties included the administration of patronage directly in the crown's gift as well as that controlled by the keeper. There was also a clerk of the faculties involved in the work of the 'patronage office': a Master Coxe was appointed to the post in 1560.[19] This clerkship carried an annual fee of £70 but most of the work was done by a deputy.[20] In 1616/17 a list of Francis Bacon's household indicates that he employed two patronage 'secretaries' or 'remembrancers', in itself indicative of the enormity of the task of distribution.[21]

Despite this permanent bureaucracy of registrar and two clerks there is evidence to suggest that the office was essentially part of the lord keeper's household: the keeper's patronage was not statutory but a favour customarily bestowed upon him by the crown.[22] During Nicholas Bacon's tenure, at least, the work of distributing patronage took place at Gorhambury, the keeper's residence, rather than at Whitehall. Quite apart from the official staff of the office a number of the rest of the lord keeper's household were also involved in its work on an unofficial but active footing.

For the formal work of the department most evidence survives for the lord keepership of Sir Thomas Coventry, 1627 to 1640. At this point procedure was probably more highly formalized than it had been during the reign of Elizabeth. It is possible that the clergy were now petitioning according to a set form of words, brief and to the point, such as that in general use in the 1680s.[23] When a petition was

[16] British Museum, Lansdowne MS. 443; Calendar of Patent Rolls, Elizabeth I, 1558–60, Pardon Roll, 1 Elizabeth, part 2, p. 209.

[17] G. E. Aylmer, The King's Servants (London, 1961), p. 217.

[18] Jones, The Elizabethan Court of Chancery, p. 165.

[19] Ibid., pp. 163–64.

[20] Ibid.

[21] J. Spedding, The Letters and Life of Francis Bacon, vi (London, 1872), pp. 336–38; chaplains: Mr Oates, Mr Lewis; chief secretaries: Mr Yonge, Mr Thomas Mewtys; remembrancers for benefices: Mr Harris, Mr Jones.

[22] H. Maxwell-Lyte, Historical Notes on the Use of the Great Seal of England (London, 1926), pp. 2, 115, 220–22.

[23] Bodleian Library, Tanner MS. 50.

made its contents were recorded upon the top of a docquet. Apparently the petition was by this date normally delivered by the petitioner in person. He was then examined by one of the lord keeper's chaplains for his learning and knowledge of the scriptures. The chaplain noted down his verdict; this was usually formalized but there is no reason to believe that the examination itself was perfunctory, the phraseology used being equivalent to set grades in an examination. Once the chaplain had performed this task another clerk was set to search the King's Books for particulars of the living petitioned for and its taxable value. This in its turn was registered on the docquet and signed by the clerk. Finally a statement of presentation was made out detailing the name of the presentee; his educational status; the benefice to which he was presented; its location; and the date of presentation. Noted beneath this was the reason for vacancy in the benefice and the basis of the lord keeper's claim to present. The presentation was signed by the lord keeper, endorsed and stored away for reference. It represented both the presentee's claim to legal presentation and the record of the office of its transaction. Such a docquet, signed by the registrar, Kempe, had cost 20s. 4d. in 1594.[24] Normally the clerks drew up a list of the keeper's presentations, based on an abbreviated form of the docquets: that for 1558/59 to 1616/17 was carefully kept and indexed. No such record survives for the later period. Enrolment of the presentation was not automatic and the registrar commanded a fee for the service. The clerks also drew up a letter of presentation directed to the ordinary of the diocese involved.[25]

If these were the processes involved in the actual drawing up of a presentation, how did the system itself operate? Clearly it was Bartholemew Kempe, under Nicholas Bacon, who decided who would have the presentation to a particular living. It is uncertain just how much control over 'policy' the lord keeper himself exercised. Of lord keeper Puckering Camden said ' . . . though he were himself a sincere and upright man, yet, by reason of the Briberies and Corruptions of his Servants in selling of Church-livings, had no good Report among the Church-men.'[26] Egerton, however, was praised for his policy of bestowing advowsons upon worthy and needy ministers—denying livings to those who already had them, rather preferring to see that 'some might have single Coats, that wanted them, before others had

---

[24] Jones, op. cit., p. 165.

[25] Numerous examples of such letters are to be found in County of Hereford Record Office, Hereford Benefice Papers (unsorted presentations), and W[orcester] R[ecord] O[ffice], 778.7324 BA2442, Index, vols 1 and 2.

[26] William Camden, The History of the Most Renowned and Victorious Princess Elizabeth (London, 1688), p. 528; British Museum, Harleian MS. 6997 (Puckering Papers) sheds little light on the problem.

Doublets'.[27] The difference between the two men as pointed by their critics was that one exercised sufficient control over the officials beneath him whilst the other merely surrendered the exercise of patronage wholly into their hands. Certainly some of the lord keepers did formulate 'policy' and envisage themselves as adhering to certain principles in distributing favour. In a letter to Mr Maxey, Fellow of Trinity College, Cambridge, Francis Bacon declared that his purpose was 'to make choice of men rather by care and inquiry, than by their own suits and commendatory letters'.[28] Egerton truly seems to have attempted to supply worthy ministers to crown livings. On two occasions in the 1590s clergymen whom he presented were made to enter into bonds for sermons. Thus on 9 November 1596 Richard Boyley was presented to Wigenholt rectory in Sussex and there a 'Bonde entred for 12 sermons to be made yerely etc.'[29] From what is known of Egerton it seems likely that he was actively seeking to promote the moderate puritan cause and the interests of a learned preaching ministry. Parkhurst of Norwich ascribed to lord keeper Nicholas Bacon attempts to ensure that simony did not enter into crown presentations.[30] Even he, however was forced to present unsuitable men to livings—the overall pattern of recruitment into the church always dictated to some extent the success of central efforts. The attempts of the lord keeper to bestow patronage only on worthy men should not be assessed in a vacuum—the calibre of ordinands in the 1560s, particularly of those willing to accept such impoverished livings, was so poor that the keeper had to accommodate some of mean qualifications, whatever his intent.[31] Moreover, there is no way of estimating how far the several lord keepers did succeed in controlling their officials or how susceptible these were to corruption.

How did clergy seeking benefices come to hear of vacancies in the lord keeper's gift and how did they bring themselves to the attention of his officials? The Royal Exchange of the clerical market—the nave of St Paul's—may indeed have played a significant role. It was said that clergymen advertised their services in the Cathedral ' . . . to see

[27] J. Hacket, *Scrinia Reserata: A Memorial . . . of John Williams, D.D. . . .* (London, 1693), part i, p. 29.

[28] Spedding, *op. cit.*, vi. p. 172.   [29] Bodleian Library, Tanner MS. 179

[30] C[ambridge] U[niversity] L[ibrary], Ee.2.34. Parkhurst Correspondence, letter 57, Bishop Parkhurst to lord keeper.

[31] See G[uildhall] L[ondon] M[anu] S[cript] 9535/1; C[heshire] C[ounty] R[ecord] O[ffice], EDA 1/3; C.U.L. E.D. R. A5/1; and L[incoln] R[ecord] O[ffice], Reg. XXVIIIA, for some idea of the calibre of ordinands in the early years of Elizabeth's reign. Ely presents a special case, most of the graduate ordinands being destined for high preferment, or the wealthier livings. Also see Owen, *op. cit.*, p. 89, for difficulties which the lord keeper encountered in filling poor livings within London.

if they can hear of some good masters, to entertain them into service.'[32] Here middlemen, often proctors and notaries public, wandered about the aisles and sought to reach agreements with ambitious clerics. In 1574 the proctor Justinian Johnson came to terms with a suitor; the latter hired a horse and rode poste haste to Gorhambury to put his case to 'Mr Kemp there whoe hath the passing of all presentacions under the Lord Keeper.'[33] Unfortunately the living had already been promised to one of Lord Howard's chaplains and his suit was unsuccessful, his money wasted.

Obviously the *Si Quis* door of St Paul's served to advertise more than crown livings, bringing to the attention of the clergy livings further afield in the hands of private patrons and also lectureships within the city of London. Equally important was knowledge garnered locally. Whereas in London it was natural for a proctor 'middleman' like Johnson to canvass in the cathedral, it was probably the ecclesiastical officials and bishops' servants in other dioceses who possessed and conveyed most knowledge of the vacancies in their areas. It was the registrar or his deputy, or the chancellor and his surrogates who were most likely to know in whose gift a living lay. The registrar kept a record of all resignations and of *caveats*.[34] Naturally enough, he who sought his first living or a promotion would approach the diocesan officials. Letters in the registrars' correspondence at Lincoln indicate the role of this important if neglected ecclesiastical official in patronage distribution.[35] Often, also, the man seeking preferment was of local provenance and knew of a vacancy from personal experience: from the bishop or from a local worthy he required reference rather than information, although he too might refer to the registry for details of the whereabouts of patronage rights.

On occasion there were specific attempts to bring particular groups of men to the keeper's attention. For example, contemporaries suspected that the movement away from the church as a career for graduates, illustrated by the great numbers entering the legal and medical professions, was due to a lack of both of finance and of adequate promotion prospects. As early as October 1560 the crown was trying to remedy this situation:

> We understand that the study of divinity is much decayed in our
> Universities of Oxford and Cambridge, by lack of provisions for

---

[32] *The Works of John Whitgift*, ed. J. Ayre, iii (Parker Society, Cambridge, 1853), p. 246.

[33] L[ondon] C[ounty] C[ouncil] R[ecord] O[ffice], DL/C/212, fo. 125r; also cited in Owen, *op. cit.*, p. 287.

[34] K. Major, 'Resignation Deeds of the Diocese of Lincoln', *Bulletin of the Institute of Historical Research*, xix (1942–43), pp. 57–65.

[35] *E.g.*, L.R.O., COR/R/3, 36.40; 48.57.

the students through late alterations, so that many leave the Universities. The Chancellors therefore are to send you the Lord Keeper a schedule of the most towardly divinity students that have need of exhibition, and you shall in our name confer on them all prebends in your disposition for one year, or longer if required, till there be some repair of this lamentable lack.[36]

The note sent to the chancellors of the universities stipulated that both 'the promotions in our gift, and the prebends in the disposition of the Lord Keeper shall be bestowed on students recommended by you'. The students thus brought to his notice did not have to seek his patronage actively.

Normally, however, the candidate for a living was faced with the problem of bringing his suit to the lord keeper's attention. The records of the keeper's presentations from 1558/59 to 1579 and of Egerton's presentations from 1596 to 1617 help here in that they list concisely who was presented to a living; who petitioned the keeper on his behalf; and the names of writers of letters testimonial or commendatory. Several historians have speculated whether petitions and commendations were really meaningful or whether they were simply a matter of form:[37] did the officials really care whether a man was able and vocationally suited; was the responsibility of reference writing taken seriously; did the passing of money either as gratuities or bribes count for more than merit or the strength of a recommendation?

In the early years of the reign the lord keeper's patronage was probably not much competed for: clergy of the meaner sort were in good supply and the officials were relieved to fill many of the financially impoverished livings at their disposal. Of 223 livings bestowed in 1558/59 some 110 were granted to clerics upon their personal petition.[38] In 1562/63 only three benefices out of 76 were thus granted away. The remaining sample years of Nicholas Bacon's keepership (1567, 1571, 1575 and 1579) reveal only one such concession out of a total of 476 presentations. This change was doubtless due to an increase in competition and growth in the importance of references may indicate a corresponding rise in standards, although by no means necessarily. Certainly those seeking preferment appear to have attached great weight to securing the help of prominent ecclesiastics or courtiers. The highpoint of episcopal influence seems to have been in the mid- and late 1560s. Just under half of the clerics preferred in 1563 were presented upon petition and / or commendation of one of the

---

[36] *Calendar of State Papers Domestic, Addenda, Elizabeth I, 1547–1565,* pp. 505, 506.
[37] See Owen, *op. cit.*; Barratt, *op. cit.*
[38] The following remarks are based upon British Museum, Lansdowne MS. 443.

bishops (36); a further 22 owed their success to some other eminent ecclesiastic. A similar picture emerges in 1567: 39 of the 110 presentations were made on the petition of bishops and a further 30, at least, on that of leading ecclesiastics and church court officials. The pattern was somewhat modified by 1571 when the names of such as Walter Mildmay, the master of the Rolls, Master Hatton, Sir Humphrey Stafford, the Earl of Huntingdon and Lord North were becoming increasingly prominent.

Moreover, there is sufficient evidence to suggest that such petitions were not simply a matter of form. The records of the period 1596 to 1616/17 note all occasions when a presentation was made without receipt of a written petition or letters testimonial. This happened in a few instances only and the reasons for presentation were filed. For example, the presentation of Edmund Gunter, M.A., to St George's, Southwark, on 16 July 1615 was 'don without any petition in writinge' because he had been commended by one of the lord keeper's chaplains.[39] An explanation was evidently required for every departure from the normal procedure and the lord keeper was clearly wont to rely upon written commendations: their writers were in some degree responsible for their clients. To assume that all petitions reflected policy would be precipitate but some at least of these patrons were conscientious in their support of worthy candidates and rejected the suits of the ignorant and scandalous. In mid-1572, for instance, Sir Henry Sidney was looking for a chaplain and Richard Dixson presented himself. Parkhurst was called up for his opinion: the result was a conscientious and discriminating reference, yet Dixson was a B.A. of Cambridge and an honest person 'of comelye personage'.[40] The forthright nature of the testimonial is repeated in many of the letters testimonial to be found in Worcester Record Office and elsewhere.[41] Sir Simonds D'Ewes refused to support one suit because he was offered a bribe.[42] To say that many patrons were scrupulous in their writing of commendations is not to say that they were particularly active in seeking out worthy ministers and pressing their causes —the initiative was almost always taken by the cleric.

Apparently the suitor for a benefice concentrated upon securing an eminent man to petition on his behalf and upon getting his suit to the lord keeper without delay. This was especially true in the later sixteenth century, when competition for the richer livings in his gift was increasing. In January 1592 Edward Houlden of Lincoln diocese wrote to the archbishop of Canterbury commenting on a vacancy

[39] Bodleian, Tanner MS. 179.
[40] C.U.L., Ee.2.34, letter 107, 20 June 1572, Parkhurst to Sir Henry Sidney.
[41] W.R.O., 732.2 (1) nos 1–40; G.L.M.S. 9535/2, fo. 155r.
[42] British Museum, Harleian MS. 385, fos 74, 75.

caused by the death of a pluralist Mr Vaise, one of whose livings was in the gift of the lord keeper 'for the which I humbly beseech your Lordship to stand my good Lord unto such as in the vacancy of that offyce have the bestowing of such lyvinges'. Houlden felt confident that his suit would not fail because of delay unless the archbishop,

> by other occasions be not mayd forgetful of this my suite unto you for the man dyed but this day and I hyred this messenger who promysed to make more speede then my horse because I would be sure to be the fyrst suitor . . .[43]

This letter well illustrates both the speed with which information regarding vacancies was often spread and the haste which was felt to be necessary in presenting a petition to the registrar. In this case also the importance of local connexion is evident.

This type of letter suggests that competition was fierce, but the formal records of presentation provide little direct support for this contention. There are but three recorded instances in the period 1596 to 1616/17: for example, there were three competitors for the rectory of Limber Magna in 1596.[44] It is by no means certain that all such occasions were noted, of course. It is probable that competition was only apparent where a fairly wealthy living was involved. The lord keeper himself seems to have been eager to claim the right to present to certain important livings, while willing enough to assign the right to nominate to other livings.[45]

In any event, the clergy who persuaded the bishops to sue on their behalf were not automatically assured of success. On 29 January 1571, Parkhurst, bishop of Norwich, presented John Armysted as 'a suter to your honor for the benefice of Westwinche', giving him a fine testimonial as 'a hansom scoller both in the Latten and greke and commended by some of the preachers nere unto hym to be of honest and sober life'.[46] Above four weeks later one John Price was presented to the living in question at the petition of Master Alvey.[47] The conditions governing the keeper's decision remain unknown and upon such slender evidence one cannot conclude that the bishops only succeeded with their suits when there was no competition.

Ministers anxious for preferment watched the situation closely. John Morlande persuaded Parkhurst to write recommending him for the keeper's living of Thelmorton, from which William Locker was to be deprived for failing to subscribe to 'theis articles of religion

---

[43] L.P.L. MS. 705, fo. 45.
[44] Bodleian Library, Tanner MS. 179.
[45] B.R.L., Croome Court Collection, vol. 901, nos 452–54 (August 1633).
[46] C.U.L., Ee.2.34, letter 57, Parkhurst to lord keeper.
[47] British Museum, Lansdowne MS. 443.

agreede'.[48] In point of fact the lord keeper made no recorded presentation to Thelmorton. Advance suits such as this may well have been common: they correspond quite closely to those occasions when patrons purchased grants of next presentation to a living just when the present incumbent seemed likely to die.

Many considerations influenced the distribution of favours. The place of simony amongst them is difficult to establish. The records for Egerton's term of office do demonstrate how carefully the officials administered the oath against simony to presentees: when they had been unable to secure a subscription personally the clerks made a point of notifying the ordinary to see that it was administered. Simoniacal contracts were difficult to prove. In the 1590s the rector of the Crown benefice of St Nicholas Acon, London, was accused of having paid thirty pounds for the living: the charge was never proved although the keeper actually went so far as to present a rival claimant; in the end, Sims remained incumbent.[49] Moreover, the distinction between simony and offering 'grateful thanks' was often blurred. Gratuities, not being fixed to the same degree as fees, may have exercised some real influence upon the official's decision regarding a living or more probably upon his willingness to bring the petition to the lord keeper's notice. In October 1571 Parkhurst drew attention to Bacon's precautions against the occurrence of simony but maintained that the keeper's practice of signing away the right of presentation to certain livings without retaining control over the presentee allowed this abuse to pass unobserved. The living of Wetherden in Suffolk had remained vacant for above six months because 'Mr John Bacon (who claymeth the gifte therof from your honor) will not bestow the same but on soche one as will geve most money.' In applying for a remedy, he ended,

> Whereof because I know your honour to have speciall care as may appeare by such articles as you have appoincted to be mynestred to suche as entre anny cure, I thought it therfore my bounden duetie to signifye thus muche trusting your honor will take it in good parte and to procure reformacon hearin accordingly.[50]

In fact it seems that the crown preferred not to grant away rights of next presentation to its livings. It favoured instead the more informal practice of allowing a third party to nominate a candidate but not to present him to the living. Thus the keeper retained a right

---

[48] C.U.L., Ee.2.34, letter 59, 1 February 1571/2, Parkhurst to lord keeper.
[49] L.C.C.R.O., Lib. Examin. 1591–94, 24 November 1592; Lib. Act. 1589–1593, fo. 292^v; British Museum, Lansdowne MS. 445; this case is described in Owen, *op. cit.*, p. 290.
[50] C.U.L., Ee.2.34, letter 57, Parkhurst to lord keeper.

of veto upon the present appointment; moreover, the possibility of confusion about the whereabouts of patronage rights was avoided because the right of presentation was rarely formally granted away. Such an arrangement was brought to light during a simony case in London diocese in 1575,[51] but little evidence of assignments of nomination is to be found in the formal documentation.

Certainly some of the presentations recorded were in fact the result of exchanges arranged with the connivance or approval of the officials. On 7 October 1600 the clerk noted that Christopher Darling was presented to Wollaston vicarage, Northamptonshire, 'at the request of Mr Butler by way of Exchange with Mr Darlynge' and the commender is duly noted as being Charles Butler, clerk.[52] The proportion of such exchanges is impossible to establish because only one of the livings involved need be in the lord keeper's gift. Once an exchange was arranged, it remained to persuade the lord keeper to approve the transaction. This was also true when what was involved was not a straightforward exchange but a resignation in favour of a particular candidate. An example of this occurs in the papers of Sir Simonds D'Ewes. In 1624 Richard Chamberlayne and others wrote to D'Ewes at the Six Clerks Office:

> The matter is this, Mr Gosse the parson of Brougham [?] growes old & crased in such sort as he is not able to discharge the cure in his owne person, & therfor is willing to resign the benefice to a sufficient man . . . he hath made choyse at the request of his only daughter Mistris Bales of a young man who is Mr Firsts sonne, of oure towne, a graduate, & one of good hope & towardnes both for learning & giftes for the ministrie & of a modest & peaceable carriadge. The living is in the Lord Keeper's gift, as your self alreadie knowes: Therforr, our humble & earnest request is that you yould be pleased to take some paynes to see if this resignation (being sent within these 3 weekes or therabouts) will be accepted of.[53]

In this case the suitor's parents and his supporters guaranteed to pay any expenses incurred in pressing the petition. The letter also illustrates a further point—that the patronage of the lord keeper might well be bestowed at three or even four removes. Perhaps there is a clue here to what is meant by 'petitioners' and commenders' in the official records: often both the physical suit and the recommendation were made by the same person but they could be put by distinct personages. D'Ewes was urged to press the suit but was not providing letters testi-

---

[51] L.C.C.R.O., DL/C/212, fo. 136r.
[52] Bodleian Library, Tanner MS. 179.
[53] British Museum, Harleian MS. 385, fo. 112. Richard Chamberlayne was a puritan preacher under D'Ewes's patronage.

monial in support of it. In 1572 Mr Sanderson urged bishop Parkhurst to provide letters of commendation for one Greves, yet Parkhurst was not asked to petition on his behalf.[54]

Contemporary opinion was that the lord keeper and his registrar gave the better livings in their gift to the chaplains of the chancellor's household or to persons supported by them or other servants. Chamberlayne assumed that D'Ewes, in the Six Clerks Office, possessed a certain knowledge of the keeper's patronage and some influence. He also expressed the opinion that 'it is the more likely that it may easily be obteyned because the living is so small, not fit for one of his chaplains & or any other of speciall note, & it standing upon so good & reasonable termes, as is resignation by one that cannot supplie it himself . . .'[55]

Preferring the lord keeper's chaplains did not imply corruption, the livings in his gift being originally intended to provide benefices in lieu of payment for his clerks and chaplains. Moreover, the lord keeper's chaplains were able men: Master Saul, for example, chaplain to Nicholas Bacon, had been in exile and was probably himself interested in improving the ministry. Nevertheless, if true, it could mean that the pool from which ministers were selected for the better livings was limited to those with court influence. Thomas Wood, in 1576, would doubtless have extended his criticism of the bishops to include the lord keeper when he said:

> Concerning the bishops' chaplens, I thinke there is scarse one mayntained of the bishops' charges but they have one or 2 benefices abrode, and so live of the sweat of other mens' browes, which perish for want of spirituall foode they ought to have at their handes . . . For God's sake therefore rid your handes of such unnessesarie chaplins . . .[56]

Certainly the lord keeper did provide his chaplains with good livings. On 25 April 1562, Arthur Sawle petitioned for a prebend in Gloucester cathedral worth £20, to which he was duly presented.[57] In September of the same year he secured his own presentation to Porlocke, Somerset, valued at £18 11s. 6d. in the King's Books. In 1564 he added Ubley rectory, Somerset (£11 11s. 5½d.), and in 1566, Dynton rectory, Gloucestershire (£14 11s. 2d.). Other chaplains did not receive quite so much at Nicholas Bacon's hands: Pervical Wyborne,

---

[54] C.U.L., Ee.2.34, letter 81, 3 September 1572, Sanderson to Parkhurst.

[55] British Museum, Harleian MS. 385, fo. 112; C.U.L., Ee.2.34, letter 81.

[56] *Letters of Thomas Wood, Puritan, 1566–1577*, ed. P. Collinson (*Bulletin of the Institute of Historical Research*, Special Supplement 5, 1960), p. 21.

[57] The material in this paragraph is drawn from British Museum, Lansdowne MS. 443, and Bodleian Library, Tanner MS. 179.

for instance, received but one living from him, although it was a wealthy one in terms of the lord keeper's patronage. Yet it is not only at the instances of their own preferment that one must look. Bacon's chaplains and those of later lord keepers successfully petitioned on the behalf of a significant number of suitors for benefices. Saul petitioned for at least 16 men between 1559 and 1575; Wyborne acted for another 16 between 1560 and 1575, in addition to commending John Sudlowe for a living in 1566. Master Pedder spoke on behalf of seven hopeful suitors during the years 1559 to 1564. On seven occasions in 1616 alone did John Williams, chaplain to Egerton, support the suits of petitioners and in the same year 'one of the chaplains to the Lord Chancellor' spoke in two further instances. In the earlier years the chaplains seem to have exercised independent patronage—they both petitioned for and recommended the men involved. A further service was performed by other members of the lord keeper's household and the staff of Chancery. For the early years (1559 to 1565) the records only give the name of the petitioner but after this date, until 1579, the name of the commender is also given. From these particulars it becomes evident that members of the household, both servants and gentlemen, from his secretary to one described simply as Geoffrey, received petitions from the bishops and others on behalf of certain candidates and themselves petitioned the registrar, no doubt for a gratuity. Thus on 2 October 1566 John Collyns was presented to Doddescombe rectory, Devon, at the petition of Master Doyley, one of the lord keeper's gentlemen, and the commendation of the bishop of Exeter.

It does not follow, however, that these men automatically controlled the more valuable livings in the lord keeper's gift. Indeed, several of the livings which Sawle, Wyborne and Pedder petitioned for were poor by any standards and the same applies to benefices for which the household gentlemen acted as intermediaries.[58] On the other hand there remains a distinct possibility that the chances of a client obtaining a living at all could in certain cases depend upon the services of these gentlemen and servants of the household: they were on the spot and in an excellent position to receive and impart information about openings; they could consistently press a particular suit and check on its progress. A cleric who petitioned for a living unsuccess-

---

[58] E.g. 16 January 1561/2, John Heywoode was presented to Beston Vicarage, Notts., worth £4 15s., at the petition of Arthur Sawle. In 1559 Edward Wyseman, one of the gentlemen of the lord keeper's household, petitioned successfully on behalf of James Hallywell for a rectory worth only £4 13s. 3d. These King's Book valuations are unrealistic but there is, from surviving evidence, little indication that the distribution of wealth as between livings changed much during the hundred years following the compilation of the *Valor Ecclesiasticus*.

fully might leave instructions to a servant to watch for a suitable vacancy and press his case in his absence. Unless their services were used in this way it is hard to see why the bishops, for example, would seek their aid when they could in normal circumstances petition directly.

The record of Egerton's presentations throws little light upon the role played by the household during the later period. The lord keeper's servants, if they appear in the lists at all, are not identified as such; even the household chaplains, apart from Williams, are not named.[59] This does not mean that no services were performed by these men: the earlier list itself does not consistently identify a petitioner as a servant or a chaplain. However, the services of such men in the later period were rarely required as physical petitioners. By this time petitions were presented in writing by the suitor himself. Where the chaplains had a role it was in commending such suits as were brought to their notice and smiling upon them in the examination. The service which gentlemen of the household had performed in allowing a cleric actually to file his petition may, however, have been just as important then as earlier.

If the lord keeper's chaplains and servants commanded some patronage they certainly did not influence all presentations. The bishops, as mentioned above, nominated men to the lord keeper. In general they sought to wield additional influence within their jurisdictions rather than to extend its bounds. An analysis of the patronage of certain of the bishops over twenty years indicates that the bishops normally petitioned for livings within their own diocese, only occasionally suing for one outside. In 1569 the bishop of Coventry and Lichfield petitioned for the preferment of John Audeley to a Leicestershire living; apart from this single instance, throughout the nineteen years of his episcopate he spoke on behalf of thirteen men for benefices within his own diocese. The bishop of Norwich similarly petitioned for one man only outside his diocese. The bishop of Worcester rarely petitioned for anyone and never succeeded (if he tried) in placing someone outside his diocese. Apart from the two archbishops only the bishop of London regularly petitioned for benefices outside his area of immediate influence: on at least thirty-three occasions he was successful. Granted that most bishops appear to have exercised influence within their own sees, one might expect that the value of livings to which they succeeded in presenting depended upon chance rather than

---

[59] John Donne was secretary to Egerton and later received favour from Lord Keeper Williams; Valentine Carey, Dean of St Paul's, and Robert Clarke had also been Egerton's chaplains. See M. Hudson, 'The Political and Ecclesiastical Activities of Bishop Williams' (unpublished London M.A. thesis, 1926), pp. 45–47.

influence. The bishop of London's wider influence may be attributable not to personal dominance but to the fact that superior national information regarding vacancies was available to London clerics.

Certainly the bishops, chancellors, archdeacons and colleges had reason to thank God for the lord keeper, for it was through him that they were enabled to prefer men of their own choosing and, in the case of diocesan officials, to some extent control their own personnel. True, their suits were not always successful, but archdeacons such as Aylmer of Lincoln; Lever of Coventry; Wattes of Middlesex; Mullyns of London; and the archdeacons of Huntingdon and Essex, were able to present numbers of men to crown livings through the chancellor's favour. However beneficial the influence of such men was to the areas which they served, it seems certain that they owed it not to their office but to their personal eminence. England and Wales contained over fifty-two archdeaconries but a mere handful of arch-deacons are mentioned in the lists of petitioners at the beginning of Elizabeth's reign. Almost all were exiles—John Aylmer, Robert Beaumont, Thomas Cole, Guido Heton, Thomas Lever, John Mullyns, Thomas Wattes and John Watson—only the occasional archdeacon, such as William Day of Nottingham, who had not been an exile, appears. To some extent this explains the comparative absence of archdeacons from the 1596 to 1617 list and their replacement by 'certain preachers' of influence. It is noteworthy that the lord keeper was granting patronage to the returned exiles and in this connexion should be mentioned the regular petitions of Alexander Nowell.[60] Nevertheless, these men tended to exercise patronage within their jurisdictions. For this reason, such petitions are one of the few ways in which we can see the policy of such men at work: few arch-deacons possessed direct patronage and their attempts to exercise influence over the gentry, if they existed, are difficult to trace. As the period progressed the bishops and officials lost the near monopoly of royal patronage which they once had and influence became frag-mented between courtiers, gentry and ecclesiastics. There is consider-able evidence that men like Huntingdon, Pembroke, Leicester and Bedford sought to extend their patronage opportunities by nominating men to livings through the lord chancellor but there is no space to develop this point further.[61] No doubt patronage exercised in this way

---

[60] Nowell petitioned for 7 livings successfully during the sample years of Nicholas Bacon's tenure alone. (1558/59; 1562/63; 1566/67; 1570/71; 1574/75; 1577/78.)

[61] See M. C. Cross, 'Noble Patronage in the Elizabethan Church', *The Historical Journal*, iii (1960), pp. 1–16; British Museum, Lansdowne MS. 443. Huntingdon petitioned successfully for 9 livings in the period 1558/59–1579; in the same period Bedford petitioned on behalf of 20 clerics.

sometimes presented policy but a full-scale study would be required to analyse the lord keeper's patronage in terms of its recipients. Moreover, it seems doomed to failure for the early years at least. Little information is readily available concerning non-graduates; also, the poor supply of educated clerics during this time means that the quality of the men involved necessarily would seem poorer than that of later presentees. The later lists were greatly affected by the rising number of graduates seeking employment in the church. For example, of 1,380 presentees to benefices between 1627 and 1640, 825 possessed M.A.'s; 301 had higher degrees; 97 had B.A.s and only 157 were non-graduate. This was a staggering increase upon the 1558/59 to 1579 list, even allowing for the failure to note all degrees in those records.[62]

From this examination of the records it is abundantly clear that the extent of the patronage in the keeper's hands made organization imperative. In effect it also meant that the keeper could not choose the recipients of his favour from personal knowledge. This gave laymen and ecclesiastics throughout the land the opportunity to exercise patronage to which they had no legal claim,[63] without the necessity of purchase. The lord keeper retained ultimate control in most cases and appears to have concerned himself with the distribution of patronage as far as was feasible. Most tried to bring it in line with some broad policy—carefully administering the oath against simony and ensuring that preaching ministers actually provided sermons for their charges. There is, however, no evidence that individual lord keepers used this patronage for political purposes, for example, to build up a loyalist party within the church. Given the organization of the 'patronage office' this would have been difficult if not impossible: the keeper's goal was limited to achieving a subscribing and preaching ministry. The examination of candidates does not appear to have been perfunctory: the responsibility of the keeper's chaplains in this matter was paramount and probably their activities warrant further

---

[62] Bodleian Library, Tanner MS. 179. The position was greatly improved before this: 1596: 76 graduates; 12 students (115 presentations); 1600: 82 graduates; (103); 1604: 93 graduates; 6 students (117); 1608: 94 graduates; 4 students (109); 1612: 99 graduates; 6 students (122); 1616: 86 graduates; 6 students (101). The proportion of university men kept fairly constant from year to year. It should be remembered that the figures do *not* represent the number of separate individuals presented. Many men received several preferments at the lord keeper's hands.

[63] J. Doddridge, *A Compleat Parson or a Description of Advowsons* (London, 1630), pp. 64–65. He establishes that the distinction between presentation and nomination is normally an artificial one but that it can be created by the patron assigning the right to nominate but not to present to another person. In such cases the nominator is to be regarded as patron. If two men are nominated and the presenter has to *choose* whom to present then he is the patron.

study. At the beginning of Elizabeth's reign there may have been a deliberate attempt to give the bishops considerable say in the distribution of patronage and the returned exiles as a group were certainly favoured. The gradual ousting of the bishops from their dominant position may have been due to increasing interest in patronage from lay puritan quarters.[64] Certain observable trends seem to have owed little to conscious policy—the rise in the number of graduates presented was, after all, commensurate with general educational expansion and the rise in graduate entry into the church.[65] The efficiency of communication concerning vacancies—both in the localities and at the centre—determined to some degree the extent of competition for benefices. This competition was in any case probably only strong where relatively wealthy livings were concerned.[66] Clearly, the lord keeper overall had access to superior information about vacancies, compared to that available to the bishops.

Whereas the lord keeper and his officials strove to organize the distribution and while they tried to attain certain minimal standards, the importance of the lord keeper's patronage as a channel for the influence of others is undoubted. The chaplains of the household and the keeper's gentlemen wielded a good deal of power but there is no way of establishing whether it was exercised in a particularly corrupt fashion. Other groups and individuals certainly found ample opportunity to press suits of their own and some (Huntingdon, Grindal, Aylmer, Lever) seem to have had a policy in mind.[67] Many more patrons were merely the semi-passive tools of clergymen anxious for preferment. The lord keeper actively encouraged this third party patronage—he had a direct interest in the system because the task of presenting to so many livings was too great for himself and his chaplains alone. For the crown its ecclesiastical patronage provided a valuable means of rewarding various individuals—a link in the chain of patronage which was much wider than the ecclesiastical world.

University of Birmingham

[64] There is, of course, always the possibility that episcopal influence was strengthened under Coventry's lord keepership.

[65] L.R.O., Reg. XXX, 1606: 19 out of 20 seeking deacon's orders were graduate; G.L.M.S., 9535/2: of 148 deacons admitted between 1620 and 1626 all were graduate.

[66] Petitioners evidently believed that it was easier to obtain an impoverished living. For examples see British Museum, Harleian MS. 6995, fos 40, 62. The efficiency of communications must have affected the degree of competition in individual instances also.

[67] Owen, *op. cit.*, pp. 97, 98, 197, 198, 200, for Aylmer's exercise of patronage as bishop of London.

APPENDICES

1. *Number of presentations granted by the lord keeper January 1558/9—December 1580**

1559	224	1565	78	1571	116	1577	108
1560	141	1566	97	1572	93	1578	126
1561	123	1567	102	1573	106	1579	163
1562	123	1568	102	1574	135	1580	248
1563	77	1569	102	1575	133		
1564	98	1570	125	1576	172		

* The modern calendar year from January 1 to December 31 has been used in the compilation of this table. The arrangement of the years into groups of high or low presentations suggests that there were complex reasons for the discrepancies between various years—epidemics; poor communications, shortage of clergy.

2. *Number of presentations granted by Lord Chancellor Egerton, 1596–1616/17*

1596	111	1602	90	1607	102	1612	122
1597	165	1603	84	1608	109	1613	112
1598	141	1604	117	1609	101	1614	98
1599	99	1605	119	1610	119	1615	89
1600	103	1606	105	1611	86	1616	101
1601	107						

3. *Indication of (a) the reasons for vacancies and (b) the basis of the lord keeper's right to present to livings appearing in the lists of presentations, 1570–80 and 1596–1616*

Year	Total	Death	Deprivation	Resignation	Lapse	Unknown	De Iure	Wardship	Simony	Promotion
1570	125	63	2	26	7	17	10	—	—	—
1571	116	68	3	25	3	1	16	—	—	—
1572	93	42	5	18	2	4	22	—	—	—
1573	106	43	7	29	2	12	13	—	—	—
1574	135	42	5	25	12	13	37	1	—	—
1575	133	50	3	21	25	7	24	3	—	—
1576	172	49	1	35	25	9	53	—	—	—
1577	108	31	1	23	13	9	30	1	—	—
1578	126	32	2	33	10	9	39	1	—	—
1579	163	33	4	37	51	3	35	—	—	—
1580	248	49	1	48	23	3	124	—	—	—
1596	115	27	(1)	27	25	4	25	2	1	3
1597	165	40	(5)	33	47	4	30	—	2	4
1598	141	43	1(4)	17	47	—	19	3	7	3
1599	99	27	(4)	17	21	1	20	—	7	2
1600	103	29	2(1)	20	31	—	11	—	7	2
1601	107	36	3(2)	20	36	2	2	1(?)	2	3
1602	90	24	(1)	17	28	9	4	2	4	1
1603	84	29	—	13	32	3	5	—	—	2
1604	117	25	(6)	22	44	2	12	—	5	—
1605	119	29	7(3)	19	36	1	19	—	5	—
1606	105	34	1(6)	19	26	1	9	—	6	3
1607	102	24	1(10)	18	36	—	9	—	3	1

Year	Total	Death	Deprivation	Resignation	Lapse	Unknown	De Iure	Wardship	Simony	Promotion
1608	109	28	(14)	14	36	1	8	—	7	1
1609	101	21	(8)	15	39	—	10	—	7	1
1610	119	34	2(4)	26	31	1	17	—	3	1
1611	86	37	(4)	11	17	1	10	—	2	4
1612	122	39	1(14)	24	28	—	12	—	5	—
1613	112	42	(10)	15	25	1	8	—	11	—
1614	98	43	(5)	21	16	—	7	—	4	2
1615	89	28	1(8)	13	24	3	7	—	5	—
1616	101	32	(5)	21	16	2	11	—	10	4

The above years were the only ones found suitable for such an analysis. Unfortunately the figures are not conclusive: the clerk regularly confused reason for vacancy with the lord keeper's claim to present—two very different things. For example, the category of 'Lapse' does not explain why the living in question had fallen vacant but why it had fallen into the lord keeper's hands. The term 'de iure' is yet more obscure—it probably means simply that the living concerned was normally a crown living valued at below £20 and therefore the keeper's by right—as such it must include many livings vacant by death, a suggestion supported by the figures for 1576 and 1580. Despite these defects the figures are very useful: the number of livings falling to the keeper for extraordinary reasons can be estimated and the rise in the number of livings presented to during lapse, dating from the mid-1570s, is particularly notable. The figures in brackets under the heading 'deprivation' indicate livings vacated by 'cession'.

THE EMERGENCE OF AN URBAN IDEOLOGY AT FLORENCE c. 1250–1450

By George Holmes, M.A., Ph.D., F.R.Hist.S.

READ AT THE SOCIETY'S CONFERENCE 14 SEPTEMBER 1972

EVERY city must in a sense have a city culture. Florence, however, was the only place in which there arose at the end of the Middle Ages what one might call a city ideology, that is to say a set of developed ideas as distinct from a way of living, which was particularly designed by and for city-dwellers. Much of the modern historical interest in Florence has centred around these ideas which emerged in the first half of the fifteenth century, the more so because even the innovations in the visual arts introduced at the same time by Donatello and his contemporaries are in part a by-product of them. The theme which I would like to develop in this paper therefore is the relationship between the city society and its ideology. This is of course a very old and well-worn theme. One of the common presuppositions of Renaissance historiography has been the understandable assumption that the ideology fitted the city, and a good deal of historical analysis has been applied to identifying the congruences between them and illustrating the growth of the humanist school out of the circumstances of Florentine life. The ideology, however, was created in the early fifteenth century, at the end of the period which I am going to discuss, when Florence had already been a great centre of industry and commerce and an independent republic for a very long time. Fruitful as it has been, this approach therefore leaves one with the disquieting feeling that a place which has been for so long and so conspicuously a centre of throbbing urban life ought to have had its ideological revolution much earlier, particularly since economic historians have emphasized the elements of commercial contraction rather than expansion in the early Renaissance period.[1] Some historians have found themselves driven into the paradoxical position of regarding the early Renaissance as a symptom of economic decline. I would therefore like to look at the old theme obliquely by deflecting attention from the great innovations

---

[1] Notably R. S. Lopez, 'Hard Times and Investment in Culture', *The Renaissance. A Symposium* (New York, 1953); R. S. Lopez and H. A. Miskimin, 'The Economic Depression of the Renaissance', *Economic History Review*, ser. 2, xiv (1961–62).

themselves and concentrating it on the factors which favoured or hindered ideological innovation in the century and a half before they appeared.

The humanist ideology of the city, as I should like to call it, received its first full expression in the second quarter of the fifteenth century and mostly in the works of three famous writers: Leonardo Bruni, Chancellor of the commune of Florence, Leon Battista Alberti, a member of an exiled Florentine family, and Poggio Bracciolini, a Florentine who was employed in the papal chancery. In their writings one can, I think without great distortion, distinguish three related sets of ideas. Firstly there is the political philosophy of the republican city state conceived not as part of a divine order of the universe in the manner of scholastic politics but as a self-sufficient secular society directed to the advancement of its citizens and their culture. Bruni was the chief promoter of this conception.[2] Alberti attached to it an architectural vision of the ideal city.[3] Secondly there is a new style of writing contemporary history, especially the political history of the city state, as an account of policies and causes and effects in which the events are ordered in a rational and artistic narrative in imitation of the historians of antiquity. Bruni's history of Florence was the first great example of this style but Poggio also practised it at an early stage.[4] And thirdly there is the artificial picture of bourgeois society which we find in Alberti's *Della Famiglia*[5] and in Poggio's dialogues,[6] where citizens discuss the problems of the family, business, society and government in a free and urbane manner with reference to the ordering of their lives within a city society. This corpus of literature was in itself remarkably complete and consistent. Of course it was limited. It was not a

---

[2] An early expression of it is *De Militia* (*c*. 1421–27), ed. C. C. Bayley, *War and Society in Renaissance Florence* (Toronto, 1961). The plainest statement is in *Della Vita Civile* (*c*. 1435–38), ed. F. Battaglia (Bologna, 1944), by Matteo Palmieri who was a second-rank amateur humanist. It was foreshadowed at the very beginning of the century in Bruni's *Laudatio Florentinae Urbis*, printed in H. Baron, *From Petrarch to Leonardo Bruni* (Chicago, 1968), pp. 232–63.

[3] In *De Re Aedificatoria* (ed. G. Orlandi and P. Portoghesi, Milan, 1966), *c*. 1444–50.

[4] Leonardo Bruni Aretino, *Historiarum Florentini Populi Libri XII*, ed. E. Santini (*Rerum Italicarum Scriptores*, xix, iii) Bk. 12, *c*. 1440–44. Cf. E. Santini, 'Leonardo Bruni Aretino e i suoi "Historiarum Florentini Populi Libri XII" ', *Annali della R. Scuola Normale Superiore di Pisa, Filosofia e Filologia*, xxii (1910), 89. *Poggii Historia Florentina* (Venice, 1715), *c*. 1453–59.

[5] L. B. Alberti, *Opere Volgari*, ed. C. Grayson, i (Bari, 1960), *c*. 1433–45.

[6] *De Avaritia* (1428–29), *De Nobilitate, De Infelicitate Principum* (1440) in *Opera* (Basle, 1538), reprinted *Opera Omnia*, i (Turin, 1964).

complete view of the world. It had nothing to say about natural science and not much about religion. It could also be argued that it was almost completely derivative. It drew very heavily on the ideas and the style of certain classical authors, notably Aristotle, Cicero, Seneca, Livy, Sallust and Quintilian. But, these limitations apart, it presented an idealized view of a way of life which was strikingly novel and was so captivating that it acquired a widespread authority in Europe as a whole.

Although two of the three leading writers, Poggio and Alberti, spent most of their lives outside Florence[7] and although other Italian cities could have supplied the humanist skill and the books necessary to evolve these ideas, still the ideology of the city was unquestionably a Florentine innovation. Behind the three protagonists there was a much larger group made up of intellectual precursors and teachers like Coluccio Salutati Bruni's predecessor as Chancellor, and Manuel Chrysoloras, the visitor from Byzantium, of wealthy patrons like Cosimo de Medici and Palla Strozzi, of friends and fellow humanists, professional and amateur, like Niccolò Niccoli, Matteo Strozzi and Carlo Marsuppini.[8] This wider humanist society was Florentine. The rapid evolution of the new type of literature was intimately bound up with the history of the ruling class of the city in the early fifteenth century. And there was also the special political factor: the new ideology could hardly have evolved in the particular way it did without the inspiration of Florentine republican politics in which many members of the group were prominently involved.

Florence was unique among the cities of medieval Europe in giving rise to such a developed set of ideas appropriate to urban life and it is this literary innovation with its attendant visual revolution which has captured the attention of historians and made Florence the most intensively studied of medieval cities. Even Davidsohn's History of Florence[9] (which must be the most elaborate and thorough investigation of any medieval or renaissance city), though it stops short at 1330, was inspired by awareness of the bourgeois consciousness to which the early developments pointed. But the striking novelties

---

[7] Full accounts in E. Walser, *Poggius Florentinus* (Berlin, 1914), G. Mancini, *Vita di L. B. Alberti* (Florence, 1911); cf. C. Grayson, *Dizionario Biografico degli Italiani*, i (1960).

[8] The most convenient survey of the group remains that in G. Voigt, *Die Wiederbelebung des Classischen Altertums*, i (1893, reprinted Berlin, 1960). Among a mass of more recent studies the most comprehensive works are H. Baron, *The Crisis of the Early Italian Renaissance* (two editions, Princeton, 1955 and 1960) and L. Martines, *The Social World of the Florentine Humanists 1390–1460* (London, 1963).

[9] R. Davidsohn, *Geschichte von Florenz* (Berlin, 1896–1927); Italian translation, *Storia di Firenze* (Florence, 1956–65).

which I have mentioned mostly appeared after 1425. It is difficult to find more than a hint of them before 1400. At that time the more mundane characteristics of an urban society, a city based on industry and commerce with a huge industrial labour force, great commercial wealth, a funded debt and a republican constitution—all these characteristics had been present for a very long time. What premonitions of the future were there in medieval Florence? Why did it take so long? Let us for the moment go back into the fourteenth century and, forgetting the future, try to pick out what possibilities of ideological development there were in medieval Florence.

A visitor to Florence a hundred years earlier in the early fourteenth century, looking for manifestations of culture, would probably have been most powerfully impressed by the number and prominence of institutions created by or associated with the religious orders. Not only would he have found the most advanced examples of painting in the Franciscan and Dominican churches of Santa Croce and Santa Maria Novella, he would also have found in them the most effective institutions for the dissemination of ideas. In the thirteenth century the religious orders had grown in great profusion and taken very deep roots in Florentine society both by importation and by native creation. A striking example of the interconnection of the orders with city society is provided by the Servites. The Servites traced their origin to 1233 when a group of seven laymen from Florentine families made an informal agreement to live piously without leaving the lay world. They later decided to live in common in a house outside the walls, then retired some miles away to Monte Senario for seclusion and finally under the influence of the Dominican evangelist Peter Martyr set up their house on the site which became the great convent and church of Santissima Annunziata and adopted the Augustinian rule with a special devotion to the Virgin and the name of Servi di Maria. The building was begun in 1250. By the end of the thirteenth century the Servites had included a Florentine saint, Filippo Benizzi, who was general from 1267 to 1285; after some vicissitudes they had secured full papal recognition in 1291 and they had a number of convents in central and northern Italy. They never became very important outside Italy. Their natural environment was the Italian city world.[10] The leader of the seven founders was Alessio Falconieri of a well-known Florentine family.

[10] The early history of the order is summarized by A. M. Rossi, *Manuale di Storia dell'Ordine dei Servi di Maria* (Rome, 1956). There is no detailed modern account to match the early work of A. Giani, *Annales ordinis fratrum beatae Mariae virginis* (Florence, 1618). Recent specialized publications are to be found in *Monumenta Ordinis Servorum Sanctae Mariae* (Brussels, 1897–1930) and in the periodical *Studi Storici dell' Ordine dei Servi di Maria*.

His niece Saint Giuliana Falconieri who died in 1341 founded a Servite Tertiary Order modelled on the Mendicant tertiaries and the Falconieri family was still claiming patronage rights which the Order found inconvenient when the Renaissance church of Santissima Annunziata was being built in the mid-fifteenth century.[11]

I mention the Servites because their history illustrates the strong impulses in Florentine lay society towards the creation of religious institutions. They could never however claim parity with the two major mendicant orders, the Dominicans and Franciscans. Perhaps more even than the cathedral it was their two churches and convents of Santa Maria Novella and Santa Croce, at both of which new and ambitious building plans were put into effect in the late thirteenth century, which dominated Florentine religious life. The vast new church of Santa Maria Novella was begun in 1279 to be succeeded in 1295 by the even vaster church of Santa Croce. Both of them took a very long time to build but in the early fourteenth century they must at least have matched the cathedral, where rebuilding started about the same time as at Santa Croce.

The establishments of the mendicants were surrounded and supported by their Third Orders, whose members observed rules and were regarded as at least quasi-clerical but lived in the lay world.[12] Santa Croce for example had a fairly well documented penumbra of Tertiaries many of them apparently living around the convent where there was a street named after them, the Via delle Pinzochere.[13] Beyond the Tertiaries and now completely in the lay world were the fraternities, many of them attached to particular churches, most of which again had sprung up in the thirteenth century. There was, for example, a *Compagnia de le laude che si rauna a Santa Maria Novella*—a 'Company for the singing of hymns of praise which meets at Santa Maria Novella'. An early account book starting in the year 1312 shows its members as a group of laymen meeting regularly at the Dominican Church and spending small contributions on candles for the services and charitable gifts.[14] The statutes of a similar group which met at the cathedral, compiled in 1326, laid down compulsory attendance at daily services and strict penalties

---

[11] G. Richa, *Notizie Istoriche delle Chiese Fiorentine*, viii (Florence, 1759), p. 29.

[12] C. Piana, 'Silloge di documenti dall'antico archivio di S. Francesco di Bologna. IV. La posizione giuridica del Terz' Ordine della penitenza a Firenze nel secolo XIV', *Archivium Franciscanum Historicum*, i (1957).

[13] Davidsohn, *Storia*, vii, pp. 65–68.

[14] Davidsohn, *Forschungen zur älteren Geschichte von Florenz*, iv (Berlin, 1896–1908), pp. 429–30. The same account contains an early entry for oil for the lamp before Giotto's Crucifixion in the church; see references in A. Smart, *The Assisi Problem and the Art of Giotto* (Oxford, 1971), pp. 74–81.

for slight moral offences.[15] The most famous of these societies was the company of the Madonna of Or San Michele, unattached to any church, whose devotions centred on a miracle working painting of the Virgin by Duccio in a shrine in the grain market and attracted some competitive hostility from the brothers of Santa Croce and Santa Maria Novella.[16] According to a chronicler's story the mortality of the Black Death brought the Company of Or San Michele legacies and gifts to the value of 35,000 florins which led to a serious financial scandal. The same chronicler says that the Compagnia della Misericordia and the hospital of Santa Maria Nuova also benefited to the extent of 25,000 florins each.[17] The sum alleged for Or San Michele seems impossibly large but the institution which commissioned the immensely elaborate tabernacle made by Orcagna for Or San Michele soon after the Black Death[18] was certainly very rich. These were only some of the more notable of a large number of similar lay societies.

Before the end of the thirteenth century the forces of urban piety and ecclesiastical organization had combined to produce an extraordinarily rich profusion of religious institutions much better adapted to city life than the diocese and the parishes. These religious organizations had proliferated during the great period of industrial growth and population expansion, in the thirteenth century, to form an elaborate and deeply rooted network. The importance of this system was that it canalized piety into forms which were appropriate to city life but which were also acceptable to ecclesiastical authority. The houses of the mendicant orders in particular linked together in one organization the brothers of the great convent of Santa Maria Novella, often members of the best Florentine families and often scholars with an advanced scholastic education, and the semi-lay men and women of the Dominican third order and the pious lay men of the confraternities attached to the convent but still in the outside world. They provided a link between different social and intellectual levels. Since the Florentine convents belonged to orders with a general European organization they also provided channels by which papal authority could be exercised in Florence and by which foreign influences such as Parisian scholasticism or the piety of the hermitages of the Apennines could flow into Florence and yet be absorbed into institutions which were securely based in the city. The variety

---

[15] Davidsohn, *Forschungen*, iv, pp. 432–33.

[16] Davidsohn, *Storia*, iii, pp. 388–90; *Forschungen*, iv, pp. 435–36.

[17] *Istorie de Matteo Villani*, in L. Muratori, *Rerum Italicarum Scriptores*, xiv (Milan, 1729), I, vii.

[18] W. and E. Paatz, *Die Kirchen von Florenz*, iv (Frankfurt am Main, 1952), pp. 500–3, 547–51.

of competitive and balancing institutions allowed a variety of impulses to be satisfied.

It is perhaps largely for this reason that, although there were a number of instances or accusations of heresy,[19] it can be discounted as a serious intellectual force in Florence in the period with which we are concerned. Even by 1250 the heroic days of the mendicant orders and of the struggles against Catharist and other forms of heresy were over and to a large extent that battle had been won by the creation of religious organizations which provided a satisfactory orthodox framework. The last really serious battle against heresy in Florence was that waged by the Dominican St Peter Martyr against the Cathars in the 1240s. Peter Martyr seems to have owed much of his success to mobilizing orthodox lay opinion in confraternities.[20] Thereafter Florence was on the whole remarkable for its orthodoxy. Even the War of the Eight Saints against the Pope from 1375 to 1378 does not seem to have produced more than a temporary and ineffectual strengthening of support for Fraticelli opinions.[21] Dangerous opinions were certainly sometimes expressed, mostly those associated with the Spiritual and Fraticelli offshoots of the Franciscan Order. Pierre Jean Olivi lectured at Florence from 1287 to 1289 and inspired the later spiritual leader Ubertino da Casale.[22] The Augustinian Simone Fidate da Cascia, who supported Spiritual views about poverty, was a popular preacher in Florence in the late 1320s and early 1330s. He has left a fine piece of rhetorical flagellation in the best Spiritual style attributing the flood disaster of 1332 to divine anger about the Florentine vices of licentiousness and avarice. He quarrelled with the Dominicans of Santa Maria Novella about doctrine but his influence with the laity is shown by the fact that he was able to persuade the commune to support a lay confraternity attached to the Augustinian convent of Santo Spirito (*Societas laudum S. Spiritus*) in setting up a house for fallen women, Santa Elisabeta delle Convertite. He was also friendly with the native canon lawyer Tommaso Corsini, a member of the family which produced St Andrea Corsini, Bishop of Fiesole, and Cardinal

[19] Recently surveyed by J. N. Stephens, 'Heresy in Medieval and Renaissance Florence', *Past and Present*, 54 (1972).

[20] The story has been most recently told by B. Quilici, *Il Vescovo Ardingo e la Chiesa di Firenze nel quarto e quinto Decennie del Secolo XIII* (Florence, 1965), p. 37 seq.

[21] M. B. Becker, 'Florentine Politics and the Diffusion of Heresy in the Trecento: a socioeconomic Inquiry', *Speculum*, xxxiv (1959), pp. 70–72. The commune was more hostile to the Inquisition than before but that does not necessarily mean a sympathy with heresy.

[22] D. C. Douie, *The Nature and Effect of the Heresy of the Fraticelli* (Manchester, 1932), pp. 89–90.

Pietro Corsini later in the century.[23] But although the inquisition attached to the Franciscan convent of S. Croce was vigilant and occasionally active throughout the fourteenth century, there is no evidence that Spiritual doctrines were very widespread or that they were influential at a sophisticated level. Such austere ideas were more suitable to the mountain hermitages of the Apennines than to the affluent society of the city. Ubertino da Casale denounced the collection of money by the Franciscans at Florence at the beginning of the fourteenth century for the building of a lavish convent[24] with good reason for S. Croce was built on the scale of a cathedral. The way of life of the Spirituals did not flourish in this ambience. On the other hand, out of their more evangelical wings, the orders could provide inflammatory penitential preachers—Fidati and later Giovanni Dominici are the most obvious examples—and satisfy an emotional need without disrupting ecclesiastical life. S. Croce is the clearest instance of a foundation which was able to absorb and render innocuous both religious radicalism and the strong currents of lay pietism but this must also have been true, less spectacularly, of many less famous orders and institutions, the Humiliati at Ognissanti and the Servites at Santissima Annunziata for example.

I emphasize the importance of the religious houses and confraternities partly in order to balance the impression of advanced secularism in Florentine life which easily follows from its association with the humanist ideology. The period of industrial growth in the thirteenth century was also a period of intense religious activity and this aspect of Florentine life continued less spectacularly but with scarcely diminished strength through the humanist period. It is one of the paradoxes of the humanist movement that its patron Cosimo set up the best classical library of the day in the convent of S. Marco which he rebuilt at great expense to house the rigorous Observant Dominicans whose champion a generation earlier had been the passionate opponent of classical learning Giovanni Dominici.[25] The humanism of the Bruni circle was in some respects a superficial phenomenon of Florentine life. At an earlier stage the convents themselves were the centres of learned culture. The most important centre for advanced study in Florence in the early fourteenth century was Santa Maria Novella. It was in the lecture room of this house that Dante ate the 'bread of

---

[23] M. G. McNeil, *Simone Fidati and his* De Gestis Domini Salvatoris (Washington, 1951), pp. 20–27; Davidsohn, *Forschungen*, iv, p. 422.

[24] *Archiv für Literatur und Kirchengeschichte des Mittelalters*, iii (1887), p. 68.

[25] R. Morçay, *Saint Antonin Archévêque de Florence (1389–1459)* (Paris, 1914), pp. 65–79.

the angels'[26] as he called the teaching of the schools and the classics which he struggled to transmute into a personal philosophy in the *Convivio* and his experience must have been shared by many lay Florentines who had to learn their philosophy and theology at home instead of going to Bologna or Paris. Santa Maria Novella had an official studium of the Order. It had a fine library.[27] Its friars included many who had been at the fount at Paris. Naturally the learning purveyed there was university scholasticism, particularly that of St Thomas. Aquinas could hardly have had more flattering pictorial memorials than the fresco painted in the Chapter House of this convent where he is enthroned above the defeated heretics Sabellius, Averroes and Arius, cringing at his feet, or in the Strozzi altarpiece painted for the same convent, where St Peter and he on either side of Christ receive from him respectively the keys and the book. Both of these were painted soon after the middle of the fourteenth century.[28]

So scholasticism had its place in Florence, primarily at Santa Maria Novella, to a lesser extent at the other convents whose members dabbled in learning. The influence of the Dominican Order and vulgarized versions of its doctrines were transmitted to the city at large by its preachers, several of whom have left substantial monuments of their teaching. Fra Giordano da Rivalto, a Pisan who had been trained at Bologna and Paris and was at Santa Maria Novella from 1303 to 1306, is known from a large collection of vernacular sermons which were clearly directed at ordinary congregations and appealed to ordinary incidents of city life. A characteristic passage is one in which he denounces the double thinking of well-to-do cloth makers who punish a poor spinster for making bad thread but condone the evil practices of their fellow guild members like stretching cloth to make it look bigger.[29] But he also made frequent attempts to convey some sense of the abstract ideas of scholasticism to his hearers. Here he is for example on 17 February 1305 trying to put over the Aristo-

---

[26] *Convivio*, I, i.

[27] S. Orlandi, *La Biblioteca di S. Maria Novella in Firenze dal sec. XIV al sec. XIX* (Florence, 1952).

[28] The Spanish Chapel frescoes were commissioned from Andrea da Firenze in 1365 (Paatz, *Kirchen von Florenz*, iii, 1952, pp. 720–22, 814–16), the Strozzi altarpiece from Orcagna in 1354 (*ibid.*, 713, 804).

[29] *Prediche del b. Giordano da Rivalto dell'Ordine de' Predicatori*, ed. D. M. Manni (Florence, 1739), p. 33. Other sermons are in *Prediche di F. Giordano da Rivalto*, ed. E. Moreni (Florence, 1831) and *Prediche Inedite del B. Giordano da Rivalto*, ed. E. Narducci (Bologna, 1867). On Giordano see Davidsohn, *Storia*, vii, pp. 128–42; A. Galletti, 'Frà Giordano da Pisa Predicatore del secolo XIV', *Giornale Storico della letteratura Italiana*, xxxi, xxxiii (1898–99).

telian concept of form to a Florentine congregation: 'charity is a form in the soul. Form: perhaps you do not understand that. It is not the form of a shoe or a cap. Certainly they are a kind of form but the learned call "form" that virtue which is in things by which they operate. So that the form of the sun is light by which it works. The form of trees is their virtue by which they bear fruit.'[30] Jacopo Passavanti, a Florentine trained at Paris, Prior of Santa Maria Novella from 1355 to 1357, was the author of the *Specchio della Vera Penitenza*—'The Mirror of True Penitence'. This is a book in the vernacular clearly designed for laymen and based on sermons delivered in Florence. It achieves most of its effect by graphic moral re-working in the vernacular of stories culled from earlier medieval authors and Passavanti's art has been compared with that of his contemporary Boccaccio.[31] But though Passavanti discourages his readers from dabbling in science his book also contains a vast number of quotations from Christian authors down to and including a great many from Aquinas and many also from the pagan classics to back up its arguments.

The last of the great Dominican preachers of the fourteenth century was Giovanni Dominici, a disciple of Raymond of Capua the Observant reformer but also an alumnus of Paris. He came to Santa Maria Novella in 1399 and eventually founded a new Observant convent at Fiesole, mostly with Florentine money. In the early years of the fifteenth century he was a frequent preacher in the city. Lapo Mazzei, the letter-writing notary, friend of Datini the 'Merchant of Prato', wrote several times in 1400 about the enormous impression which he created: the congregation 'all wept or stood stupefied'; he 'says things about the Nativity of Christ which draw the living soul out of the body'.[32] Besides being a powerful evangelist Dominici, who was himself a learned man, regarded the study of the classics as one of the great evils of his day and fought a bitter rearguard action during the first years of the humanist movement against the increased attachment

---

[30] 'Perocchè la carità, si è forma nell'anima; forma, forse non intendete bene, forma non è pur quella del calzolaio o della birretta; ben sono queste alcun modo di forma; ma forma chiamano i savî quella virtù che è in tutte le cose, per le quali tutte l'operazioni si fanno. Onde la forma del sole si è la luce, colla quale opera. Forma degli alberi si è la virtù loro, colla quale fa quello frutto' (*Giornale Storico*, xxxiii, p. 197).

[31] *Lo Specchio della vera penitenza*, ed. F. L. Palidori (Florence, 1863). Cf. A. Monteverdi, 'Gli Esempi dello "Specchio di vera penitenza",' *Giornale Storico della letteratura Italiana*, lxi, lxiii (1913–14). For Passavanti's biography "Necrologio" *di S. Maria Novella*, ed. S. Orlandi (Florence, 1955), i, pp. 450–71.

[32] *Ser Lapo Mazzei. Lettere di un notario a un mercante del secolo XIV*, ed. C. Guasti (Florence, 1880), i, pp. 228, 316.

to Latin literature.[33] In this he presents an interesting contrast to one of his predecessors at Santa Maria Novella, just a century earlier, Remigio de' Girolami who has a place among those who introduced ancient literature into Florence. The writings of Remigio de' Girolami, who was both a Florentine by birth and a friar of Santa Maria Novella where he died in 1319, are the nearest thing to a serious attempt by a university-trained scholastic to adapt the learning of the schools to the specific problems of Florentine city politics. He was active as a preacher around 1300, during the period of Boniface VIII's attempts to gain control of Florence. Unlike his contemporary Giordano da Rivalto, Remigio came himself from a prominent Florentine family and probably because of this his sermons contain a lot of lively comment on the politics of the city. Apart from his sermons he has left a political treatise *De Bono Communi*, written about 1302 in the period of discord in the city caused by relations with Boniface VIII. It is an intellectual's reaction to political faction, a collection of arguments in favour of the view that the common good was to be preferred to the good of individuals. Aristotle's *Ethics* figure prominently and so do some of the classical Latin writers. In this book, admittedly unsystematically and obliquely, the scholastic interpretation of classical political thought touches city life.[34]

One kind of sophisticated thought available to Florentines then was theology and philosophy transmitted by the Orders. But beside this culture of the clerics there existed also a culture of the laymen which Florence shared with other Italian cities. One of the characteristics of Florentine society was widespread lay literacy, essential for a population whose way of life depended on contracts and accounts. Here, by way of illustration, is one of the laconic record entries which provide most of our information about early Florentine primary education. In 1304 Domina Clementia 'doctrix puerorum' contracted for the sum of forty shillings to teach Andrea Casini 'to read and write so that he shall be able to read the psalter, Donatus and

---

[33] On Dominici's life A. Roesler, *Cardinal Johannes Dominici, O. Pr. 1357–1419* (Freiburg-im-Breisgau, 1893). His attacks on contemporary humanism are contained in *Lucula Noctis*, ed. E. Hunt (University of Notre Dame Publications in Medieval Studies, no. 4, 1940) and *Regola del Governo di cura familiare*, ed. D. Salvi (Florence, 1860).

[34] L. Minio-Paluello, 'Remigio Girolami's *De Bono Communi*', *Italian Studies*, xi (1956); see further C. T. Davis, 'An early Florentine political theorist: Frà Remigio de' Girolami', *Proceedings of the American Philosophical Society*, civ (1960) and G. Salvadori and V. Federici, 'I sermoni d'occasione, le sequenze e i ritmi di Remigio Girolami fiorentino', *Scritti vari di filologia a Ernesto Monaci* (Rome, 1901).

instruments and to write'.[35] There are several things worth noting in this passage. It is already possible for a woman to be teaching Latin. Her pupil, who was a prominent member of the silk guild some twenty years later and a prior of the city thirty-six years after this education started, was to be able to read 'instrumenta'—legal documents—and also to learn Latin grammar. We have unfortunately no systematic information about literacy or primary education in Florence. Giovanni Villani said that in 1339 there were between 8,000 and 10,000 boys and girls learning to read, between 400 and 1,200 boys learning the abacus and arithmetic in six schools and between 550 and 600 learning grammar and logic in four schools. These figures are probably great exaggerations, but even if they are drastically reduced they imply a substantial degree of literacy in a population of the order of 100,000.[36] More important, they enumerate the types of education which were available: firstly basic reading and writing, secondly arithmetic for business, thirdly an initiation into the first stages of medieval higher education, grammar and logic. Reading, writing and arithmetic must have been very common accomplishments. The rudiments of a classical education were not rare. Giovanni Morelli, an otherwise undistinguished merchant without humanist connexions, who wrote down his recollections in the early part of the fourteenth century said that a man should not lose touch with the great authors when he left school: he ought to set aside time for reading Virgil, Boethius, Seneca, Cicero, Aristotle.[37] Impossible to say of course how many merchants were capable of following this idealistic advice. But at least by the early fifteenth century the idea did not seem absurd.

Apart from the merchants whose calling demanded an ability to write letters and keep accounts there was a more specialized profession which was particularly associated with education: the notaries. Flor-

---

[35] 'Legere et scrivere, ita quod convenienter sciat legere Psalterium, Donatum et instrumenta, et scrivere', S. Debenedetti, 'Sui più antichi "doctores puerorum" a Firenze', *Studi Medievali*, ii, pp. 1906, 333, 344. Other general accounts of Florentine education in Davidsohn, *Storia*, vii, ch. 3; C. Bec, *Les marchands écrivains, affaires et humanisme à Florence 1375–1434* (Paris–the Hague, 1967), pp. 383–415; C. T. Davis, 'Education in Dante's Florence', *Speculum*, xl (1965).

[36] *Historie Fiorentine di Giovanni Villani,* in Muratori, *Rerum Italicarum Scriptores,* xiii (Milan, 1728), XI, xciii: 'Troviano ch' e fanciulli e fanciulle, che stavano a leggere dalle otto mila a dieci mila. E i fanciulli che stavano ad apparare l'abbaco e algorismo in sei scuole, da mille in mille ducento. E quelli, che stavano ad apprendere Grammatica e loica in quattro grandi scuole da 550 in sei cento.' Cf. A. Frugoni, 'G. Villani. "Cronica" XI. 94', *Bullettino dell'Istituto Storico Italiano,* lxxvii (1965), p. 251.

[37] Giovanni di Pagolo Morelli, *Ricordi,* ed. V. Branca (Florence, 1956), pp. 271–73.

entine notaries have not been very much studied though they make their existence clear enough to the historian by the vast quantities of records which still survive in their registers. In the later fourteenth century about 400 were registered in the *Arte dei Giudici e Notai* which was one of the major guilds of the city, so Villani's figure of 600 notaries for 1339 may not be a great exaggeration[38] and they were certainly very much more numerous than the other learned professions of lawyers and physicians. The notaries' job was to write formal documents of all kinds, varying in importance from the wills of humble citizens to the legislative acts and diplomatic correspondence of the commune. All of them therefore had to have the basic skill of composition in Latin on which they were examined for matriculation in the guild.[39] Their professional interest in Latin composition encouraged in some of them a more advanced interest in rhetoric and in Latin literature. Throughout Northern Italy they constituted a fairly large class with professional standards of education and with a professional interest in classical literature which as laymen they could pass on to their children. This was a crucial social factor determining the form of higher culture in medieval and Renaissance Italy both because the notaries were a large educated class and because of their tendency to emphasize the literary rather than any other aspect of classical culture. The prototype Renaissance man of letters, Petrarch, and the prototype learned artist, Brunelleschi, were both sons of Florentine notaries. Among the members of the famous group which initiated the humanist revolution in Florence around 1400 Salutati, the Chancellor of Florence, was a notary by training and profession and both Poggio and Bruni started life with a legal training which would have made them either notaries or lawyers if they had not acquired the outstanding skill in Latin composition which freed them from ordinary professional restrictions.[40] The notarial class was prominent in Florentine life long before the humanist revolution. It was a notary, Brunetto Latini who died in 1294, who was singled out by Villani in a famous passage as the man who began to 'civilize' (*digrossare*) the Florentines. This he did so far as we know primarily

[38] L. Martines, *Lawyers and Statecraft in Renaissance Florence* (Princeton, 1968), p. 41; Villani, XI, 113.

[39] Martines, *ibid.*, pp. 34–35, referring to the Statutes of 1344.

[40] For Salutati see B. L. Ullman, *The Humanism of Coluccio Salutati* (Padua, 1963), ch. 1; the early careers of Poggio and Bruni are sketched by Martines, *Social World of the Florentine Humanists*, pp. 123–24, 166–67. The general importance of the connexion between law, rhetoric and culture is discussed by J. E. Seigel, *Rhetoric and Philosophy in Renaissance Humanism* (Princeton, 1968), ch. 7, and by H. Wieruszowski, 'Rhetoric and the Classics in Italian Education of the Thirteenth Century', *Politics and Culture in Medieval Spain and Italy* (Rome, 1971).

by introducing them to Cicero's *De Inventione*, and Aristotle's *Ethics* in his *Rettorica* and *Livres dou Trêsor* which are vulgarizations of the classics.[41] Brunetto was an unusually creative notary and had the advantage of travel which brought him into contact with the schools of Paris. A more commonplace example, over a century later, is Lapo Mazzei, Datini's friend, whom we have already encountered under the spell of Dominici's sermons in 1400. Mazzei's correspondence is mostly about everyday matters but he is quite capable of quoting Boethius, Cicero, Seneca or Virgil to drive home a point.[42] There must have been hundreds of Florentine notaries in the fourteenth century with the same broad smattering of theological and classical culture.

In the period 1250 to 1400, then, there were two parallel streams of high culture in Florence: the university scholasticism of the religious orders and the rhetorical literature of the lawyers, a clerical culture and a lay culture. It is, I think, quite proper to see the humanist revolution as a great deepening and strengthening of the second of these two traditions, the lay culture of the rhetoricians, an intensification of this lay culture which eventually produced a lay ideology. But to put it in this way gives a misleading impression of continuity, as if the rhetorical tradition with its appreciation of the political and social teaching of Cicero gradually grew stronger until it blossomed in Bruni and his circle. That was not how it happened. To put the humanist revolution in perspective one has to appreciate both the obstacles to the creation of an independent lay ideology in fourteenth-century Florence and the novelty of the changes in the next century.

To the historian of ideas the most striking feature of fourteenth-century Florence is the contrast between, on the one hand, its pre-eminence as a European centre of industry and commerce and its fertility in aesthetic innovation which produced the painting of Giotto and the stories of Boccaccio and, on the other hand, its severe limitations as an intellectual centre. In both the clerical and the lay traditions of thought the Florentine participation, though it was widespread among the citizens, was provincial and peripheral. In comparison with a number of other cities Florence was poorly equipped to be a centre of creative thought. The first serious attempt to found a university started in 1321, the year of Dante's death. It was entirely a communal project, promoted and financed by the city government, and the aim seems to have been to found a centre chiefly

---

[41] H. Wieruszowski, 'Brunetto Latini als Lehrer Dantes und der Florentiner', in *Politics and Culture in Medieval Spain and Italy*; Villani, VIII, x.
[42] This aspect of the correspondence is analysed by Bec, *Marchands Écrivains*, pp. 115–32.

for the study of the useful sciences of law and medicine in competition with Bologna. In the 1320s and 1330s a few teachers were attracted but the enterprise petered out. It was revived in 1348 and collapsed again very quickly. The continuous existence of a university at Florence started only with the third attempt in 1359. There was therefore no university in Florence during the great period of university scholasticism elsewhere in Europe. When the *Studio* did come into being it was small, entirely controlled by the commune and remembered only for its lectures on Dante and the visits of great classicists like Chrysoloras, Guarino and Filelfo in the humanist age.[43] So the scholastic culture of Florence was a second-hand affair.

The position of proto-humanist learning was somewhat similar. In 1355 or thereabouts Petrarch wrote a letter to a Florentine humanist friend in which he commented on the indifference to letters shown in that 'commercial and clothmaking' city (*mercatrix et lanifica*).[44] Of course it would be absurd to suggest that humanist learning was absent in the city in which Dante acquired his knowledge of the Latin poets. At a certain level it was in fact rather widespread and Petrarch's own father was an example of it. In addition several prominent proto-humanists of the early fourteenth century from other places had spent some time in the city.[45] Still it remains true that Florence had a rather unimportant place in the history of humanism before the later fourteenth century. It has been pointed out that the geography of early humanism was much affected by the distribution of manuscripts surviving from the early Middle Ages. Florence, especially in comparison with Eastern Lombardy, was poor in this respect,[46] which accounts in part at least for the fact that it produced nothing comparable with the lively humanism of Padua in the age of Dante. The books which were common in the Middle Ages were no doubt well represented in its libraries but the accumulation of rare works and superior texts had to wait for the activity of Boccaccio and his friends in the later fourteenth century. In 1387 Boccaccio's books went to the convent of Santo Spirito where they were made available to

[43] The story up to 1359 is told by Davidsohn, *Storia*, vii, pp. 269–79. For the later university, A. Gherardi, *Statute della Università e Studio fiorentino* (Florence, 1881).

[44] 'Epycurum ac Democritum studiosissime urbium, Athene, famosos mundo accolas, sibi autem incognitos habuere; miremur si te mercatrix et lanifica nostra non noverit?' (to Francesco Nelli, Prior of Santi Apostoli, *Familiari*, XVIII, 9).

[45] R. Weiss, 'Lineamenti per una storia del primo umanesimo fiorentino', *Rivista Storica Italiana*, lx (1948).

[46] G. Billanovich, *I Primi Umanisti e le Tradizioni dei Classici Latini* (Freiburg, 1953).

enthusiasts. About the same time the great amateur Niccolò Niccoli began to found his library, eventually of 800 volumes, which after his death was turned into the outstanding public library at San Marco by the munificence of Cosimo de Medici.[47] The collection of books went together with the establishment of a distinguished humanist tradition. Neither existed in Florence before the late fourteenth century.

It is this provincialism, the sense of being at the receiving end of intellectual movements, which makes Dante a typical Florentine of the early fourteenth century. If one can forget for a moment Dante's overwhelming power of poetic synthesis and think only of the pieces which he tried to synthesize, he presents himself in his works as a man who has picked up the fragments of thought which happened to be available to an enquiring Florentine. He had the Latin books of the notaries and poets: Cicero, Virgil, Ovid and so on. He knew about Aquinas from the brothers of Santa Maria Novella and he knew a good deal about Aristotle. He had heard about Averroist medicine and philosophy from the Florentines who went to Bologna. He knew about the prophetic and ascetic ideas of the spiritual Franciscans, perhaps because he had heard Pierre-Jean Olivi lecture at Santa Croce. But he was a long way from the centres of thought and he found it difficult to make a coherent pattern of it all to suit his own experience. His synthesis was a personal, poetic one which, for all the reverence accorded to him as a poet, had very little importance in the subsequent history of ideas.

A fourteenth-century thinker trying to evolve a social or political theory for the city might have done it either by adapting university aristotelianism (in the manner brilliantly exemplified by Marsilius of Padua's *Defensor Pacis*) or by adapting Cicero and other Latin writers (in the manner of the later humanists). Unlike Marsilius, who was at home in the two great centres of Paris and Padua, Florentine thinkers did not have the self-confidence or the intellectual daring needed to follow up these possibilities. So if we look at the instances of native social theory in fourteenth-century Florence we shall find only incipient suggestions of ideas, men trying occasionally to grapple with the implications of their environment but quite unable to construct an adequate intellectual framework for it. Dante's *Convivio* contains a *canzone* and an interpretative chapter in which he tried to evolve a theory of nobility as a quality based entirely on individual

---

[47] On these two libraries see A. Mazza, 'L'inventario della "parva libraria" di Santo Spirito e la Biblioteca del Boccaccio', *Italia Medioevale e Umanistica*, ix (1966) and B. L. Ullman and P. A. Stadter, *The Public Library of Renaissance Florence: Niccolò Niccoli, Cosimo de' Medici and the Library of San Marco* (Padua, 1970).

virtue and not at all on wealth or birth.[48] He was not doing this with the purpose of establishing an egalitarian social theory—his interest was in the concept of virtue rather than in the social implications of his argument. He was however inspired by a reading of Aristotle's *Ethics* and Cicero which was more radical in its conclusions than that of Aquinas, and his interpretation suggested the possibility of an egalitarian social theory. Many years later (*circa* 1377–78), we find another Florentine, better educated than Dante, Lapo da Castiglionchio, who was both a canon lawyer and a friend of Petrarch, trying to make sense of the concept of nobility from the point of view of a city dweller, with Dante's *canzone* in mind. Lapo was a keen humanist. He had taken time off on an embassy to the Pope in 1377 to visit Cicero's birthplace and like Dante he used Cicero as an outstanding example of the plebeian who made good.[49] But when he came to discuss the concept of nobility he rejected Dante's extreme argument and fell back on the writings of his fellow lawyer Bartolus of Sassoferratta and Aquinas's commentary on Aristotle's *Ethics*. Like Bartolus, Lapo rejected Dante's idea of nobility as a quality conferred by virtue and accepted the idea of nobility as a rank conferred by authority and accepted by inferiors. He did this in spite of the difficulties which he admitted it caused when he considered a communal city regime because in Florence for example, as he pointed out, nobility was actually a legal disadvantage since it carried higher penalties for certain offences and exclusion from certain offices.[50] This was a clear demonstration of the difficulty of making a city social theory without drastically revising theories developed for a different kind of society. Lapo was not prepared to do this. A way out of the

---

[48] *Convivio,* IV; *e.g.* 'che'l divino seme non cade in ischiatta, cioè in istirpe, ma cade ne le singulari persone, e, sì come di sotto si proverà, la stirpe non fa le singulari persone nobili, ma le singulari persone fanno la stirpe' (IV, xx).

[49] *Epistola o sia Ragionamento di messer Lapo da Castiglionchio Cittadino Fiorentino,* ed. L. Mehus (Bologna, 1753), p. 6.

[50] '. . . La nobiltà consiste e sta in questio cioè che il Superiore fa alcuno a se grato et accetto, come di sopra dissi. Ma insorge uno dubbio: perocchè in queste città che si reggono per popolo, coloro che si chiamano nobili, sono meno accetti, come appare nell'imporre delle pene, ove appare che è più punito il nobile, che lo ignobile. Apparisce ancora nel concedere di molti ufici, da' quali i nobili sono esclusi. E per questo appare che costoro non possono essere detti nobili, conciossia cosa che essi non sieno più accetti anzi meno. E secondo questo la diffinizione predetta della nobiltà non si confà a loro' (*op. cit.,* p. 26). The earlier part of Lapo's argument about nobility (pp. 11–17) is translated into Italian from a passage in Bartolus's *De Dignitatibus.* The passage is printed in K. Witte, *Dante–Forschungen,* i (Halle, 1869), pp. 462–71. Thereafter Lapo's argument becomes more original. Both Bartolo and Lapo appear to refer only to the *Canzone* and not to Dante's prose explanation.

impasse was shown in the next century in Poggio's *De Nobilitate* where seigniorial conceptions of nobility were simply rejected in favour of a stoic view of nobility based on individual worth[51] but it required the humanist revolution and a writer prepared to ignore scholasticism to make this possible.

A parallel example of a more trivial kind is the canon law of usury. Florentine society was inevitably riddled with usurious practices or practices suspected of being usurious. It is therefore interesting to find a Florentine canon lawyer Lorenzo Ridolfi in 1403 composing a book which is designed to assemble canonists' opinions about usury relating particularly to problems met by his fellow citizens. Ridolfi's book has a place in economic history as the first technical study of exchange and credit: in the course of his investigations he had to explain, rather helpfully for the historian, exactly what was meant by 'cambium ad Venetias', the device by which a loan at interest was fictitiously disguised as an exchange between Florence and Venice, and how the Florentine state debt worked by levying forced loans which became interest bearing and negotiable credits in the 'Monte'.[52] But the main impression which the book leaves is of the incongruity between the activities of the business world which it describes and the ethical and legal structure which the author is attempting laboriously to fit to them. Again if one moves on into the humanist world one finds Poggio in *De Avaritia* able to set up, rather playfully but not entirely without seriousness, a defence of the view that avarice is essential for the economic basis of civilized life.[53]

One great body of original and semi-learned writing in the fourteenth century was more or less unconnected with the scholastic structure: this was history. Florentine writers from Dino Compagni

---

[51] Poggio, *De Nobilitate*, in *Opera*.

[52] *Laurentii de Rodulfis Civis Florentini de Vsuris*, in *Tractatus Illustrium in utraque tum pontificii, tum Caesarei iuris facultate Iurisconsultorum, De Contractibus, et aliis illicitis*, vii (Venice, 1584), fos. 37ᵛ, 38ᵛ. For its place in the literature on usury see R. de Roover, *L'Evolution de la Lettre de Change, XIVᵉ–XVIIIᵉ siècles* (Paris, 1953), esp. p. 197; J. T. Noonan, *The Scholastic Analysis of Usury* (Cambridge, Mass., 1957), pp. 69, 121–25, 185–87. Instances of hostility to ecclesiastical laws on usury in fourteenth-century Florence are discussed by M. B. Becker, 'Three Cases concerning the Restitution of Usury in Florence', *Journal of Economic History*, xvii (1957); 'Some Economic Implications of the Conflict between Church and State in Trecento Florence', *Mediaeval Studies*, xxi (1959).

[53] The extent to which attitudes in humanist dialogues are to be taken seriously is an interesting question. In this case there happens to be some information about the evolution of the dialogue into its final form which is revealing. See H. Harth, 'Niccolò Niccoli als literarischer Zensor. Untersuchungen zur Textgeschichte von Poggios "De Avarita"', *Rinascimento*, vii (1967).

and Giovanni Villani in the first half of the fourteenth century to Gregorio Dati and Gino Capponi in the early fifteenth produced a magnificent series of narratives written in Italian and describing the life of their city with a natural sensitivity both to the nature of internal party conflict and to the distinctions between the political activities of communes and tyrants. Florentine vernacular history has very much the same relation to city society as Froissart's contemporary chronicles have to Anglo-French seigniorial society: it describes events within a particular social framework but it does not have an explicit theoretical bias like humanist history. Villani does indeed tell us in one famous passage how he was inspired to write the history of the city by a visit to Rome during the jubilee of 1300. On that pilgrimage he saw the monuments of ancient Rome and, so he tells us, read 'the great deeds of the Romans written by Virgil, Sallust, Lucan, Livy, Valerius Maximus and Orosius'. And then, he says, he was struck by the contrast between the decline of Rome and the rise of Florence and decided to write the history of his native city.[54] In spite of this curiously Gibbonian moment of inspiration and in spite of the fact that Villani and numerous other Florentine historians of the fourteenth century were excellent chroniclers of the politics of republican city life none of them was able to make that crucial imaginative leap, made by the humanists and so well described by Hans Baron, from seeing Florence as the descendant of the Roman Empire to seeing it as the inheritor of the social values associated with the Roman republic.[55] They remained mesmerized by Caesar and the conventional glory of the Empire. They did not establish a theoretical preference for city society or a theory of republican politics. The official propaganda of the commune, although it made free use of the word 'Libertas' in its appeals to other communes, did not advance beyond using that word in a vague and ambiguous sense embracing both internal republicanism and external political independence.[56]

Although the vernacular historians were highly successful in writing the history of the republic I think it is a mistake to see them as some have done as the precursors of the humanist historians. On the contrary the distinction between them seems to me to illustrate very

[54] Villani, viii, 36.

[55] H. Baron, *The Crisis of the Early Italian Renaissance* (Princeton, 1955), i, ch. 3; N. Rubinstein, 'The Beginnings of Political Thought in Florence', *Journal of the Warburg and Courtauld Institutes*, v (1942).

[56] N. Rubinstein, 'Florence and the Despots. Some Aspects of Florentine Diplomacy in the Fourteenth Century,' *Transactions of the Royal Historical Society*, 5th ser., ii (1952), especially pp. 29–32; R. Witt, 'The Rebirth of the Concept of Republican Liberty in Italy', *Renaissance Studies in Honor of Hans Baron*, ed A. Molho and J. A. Tedeschi (Dekalb, Illinois, 1971).

clearly the general qualitative difference between Florentine thought progressing under its own steam in the fourteenth century and the new direction which it took after it had received a massive new injection of classicism from the humanist enthusiasts. A good basis for comparison is provided by the two accounts of one of the great political crises of the republic, the final war against Giangaleazzo Visconti in 1400–1402 written by Gregorio Dati in 1407–8 and by Bruni in 1440–44. Dati was an educated silk merchant and his account represents the business man's view of a recent political crisis. It is a good narrative, well aware of the political situation in Italy and full of shrewd analytical comments. What impresses one most is his acute and explicit appraisal of political situations and of the economic forces underlying them. He knows for example how Florence's economic and political success have made her envied by her neighbours and therefore vulnerable to Milanese infiltration into Tuscany. He reports the Florentine calculation that in the final crisis Giangaleazzo's ambition and hatred had clouded his judgment so that he was financially overstretched whereas Florence knew she could keep up her defence expenditure indefinitely. We could hardly expect a better rational analysis of a political situation.[57]

Some years later Bruni wrote an account of the same episode in Book 12 of his History of the Florentine People. As one reads his narrative what strikes one most is the artistic arrangement and the elegant Latin. In 1399 the Florentines' attention is taken up by the strange religious movement of the Bianchi. They wake up from this to see that they are being surrounded by Milan with its hands on Pisa, Siena and Perugia. In 1400 there are changes of allegiance in various surrounding cities, some favourable to Florence, some unfavourable. Then comes a new factor from outside, the possibility of an Italian expedition by Rupert of the Palatinate. Bruni explains the German background and intertwines the Italian events with the parallel story of the Florentine efforts to create a diversion by encouraging Rupert's invasion until his defeat at Brescia in the autumn of 1401. This is followed by the centre piece of the chapter. Ambassadors of Florence and Milan are at Venice at the same time. They are made to present their cases to the Venetians in long set speeches in humanist Latin, the Milanese speaking as defenders of Italy against the barbarians, the Florentines as defenders of the independence of the Italian cities against Milanese aggression. Then back to Tuscany, the tightening ring of the Milanese attack ending with the sudden denouement of Giangaleazzo's sudden death.[58]

[57] 'L'Istoria di Firenze' di Gregorio Dati, ed. L. Pratesi (Norcia, 1902), pp. 56–76.
[58] Historiarum Florentini Populi Libri XII, Bk xii.

Each of these accounts has its virtues. But they are not at all the same. Dati conveys the feel of life in besieged Florence and shrewdly weighs the political and economic factors. Bruni moulds events into a flowing narrative and uses the episode as an excuse for an artistic presentation of the Florentine case. His account has perspective, grace, less realism than Dati's. Both of the accounts are of course rational narratives as opposed to annals but they exemplify such different kinds of rationalism that they are better seen as two different kinds of history. Bruni's way of writing is not a development of Dati's but an abrupt diversion from it.[59]

Bruni wrote his piece of history in the early 1440s. By that time the humanist movement had grown out of the beginnings around 1400 into a full flood. When the humanist revolution came it came rather quickly. Petrarch's 'commercial and cloth-making' city on the fringes of culture became within a generation the capital of a brilliant cultural movement. Why did this happen? The most important factor was the most obvious and least mysterious one: a collection of individuals. Salutati, a disciple of Petrarch, was responsible for bringing Chrysoloras to Florence to teach Greek in 1397. The legend which ascribed to Chrysoloras's visit the revival of Greek and the beginning of the Renaissance in Western Europe goes back to the account written by Bruni, his most successful pupil.[60] It may exaggerate the Greek element because the culture of the Florentine group remained predominantly Latin, but it does not exaggerate the influence of Salutati and Chrysoloras in creating a school of passionate classicists. From that point there is a clear continuity to the well-established humanist cult of the 1430s and 1440s. Bruni and Poggio, pupils of Salutati at the very beginning of the century, lived until 1444 and 1456. Niccoli the great book collector who was also one of the original group lived until 1439 when his library went into the keeping of Cosimo de Medici, who had been a devotee for at least twenty years and was by then the most powerful and richest man in Florence. These men were successful partly because they were the successors of the *dictatores*, the notaries and rhetoricians. Like Petrarch before them they succeeded by giving an enormous acceleration to a force which already existed and because there was already a large educated public which could enjoy their writings. But, like

[59] Other analyses of Dati and Bruni from a different point of view are in Baron, *Crisis of the Early Italian Renaissance*, i, ch. 8 and Bec, *Marchands Écrivains*, pp. 151–73.

[60] 'Litterae quoque per huius belli intercapedines mirabile quantum per Italiam increvere, accedente tunc primum cognitione litterarum graecarum, quae septingentis iam annis apud nostros homines desierant esse in usu' (*Rerum suo tempore gestarum commentarius*, ed. C. De Pierro, *Rerum Italicarum Scriptores*, xix. iii (Bologna, 1926), p. 431).

Petrarch also, they were essentially literary men, interested primarily not in politics or society or religion or philosophy but in writing. They have to be understood as a literary movement.

Can one point to any less personal factors which determined the chronology of intellectual change? One important influence was certainly the strength of republican self-consciousness in Florence which was intensified by the long wars with Visconti Milan stretching intermittently through the first half of the fifteenth century. The political philosophy of Aristotle and Cicero and the republican history of Livy and Sallust were very easily assimilated to the Florentine experience and provided a natural encouragement to a wholesale adoption of classical conceptions. But of course this would have been true up to a point at any time in the previous hundred years. Florence was no more republican and Aristotle and Cicero were not much more available than they had been in the time of Dante. I think that one should beware of ascribing too much intellectual influence to the defence of the Florentine republic in the early fifteenth century.[61] But, although the political explanation is inadequate, I do not think that the success of the humanist movement was simply a matter of a happy combination of individual talents. There were new circumstances in the early fifteenth century which made their work extravagantly successful; but the new circumstances were not in the internal history of Florence. It is quite futile to look for them in the growing self consciousness of the mercantile bourgeoisie, in the growing political awareness of an embattled republic, in the development of a leisured *rentier* class or in any other internal social development. The difficulty in approaching the new circumstances is that they were changes of a general kind in the European world which can hardly be described except in impressionistic terms and in invoking them the historian lays himself more than usually open to the charge of using vague and unverifiable generalizations. Nevertheless they must be invoked.

---

[61] The political explanation of the humanist revolution has been developed at length by H. Baron in *The Crisis of the Early Italian Renaissance*. One important part of his argument, the ascription of a primarily political inspiration to Bruni's early works, the *Laudatio Florentinae Urbis* and the *Dialogi ad Petrum Paulum Istrum* has been criticized by J. E. Seigel ' "Civic Humanism" or Ciceronian Rhetoric?', *Past and Present*, no. 34 (1966); reply by Baron, 'Leonardo Bruni: "professional rhetorician" or "civic humanist"?', no. 36 (1967). Seigel rightly points out that Bruni was primarily a rhetorician. This does not necessarily reduce the importance of the political background, though it does change the nature of its impact on Bruni. Faith in republicanism is certainly an important element in Florentine humanism throughout the first half of the fifteenth century, but not a sufficient explanation for the prestige and success of the humanist school.

What had happened was a general change in the external balance of forces which I think one can only appreciate by comparing the situation of Cosimo's Florence with that of Florence in the century before. Although it was the financial capital of Europe and perhaps its greatest industrial city, fourteenth-century Florence was not a very strong political force in the European world. In 1301 Dante's Florence had quaked before the emissaries of Boniface VIII and Charles of Valois.[62] In the War of the Eight Saints against Gregory XI in 1375–78, though by no means as easy a prey as in the days of Boniface VIII and though enjoying the powerful support of Milan, Florence was very hard pressed both by the commercial effects of an interdict and by the heavy financial burden of dealing with the armies of French and English mercenaries imported into Italy by the pope, and the political and social tensions caused by the war prepared the ground for the revolutions of Salvestro de' Medici and the Ciompi.[63] How impossible it would have been to predict at that time that the humbled papacy should become politically dependent on Cosimo's republic or that political intervention from Northern Europe should become a negligible factor in Tuscan politics. That is what happened. The reason of course was the general weakening of the seigniorial world in the early fifteenth century which left the Italian cities standing for a generation above the wrecks of those powers which had overawed them in the previous century. This is not merely a Florentine or an Italian phenomenon. In terms of the balance of power the early fifteenth century was the golden age of the cities. It is not an accident that the humanist ideology of the city was evolved at this time. The social and political balance of power affected the intellectual climate. The papal court became not only a political equal but also a cultural satellite of

[62] Charles of Valois's entry into Florence (see Davidsohn, *Storia*, iv, 213–285) is described by Dino Compagni, one of the priors at the time, whose narrative vividly conveys the feeling of impotence in the city partly because of fear of papal and French power, partly because of political divisions within the city (Dino Compagni, *Cronica, Rerum Italicarum Scriptores*, IX, ii, pp. 118–35).

[63] The best general account of the external history of the war remains that by F. T. Perrens, *Histoire de Florence*, v (Paris, 1880), pp. 96–181. It depends on the narrative and records published by A. Gherardi, 'La Guerra dei fiorentini con papa Gregorio XI detto la guerra degli Otto Santi', *Archivio Storico Italiano*, ser. 3, v–viii (1867–68). Some impression from the papal side of the activities of foreign troops in central Italy at this period can be obtained for example from L. Mirot, 'Sylvestre Budes et les Bretons en Italie', *Bibliothèque de l'École des Chartes*, lviii–lix (1897–98). The internal political history of Florence at this time has recently been described by G. A. Brucker, *Florentine Politics and Society 1343–1378* (Princeton, 1962), chs 7–8.

Florence.[64] This new and of course temporary atmosphere of self-confidence in the city world was, I think, an essential ingredient of the environment of the humanist movement. In these circumstances it was possible for quite a small group of literary men to establish an authoritative new set of values which was astonishingly free from those limitations which had circumscribed the Florentine mind in the previous century.

St Catherine's College, Oxford

[64] I have sketched some aspects of the relations between Florence and the papacy at this period in *The Florentine Enlightenment* (1969).

PATRICIAN CULTURE: VENICE AND AMSTERDAM IN THE SEVENTEENTH CENTURY

By Peter Burke, M.A., F.R.Hist.S.

READ AT THE SOCIETY'S CONFERENCE 15 SEPTEMBER
1972

IN the seventeenth century, visitors to both cities were struck by the obvious physical similarities between Venice and Amsterdam.† The social similarities were no less great. In a Europe mainly composed of monarchies, each was the greatest city of a republic. In a Europe where the ruling class still tended to identify with warriors, the patricians of Amsterdam and Venice were predominantly civilian. In a Europe whose political leaders usually despised trade, Venice and Amsterdam stood out as places where trade and politics could be combined with success, at least early in the seventeenth century. In a Europe whose ruling classes tended to spend most of their time on their country estates, the patricians of Venice and Amsterdam lived mainly in town.[1]

What follows, then, is a comparison of two seventeenth-century urban elites, defining 'elite' as a small group high on three criteria, status, power, and wealth. This paper will concentrate on questions of social and cultural history, describing the style of life of the two groups, their intellectual interests and their patronage of the arts. In short, it will discuss how far the patricians of Venice and Amsterdam were urban and how far they were civilized, or rather, what forms their culture took. To answer these questions I shall employ the method of collective biography, looking at the *vroedschap*, or town council, of Amsterdam, and in Venice at the doges and the *procuratori di S. Marco* (henceforth referred to as 'proctors'). These groups consist of 244 Venetians and 319 Amsterdammers in a long seventeenth century stretching from 1580 to 1720. If this group does not

† This paper reports some of the results of a wider study of the ruling classes of Venice and Amsterdam which should be published in book form by Maurice Temple Smith in 1974. The research in Venice and Amsterdam on which it is based was made possible by a research award from the Leverhulme Trust Fund.
[1] Venetian ambassadors to the United Provinces frequently made comparisons between the two cities. See *Relazioni veneziane*, ed. P. J. Blok (The Hague, 1909), pp. 15, 35, 112.

include everyone with status, power and wealth in the two cities, at least it contains a sizeable proportion of them. Statements about 'the elite' or 'the patriciate' should henceforward be taken as statements about these 563 men.[2]

For each of these 563 it is possible to discover something about family, political career and wealth; you can imagine how much harder it is to discover their taste in paintings or their conception of God. Only a few individuals in each city have left abundant evidence. I shall start from these well-known individuals but try not to assume that they are typical, and then work outwards to the rest.[3]

The Venetian elite was the upper part of the formally defined Venetian nobility, which included about 2,000 adult males in the seventeenth century. A proctor was something like a life peer. The proctors ranked immediately after the doge, wore special robes with enormous sleeves, and on appointment made a ceremonious entry into their new status. By European standards the Venetian nobility as a whole was an unusual one. They dressed in long gowns which made it clear that they belonged to the robe rather than the sword, and they had traditionally bad seats on horses. Equally unusual, their traditional style of life was one of frugality rather than display. Doge Leonardo Donà* told his heirs to live simply and bought his own carriage second-hand.[4] When Giovanni Sagredo* was ambassador at Paris, so the contemporary story went, he would come back from audience with the king and tell his footmen to take off their liveries, to save wear and tear.[5] Gravity and dignity were also valued highly. It was noted that doge Francesco Morosini* would never cross his legs in public.[6] Taciturnity was a virtue, and a studied inscrutability the ideal. It was not only at Carnival that Venetians wore masks. This style of life, marked by frugality, gravity and caution, struck one seventeenth-century observer as a 'Spanish' style. But during the century a rival 'French' style came to emerge, more open, more

---

[2] There are brief biographies of the Amsterdam elite in J. E. Elias, *De vroedschap van Amsterdam* (Haarlem 1903–5) and biographies of the doges in A. da Mosto, *I dogi di Venezia* (2nd edn, Milan 1960). From now on, members of the elite will be signalled in the text by an asterisk.

[3] Biographies of members of the elite include G. Cozzi, *Il doge Nicolò Contarini* (Venice and Rome 1958); F. Seneca, *Leonardo Donà* (Padua, 1959); H. A. Enno van Gelder, *De levensbeschouwing van C. P. Hooft* (Amsterdam, 1918); J. F. Gebhard, *Het leven van Mr Nicolaas Witsen* (Utrecht, 1881).

[4] A. Cutolo, 'Un diario inedito del doge Leonardo Donà', *Nuova Antologia* (1953), p. 278.

[5] This story in the 'Relazione del' Anonimo' (henceforth *R.A.*), ed. P. Molmenti in his *Curiosità di storia veneziana* (Bologna, 1919), p. 414.

[6] Da Mosto, *I dogi di Venezia*, p. 435.

flamboyant, more generous, more relaxed.[7] Nicolò Corner* was described as friendly, even jovial; Piero Dolfin* was gay, pleasant, full of promises which he did not keep; doge Domenico Contarini* impressed a French visitor by his *douceur* and his *affabilité*.[8]

Amsterdammers had no such conscious traditional style. They were not nobles but merchants, not an estate but a class, in the sense of an informally defined group whose wealth tended to give them power, whose wealth and power tended to give them status. It is true that some members of the elite tried to prove their descent from foreign nobles or bought country estates with titles attached, but this group within the elite was not formally distinct from the rest. The Amsterdam patricians wore no official robes like the doge and proctors of Venice. Their movements were less ceremonious, for they went about the streets like everyone else. The British ambassador Henry Sidney remarked with surprise that burgomaster Gillis Valckenier* 'walks about without a footman'; 'he walks about the streets just like an ordinary shopkeeper'.[9] Another British ambassador, Sir William Temple, generalized the point when he wrote that the burgomasters of Amsterdam 'are obliged to no sort of expense, more than ordinary modest citizens, in their habits, their attendance, their tables'. On the contrary, they 'appear in all places with the simplicity and modesty of other private citizens'. The Amsterdam style became a little grander during the century. Like the Venetians, the Amsterdammers were feeling the influence of the French.[10]

Venetian patricians were an essentially urban group. The main residence of each family was the palace in Venice, not the villa or villas on the mainland. Branches of a family might be named after the part of town in which they lived; the Foscarini *ai Carmini*, the Giustinian of *campiel dei squellini*, and so on. It was the town palace on which most money was spent, and the town palace where the family spent most of their year. The elite had to stay in town, for political reasons in particular. The state was governed from the Doge's Palace, where the Great Council met, and the Senate, and the College, and the Council of Ten. The doge could not leave Venice without

[7] The terms *genio spagnuolo* and *genio francese* are used throughout the anonymous *Esame Istorico Politico* (MS. in Venice, Museo Correr, Gradenigo 15; henceforth *E.I.P.*).

[8] On N. Corner*, *R.A.*, p. 399; on P. Dolfin*, *R.A.*, p. 374 and *E.I.P.*, p. 49; on D. Contarini*, A. de St-Didier, *Venise* (Paris, 1680), p. 180.

[9] H. Sidney, *Diary*, i (London, 1843), pp. 63–66, reproduces letters written in August 1679.

[10] Sir William Temple, *Observations upon the United Provinces*, ed. G. N. Clark, (Cambridge, 1932), pp. 59–60.

permission. The other patricians could leave when they wanted, but the Senate usually met every Saturday, and the Great Council every Sunday morning. Of course a council with some two thousand members could not do all its business in one morning a week; hence the crucial importance of another urban institution, the *broglio*. Foreign visitors noticed that the piazza S. Marco was full of patricians 'in great troops' every day between five and eight in the evening. It was here that the upper nobility paid court to the lower, soliciting their votes for the following Sunday: a political market-place, as more than one visitor remarked.[11]

It was also the city where two important leisure institutions of the Venetian nobility were located, the gambling saloon and the academy. In the sixteenth century, gambling might take the form of bets on elections in the Great Council; in the seventeenth century, it took the politically more innocuous form of playing cards for money in public rooms or *ridotti*. Among the patrician enthusiasts were the two Valier doges, Bertucci and Silvestro, and Giacomo Correr*, who spent his winnings paying his fines for refusing political office.[12] As for the academy, by the seventeenth century it was a club with a fixed meeting-place, 'protectors' and an *impresa*. It was organized by nobles, although commoners were invited to join. The Delphic Academy, for example, met in the palace of senator Francesco Gussoni; its protectors were the proctors Gianbattista Corner* and Alvise Duodo*, its *impresa* was a tripod with the motto *hinc oracula*. One of the most famous academies was that of the *Incogniti*, founded by Gianfrancesco Loredan and meeting in his palace. Its members did indeed come incognito, wearing masks, which at once solved the problem of ceremony in a mixed gathering of nobles and commoners, and made it possible to express unorthodox religious opinions without fear of the consequences. Even women were allowed to go to meetings of the *Incogniti*, which made it more like a French *salon* than other Venetian academies of the time.[13]

This is not to deny, but only to limit the importance of another Venetian social institution, *villeggiatura*. Villas were investments but they were also holiday residences. The 'ebb and flow' of the nobles along the Brenta was a regular event. The summer season began on 12 June and ended with the end of July. The autumn villa season

[11] T. Coryat, *Crudities*, i (Glasgow, 1905), p. 318, and A. de St-Didier, *Venise*, p. 33, describe the *broglio* in 1608 and *c*. 1672 respectively.

[12] A. da Mosta, *op. cit.*, pp. 391, 441, on the Valiers;* on G. Correr,* *R.A.*, p. 405.

[13] On Venetian academies, M. Battagia, *Della accademie veneziane* (Venice, 1826); on the Delphic Academy, F. Sansovino, *Venezia città nobilissima*, ed. G. Martinioni (Venice, 1663), p. 396; on the *Incogniti*, A. Lupis, *Vita di G. F. Loredano* (Venice, 1663), p. 17.

began on 4 October and ended in mid-November. A villa was a refuge from city life, a means of escape from plague, from summer heat and from politics. Near the villa the patrician could shoot hares or waterfowl. In the villa he could study or drive away the almost inevitable boredom with chess or cards, parlour games or practical jokes.[14]

Amsterdam patricians were still more of an urban group than Venetians. They tended to congregate along a few canals; the Heerengracht, the Keizersgracht, the Singel. They needed to be within easy reach of the Town Hall, where burgomasters, councillors and magistrates all had their chambers. They also needed to be within easy reach of the Bourse, which was surely the Amsterdam equivalent of the *broglio*, since the Amsterdam elite was more concerned with trade than the Venetian one was, and in any case the ruling group was too small to need a meeting-place outside the Town Hall. However, the Amsterdam elite was not entirely urban. They too had their estates and their villas; *hofsteden* (farms), *buitenplaatsen* (country places), *lusthuizen* (pleasure houses) or *speelhuizen* (play houses) as they called them.[15] As the last two names suggest, these villas were places for recreation, an impression confirmed by such names of individual houses as *Buitensorg (Sans Souci)*, *Tijdverdrijf* (Pass-Time) and *Vredenhof* (Peacehaven).[16] At the end of the seventeenth century one finds the town council meeting relatively rarely, if at all, in June and August. It is likely that its members had disappeared to their *speelhuizen*.[17] But it should be emphasized that, like Venetian villas, what these houses offered was a temporary escape, and not a permanent alternative to urban life.

One of the advantages of villas was that they offered an attractive environment for study and for writing. The Venetians seem to have been more inclined than most nobilities in seventeenth-century Europe to go to university, which in their case meant Padua, to write books, and even to publish them. At least 8 out of the 25 doges of the period studied at Padua.[18] The books published by members of the elite

[14] G. Sagredo*, *Arcadia in Brenta* (Venice, 1669), describes the *flusso e riflusso della nobiltà*; I used the Bologna, 1693 edition, p. 1. The dates of the villa season in P. Molmenti, *La storia di Venezia nella vita privata*, 4th edn, iii (Bergamo, 1908), p. 253.

[15] R. van Luttervelt, *De buitenplaatsen aan de Vecht* (*s.l.*, 1943) describes them from an architectural point of view.

[16] These three houses owned by William Backer*, Nikolaas Witsen* and Andries de Graeff* respectively.

[17] Amsterdam, Gemeente Archief, Resolutiën. The volumes of 'resolutions' from 1650 to 1700 show the *vroedschap* meeting more and more rarely in June and August.

[18] N. da Ponte*, L. Donà*, N. Donà*, F. Contarini*, N. Contarini*, F. Erizzo*, D. Contarini*, M. A. Giustinian*.

include Nicolò Contarini*'s *De perfectione rerum*, a general survey
of God, man, the angels and the universe;[19] Paolo Paruta*'s *Perfezione della vita politica*, his *Discorsi*, and his history of Venice,[20]
Battista Nani*'s history of Venice;[21] Giovanni Sagredo*'s romance,
Arcadia in Brenta, and his history of the Ottoman Empire;[22] and a
book on geometry by Nicolò da Ponte*.[23] The unpublished treatises
by members of the group include the poems of Simone Contarini* and
Antonio Ottobon*, Daniele IV Dolfin*'s *Esercitio militare*, Paolo
Tiepolo*'s history of Cyprus and, of course, Nicolò Contarini*'s
history of Venice.[24]

In spite of an impressive list of publications, the patricians of
Venice liked to emphasize that they were just amateurs. As one of
them put it, 'I am a Venetian gentleman and I have never hoped to
be known as a literary man'.[25] Giovanni Sagredo* described the
noble heroes of his romance as 'well-informed but not academic, and
carrying their learning lightly'.[26] That leading literary figure of the
mid-century, Gianfrancesco Loredan, was said to devote his days to
the serious business of politics and write his stories and other works
only at night.[27] Battista Nani*'s history of Venice gave one contemporary the impression of having been written in haste by a
man preoccupied with other matters; perhaps the impression was
deliberate.[28]

The books published by the Venetian elite give the impression that
their chief intellectual interest was in history, an impression confirmed
by the fact that the Venetian government regularly appointed official
historians. The histories of Paruta*, Contarini* and Nani* were in

[19] N. Contarini*, *De perfectione rerum* (Venice, 1576).
[20] P. Paruta*, *Della perfezione della vita politica* (Venice, 1579); *Discorsi
politici* (Venice, 1599); *Historia Vinetiana*, (Venice, 1605). He died in
1598.
[21] B. Nani*, *Historia della Republica Veneta*, i (Venice, 1662).
[22] G. Sagredo*, *L'Arcadia in Brenta* (Venice, 1669), published under the
pseudonym 'Ginnesio Gavardo Vacalerio'; *Memorie istoriche de' monarchi
ottomani* (Venice, 1673).
[23] All copies of this book seem to have disappeared, but it was published
in 1585, the year of the doge's death, according to P. A. Zeno, *Memoria de'
scrittori veneti patritii* (Venice, 1662), *s.v.* Ponte.
[24] The poems of S. Contarini* and A. Ottobon* are in the Marciana in
Venice; there are copies of N. Contarini*'s history in the Archivio di Stato in
Venice, in the British Museum, and elsewhere.
[25] G. F. Sagredo (brother of Zaccaria Sagredo*) to M. Welser, 1614, quoted
by W. J. Bouwsma, *Venice and the defense of republican liberty* (Berkeley,
1968), p. 87.
[26] *Dotti senza professione, eruditi senza ostentatione: Arcadia in Brenta*,
p. 1.
[27] Lupis, *Vita di G. F. Loredano*, p. 25.
[28] *E.I.P.*, p. 34.

fact commissioned in this way.[29] The same impression is given by the historical introductions to the reports which returning diplomats and administrators had to read out in public. They suggest a pragmatic interest in political history, written, as Contarini* remarked, not to exhibit eloquence but to help in political affairs.[30]

There is much less evidence of patrician interest in science, which has received somewhat more emphasis from historians than it deserves. It is true that Gianfrancesco Sagredo was a friend of Galileo, interested in astronomy and magnetism, and a man who made his own scientific instruments;[31] that Nicolò Contarini* was interested in medicine and hydraulics; that he and Leonardo Donà* were regular visitors to the house of Andrea Morosini, home of an academy where discussions on the natural sciences took place. But this academy was equally concerned with questions of theology and ethics, and it is difficult to find any more patricians with serious scientific interests.[32] The ethos of the aristocratic amateur was a discouragement to scientific research and allowed only two attitudes to the subject. The first was a collector's interest. Federico Contarini* had a typical undiscriminating *Wunderkammer* of the years around 1600 which included minerals and bones, a cat's testicles and a buffalo's horn.[33] The second possible attitude to science was the utilitarian attitude of a governing class. When Galileo was professor at Padua, Antonio Priuli* went up the campanile of S. Marco 'to see the marvels and singular effects of the telescope of the said Galileo', but then, for a naval power, a telescope was of practical value.[34] This utilitarian attitude is summed up in a treatise on education written for Venetian nobles, which recommends the student to leave 'subtle and over-curious investigations' to others, and study mathematics only insofar as it is relevant to 'the interests of the commonwealth'.[35] Mathematics

---

[29] On official history, see G. Cozzi, 'Cultura politica e religione nella pubblica storiografia veneziana', *Bollettino della storia della società veneziana*, v (1965).

[30] *Relazioni degli stati europei*, ed. N. Barozzi and G. Berchet (Venice, 1857 onwards). Contarini*, quoted by Cozzi, *Il doge N. Contarini*, p. 203.

[31] A. Favaro, 'G. F. Sagredo e la vita scientifica in Venezia', *Nuovo Archivio Veneto*, new series, iv (1902).

[32] A. Morosini described his academy as holding discussions *de rerum natura, de moribus, de divinis rebus*; quoted in G. Cozzi, 'Federico Contarini', *Bollettino della storia della società Veneziana*, iii (1961), p. 279.

[33] The inventory of Contarini*'s collection is edited by M. T. Cipollato as an appendix to Cozzi's article about him.

[34] A. Priuli*'s memoirs are quoted in A. Favaro, 'Galileo e la presentazione del cann occhiale alla repubblica Veneta', *Nuovo Archivio Veneto*, i (1891), p. 69.

[35] *Dimettendo ad altri le sottili e troppo curiose investigationi*: A. Colluraffi, *Il nobile veneto* (Venice, 1623), p. 56.

was associated with military studies in a Paduan academy for Venetian nobles, the *Delia*.

The books published by the patricians of Amsterdam give a rather different impression. They include Laurens Reael*'s book on magnetism;[36] Nikolaas Tulp*'s *Observations* on medicine;[37] Joan Commelin*'s books on botany,[38] the atlases of the publisher Joan Blaeu*;[39] Jan Six*'s tragedy *Medea*;[40] Coenrad van Beuningen*'s religious writings;[41] Johannes Hudde*'s published letters on algebra and geometry;[42] and, best known of all, two books by Nikolaas Witsen*, on ship-building and on Tartary.[43] This list suggests a much greater interest in the natural sciences than there was in Venice, and rather less interest in history. The last point should not be exaggerated; one of the most distinguished historians in seventeenth-century Europe, P. C. Hooft, 'the Dutch Tacitus', was the son of a burgomaster of Amsterdam, and his father Cornelis was not ignorant of history either. The papers of C. P. Hooft* refer to sixteen historical works including Livy, Josephus, Guicciardini, Sleidan (the *Commentaries*), Foxe, Camden (the *Annals*) and Bor.[44] His still more learned colleague, burgomaster Martin Coster*, whose library at his death contained 565 works in nine languages owned copies of Herodotus, Thucydides, Xenophon, Livy, Plutarch and Josephus among the ancients; among the moderns, he had books by Biondo, Giovio, Commynes and Sebastian Franck; the history of France by Paolo Emilio, the history of Poland by Martin Cromer, the history of England by Polidore Vergil, and the history of Florence by Machiavelli.[45] C. P. Hooft* regularly argues from history, Biblical and classical. The fact that Moses was above Aaron is an 'example' which proves that the preachers of Amsterdam should not tell the town council what to do.[46]

This attitude to history as a storehouse of political examples is of course common enough in seventeenth-century Europe. What is much

---

[36] L. Reael*, *Observatiën aen de magnetsteen* (Amsterdam, 1651). Reael died in 1637.

[37] N. Tulp*, *Observationes medicae* (Amsterdam, 1641).

[38] J. Commelin*, *Catalogus plantarum indigenarum Hollandiae* (Amsterdam, 1683), and other works.

[39] J. Blaeu*, *Geographia* (Amsterdam, 1662), and other works.

[40] J. Six*, *Medea* (Amsterdam, 1648).

[41] C. van Beuningen*, *Alle de brieven ende schriften* (Amsterdam, 1689).

[42] J. Hudde*, 'de reductione aequationum' and 'de maximis et minimis' in R. Descartes, *Geometria*, ed. F. Schooten (Leiden, 1659), pp. 407–516.

[43] N. Witsen*, *Scheepsbouw en bestier* (Amsterdam, 1671); *Noord en Oost Tartarye* (2nd edn, Amsterdam, 1705).

[44] Enno van Gelder, *De levensbeschouwing van C. P. Hooft*, appendix 2.

[45] Amsterdam, Gemeente Archief, Weeskamer, Boedelpapieren, Lade 139, contains the 1594 inventory of Coster*'s books.

[46] C. P. Hooft, *Memoriën en Adviesen*, i (Utrecht, 1871), p. 97.

less common is to find a ruling group so interested in the natural sciences. This interest has a good deal to do with their education. New ideas and new interests tend to flourish most in new institutions. The Amsterdam Athenaeum was founded in 1632, and it is likely that many of the elite studied there before going to university, usually to Leiden. The curriculum of the Athenaeum in the mid-seventeenth century included mathematics, astronomy, botany and medicine. Some of the teachers were Cartesians, and in 1694 an edition of Descartes was published for the use of the students there. In any case, Amsterdam was a new city, its elite were new families which would have less emotional investment in tradition than Venetian patricians did. A new society has less resistance to new forms of culture, particularly when, as in the case of Amsterdam, it is a relatively open society. Professional doctors like Coster* and Tulp* could sit on the town council in Amsterdam; in Venice they could not have done so. In his book on ship-building, Witsen* showed an interest in technical details such as the exact measurement of planks which elsewhere might have been thought beneath a gentleman. He even drew a number of the illustrations himself. Johannes Hudde* was one of the best mathematicians of his day, on friendly terms with Huygens, Leibniz and Spinoza; he clearly had no inhibitions about these 'subtle and over-curious investigations'. Witsen* and Hudde* were perhaps able to indulge their interests because they did not identify themselves as noblemen.

The religious attitudes of the two groups were more alike than one might have expected, since one city was officially Catholic and the other predominantly Protestant. In Venice 'Catholic' and 'papist' were not the same, observed the French ambassador just before the interdict, an event which only confirmed his judgment.[47] During the interdict the Venetian position was defended by the Republic's official theologian, Paolo Sarpi. Sarpi believed that the primitive church had been democratic, poor, unworldly and austere, while the contemporary church was monarchical, rich, worldly and corrupt; that the great obstacle to the reform of the church was the triple alliance of the pope, Spain and the Jesuits; that the Augustinian emphasis on man's need for grace was nearer the truth than the Jesuit emphasis on free will. Was this the attitude of the patriciate? The case has been argued powerfully in a recent book.[48] A similar cluster of attitudes to Sarpi's can certainly be found in Nicolò Contarini*; a man of austere morality who wanted the church to keep out of temporal affairs and hated the Jesuits for their use of religion

[47] This observation made by Philippe Canaye de Fresnes in 1604, quoted by Cozzi, *N. Contarini*, p. 44.
[48] Bouwsma, *Venice and the defense of republican liberty*.

as a political tool. Augustinian on the grace issue, he followed the synod of Dort with interest and his sympathies were with the Gomarists. His was an interior religion; his will makes an unusually brief mention of the Virgin and the saints.[49] Some of these attitudes of his can be found among other Venetian patricians of the time. Doge Leonardo Donà* was equally anti-Spanish and critical of the papacy and he was a man of equally austere morality.[50] Antonio Priuli*, according to his will, hoped to reach heaven 'thanks only to the blood shed for us by our Lord Jesus Christ'.[51] The reports of some patricians who had served as ambassador to Rome show that they were anti-Spanish and hostile to the popes for their support of Spain; examples which spring to mind are Paolo Tiepolo*, Paolo Paruta*, Agostino Nani* and Simone Contarini*. An anti-papal group, one might say.

However, it would be misleading not to point to equally outstanding examples of an opposed religious attitude. There was a devout party, or, if 'party' is too strong a term, a group of patricians who were more favourably disposed to the pope. They included Zuanne Dolfin*, who ended his life as a cardinal; doge Marin Grimani*, who was knighted by pope Sixtus V; Giacomo Foscarini*, who wanted to have the Jesuit college at Padua reopened; Federico Contarini*, and others equally well known. If one looks at the wills of the proctors over the whole seventeenth century, it is to find in the majority of cases considerable emphasis on the outward forms of religion. The proctors want to be buried in the habit of a Franciscan or a Capuchin; they leave money for 300, 500, or even 3,000 masses; they express their devotion to patron saints and guardian angels.[52] Doge Giovanni Bembo* once offered a silver ship to the Holy House of Loreto; doge Giovanni I Corner* asked for someone to make a pilgrimage there in his name; Alvise Barbarigo* kept the relics of S. Sulpicio in his villa.

Individual examples like these are of course a poor substitute for a questionnaire. The nearest approach to a questionnaire on this subject we owe to the Jesuits, who made a survey in 1620 about the attitude of senators to the readmission of the society to Venice; they estimated that at least half the senators were opposed.[53] The fact that Venice was laid under interdict in 1606 suggests that over half

---

[49] Cozzi, op. cit., pp. 211–18: Contarini's will, 1630 (I give no references for wills which can be found in the card-index of the Archivio di Stato in Venice).

[50] Seneca, Leonardo Donà, pp. 27–38.

[51] A. Priuli*, will (1623).

[52] A reference to his angelo custode, a new devotion in the seventeenth century, in G. Basadonna*, will (1694).

[53] Rome, Jesuit Archives, Venezia 109 c. 413, cited by Cozzi, 'Federico Contarini', p. 204.

the leading patricians at that point supported an anti-papal policy. Yet the wills of the proctors suggest that most of them accepted an exterior religion, an impression confirmed by such a collective act of devotion as the building of the church of the Salute, by order of the Senate, as 'an appropriate means to placate the wrath of heaven'.[54] How is one to reconcile this apparent contradiction? It looks as if what happened in 1606 was that at a time when Venice seemed threatened by Spain and the pope was a friend of Spain, the silent majority of patricians was prepared to accept the leadership of a hard-line anti-papal group whose other religious attitudes they did not share.

Curiously enough, this was just the situation in certain Dutch towns during the revolt of the Netherlands; the fear of Spain persuaded the silent majority to accept the leadership of a minority of Calvinists. In Amsterdam in 1578, a group of former religious exiles took over the city government. But for some years it was still possible for Catholics to serve on the town council,[55] and when they disappeared, a group within the elite still stood up for religious toleration. The most famous of them was C. P. Hooft*. With his dislike of intolerance went his dislike of subtle theological disputations and of the ambition of the clergy; his conception of Christianity as a matter of 'good conscience' rather than a matter of deep theological questions; in short, his 'interior religion' (the term *innerlycke religieusheydt* is his own). He might, like Sir Thomas Browne, have declared that 'I condemn not all things in the Council of Trent' (he owned a copy of Baronio) 'nor approve all in the synod of Dort'.

In the controversy between Professor Arminius and Professor Gomarus over the deep questions of grace and predestination, which came to a head about the year 1608, it is tempting to see an analogy with the Venetian crisis of 1606. In both cities the theology of grace was entwined with a political question, whether the state was to control the church or not—or better, whether the patriciate was to control the clergy or not. It is equally tempting to take the gentle Hooft* as typical of Amsterdam patrician attitudes, in the same way that it is tempting to take Nicolò Contarini* as typical of Venetian ones. This too would be misleading. It is true that Arminius himself had married into the Amsterdam patriciate.[56] It is true that Oldenbarnevelt supported both the Arminians and the power of the Dutch regent class; that the Prince of Orange supported the Gomarists and

---

[54] The phrase is that of the *deputati alla fabrica* in 1679, quoted by G. A. Moschini, *La chiesa e il seminario di S. Maria della Salute* (Venice, 1842), p. 27.

[55] Ysbrant Dommer*, for example, who died *c.* 1582.

[56] In 1590 Arminius married Lijsbeth, daughter of Laurens Reael*.

that in 1618, when the controversy was at its height, he purged the *vroedschap* of Amsterdam and other cities of supporters of Arminius. When the Remonstrants were forced into founding a separate church, twelve members of the town council of Amsterdam had their children baptized there between 1633 and 1673.[57]

All this is true, but not the whole story. In the Amsterdam patriciate no less than in the Venetian there was a devout party or faction.[58] In Amsterdam it was led by Reynier Pauw*, one of the key figures in the convocation of the synod of Dort, where the Remonstrants were excommunicated. Pauw*'s papers have not survived, so that it is difficult to describe his religious attitudes in any detail, but we do have some evidence from his circle. Dr Pieter Schaep*, for example, wrote a letter to his son when Gerard Schaep* went up to Leiden university in 1617.[59] It is difficult to avoid the word 'puritan' when describing the cluster of attitudes expressed in this letter. Dr Schaep* is concerned that his son should organize his studies well, avoid wasting time, drunkenness, and 'whoredom', and, above all, that he should 'fear God'. Quotations from the Old Testament about the fear of the Lord echo through the letter. Gerard Schaep*'s papers have also survived. The image of God which emerges from them is that of a being who intervenes constantly in daily life. It is very different from the God of C. P. Hooft*, who liked to stress man's ignorance of the divine.

Thus in Calvinist Amsterdam as in Catholic Venice there was both a devout group and an anticlerical group within the patriciate. Where the fear of Spain played into the hands of the Venetian anticlericals, in Amsterdam it played into the hands of the devout. When the controversies died down, the two groups continued to exist in each city. The differences between them even affected their patronage of the arts.

Art patronage was also much influenced by the fact that the Venetian elite was noble, while the Amsterdammers were a bourgeoisie. Despite their ideal of personal frugality, Venetian patricians were believers in the ethos of 'magnificence', which they defined themselves in terms of 'conspicuous consumption' (*spendere largamente*). The great occasions for displaying this magnificence were 'banquets, weddings, and buildings, where it is right to spend without thinking

---

[57] H. Bontemantel, *De Regeering van Amsterdam*, ed. G. W. Kernkamp (Utrecht, 1897), lxiv, lists H. Bontemantel*, J. van Hartogvelt*, G. Hasselaer*, H. Hooft*, S. van Hoorn*, J. Hulft*, N. van Loon*, W. van Loon*, J. van den Poll*, W. Schrijver*, and C. van Vlooswijk*.

[58] The importance of this group is emphasized, indeed overemphasized, by R. B. Evenhuis, *Ook dat was Amsterdam* (Amsterdam, 1965–67).

[59] Amsterdam, Gemeente Archief, Bicker papers, 717, pp. 218–20.

of the expense'.[60] The great motive for this magnificence was family pride, 'the honour and . . . the splendour of the house'.[61] The family palace or *casa dominical* was at the centre of their attention. They would dream for entire generations of enlarging it and redecorating it, buying up the neighbouring houses and exhorting their descendants to carry on the good work.[62] The house was not just a residence, it was a symbol of the family. Hence Antonio Grimani* wrote of his, 'I do not want it ever to be rented out; it must be inhabited by my sons and their dependants for ever'.[63] Some spectacular new palaces were built in seventeenth-century Venice, including Palazzo Pisani on Campo S. Stefano, and Palazzo Pesaro on the Grand Canal, planned by doge Giovanni Pesaro* and built by Longhena for his nephew Leonardo*.[64] Sumptuous monuments were another way of glorifying the family. The one to Silvestro Valier* at S. Zanipolo, for example, was erected at a cost of 20,000 ducats.[65] One might give one's parish church a new façade and commission sculptors to turn it into an enormous monument, as Vincenzo Fini* and his brother did at S. Mosè, at a cost of 90,000 ducats, possibly a record for seventeenth-century Venice.[66] Even the country villa was turning into a palace during the period. A famous example is the villa Pisani at Strà, built in the early eighteenth century.

The works of sculpture and architecture commissioned by the patricians of Amsterdam show, as one might have expected, less magnificence, less display and less desire for the conspicuous glorification of the family. There were some fairly grand town houses, it is true, like Heerengracht 446, the house of Andries de Graeff*; the Trippenhuis or the house Vingboons built on the Singel for Joan Huydecoper*, which took up the space of three houses and had a magnificent garden which gave it the appearance, from the rear, of a country house.[67] But in general the houses of the Amsterdam elite were not on the scale of the Venetian *palazzi*, nor were they so expensive. 14,000 florins seems to have been the normal price for houses

---

[60] P. Paruta*, *Della Perfezione della vita politica*, p. 282; the speaker in this dialogue is Michele Surian.

[61] *L'honorevolezza et . . . la splendidezza della casa*: G. Bembo*, will (1617). There are many similar phrases in proctors' wills.

[62] G. de Lezze*, will (1624) mentions buying the house next door, as does G. Pesaro*, cited by E. Bassi, *Architettura del '600 e del '700 a Venezia* (Naples, 1968), p. 124.

[63] A. Grimani*, will (1624); cf. the will of G. da Lezze* (1624).

[64] Bassi, *op. cit.*, p. 58 and p. 124.

[65] Da Mosto, *I Dogi di Venezia*.

[66] Bassi, *op cit.*, p. 233.

[67] On the Huydecoper* house, see P. Vingboons, *Gronden en afbeeldsels der voornaamste gebouwen* (Amsterdam, 1688), fo. 2ʳ.

on the Keizersgracht in the seventeenth century; that would be about 7,000 ducats, little enough by Venetian standards.[68] A house was simply a place for the nuclear family to live in and does not seem to have had the symbolic importance of the Venetian *casa dominical*. Nor did the Amsterdammers spend much on family tombs, and their country houses seem to have been modest affairs compared with seventeenth-century Venetian villas. Take 'Vredenhof', for example, Andries de Graeff*'s country house near Voorschoten. In 1733 it was valued at 9,000 florins, including the gardens and the other land around it. The inventory of that year lists the rooms; only eleven of them altogether, including four service rooms—kitchen, cellar, servants' room and coach-house.[69]

The patronage of painters and writers was less a matter of family honour and rather more a question of personal taste, likely to reflect a genuine interest in the arts. The two groups were both in a favourable position to be patrons because they were urban, living in cities where painters and writers were concentrated. Here again the patronage of each of the elites has a certain pattern or style to it. A visitor to the house of a Venetian patrician would have been struck by the number of portraits. Some of them celebrated the family, but others, portraits of the Grand Turk, for example, gratified an interest in history. Religious paintings were much in evidence, many of them pictures of saints, probably including St Francis and the Magdalen, and possibly a local favourite like S. Marina or the blessed Lorenzo Giustinian. The rest of the collection would have been made up of classical mythologies, such as paintings of Venus or Apollo; of 'moral inventions' with titles such as *Time, prudence and fame*; and history-paintings like *Alexander and the family of Darius* or *Scipio and the Spanish slave*, both illustrating the virtues of a conqueror, continence and clemency. There might be a few landscapes in seventeenth-century Venetian collections, but they were very much in the background of attention.[70]

Literature was very much part of the daily lives of Venetian patricians. Books were dedicated to them, and they would receive somewhat nauseating complimentary verses celebrating their marriages and their political appointments.[71] Some of them took a lively interest in the opera. In the late seventeenth century there were

---

[68] The houses of J. Bisschop* and D. Bernard* were valued at this amount in 1623 and 1714 respectively.

[69] Amsterdam, Gemeente Archief, de Graeff papers, 608, fo. 82r.

[70] For Venetian collections, S. Savini-Branca, *Il collezionismo veneziano nel '600* (Padua, 1964); the appendix includes descriptions of the collections of fifteen members of the elite.

[71] C. Ivanovich, a prolific writer of such verses, prints some in his *Minerva al tavolino* (Venice, 1681).

twelve opera houses in Venice, of which eight were owned by noble families, including two members of the elite; Alvise Duodo*, who opened the theatre of S. Apollinare in 1651, and Marcantonio Giustinian*, in whose family theatre at S. Mosè Monteverdi's *Arianna* had its première in 1640.[72] Marco Contarini* had a theatre and music-room constructed on his country estate at Piazzola, and his collection of opera scores was a famous one.[73] This collection suggests that subjects from Roman history were particularly popular; Scipio and Alexander among them. The analogies with the paintings collected by patricians are obvious enough.

It is difficult to find out much about Amsterdam patricians as collectors in the first half of the period, but by the later seventeenth century they seem to have equalled the Venetians. What they collected was rather different. There were portraits of course, but the emphasis was on the group portrait, particularly the *schutterstuk* or painting of the town militia in their uniforms. As might have been expected, Old Testament subjects were rather more popular in Amsterdam collections than in Venetian ones, and there was also much more emphasis on landscapes, on still-lifes and on genre paintings. It is more surprising to see the occasional St Sebastian or St Stephen, or to find the occasional patrician, like Andries de Graeff*, with paintings of Venus and Diana in his house.[74] The strongly Calvinist burgomaster Tulp* once protested against the floats of 'heathen gods and goddesses' laid on to entertain the prince of Orange, so one wonders what he thought of his colleague's collection. Tulp* too patronized the arts. Rembrandt's famous *Anatomy Lesson* was painted for him, and he was particularly fond of the work of Paul Potter, who specialized in painting animals in landscapes.[75] This contrast in collections furnishes some support for the argument that Calvinism indirectly encouraged the rise of landscape painting.[76]

Amsterdam patricians, like Venetian ones, received 'poetic applause' when they married or were appointed to office. A vast quantity of this occasional verse was produced. For example, at least twenty-four people wrote poems about the burgomastership

---

[72] S. T. Worsthorne, *Venetian opera in the seventeenth century* (Oxford, 1954), is a valuable study but identifies the owner of the S. Apollinare theatre wrongly as a Dandolo, p. 33; contrast Ivanovich, *op. cit.*, p. 398.

[73] T. Wiel, *I codici musicali contariniani* (Venice, 1888), catalogues 120 MSS from the Contarini collection now in the Marciana.

[74] J. Vos, *Alle de gedichten* (Amsterdam, 1726), pp. 323f, describes a number of collections in verse.

[75] Tulp*'s protest quoted by K. Fremantle, *The Baroque Town Hall of Amsterdam* (Utrecht, 1959), p. 64; for his patronage of Potter, see A. Houbraken, *De Groote Schouwburg*, ii (Maastricht, 1944), p. 102.

[76] A. Cuyper, *Calvinism* (London, 1932), chapter on 'Calvinism and art'.

and death of Willem Backer*.[77] The dedications of the works of Vondel suggest that a small group of patricians were very much interested in the theatre; among them Andries de Graeff*, Simon van Hoorn*, Joan Huydecoper*, and Cornelis van Vlooswijk*.[78] One finds the same mixture of biblical and classical themes in the plays written for the Amsterdam theatre as in the galleries of Huydecoper* and de Graeff*.

It is natural to wonder whether the patricians had any influence on the plays dedicated to them, and what they wanted. In one case at least there is evidence for an answer; the case of Vondel's *Palamedes*. One day in 1625 Vondel was talking to Dr Albert Burgh* about Oldenbarnevelt, and Burgh said,

' "Write a tragedy about it". Vondel answered, "It isn't the moment". The other replied, "Just change the name".'

In an age accustomed to historical parallels there was no difficulty in recognizing the 'injured innocent' Palamedes as Oldenbarnevelt, Agamemnon as Prince Maurice, or Megeer as ex-burgomaster Reynier Pauw*. Vondel was called before the magistrates to answer for his play. Some of them wanted him acquitted, while others, the Counter-Remonstrants, wanted him punished severely. In the end he was simply fined.[79] The town council was not only divided about *Palamedes*, but about the question whether to have a theatre at all. The devout party wanted to pull the building down and erect a church in its place. The divergence between de Graeff* and Tulp* extended to the drama.

Much has beeen written about the possible relationship between the Counter-Reformation and the baroque style, and something about Calvinism and the classicism.[80] A comparative study of the taste of two seventeenth-century patriciates, one Catholic and one Protestant, seems an obvious way of attacking the problem. For the sake of brevity and clarity I shall confine myself to the visual arts; assume that to commission a work of art involves approving its aesthetic values; and operate with a simple contrast between a preference for the ornate, exuberant, emotional and idealizing, versus a preference for the plain, sober, reasonable and down-to-earth. In

---

[77] Amsterdam, Gemeente Archief, Backer papers, 70.

[78] Vondel dedicated *King David in Ballingschap* to A. de Graeff*; his translations of *Oedipus Rex* and *Iphigenia in Tauris* to J. Huydecoper*; the *Batavische Gebroeders* to S. van Hoorn*; and *King David Hersteld* to C. van Vlooswijk*.

[79] G. Brandt, *Leven van Vondel*, ed. S. Leendert, jr. (Amsterdam, 1932), p. 14.

[80] W. Weisbach, *Der Barock als Kunst der Gegenreformation* (Berlin, 1921), and L. Wencelius, *L'esthétique de Calvin* (Paris, 1937), opened the discussion.

Venice there were influential patricians of sober taste in the late sixteenth century, Federico Contarini* for example, but the taste for the ornate soon became dominant. Tintoretto had been a controversial painter, but in the next generation his follower Sante Peranda became quite fashionable for religious paintings. His patrons included such prominent members of the devout faction as Marin Grimani* and Renier Zen*. For portraits, the man was Tiberio Tinelli, a painter much influenced by van Dyck.[81] From about 1640 onwards, the popularity of opera, which was surely spectacle more than it was drama or even music, shows the rising taste for the exuberant. The most famous of baroque sculptures, Bernini's *S. Teresa*, was commissioned by cardinal Federico Corner, son of doge Giovanni I*. It was a patrician, Vincenzo Fini*, who commissioned the façade of S. Mosè from the architect Tremignon and the sculptor Meyring, a Flemish follower of Bernini. Richness of decoration could hardly go further. The columns on the façade of S. Mosè are not only fluted, they have ornamental bands across them, and these bands are themselves ornamented with rosettes. It may be significant that the patrons of this truly monumental piece of expensive bad taste had only been ennobled twenty years before.[82]

In Amsterdam the plain style seems dominant throughout the period, in the architecture of Vingboons and van Campen, the landscapes of Potter, the flower pieces of the van Huysums, or the portraits of van der Helst. Van der Helst seems to have been the most fashionable portrait painter among the Amsterdam elite between the 1640s and the 1660s, producing perceptive works which do not appear to idealize the sitters.[83] A small group of patricians seem to have been attracted by a more flamboyant style. Andries de Graeff* employed the painter Jordaens and the sculptor Quellin, both, significantly, from Antwerp, and he was on friendly terms with Govert Flinck, a painter who borrowed elegant poses from van Dyck to make his sitters look more aristocratic. For example, there is a portrait of an unidentified member of the Munter family, which contributed four members to the elite, in which the sitter has one hand to his breast and the other elegantly drooping.[84] The general impression of

---

[81] Paintings by Peranda were also owned by G. Pesaro* and A. Nani*; paintings by Tinelli were owned by G. B. Corner*, A. Nani*, A. Priuli*: Savini-Branca, *Il collezionismo veneziano nel '600*.

[82] Bassi, *Architettura del '600 e del '700 a Venezia*, p. 233.

[83] See J. J. de Gelder, *B. van der Helst* (Rotterdam, 1921). His sitters included D. Bernard*, R. Bicker*, F. B. Cocq*, J. Huydecoper*, J. van den Poll*, A. Pater*, C. van Vlooswijk*, C. Witsen*.

[84] See J. W. von Moltke, *Govert Flinck* (Amsterdam, 1965); the Munter portrait is no. 212 in his catalogue. De Graeff*'s friendship with Flinck is mentioned by Houbraken, *De Groote Schouwburg*, ii, p. 18.

Amsterdam patrician taste is predominantly sober but with a touch of something different, an impression summed up by the Town Hall, a plain building whose simple lines do not harmonize with the enormous pediments full of allegorical sculptures, again by Quellin.

The cultural differences between Venice and Amsterdam have something to do with the fact that one patriciate was Catholic and the other Protestant, but surely even more with the fact that one was a nobility and the other a bourgeoisie. The noble Venetians, more concerned with the splendour of their family, were bound to make different demands on artists from patrons who were members of the third estate. That a few Amsterdammers with titles should have behaved more like Venetians only reinforces the impression that the greatest difference between the two groups was not religious but social.

University of Sussex

THE ROLE OF RELIGION IN THE CULTURAL STRUCTURE OF THE LATER VICTORIAN CITY

By Revd. J. H. S. Kent, M.A., Ph.D., F.R.Hist.S.

READ AT THE SOCIETY'S CONFERENCE 15 SEPTEMBER 1972

ONE obviously cannot make generalizations covering all the towns and cities of late nineteenth-century England. London was a case by itself; Liverpool a very different port from Bristol; an industrial town like Rochdale seems very remote from Dorchester. Nor is it possible to give a single brief definition of a city, though many have tried. 'Just as there is no single form of the pre-industrial city,' wrote R. E. Pahl, 'urbanization as concentration of population does not lead to any single pattern of class action and conflict.'[1] Attempts to provide a definition of a city culminate in David Riesman's comment that the city is what we choose to make it for the purposes of analysis. One has to accept that Bristol, Dorchester, Rochdale and Liverpool were towns without exaggerating what they had in common.

Most Victorian towns prospered and their population increased. Religious institutions multiplied at the same time. In Liverpool, for example, in 1800 there were twelve Nonconformist chapels in a population of 77,000; in 1840 sixty chapels in a population of 223,000; in 1900, three hundred and twenty-five chapels in a city of 716,000. This does not mean that religious institutions expanded at the same pace as urban society in general: in the case of Liverpool itself, the increase in chapels had been erratic and unplanned, so that the *Daily Post*'s religious census of 1908 showed that there was a total morning attendance in the Free Church chapels of 20,000 and an evening attendance of 47,000, which meant an average attendance per chapel of 62 and 145 respectively.[2] Robert Currie argues that, looked at in terms of a membership–population ratio, Wesleyan Methodist membership declined continuously from 1841 to 1921; the second largest Methodist body, Primitive Methodism, declined from 1881 to 1931; the smaller Methodist Free Church, in its various guises, declined in

---

[1] R. E. Pahl, *Readings in Urban Sociology* (London, 1968), p. 4.

[2] I. Sellers, 'Nonconformist Attitudes in later 19th Century Liverpool', *Trans. Hist. Soc. Lancashire and Cheshire*, cxiv (1962), pp. 216–17.

Currie's absolute sense from 1871.[3] As for the Anglican Church, the comparison that stands out is between the two attempts in our period to calculate the size of religious groups in London: the *British Weekly* survey of 1886 and the *Daily News* census of 1902–3. It was claimed that for a comparable 'London' the estimated total attendance at all kinds of religious institutions fell from a *British Weekly* total of 1,167,312 to a *Daily News* total of 1,003,361, while the population of the area had risen by about 700,000. Within these figures, which no one at the time challenged very seriously, Anglican attendances had decreased from about 535,000 in 1886 to 396,000 in 1902–3.[4] At the time it seemed very important that during the same years Free Church attendances in 'London' had hardly fallen at all, but this was misleading: the Baptist and Congregationalist groups had just come to a peak from which they were to decline continuously.[5] It is fair for Professor Owen Chadwick to remind us that for many at the time what seemed most evident was the increase in the number of churches and chapels and of the number of people using them,[6] but the period of substantial growth had lain between 1800 and about 1860. There is no question of any second evangelical awakening in England in 1859,[7] and from 1870 at the latest the leaders of the religious institutions were aware that development was at least slowing down—and they did not need E. R. Wickham's *Church and People in an Industrial City* (1957) to tell them that the urban working-classes had largely withdrawn from contact with them.[8]

In any case, it may be regarded as axiomatic that the strength of religious institutions depends, not on the number of people who are existentially committed to a particular theological outlook, Christian, Buddhist or Islamic, but on the social roles which are available to the institutions as such. Apart from the increase in population, social conflicts, not a sudden change in the number of people prepared to accept Christian beliefs, or, more generally, a 'religious' outlook, explain the expansion which can be seen taking place in some cities. A good example of what this could mean can be found in Bristol. The principal Victorian middle-class expansion of Bristol was on to the higher ground overlooking the medieval city on the western side.

[3] R. Currie, *Methodism Divided* (London, 1968), pp. 85–103.

[4] R. Mudie-Smith, *The Religious Life of London* (London, 1904), p. 281.

[5] Peak year for the Baptists, for example, was 1906, when the United Kingdom membership was 434,741; in 1967 the equivalent figure was 290,313.

[6] O. Chadwick, 'The Established Church under Attack', in *The Victorian Crisis of Faith*, ed. A. Symondson (London, 1970), pp. 91–107.

[7] *Cf.* J. E. Orr, *The Second Evangelical Awakening in Britain* (London, 1949).

[8] Wickham's city was Sheffield.

Here the main road ran fairly straight for about a mile, culminating in Blackboy Hill. Along this road, which came to divide Clifton, on the left, from Cotham and Redland on the right, a number of churches and chapels were built during the Victorian period. On the Clifton side the parish churches were St John's (1841, morning attendance 1881,[9] 520, evening attendance, 380) and St Paul's (built in 1853, given a parish in 1859, burned in 1867, replaced with a second church 1868, a.m. in 1881, 920, p.m., 726); further into Clifton were Christ Church (1841, a.m. 923, p.m. 920), Emmanuel (1865–69, a.m. 740, p.m., 537), and All Saints, which replaced an older building in 1868 and was designed by G. E. Street (a.m. 652, p.m. 820): this was the only High Church parish in the area. On the other side of the Whiteladies Road there were St Mary the Virgin, Tyndall's Park (1874, a.m. 715, p.m. 664), and St Nathanael's, Cotham (1875, a.m. 241, p.m. 301).

The Wesleyan Methodist chapels were Victoria, at the start of the Whiteladies Road (1862/63, a.m. 320, p.m. 312); Trinity (1866/67, a.m. 347, p.m. 405), about half the way to the Blackboy Hill; and at the top of the hill the Methodist Free Church opened a chapel called The Mount of Olives in 1855, six years after the Wesleyan schism of 1849, (a.m. 60, p.m. 110), but this chapel passed into the hands of the Wesleyan Methodists in 1892. A second and more successful Methodist Free Church chapel was built in Redland in 1876 (a.m. 242, p.m. 219), before the Redland Court estate was finally broken up and built over. In Cotham (1878, a.m. 273, p.m. 304) was a third Wesleyan chapel. Wesleyan Methodism suffered badly from the 1849 schism in Bristol: the communicant roll fell from 3,849 in 1850 to 1,453 in 1854, and it was 1891 before the higher figure was reached again.

There were three Baptist chapels: Tyndale (1867/68, a.m. 372, p.m. 320), started with 38 members from older Baptist chapels in the city; Cotham Grove (1872, a.m. 267, p.m. 192), also founded with 45 members from older Baptist chapels; and Buckingham chapel, on the Clifton side, built in 1847 (a.m. 273, p.m. 193). The first Congregational chapel in the district was Highbury in Cotham (1841, a.m. 621, p.m. 426), the first major commission of the High Church architect, William Butterfield: members from this church established Redland Park (1861, a.m. 552, p.m. 486), on the Redland side of Whiteladies Road, where Tyndale Baptist, Trinity Wesleyan and Redland Congregational appeared, close together, in rapid succession. In Clifton there was a Unitarian chapel, Oakfield Road (1864, a.m. 85, p. m. 76), and a meeting of the Christian Brethren, Bethesda (a.m. 312, p.m. 133.

[9] J. F. Nicholls and J. Taylor, *Bristol Past and Present* (Bristol, 1881), pp. 305–8. For another view of D. Carter, 'Social and Political Influences of the Bristol Churches' (M.Litt. thesis, Univ. of Bristol, 1970). Bristol population 1881, 211,659.

The absence of Bible Christian, Primitive Methodist or Salvation Army groups helps to characterize the area.

For Anglicanism the seven new parish churches mentioned were part of the 19th century drive to extend the small-parish system which was the bane of Victorian Anglican planning: between 1823 and 1903 41 new parish churches were built in Bristol, which, with mission chapels, provided about 36,000 sittings. The predominantly middle-class nature of the area is shown by the fact that here Anglican gross attendances in the religious census of 1881 exceeded Free Church attendances by about 9 to 7, whereas in Bristol as a whole Free Church attendances exceeded Anglican by about 61,000 to about 45,000.[10] It was significant of the social prestige of the area and of the price of having a bishop that when the Bristol see was restored in 1897 (having been combined with that of Gloucester since 1836), the new palace, costing £14,000, was placed on one side of Redland Green, and built 'in the style of the simple old manor houses in districts where stone is the local building material'.[11]

For the Bristol Free Churches, however, the establishment of this series of strong chapels meant the formation of a new middle-class social and political leadership which carried more weight than did the leadership of the older chapels in the central part of the city, or of the new Victorian chapels standing on the southern side of the river Avon in the poorer districts of Bedminster and Totterdown. A hard core membership of three to four hundred was good for any of these chapels, but larger numbers passed through them—for example, between 1868 and 1894 Richard Glover, pastor at Tyndale Baptist, made about 800 members, but in 1901 the three Baptist chapels had total memberships of Buckingham, 117; Cotham Grove, 259; and Tyndale, 321.[12]

The strength of these Free Church chapels lay not in numbers but in their ability to organize and lead a pressure-group whose urban programme they legitimized on religious grounds, and pressed on the amorphous Liberal Party of the late nineteenth century. Standish Meacham has suggested that Nonconformity accepted the development of the industrial city in a sense that Anglicanism did not. The social groups from which Anglican leadership came clung to the feeling that the city was vulgar and *for* the vulgar.[13] What Meacham said about Anglicanism was probably true, but although Nonconformists

[10] J. F. Nicholls and J. Taylor, *Bristol Past and Present* (Bristol, 1881), pp. 305–8.
[11] C. S. Taylor, *Bristol. Illustrated Guide to the Church Congress* (London, 1903), p. 115.   [12] *The Baptist Handbook for 1901* (London, 1900), p. 256.
[13] S. Meacham, 'The Church in the Victorian City', *Victorian Studies*, xi (1968), Summer Supplement (on Victorian urban history).

accepted the city as an arena of conflict they also rejected it, because the city made them conscious of their lack of social power. Their social programme, which demanded the abolition of Anglican and Roman Catholic day-schools, the stamping out of prostitution, the closure of public-houses, the prohibition of gambling and in general a kind of frozen Sunday, reflected this dislike of the city as it was, part 'Anglican' and 'upper-class', part 'working-class'. Nevertheless, Meacham is right in so far as one must distinguish between anti-urbanism of an Anglican kind, its roots in the English governing class's arcadian attitudes and low view of commerce and industry, and a Nonconformist anti-urbanism, its sources to be found in social and political frustration. Where one differs from both Meacham and Asa Briggs, who advanced similar views of the urban role of Nonconformity in terms of Birmingham, is in doubting that one can distinguish between a negative Anglican and a positive Nonconformist attitude to the changing urban situation.[14]

In any case, one must be cautious about generalization. In Bristol the Free Churches retained through the second half of the nineteenth century the leadership and support of a number of local businessmen of various kinds, but if one took Liverpool, much the more successful port of the two in the Victorian period, as an example one would find a different picture. Ian Sellers writes:

> 'Nor can it be said that in the later years of the century Liverpool Nonconformity contained within its ranks the numbers of successful, self-made businessmen who elsewhere financed Nonconformity and also provided it with vigorous lay leadership. Throughout this period most denominations in Liverpool complained of impoverishment or the lack of wealthy adherents, and their complaints are borne out by the testimony of independent witnesses. Thus, when the Baptists closed down Comus Street chapel in 1877, a most pathetic letter was sent round the churches, begging them to allow the proceeds of the sale to be used as a nucleus for the support of their many impoverished churches. "The number of rich Baptists in Liverpool," the circular concludes, "is diminishing; we now have very few". The only two really prosperous congregations which, if the figures for Hospital Sunday collections are an accurate guide, far outsripped the rest in material sources—Sefton Park Presbyterian and Ullet Road Unitarian—were curiously isolated from the rest of Liverpool Nonconformity, and pursued singular patterns of political behaviour.'[15]

Sefton Park (1880), was dominated from its foundation to 1905 by the Reverend John Watson, whose original Jacobitism became in

[14] *Ibid.*   [15] I. Sellers, *op. cit.*, p. 217.

Liverpool a sanctimonious vision of England as a peasant utopia
presided over by a benevolent Tory government; he backed the Boer
War as a cure for national debility and loved to appear in full-
dress uniform in the streets of Liverpool as chaplain of the Liverpool
Scottish.[16] The social role of urban Presbyterianism, however, like
that of urban Roman Catholicism, was very much a racial question.

These expanding religious institutions took a place in a new urban
structure. How far one can speak of a Victorian urban civilization
is another question; one could hardly compare the cities that I have
mentioned with Florence, Venice, Amsterdam or Paris. Culture, however, is a term subject to definition, and the following may serve as
headings here. An urban culture will combine elements of government, economic patterns, education, recreation and religion. In the
late Victorian period institutionalized religion (as distinct from more
diffuse 'religious' behaviour of all kinds) came so frequently into
conflict with other institutions in matters which affected the other
elements in the urban culture (as I have already suggested in referring
to the social programme of the Nonconformists) that not only is the
idea of cultural conflict an important qualification of the urban role
of institutionalized religion, but it also becomes necessary to ignore
denominational differences to some extent and think instead in terms
of a religious sub-culture which was slowly separating itself, institu-
tionally, from the dominant, largely secular culture. This was an
urban phenomenon, partially concealed at the time by special circumstances. In the case of Anglicanism, this shift towards a common
identity with other religious institutions was modified psychologically
by persistent memories of having been part of the dominant culture
in the past, and this explains why it was especially Anglican digni-
taries who felt it their role to insist on the essential unity of society.
Thus in 1876, for example, Canon, later Bishop, Westcott told the
Peterborough Volunteers of the vital unity of the nation:

> 'I do not forget [he told them] that there are forces at work among
> us which tend to separate class from class, and to set one against
> another in fratricidal rivalry, I do not forget that some would repre-
> sent loyal homage to rank and blood as derogatory to the generous
> spirit which it purifies. But I am sure that the great heart of England
> is sound still. I am sure that the unity of which I speak is real, if
> often concealed, and that reverence is as yet powerful among us
> if often dissembled . . . There is a living circulation between our
> many ranks which makes mutual understanding easy. On the other
> hand, there is an age-long tradition round each one which preserves

[16] See the life of Watson by W. R. Nicholl (1908), entitled *Ian McLaren*
(Watson's pseudonym as an author).

its distinctions intact. We do not yet think that we have made or that we can unmake the dignity of the throne. . . . We believe— the whole framework of our life helps, nay forces, us to believe— that our manhood is one, and at the same time, in order that the whole may be one, differentiated in countless fragments of which each fulfils its proper office'.[17]

In the case of the Free Churches the complicating factor was that between about 1890 and 1914 the clerical leaders went through a period of intense and disastrous exaltation, when they believed that their denominations were about to inherit the place of Anglicanism (which they accepted as still being part of the dominant culture) and even to impose their own patterns of behaviour upon British society as a whole. Despite this inner conflict, and the suspicion with which many in both groups viewed Roman Catholicism, urban religious institutions were beginning to approximate to one another in social composition and ethos in the late Victorian period, and it is this process which explains the movement towards institutional unity (which also began before the end of the nineteenth century), and not, as has been suggested by Bryan Wilson and Robert Currie, falling membership figures combined with a clerical conspiracy.[18]

Looked at from the point of view of institutional religion, therefore, one cannot describe Victorian urban culture as a unity: the religious sub-culture was not simply the religious expression of the dominant cultural pattern. Conflict emerged at the level of local government, for although religious institutions sympathized with the general middle-class Victorian desire for order, they also tried, especially in the 1890s, to use local authorities to enforce their own moral aims. The Reverend Charles F. Aked, left-wing pastor of the Pembroke Baptist chapel in Liverpool from 1890 to 1906 (when he left for the Fifth Avenue chapel in New York), told the first National Council of the Evangelical Free Churches in 1896:

'Law is one thing, but the enforcement of it is another. The experience of Liverpool by this time is well known . . . The civic authorities protected vice . . . the policy of concentration was the one followed. Two districts were given up to the trade in vice. If the evil-doers opened business in other neighbourhoods they were prosecuted, but so long as they kept within the infected areas they were safe . . . When we were exploring I was accosted by women at ten different houses in one street, and at five houses out of six

---

[17] B. F. Westcott, *Peterborough Sermons* (London, 1904), pp. 364–65.
[18] For these ideas, see B. Wilson, *Religion in Secular Society* (London, 1969), pp. 151–205; and R. Currie, *op. cit.*, especially pp. 293–316.

standing together . . . I counted one night forty-four fallen women coming out of one liquor place in ten minutes, and sixty-six at closing-time. But at last the conscience of Liverpool was touched. The Churches put on strength. The people arose. Then a political party inscribed "social reform" upon its banners, won seats at elections . . . The old gang was broken up. The Watch Committee had a new chairman and a new policy. The law was set in motion . . .'[19]

Setting the existing laws on prostitution, drink and gambling in motion and campaigning for new laws as well dramatized the cultural conflict between strongly opposed views as to how the industrial city should be organized. At the economic level, however, the intensive but selective exploitation of urban space which characterized the 19th century tended to be taken for granted by the religious institutions precisely because their most sophisticated and influential leadership came from the protected areas. As H. J. Dyos has written: 'the middle-class Victorian suburb was both an invention for accentuating social distinctions and a means of putting off for a generation or two the full realization of what was entailed by living in a slum'.[20] There was never any real question of there being an organic whole, 'the city'. In Bristol, for example, the nineteenth-century city expanded from the medieval, low-lying port up steep escarpments into Clifton, Cotham and Redland, while at the same time forming new industrial areas at a distance from this middle-class citadel. The city moved both westward (bourgeois) and south and east (industrial). The role of religion could not be described as the same in both directions, nor were the two areas at all profoundly related, still less united, in the consciousness of most individuals. But a city like Bristol did not only exist as a kind of class system—as was very obvious in other new towns like Swindon, where the poor and the better-off crept towards one another's proximity for most of the century: the city also existed less as economic structure than as the momentary product of many economic stresses. From one point of view everything in a Victorian town was constantly in decline, moving away from being new, fashionable, solid. Railway building ripped into the core of many large cities. destroying housing and worsening the lives of the poor. There was often more stress than structure. The older forms of the western religious tradition had been able to rationalize what seemed, down to the eighteenth century, to be an almost changeless economic structure; they were not so well adapted to rationalize rapid

[19] *Proceedings of the First National Council of the Evangelical Free Churches* (London, 1896), pp. 199–200.
[20] H. J. Dyos, 'Slums of Victorian London', *Victorian Studies*, x (1967), p. 27.

and unpredictable economic change and growth. This did not seem to matter very much in the eyes of the institutional leaders themselves until, towards the end of the century, it emerged that industrial workers were capable of organizing themselves: a further cultural clash became inevitable at this stage as it became clear that what the pamphleteer had meant by 'the bitter cry of outcast London'—a Macedonian call for help in his religious vocabulary—had only existed in his own clerical imagination.[21] Even so, the response of the religious institution could expose the cultural conflict in bizarre forms. In 1894 the Baptist popular preacher, F. B. Meyer, pastor of Christ Church in Westminster Bridge Road, instituted a 'People's Drawing Room' for working women, to balance the 'Pleasant Sunday Afternoon' which he already provided for the men. 'I have a number of palms for decoration,' he said, 'and shall try to procure one or two canaries to make the surroundings as comfortable and homelike as possible. Babies will have to be given up at the door, and for them we have our crêche, where feeding-bottles, rattles and other toys will be provided, and our kind amateur nurses will set the mothers free for an hour of quiet self-culture and social intercourse. I hope to read them selections from Tennyson and Longfellow . . .'[22] This recipe for social reconciliation was repeated with breathless admiration by the *Bristol Christian Leader* (April 1894), the monthly organ of Bristol's Nonconformist institutions in the 1890s. The conflict really sharpened when organized labour challenged the political role of the Free Churches by breaking with the Liberal Party, to which Nonconformity had seen itself offering the labour vote; but the independence of the new labour movement, and of the trade unions, was equally a cultural split from the Anglican and Roman Catholic institutions.

The bulk of the urban middle-class absorbed nineteenth-century economic change without excessive physical or psychological suffering; those among them who identified with religious groups did not regard economic development as threatening the significance of their religious institutions; the liberal, non-dogmatic theology which many of them favoured in the last quarter of the century approved of 'progress'. This meant that the middle-class leaders of religious institutions concentrated their moral attention on leisure, not work. Paradoxically, industrial workers, and even more those who lived in urban poverty, also concentrated their vitality on leisure, but did so because they could not accept the consequences of economic

[21] *The Bitter Cry of Outcast London* (London, 1883) has been attributed to several authors, but A. Mearns and W. C. Preston, the probable co-authors, were both Congregationalist ministers.

[22] F. B. Meyer, 'The People's Drawing Room', *Bristol Christian Leader* (1894), p. 132.

change, and especially the Victorian industrial town, as moral. There was a mutual, but incompatible, repudiation of the town as it was. Over leisure and recreation the conflict between the articulate leadership of religious institutions and the poorer groups of society (together with the small group of the aristocracy proper, a favourite target of the popular preacher), became absolute towards the end of the century, even if the absoluteness was sometimes the absoluteness of unreality, as when the Free Church Congress of 1896 demanded legislation to close public-houses on Sunday. For example, in Middlesbrough (population at the turn of the century 97,000) a local census recorded that on a given Sunday 22,000 people attended 60 different chapels, churches, etc.; about 90,000 were seen to enter 106 public-houses and 36 off licenses during the same day.[23]

But the vigour with which religious institutions denounced public-houses, 'blood-tubs' and music-halls, bookmakers and betting in general, prostitution (though this was partly because of the attraction to middle-class boys), professional football (though not cricket, which remained part of the wealthier classes' cultural scene), also reflected a confidence born of an awareness that the cultural structure of a Victorian city was so deeply divided that religious institutions could expect outside support as long as they were seen to be criticizing working-class (or aristocratic) conventions of behaviour.

Here an Anglican comment on football may balance the references made to Nonconformity. *Commonwealth*, started in 1896 as a journal which believed itself to be Christian Socialist, said, during the South African War:

> 'War rages, great social changes are toward, disasters intervene, there are discussions on bread and education, but the adult male population of England and Scotland is watching its football matches. The sight is a portent, a hundred thousand young adult males, all in black roundhats, small moustaches and short pipes, gazing with painful intensity at the twenty-two combatants they have hired to compete before them. So long as the Saturday afternoon is preserved, and the sixpence for the match secure, England need never fear revolution.'[24]

No doubt Scott Holland,[25] who was a parson, wrote this, but the distancing of the young men in their bowler hats with their short pipes, and their intensity which is painful, not to them, but to the journalist, is significant of the cultural conflict. It was, after all, a parson who

---

[23] Lady Bell, *At the Works* (London, 1911), pp. 33, 187.
[24] *Commonwealth* (1902), p. 146.
[25] H. S. Holland (1847–1918) was Regius professor of divinity at Oxford from 1910 to his death, a comment on Anglicanism rather than on Holland.

was supposed to have gnawed through the handle of his umbrella while watching Spofforth, the Australian fast bowler, wreck the English batting in 1882, but *his* intensity was thought to be a proper reaction to an epic situation. One finds a similar attitude in the *Bristol Christian Leader* in November, 1893, during a local mining strike, when trade union leaders had criticized Bristol religious institutions for alleged indifference. 'It seems to be the toilers' grievance that employers form the bulk of the ruling element in the Churches, and the Churches, they reason, are therefore against them. We cannot agree with this.' The *Leader* said that it would support 'any safe course to take towards bringing in a happier temporal state for the toilers'.[26] Of the whole way of life to which both secular and religious institutions wanted to bind the industrious poor, Alexander Paterson wrote: 'How low are the civic standards of England, how fallen the ideals and beauties of Christianity. No man that has dreams can rest content because the English worker has reached this high level of regular work and rare intoxication.'[27]

What had happened was that the bringing together of masses of working-class people—the steelworkers of Middlesbrough and the Great Western Railway factory workers at Swindon, for example— in similar streets, factories and workshops produced a psychological situation different from that produced by the traditional presence in the countryside of agricultural labourers, always thinly scattered on the ground, often living in detached groups of cottages, and isolated from one another much of the time by the jobs they were doing. In the late Victorian town a middle-class, or suburban conscious-ness of the working-class was quite as real, if not a more real, phenomenon, than a proletarian class-consciousness. Despite the sentimentality of a writer like Richard Hoggart, one doubts the exis-tence of a significant working-class culture as such, to be identified, for example, as *'for'* life'.[28] The state of mind of the majority of the poorer people living in places like Bristol, Liverpool or Swindon seems to have been more a consciousness of not belonging fully to the dominant, though sub-divided culture.[29] Given that these were posi-tive and negative forms of the same culture, the difference between them was partly imposed by the controlling groups. Suburban society in general believed, and may have needed to believe for the sake of

[26] *Bristol Christian Leader* (1893), p. 324.

[27] Alexander Paterson, *Across the Bridges* (London, 1914), p. 146.

[28] As supporting evidence here, cf. H. J. Gans, 'Culture and Class in the Study of Poverty', in *People and Plans* (London, 1972), pp. 298–330.

[29] Since it seems usually to be held that an articulate working-man is not typical it is difficult to justify this statement from such writers as Alfred Williams (see below, p. 169) or Thomas Wright; the journals of city missioners suggest the same conclusion.

its own identity, that the poor had a different way of life which suited their limited capacities: the poor were not supposed to present a reflection, however inadequate, of suburban culture. Popular education, which in Victorian times was meant to act as a limiting factor on the development of the poor, and which was deliberately remoulded in a more élitist direction by the 1902 education act, was the secular means of imposing cultural forms: Robert Roberts, for instance, in his fascinating description of Salford at the opening of the century, emphasizes how the slum school which he attended indoctrinated its pupils with the cult of empire.[30] The role of the major religious institutions, one which they seemed to accept, was that of legitimizing suburban attitudes while rejecting as incompatible with religious behaviour the normal leisure activities of the working-classes (and the aristocracy).

This steady criticism of secular leisure had a financial basis as well. Victorian chapels were built on debt, and in the course of the century two and even three buildings were put up by the same local group; the Anglican equivalent was usually the 'iron church' which preceded a hardback building. The cost of paying for buildings, ministers, and also for overseas missions had to be found by a comparatively small group on an annual basis. The feeling that the religious society should separate itself from the secular society, a feeling powerful in the Catholic, Protestant and small-sect groups, was now reinforced by financial pressures. The survival of all these groups depended upon their absorbing the time and money of their adherents, and secular leisure ate away at both. And if working-class men and women patronized public-houses, bet on horses (the typical form of gambling of the period) and went to football matches they were unlikely to support financially the parish churches and mission-chapels which middle-class religious institutions erected in working-class areas.

The education of the children of the poor, the final element which I suggested as part of an urban culture, had been a constant source of conflict. In the 1840s, as one sees clearly, for example, in the reports on the mining areas in Staffordshire and the north-east,[31] the ministers of all religious institutions saw the working-classes as ignorant, easily led astray by agitators (Chartists, of course, at that time), unaware of their best interests (and therefore tempted to strike, which, as middle-class commentators were already willing to tell them, was never in their best interests). The ministers saw themselves, and wanted government to see them, as the agents of civilization in a

---

[30] R. Roberts, *The Classic Slum* (London, 1971), pp. 101–15.
[31] See the report on the South Staffordshire mining area by T. Tancred in 1843, and *The Report of the Commissioner into the State of the Mining Districts* (1846) by H. S. Tremenheere.

society which was falling apart, and therefore they favoured more schools of an elementary kind as long as they themselves controlled them, and as long as some variety of Christianity was taught in them. For a brief period in the 1840s government was sufficiently alarmed to welcome this support, but between the 1840s and the 1880s the situation changed and religious institutions ceased to play a vital part in the strategy of the English ruling groups. Thus Bishop Westcott's 'Christian Socialism' was not a move to obtain concessions from the state by threatening to support urban revolutionary societies, but expressed the hope that by showing sympathy for trade unionism and preaching industrial conciliation (not strikes) institutionalized religion might still put in a claim to be playing an important role in the structure of the state. In education, the act of 1870 did not finally decide the future, but wrote off the past, that is, the hope of the leaders of the religious bodies that their fundamental role in the new urban structure might be in providing education, especially at the level of the poor. The Board School system pointed towards new secular institutions in which the schoolmaster would finally replace the priest: the decline in the number of ordination candidates began then and has gone on ever since.

From this point of view Forster gave his Nonconformist friends a last chance: if, out of fear of Anglicanism, and especially of Anglicanism in the villages, where they did not believe in the possibility of a conscience clause, they abandoned denominational schools, for which in any case they could not pay, the system of local, and especially urban, Board Schools might give them the chance, at least in some cities—Bristol, for instance, where the non-Anglicans held a majority most of the time, or Swindon, but not Salisbury, where an Anglican local majority prevented competition from non-Anglican schools in the name of the theory that cathedral towns were now the last fortresses of the Church of England proper—to destroy or at least greatly weaken the Anglican and Roman Catholic denominational schools, without surrendering all religious content in education at the same time. And if they could break the hold of the Anglican/Roman Catholic groups on elementary education in the towns they would have changed their own urban role profoundly. In other words, the struggle between religious institutions in the towns over the education of the children of the poor was not primarily about education, but about social power: it was a contest for a social role in late Victorian cities between two groups for whom educational policy was a convenient and natural way of expressing conflict. While they fought one another for social and cultural control, however, the dominant culture slipped further and further out of the reach of both of them. In urban terms, between 1870 and 1902 Nonconformity certainly succeeded in weakening Anglicanism, but the conflict only damaged the religious sub-culture of which both were part.

Two quotations from the Anglican journal, *Commonwealth*, may help to fix the conclusion here. C. F. G. Masterman, writing in 1902 against the background of renewed education controversy, still romantically defended the ideal of total religious education which was rapidly disappearing: he longed for a religious school in which a lesson in arithmetic would somehow be different from a mathematics lesson in a secular school. The London School Board had made 'religious instruction' a brief subject among subjects. He continued:

> 'We have the one damning fact of the religious position of South London today after thirty years of this admirable instruction: a population practically heathen, with little knots of worshippers in a great ocean of indifference . . . The children learn of a book or a creed . . . the knowledge remains with no relation to the real world of their daily existence; and it sloughs off as the benefit of three quarters of school life sloughs off in the two or three years succeeding school . . .'[32]

This was romantic because Masterman was writing as though the 'religious school' was still a credible alternative in what was no longer simply a state system for the teaching of poor children. As middle-class children began to enter what was becoming a national education system it was no longer possible to impose the form of the 'religious school' on what were ceasing to be really local schools. What Scott Holland called 'the religious half-hour in the secular school' spread through the surviving denominational network: it was an open secret by 1902 that at the level of the urban day school the religious teaching of many denominational schools hardly differed from that in the Board Schools.

My second quotation is from Scott Holland, writing as editor of *Commonwealth* in November 1902. 'The melancholy lesson is forced upon us by the present education controversy that Dissenters do really hate the Church'—by which he meant Anglicanism—'so that their opposition to it is the one thing that rouses them to special enthusiasm'.[33]

Holland was correct in implying, on this particular occasion, that education was not the point, and correct in stressing the intensity of feeling; but he was mistaken in putting the issue in clerical terms, as between Anglicanism and Dissent. This was how the clerical

[32] C. F. G. Masterman, 'The Fight for the Schools', *Commonwealth*, vii (1902), p. 164.
[33] *Commonwealth*, vii (1902), p. 339.

leaders of the religious institutions wanted to have the controversy understood. But there were at least four parties involved: the religious sub-culture split into two parties by an urban conflict between middle-class groups; a secular Conservative political party, prepared to rescue the Anglican/Roman Catholic alliance from defeat but not interested in imposing the 'religious school' in the state system on an urban level; and the working-class, whose representatives on education commissions normally objected to what they called dogmatic teaching and supported the Board School tradition. In 1902 Nonconformity finally discovered that it had lost its power-base in the cities, while the other major religious institutions averted similar catastrophe.

At the urban level all these cultural conflicts can be consolidated in a single example, the differing time-structures to be found in the city. There was a superficial unity, because, in theory, if not in practice, every one was subject to traditional clerical time, modified in England by a Protestant willingness at the Reformation to sanction the disappearance of many religious holidays. During the nineteenth century there had been a renewed campaign to impose a complete Sunday shut-down, and this had largely succeeded, partly because this was an issue on which the religious sub-culture remained united, and partly because the campaign fitted into a middle-class desire for the establishment of urban public order.

Thus Sunday became the urban working-man's day of leisure, given him by tradition, sabbatarianism and public convenience. Theoretically, the time-structure of his life was similar to everyone else's: a working-week rhythmically interrupted by a silent Sunday on which, after all, the religious institutions were theoretically open to him. Leisure or no leisure, however, he was not to be entertained, though innovations like the Pleasant Sunday Afternoon revealed a clerical awareness that this denial of the demand for entertainment could not be maintained indefinitely. During the nineteenth century liberal pressure from outside the religious sub-culture mounted in favour of at least intellectual concessions, and one finds *Commonwealth*, in its initial liberal mood of 1896, welcoming the vote of the House of Commons in favour of the Sunday opening of museums and art galleries: only small amounts of labour would be required and Jews, who allegedly operated the Birmingham public library on Sundays, could always be employed. In Bristol, however, the religious institutions remained broadly against a proposal made in 1892 to open municipal library and museum on Sunday. It was a step towards the secularization of the Sabbath, said the *Bristol Christian Leader*: 'The working-classes neither demand nor appreciate the opportunities which are claimed for them'—while to see the neighbourhood of the

Suspension Bridge on a Sunday evening 'is enough to make a Christian's heart sink within him'.[34] Out of 107 Free Church ministers in the city (55 Methodist, 35 Congregational, 15 Baptist, 1 Moravian and 1 Presbyterian), only one replied in favour of Sunday opening when sent a questionnaire in 1893, and the local council finally rejected the proposal by a vote of about two to one.

Nor was this simply the conservatism of the south-west: in Lady Bell's Middlesbrough about 1907 the theatres, the working-men's clubs and the museum all had to close on Sunday and only the newspaper rooms at the Free Library opened its doors.[35] And although a Joint Committee of Convocation had reported in favour of the change in 1893, in 1902 one finds Scott Holland in *Commonwealth*, no longer so liberal, pointing out that Anglican liberals had only meant to make Sunday joyfully religious, not to introduce a secular Sunday. Which again suggested a misunderstanding on his part of the role of the religious sector, for the movement to alter the tone of Sunday had been a response to the secularizing tendency of the dominant culture: to preserve a role in the urban structure religious institutions were expected to legitimize changes of this kind. Now, however, Holland wanted to fight for Sunday—'its social value as enforced relief—its religious value as spiritual necessity'—quite forgetful of the working-classes against whom he was really fighting.[36]

The first article in the series which he commissioned on the issue touches directly on the underlying problem of time-structures. Armitage Robinson, as a canon of Westminster, was perhaps not the best person to write it. Special services on a Sunday afternoon—no doubt he was thinking of his neighbour F. B. Meyer among others—drew in some working-class people, but their neglect—so he worded it, somehow supposing them to be Christians in any case—their neglect of the first half of Sunday must be remedied. It emerges at one stage of his argument that he knew that working-class people in London did not only stay up late on Saturday night in order to enjoy themselves, but that people waited as late as possible before buying meat which had cheapened as the night wore on, but nevertheless he felt that 'we' must teach the working-man how to spend his Saturday night better. 'He now sleeps late because he has supped so late', the Canon concluded.[37]

It should be added here that in discussions of working-class behaviour at this time religious writers were still obsessed with the concept of conversion as a rapid change of life-direction. This, after all, was

[34] *Bristol Christian Leader* (1893), p. 62.
[35] Lady Bell, *op. cit.*, pp. 186–87.
[36] *Commonwealth*, vii (1902), p. 226.
[37] *Ibid.*, p. 227.

the revivalist period *par excellence*, of Moody and Sankey, Torrey and Alexander, and 'converting' preachers like H. P. Hughes. Thus Armitage Robinson really thought that the working-man had only to will a difference in his own behaviour, and largely ignored the extent to which individual conduct is enmeshed in an economic and social structure.

As the problem of food prices implies, there was a distinct working-class time-structure, and this is most easily illustrated by a particular example. This comes from Alfred Williams' description of *Life in a Railway Factory*, an account of the Great Western Railway works at Swindon in the last year of the nineteenth century. Williams was born in 1877 and worked there for more than twenty years.

Williams said that the factory-year was divided into three general periods, *i.e.* from Christmas till Easter, Easter until the 'Trip', which took place in July, and from 'Trip' until Christmas. It will emerge incidentally, however, that it was only partly Christmas which marked the second turning-point. All three were breaks in the factory routine, but there was little travelling at Easter; instead men put their gardens and allotments in order. Despite the prominence of ecclesiastical names, the factory revolved around the July 'Trip': over 20,000 people left the town, many going to London, many to Weymouth. About half the total came back the same night, but the remainder usually stayed for the eight days of the unpaid holiday. The Trip trains were free. By the time they came back most of the men had little or no money at all. They saved up for months beforehand, and whatever new clothes were bought for the summer were first worn on this occasion. From Christmas until Easter, Williams said, was a time of rising spirits; from Easter to the July Trip one of comparative ease and satisfaction; 'from August till December the feeling is one almost of despair. Day after day the black army files in and out of the entrances with the regularity of clockwork'.[38] The popularity of the Saturday football match (rather than the canon's morning service at Westminster) explains itself in the existential context. It is not surprising that Williams noted that 'many a workman boasts that he has denied himself a Sunday dinner in order to find the money . . . to attend Saturday's match'.[39] The stress involved is clearer when it is realized that the time until Christmas, the first half of the football season, was also the time when whatever money was to be saved had to be saved.

As for the week, there was a lethargic Monday, a productive

[38] A. Williams, *Life in a Railway Factory* (London, 1915), p. 250.
[39] *Ibid.*, p. 287.

Tuesday, and then a series of variable days ending in a wasted Saturday half-day which was still worked at the end of the century.

'Sunday is the day of complete inactivity with most of the workmen, and it is possibly the weakest and least enjoyed of all. If the day is dull and wet a great number stay in bed till dinner-time, and sometimes they remain there all day and night till Monday morning comes. This will not have done them much harm'.[40]

The mention of despair in the weeks between August and December is interesting because Williams, without being quite conscious of it, goes on to describe a kind of New Year Festival. He wrote:

'New Year's Eve was always suitably observed and celebrated by those on the night-shift.' The work came gradually to a halt. 'The steam-hammers were silenced, the fires were damped and the tools were thrown on one side. All that could be heard was the continual chu-chu of the engine outside forcing the hydraulic pumps, and the exhaust of the donkey engine whirling the fan. Then an inventive and musical-minded workman stretched a rope across from the principals, and came forwards with two sets of steel rods, of varying lengths and thicknesses, capable of emitting almost any note in the scale . . . Some one fetched a big brass dome from a worn-out boiler, while several others had brought old buffers from the scrap waggons.

'Shortly before midnight, when the bells in the town and the far-off villages began to peal out, the workmen commenced their carnival. Bells were perfectly imitated by striking the bars of steel . . . the buffers contributed their sharp notes, and the brass dome sounded deeply and richly. When the noise had been continued for a sufficient length of time food was brought out.' They ate, drank and slept. 'They seldom started work any more that morning. The foremen and the watchmen were usually missing on New Year's Eve . . . All this happened some twenty years ago and would not be permitted today . . .'[41]

The whole pattern, the year, the week, the Sunday, the New Year Celebration, with music and feasting, the annual Trip with its spend-out atmosphere, produced a time structure subtly different from that which contained the lives of those who served in religious institutions and sometimes took up their pens to write about the English Sunday—now, as the vicar of St John the Divine, Kennington, told *Commonwealth* readers, 'lost, and it can never be restored'.[42] I don't want to

[40] A. Williams, *Life in a Railway Factory* (London, 1915), p. 254.
[41] *Ibid.*, pp. 271–73.
[42] *Commonwealth*, vii (1902), p. 229.

conclude this section by making exaggerated claims for the existence of a Victorian working-class 'religious attitude', which, though it was sometimes parasitic on institutionalized religion, as in the use of christian passage rites, was, nevertheless, not essentially christian at all. But there are parallels for this enthusiasm for the New Year festival, while the Harvest Festival, for a few years towards the end of the century, seems to have filled many urban chapels and churches with working-class people for one service only. The role of religion in the working-class world proper still waits for full investigation.

In earlier periods of European history, religion, while not necessarily directly inspiring outbursts of aesthetic achievement, had at any rate offered symbols and ideas through which painters especially could express themselves. If one goes to the cathedral in Antwerp, for example, one can see in Rubens's three great paintings, *The Planting of the Cross* and *The Descent from the Cross* which flank the altar-piece, *The Assumption,* the extent to which the western religious tradition still offered symbolic clothing to the vitality of an urban culture. The situation had changed by the nineteenth century but Victorian religious institutions still hoped to reverse what had become a firmly secularizing trend. Such hopes had to be realized in the new urban society and comment is necessary because we are discussing urban civilization. At the level represented by Rubens little was achieved. The claim that the Catholic revival inspired a movement of artistic renewal in England was not supported by the meagreness and derivativeness of much of what was collected for the Victoria and Albert Museum's 1971 exhibition of 'Victorian Church Art'.[43] There were efforts, nevertheless, and one of them is the chapel of Keble College in Oxford. In his recent biography of the architect of the college, William Butterfield, Paul Thompson says of the chapel:

'It is the mosaics which dominate the interior . . . and make it at first sight one of the least attractive of Butterfield's later displays of polychrome. Yet it is well worth a longer look. The chapel is treated as a single, vast space, the whole effect concentrated on the outer surfaces. All the furniture is kept deliberately low: only dark long lines of seats, and a light open wrought metal pulpit and altar rails. The choir seats are pushed back to form a great open floorspace at the east end, paved in white and grey stone, with encaustic tile patterns in yellow, plum, emerald green and seagreen. These colours are taken up in the walls. The lowest stage is a bold wall-arcade, the surface behind of glazed plum-coloured brick, with thin seagreen strips and broader bands of formalized mastic pattern-

---

[43] The exhibition catalogue, *Victorian Church Art* (London, 1971), was excellent.

ing set in stone-flowers, suns and tendrils. Next come the mosaics, rather softer in colour: green, pink, pale blue, a limp yellow, red and white. The colours seem in fact too soft for the strong archaic lines of the figures and their powerful architectural setting. Surely the white ground is especially mistaken? Above the mosaics, however, the colouring reaches a superb climax'.[44]

Here a modern enthusiasm for polychrome in the abstract unduly distracts Dr Thompson from the archaic lines of the mosaics which, though they present deliberately impersonal images of the christian past, were meant to seize and hold the attention of the observer by their restless activity, to persuade him that the empty chapel was filled with an invisible but overwhelming presence. I doubt if the white is a mistake: it is the whiteness of the ground that finally rules out the possibility of any kind of naturalism; the whiteness is also essential to the restlessness of the whole. Inflexible, unecstatic, appealing to dogma, not reason, and to authority, not emotion, the chapel as Butterfield conceived it perfectly translates John Keble into architecture. Whether Keble of all men had anything to say to urban society is questionable, but the almost unanimous rejection of the chapel in Oxford for nearly a hundred years—the mosaics were finished in 1876—shows how much more vibrantly Butterfield made his point than Keble made his own in the long-forgotten, mediocre verse of *The Christian Year*. If there had been no more to the chapel than Keble it would, like Balliol Chapel, which Butterfield also designed, have been forgotten long ago.

For Butterfield's intention was to reassert the centrality of the western religious tradition to urban as well as rural culture. He described the 1870's as 'an age terribly subjective and sensational'; he deplored the point at which medieval painters' versions of Christ became 'anatomical and aimed at affecting the emotions';[45] the primitive atemporality of the chapel mosaics was intended as an affront to the 'modern mind'. The irony was that those whom he had thought were his own supporters were quite ready to use his chapel as a back-cloth for *The Light of the World*, which Holman Hunt had painted in 1854, which reeked of the subjective, the sensational and the democratic and which might be described as Sankey and Moody in oils. 'Being a sentimental picture', Butterfield wrote, 'it is much more appropriate in my judgment to some other room, such as the library.'[46] *The Light of the World* duly hung in the library until Butterfield was safely out of the way, when it was transferred to a shrine specially added to the south wall of the chapel. But the College

---

[44] Paul Thompson, *William Butterfield* (London, 1971), pp. 246–47.
[45] *Ibid.*, p. 33.   [46] *Ibid.*, p. 304.

was right and Butterfield's only a superb failure, for when people visit the chapel they do so to see *The Light of the World*. And that is the measure of the failure of the religious sub-culture to maintain its ancient status in the urban world of the twentieth century.

University of Bristol

THE PURSUIT OF HAPPINESS IN THE CITY: CHANGING OPPORTUNITIES AND OPTIONS IN AMERICA
The Prothero Lecture

By Professor Eric E. Lampard, B.Sc.(Econ.), Ph.D.

READ AT THE SOCIETY'S CONFERENCE
16 SEPTEMBER 1972*

If everything occurred at the same time there would be no *develop-ment*. If everything existed in the same place there could be no *particularity*. Only space makes possible the particular, which then unfolds in time. Only because we are not equally near to every-thing; only because everything does not rush in upon us at once; only because our world is restricted, for every individual, for his people, and for mankind as a whole, can we, in our finiteness, endure at all. The extent of this horizon differs, of course, from man to man. But in economic affairs, as in all other affairs, our ken is limited for acting intelligently and for finding our way through the complexities of life. And even within this little world, we are familiar with not more than its innermost circle. Depth must be bought with narrowness. Space creates and protects us in this limitation. Particularity is the price of our existence.

To let this space-conditioned particularity grow without letting the whole run wild—that is political art.

AUGUST LÖSCH, Autumn, 1939
(*Die räumliche Ordnung der Wirtschaft*)[1]

IN 1790 a population numbering less than four millions was said, according to a later census calculation, to be almost 95 per cent rural in residence and, by implication, proportionately agricultural in occu-pation. By 1970 a population well in excess of 204 millions was almost 75 per cent urbanized and, in terms of labour force, less than 5 per cent involved in agricultural pursuits.

---

* The Society expresses its warmest thanks to the Prothero lecturer for the generous help which has made it possible to print this extended version of his lecture in the *Transactions*.

[1] Transl. by W. H. Wogrom as *The Economics of Location* (New Haven, 1958), p. 508 (quoted by permission of Yale University Press). I would like to acknowledge the helpful comments of Maldwyn Jones, Peter Mathias, and J. R. Pole, among others, when this lecture was given.

It is a commonplace of American literature and historiography that the United States was born in the country, that its characteristic values and institutions were bred in a rustic mould of life. Even before the Republic, American principles of religion, government and political economy, of family and community, even of work and recreation are said to have been rooted in, and nourished by, rural ways of life and livelihood. The wilderness, the farm, Nature, the western 'frontier', were all invoked at one time or another as the decisive, if not unique, influence on the development of an exemplary national culture. Similarly, the pioneer, the frontiersman, the yeoman cultivator, the family farmer, and their near neighbours, the independent craftsman, mechanic, or enterpriser have been the idealized type of American rôle, and in behavioural terms, the original and most authentic representative of republican spirit and virtue. Other moulds of life and different social rôles, while adding perhaps to the variety of American life and accomplishments, were for long suspect as deviant or factious and, until rendered molten and malleable according to the older pattern, potentially un-American.

In propagating so much of this pastoral imagery, *littérateurs* and historians not only struck a cherished chord in the folk-memory, they have embellished a literal and statistical fact. In 1790 the population was overwhelmingly rural in residence and in terms of measurable product largely agricultural. Not before 1840, when population already exceeded 17 millions, did fewer than nine out of every ten Americans live in census rural areas, although only four in every five members of the work force (10 years old and over) could by this date be classified as husbandmen. Nevertheless, 72 per cent of real value added to materials by commodity production was contributed by agriculture and the bulk of value added by manufacture arose from the primary processing of farm-grown foods and fibres or forest products.

At midcentury, independence still provided the cement of an increasingly interdependent social order. Only 30 per cent of the working population of town and country were yet hired hands; the rest were either self-employed or legally enslaved. By 1860, when the expansive Republic could no longer contain its diverse and deviant sections within the old political frame of Union, one in every five of its 31 million inhabitants was some sort of a city dweller and almost half the work force was employed outside husbandry. Still, farming contributed almost 60 per cent of value added by commodity production, while King Cotton alone was regularly earning from 55 to 60 per cent of the nation's export value, compared with only 10 or 12 per cent from manufactures of all kinds.

But in important respects, the statistical preponderance of rural life obscured the already declining share of agricultural production. If Lincoln had allowed the wayward sisters to go in peace, the remaining United States of 1870 would have been among the most urbanized populations of the globe and the Confederacy might have applied for a charter membership in the underdeveloped fraternity of the Third World. While this is not advanced as a contrafactual conditional hypothesis, it is noteworthy that in 1870 the unredeemed South, including Texas, contained well over 30 per cent of the nation's population but scarcely more than 10 per cent of its assorted city dwellers. The detail of the South's industrial structure, moreover, now departed from its antebellum trend. Every postbellum census but one has revealed that the *absolute* size of the nation's incremental urban population was larger than corresponding increments to rural population. When, in 1890, the census reported the disappearance of a continuous 'frontier' line of unsettled land in the West, more than one-third of the Republic's 63 million population was classified as 'urban' by residence; cultivators comprised less than 43 per cent of the work force, barely a third of commodity value added originated directly in agriculture.[2] It was at this point in the nation's development that the Wisconsin historian, Frederick Jackson Turner, advanced his *mal du siècle* frontier interpretation of American history amidst the celebrations of the World's Columbian Exposition in Burnham's 'White City' at Chicago. Meanwhile, of course, the lofty agrarian myth of the Republic had for several decades been hardening into the narrower sectoral ideology of the agrarian crusade.

If the closing of the frontier, in Turner's phrase, sealed 'the first period of American history', it did not close off opportunity to the nation's farmers in the second period.[3] Far more final land entries under the terms of the Homestead Act were made in the 27 years after 1890 than in the preceding 27 since the Act first went into effect. The absolute number of farm operators and workers did not, in fact, peak until around 1910 when the farm sector was enjoying the

[2] Sources of concepts and data are given in E. E. Lampard, 'The Evolving System of Cities in the United States: Urbanization and Economic Development', *Issues in Urban Economics*, ed. H. S. Perloff and L. Wingo, Jr. (Baltimore, 1968), pp. 81–139. The classic analysis of agrarian sentiment is P. H. Johnstone, 'Old Ideals versus New Ideas in Farm Life', *Yearbook of Agriculture 1940* (Washington D.C., 1940), pp. 111–67.

[3] F. J. Turner, 'The Significance of the Frontier in American History', American Historical Association *Annual Report for 1893* (Washington, D.C., 1894), pp. 199–227. On antebellum 'space' and 'time' dilemmas: M. L. Wilson, 'The Controversy Over Slavery Expansion and the Concept of the Safety Valve: Ideological Confusion in the 1850s', *Mississippi Quarterly*, xxiv (1971).

longest and most prosperous period, *vis-à-vis* the rest of the economy, in American economic history. Of course, its relative contribution to commodity value added had continued to decline. The absolute size of the manufacturing labour force had also increased but, whereas manufacturing's share of all commodity value added continued to grow absolutely and relatively, the share of manufacturing in the non-agricultural work force had also been declining—falling behind the combined share of the mining, construction, and service sectors—since around 1880. By 1920, when the Republic's numbers surpassed 105 millions, every other American was living out his or her life in cities. Only one in every four occupied persons over 10 years of age remained on the farms, while the other three were almost always to be found, employed or otherwise, in the manufacturing, construction, and service industries.

No urban historian stepped forward in 1920 to explain the emblematic significance of this latest artifact of census enumeration. But in 1910 Turner himself had already made, as it were, a 'half-minded' concession to the 'revolution in the social and economic structure of this country during the past two decades' and he expressed 'the shock' with which 'the people of the United States are coming to realize that the fundamental forces which have shaped their society up to the present are disappearing'.[4] The familiar chord struck repeatedly in the folk memory by *littérateurs* and historians up to that day had, under the force of the urban impact, apparently become the Lost Chord.[5]

Turner, to be sure, was well aware of the gathering controversy over industrialism and the problems of cities, real or imagined, that had gone on in American public life in one form or another since shortly after the Revolution. Yet for one who had always thought of his work as 'dealing with the processes of American history rather than with a geographic section', and who had often wanted 'to start

[4] Turner, 'Social Forces in American History', *American Historical Review*, xvi (1911), pp. 217–33. Earlier historians such as W. H. Prescott, George Bancroft, Francis Parkman, and Henry Adams had all expressed misgiving or hostility to large cities and elements in their populations.

[5] The long and influential 'booster' tradition has had little impact on literature or historiography. But Frank Freidel, 'Boosters, Intellectuals, and the American City', *The Historian and The City*, ed. O. Handlin and J. Burchard (Cambridge, Mass., 1963), pp. 115–20, offers an illuminating synopsis of its possibilities in response to M. White, 'Two Stages in the Critique of the American City', *ibid.*, pp. 84–94. An early urban booster was Jesup W. Scott of Toledo, Ohio: see *Hunt's Merchants' Magazine*, xix (1848), pp. 383–86, and xxv (1851), pp. 559–65. W. B. Hesseltine, 'Four American Traditions', *Journal of Southern History*, xxvii (1961), pp. 3–32, suggests a wider range of public rôles.

something in agricultural history', Turner came late to his awareness of the process of urbanization and its intimate relation to the entire Westward Movement since late colonial times.[6] Although 'the city problem' had long exercised reform-minded social scientists, critics, and authors of realistic fiction, neither the problems nor the processes of urbanization excited much concern among professional historians until well after World War I.

The young Hoosier, Charles A. Beard, had been conscious—since his early connexion with Ruskin Hall—of 'the social question' as it affected the working classes of London and the great manufacturing centres of the provinces. He was well acquainted with the researches of Booth and Rowntree; yet he appreciated 'the marvellous mechanical and scientific progress' that had made material abundance possible for all the crowded classes of men in the industrial cities.[7] Beard later became a rather harsh critic of Turner's romantic individualism and Turner clearly had Beard in mind when he complained to the young but senior Arthur M. Schlesinger in 1925 of recent 'attempts to minimize' the broad frontier theme. He attributed the tendency to:

'the pessimistic reaction against the old America that [has] followed the World War—the reaction against pioneer ideals, against distinctively American things historically in favor of the Old World solutions of 'the promise of American life'—to write in terms of European experience, and of the class struggle incident to industrialism. There seems likely to be an urban reinterpretation of our history. But we cannot altogether get away from the facts of

[6] Turner, letter to Merle Curti, 11 June 1927, in *The Historical World of F. J. Turner: With Selections from His Correspondence*, narrative by W. R. Jacobs (New Haven, 1968), pp. 238–39. In his introduction to *Frontier and Section: Selected Essays of Frederick Jackson Turner* (Englewood Cliffs, N.J., 1961), pp. 8–9, R. A. Billington suggests that, shortly before his death in 1932, Turner had planned an essay on 'The Significance of the City in American Civilization'.

[7] C. A. Beard, *The Industrial Revolution* (London, 1901), *passim*. Beard became too preoccupied with the political problem of democratizing the capitalist system to make any enduring contribution to economic or urban history. His 1912 text *American City Government* is scarcely a footnote today. In his 'The City's Place in Civilization', *The Survey*, lxi (1928), pp. 213–15, Beard accepts Jefferson's strictures on eighteenth-century cities in Europe but reaffirms the rôles of science and the machine in fulfilling the promise of city civilization. He concludes, *pace* Lord Bryce, that: 'County, not city, government is the most conspicuous failure of American democracy'. An early example of faith in education and knowledge as the mutually beneficial solvents of town and country relations is Roberts Vaux, 'Importance of Education', address to the Philadelphia Society for Promoting Agriculture, *The Agricultural Almanack for 1827* (Philadelphia, 1827).

American history, however far we go in the way of adopting the Old World!'[8]

There was no 'urban reinterpretation' of American history, not much urban history of any kind, in the immediate postwar decade. It remained for essentially political historians to accommodate the diverse processes reshaping America: industrialization, westward migration, immigration to the farms and cities, and the ensuing era of 'Progressive' reform. Not before the publication in 1933 of A. M. Schlesinger, Sr.'s *The Rise of the City, 1878–1898*, was there much scholarly interest in a general field of urban history. Schlesinger then offered a building-block topical narrative of the industrial-urban transformation which seemed to fit in very conveniently between Allan Nevins' buoyant *Emergence of Modern America, 1865–1878*, and Harold U. Faulkner's sombre *Quest for Social Justice,1898–1914*. Meanwhile, the rather aimless debate over Turner's frontier hypothesis was part of the adaptation to these same industrial themes and, if it shed little light on the process of industrial-urban transformation at any time, it nonetheless served to undermine conventional wisdom concerning the exclusively rural-agrarian matrix of American institutions and identity. Curiously enough, it invoked English precept and wider European tradition not, to be sure, in terms of class struggle, but rather to stress an original consensus and agreement on civic fundamentals underlying strong differences on immediate issues.[9] But in registering their various dissents from Turner's grand theme of 'westward process', most of the new interpretations made indirect obeisance to the old. Notwithstanding their express concern with social and economic trends, historiographical issues were usually couched in broad political terms and the currents of change were too readily absorbed into mainstream clashes of sections and interests, partisan electoral strife, social problems and reform movements.

Even when historians, like Turner himself, recognized the social strains incident to industrialism, big business, and the flood of 'new' immigration, their resort to metaphors of urban 'impact'—with their connotations of collision with something from outside—underlined the provincial rurality of American republicanism. Rural life outside the Old South was usually depicted in Arcadian terms down to some

[8] Turner, letter to A. M. Schlesinger, Sr., 25 May 1925, in *Historical World of F. J. Turner*, pp. 163–64. On American usage of the word 'frontier' see J. T. Jurick in American Philosophical Society *Proceedings*, cx (1966), pp. 10–34.

[9] G. M. Gressley, 'The Turner Thesis—A Problem in Historiography', *Agricultural History*, xxxii (1958), pp. 227–49. Also, B. F. Wright, Jr., *Consensus and Continuity, 1776–1787* (Northampton, Mass., 1958).

suitably critical date between, say, the Tariff Acts of 1862–64 and McKinley's defeat of Bryan in the presidential campaign of 1896. The urban impact historians—especially contributors to college textbooks of the 1940s and 1950s—appear to have been profoundly impressed by the polemical writings of late nineteenth-century social critics and the prescriptive formulations of early social scientists. They compressed the industrial-urban transformation into a few decades and stigmatized it as an unequal struggle between opposing ways of life, between urban and rural 'cultures'.

While shunning social science jargon historians, nevertheless, adapted many of the same lines of inquiry, asked broadly similar questions of like kinds of data, and came up with much the same findings as their earlier counterparts in economics, sociology, or political science. Transposed into the letristic key of metaphor, the conflict was one of polarized cultures, one in which the old American values and institutions—equality, independence, conscience, the family, the community, and local democracy—had been at stake. Out of the industrial-urban impact arose the need for order and efficiency in business, politics, administration, religion, philanthropy, education, and social relations.[10] Thanks largely to the Progressive movement, the original 'promise of American life' was upheld and eventually consummated in the New Deal achievement. Indeed, in recognizing the South as 'the nation's economic problem No. 1' and through his programmes to give the farmer 'economic parity' with industry, Roosevelt II went far to restore the agricultural remnant to that larger parity in the Great American Welfare Coalition promised by Roosevelt I's appointment of the Commission on Country Life at the height of the first Progressive surge in 1908.

Before the 1950s the leading historiographical ideas on inter-war society were again very much like those of contemporaries who had endured the transformation. Now that society was almost wholly industrialized, however, conflict of any sort between town and country could no longer be regarded as the mainspring of social change. With the disillusionment that followed the frustration of Woodrow Wilson's crusade to impress American values on a wayward and benighted world, and after the collapse of the 'New Economic Era' of prosperity into the interminable Depression, faith in 'Old Stock' American ideals and potencies was badly shaken. The plain people of town and country were alike the victims of business

[10] E. E. Lampard, 'American Historians and the Study of Urbanization', *American Historical Review*, lxvii (1961), pp. 49–61, and in a broader context, *idem*, 'Urbanization and Social Change', *The Historian and The City*, ed. Handlin and Burchard, pp. 225–47.

cupidity and waste. Present-minded historians found the Beardian political interpretation of class interests and social conflict much more to their taste. Beard's liberal-progressive critique of American institutions made a much broader appeal than Morris Hillquit's liberal Marxism or Father John A. Ryan's liberalized corporativism. It is not surprising that Beard's, as he believed, Madisonian view of American capitalism *throughout* its history now coloured the dominant interpretation of the American past in both its agrarian and industrial periods.[11]

It is historiographically significant, again, that scholars have devoted far more attention to Roosevelt I's National Conservation Commission than to his Commission on Country Life, both of which were appointed in 1908.[12] The latter commission, while catering to the agrarian narcissism of rural America and its small towns, had announced the urgent need to reform country attitudes and ameliorate country-life conditions. In the country, no less than in the city, health, housing, education, social relations and even religion were found to be in a deplorable state. Judged by the findings of both early rural and urban sociologists, much was rotten in both 'types' of American community and the Republic no longer had an equilibrium to which it might return—unless it be the 'small town' on whose model proportions most social critics, except Thorstein Veblen, seemed to agree.[13]

The country-life movement was not just another sentimental journey back to the land, nor a romantic village renovation programme. Liberty Hyde Bailey, its chief protagonist, described its motivation as 'the working out of a desire to make rural civilization as

---

[11] C. A. Beard, *The Economic Basis of Politics* (New York, 1922), went through many printings and was re-issued in 1945, when Beard added his reflections on the recent politicization of economics.

[12] R. H. Wiebe's influential study *The Search For Order, 1877–1920* (New York, 1967), for example, makes full reference to the conservation movement and agricultural interest groups but not to the country-life movement.

[13] Veblen's sour comments appear in *Absentee Ownership and Business Enterprise in Recent Times: The Case of America* (New York, 1923), chap. 7, on the 'independent farmer' and the 'small town'. Also, W. L. Anderson, *Country Town, A Study of Rural Evolution* (New York, 1906); C. J. Galpin, 'The Social Anatomy of an Agricultural Community', *Research Bulletin 34,* (Wisconsin Agricultural Experiment Station, Madison, May, 1915). The predicament of the small Midwestern town is presented by L. Atherton, *Main Street on the Middle Border* (Bloomington, Ind., 1954). The decline of the small town has long been deplored: H. J. Fletcher, 'The Doom of the Small Town', *Forum*, xix (1895), pp. 214–23, and *The Christian Science Monitor*, Aug. 30, 1972, p. 7. But see L. F. Schnore, 'The Rural-Urban Variable: An Urbanite's Perspective', *Rural Sociology*, xxxi (1966), pp. 131–55. But the small town lives in the ideal of the city 'neighbourhood'.

effective and satisfying as other civilization'. In G. Walter Fiske's words, the movement sought 'to make country life as satisfying as city life and country forces as effective as city forces'. The pursuit of happiness in the city had evidently acquired a relevance, if only as a measuring rod, for the conservation of happiness in the countryside. Bailey found the 'general absence of . . . common feeling' among rural people to be as critical as the divorce between town and country and the resultant bondage of the cultivator. The recommendations of the Commission, which needless to add were never implemented, sought not only to accomplish an economic parity between agriculture and 'industry' as the necessary condition for ensuring an urban nation its food supply, but also the achievement of those wholesome conditions of social life which urban critics had often attributed to rural communities and which the rural critics now thought were available to city people.[14] It was unfortunate that both types of social doctor focused so narrowly on the pathologies of their respective laboratories. It was regrettable from the standpoint of historiography, at least, that 'urban' and 'rural' phenomena should have been thus compartmentalized and then rather abruptly dropped from consideration, since it proved impossible for historians to determine the differential effects of social change without first understanding its secular processes.

When A. M. Schlesinger, Sr., sketched his interpretative essay 'The City in American History' in 1940 he had available to him a much larger array of historical and sociological monographs than any previous commentator. In the amplified version, published in 1949, he had the benefit of an even richer monographic fund. Yet for all the intellectual capital accumulated by years of research, Schlesinger had not yet found a frame of reference appropriate to the study of social change. American urban history now extended from the first colonial days down into the troubled years of the New and Fair Deals. The spread of cities was placed in a context of westward movement from the Atlantic to the Pacific's shores: 'a true understanding of America's past demands this balanced view—an appreciation of the significance of both frontier and city'. Economic opportunity had been everywhere, culture and complexity particularly, almost generically, in the city, but the whole interpretation was rendered in a rather optimistic Hegelian dialectic of urban–rural conflict, the outcome of which was

14 U.S. *Senate Document* No. 705, 60 Cong., 2 Sess. L. H. Bailey, The *Country Life Movement in the United States* (New York, 1911), pp. 1–30, 97; G. W. Fiske, *The Challenge of the Country: A Study of Country Life Opportunities* (New York, 1913), pp. 1–58, and H. Paul Douglass, *The Little Town, Especially in Its Rural Relationship* (New York, 1919), which postulated the need for a 'half-way' house between town and country.

always the greater dominion of the city—with a continually post-dated synthesis for 'community.' But, Schlesinger went on:

'the twentieth century has been spinning a web in which city and country, no longer separate entities, have been brought even closer together. When the city encroaches sufficiently on the country and the country on the city, America may hope to arrive at a way of life which will blend the best features of both the traditional ways.'

Did he mean the suburbs? But, he concluded, whereas in Europe:

'the modern urban community emerged by gradual steps out of the simple town economy of the Middle Ages . . . the American city leaped into being with breath-taking speed. At first servant to an agricultural order, then a zealous contestant, then an oppressor, it now gives evidence of being a comrade and a cooperator in a new national synthesis. Its economic function has hardly been more important than its cultural mission or its tranforming influence upon rural conceptions of democracy. The city, no less than the frontier has been a major factor in American civilization. Without an appreciation of the role of both, the story is only half told.'[15]

In historiography, at last, the city had achieved parity with the country. Urban America need no longer choose between Hamilton and Jefferson-worship, Benjamin Franklin, the pioneer of conglomerate business in America, was restored to the pantheon. Historiography was moving beyond Beard and its interpretative options were enlarged. Schlesinger's essay is a landmark.

Certainly the New Deal was a new national 'synthetic'. It was a belated and, on the whole, unsuccessful effort to improvise a public institutional structure in which the largely private, and still potentially corporate, interests of town and country could renew the quest for happiness in an industrial-urban society. It attempted to incorporate a nationwide structure in which America's highly differentiated and comparatively specialized populations—individuals, voluntary groups, business associations, trade unions, localities, and whole regions—could function and prosper under a federally erected bureaucratic arch. Even the Southern Negro could begin to participate *via* federally tolerated forms of social segregation.

---

[15] 'The City in American Civilization', in Schlesinger, *Paths To The Present*, pp. 210–33, 297–99. The original essay in the *Mississippi Valley Historical Review*, xxvii (1940), p. 43–66, was criticized by W. A. Diamond, 'On the Dangers of an Urban Interpretation of History', *History and Urbanization*, ed. E. F. Goldman (Baltimore, 1914), pp. 67–108, for loose use of terms and neglect of economic and class conflicts. Schlesinger did not feel that 'the urban and class interpretations' were 'mutually exclusive'.

But the New Deal erected its institutional scaffolding not so much out of the processes of social change in America as upon the shaky foundations inherited from the Progressive era and the exhilarating memory of alphabetical agencies and expedients that had served to defeat the Kaiser in 1916–18. It never really worked, but the gentleman farmer from Dutchess County, N.Y., held the urban Republic together long enough until the combined impacts of Hitler and Tojo imparted a dynamism and consensus in Washington to restore the nation's momentum onward and *outward*. The Employment Act of 1946, federal keystone for an American pluralistic consensus in peacetime, could probably not have held the rickety structure together without the renewed momentum of the Cold War and Sputnik.

There was little effective concern for cities as such under the New Deal, although they figured quite largely in the purposeful projects of the National Resources Planning Board, aborted by the Congress, once the economy had experienced the tonic effect of Europe's latest war between the states.[16] Most of the interpretative historical writing of the 1940s was enlisted for the duration and urban history was likewise adjourned. When peace broke out many historians almost immediately re-enlisted in the Cold War to preserve embattled democracy from Red malefactors at home and abroad. Professionally-conscious, more local-minded, urban historians resumed their modest diggings, enjoyed annual lunches together, and eventually consoled each other in the mimeographed pages of Blake McKelvey's *Urban History Group Newsletter*, one of the few historiographical landmarks of private cooperative enterprise during the first Eisenhower term.

The New Deal had supposedly tamed the excesses of American 'Business' and the country might have expected to enjoy, what would come to be called, a period of 'political stability and economic growth'. There was nervousness all round, but the progressive-minded historian, Arthur M. Schlesinger, Jr., called upon citizens to be vigilant against 'business' and conservative of republican democracy, which alone among 'modes of organizing society' could by bargaining

---

16 R. Lubove, 'New Cities for Old: the Urban Reconstruction Program of the 1930s', *Social Studies*, liii (1962), pp. 203–13; J. A. Arnold, *The New Deal in the Suburbs: a History of the Greenbelt Town Program* (Columbus, Ohio, 1971). V. L. Perkins, *Crisis in Agriculture: The AAA and the New Deal, 1933* (Berkeley, 1969), attempts a realistic defence of the early farm policy, but see L. J. Arrington, 'Western Agriculture and the New Deal', *Agricultural History*, xliv (1970), pp. 337–53, which shows that per capita loans and expenditures by federal farm agencies, 1933–39, were directed towards *richer* rather than poorer farm states, to those which had experienced the greatest *drop* in per capita farm incomes, 1929–32. Also, D. Holley, 'The Negro and the New Deal Resettlement Program', *ibid.*, xlv (1971), pp. 179–93.

and compromise keep 'alive enough hope among discontented minorities to deter them from taking up the option of revolution'. It was still not clear in 1944 what difficult tests would be imposed upon the Republic after victory but its survival would 'bear a vital relation to its attacks on similar (if less intense) crises of its past'. Schlesinger, Jr.'s *The Age of Jackson*, published in 1945, had originated in a series of lectures delivered, somewhat ironically, at the Lowell Institute in Boston in the months before the bombs at Pearl Harbor finally terminated the social crisis of the 1930s. The book was an interpretation in the spirit, to say the least, of the New Deal although 'the actual issues, political and economic, of Jackson's day have now an almost Arcadian simplicity'. Its author had little to say about town and country other than conflict but, like the New Deal, Schlesinger was taken up with the industrial order and the predicaments of 'humble people' regardless of where they lived. *The Age of Jackson* was perhaps the last truly Progressive historical tract, an example of the higher journalism in the service of the Republic.[17]

But history and historiography were to manifestly, in Schlesinger Jr.'s words, 'thrust a world destiny on the United States' to which, however reluctantly, the Republic must accede. Early in 1949, he was still persuaded that 'the restoration of business to political power in this country would have calamitous results' as in the past. He expected the Republic to remain 'a New Deal country' but, if business got power, 'this time we might be delivered through the incompetence of the right into the hands of the totalitarians of the left'. The anti-communist purges were already public policy during the first Truman administration but 1948 had been a bitter-sweet year. The incompetent right under Thomas E. Dewey had only just been fended off and the Democracy itself had barely survived its own internal 'totalitarian' threat from Henry A. Wallace on the left and Strom Thurmond on the right. The bass black Paul Robeson was not yet a non-Person and was still singing a Pied Piper's black and red tune.

Schlesinger Jr.'s expectation that the Republic would remain 'a New Deal country' was borne out by Truman's second administration and even by the business-venerating General Eisenhower. History, as Schlesinger, Jr., affirmed, had 'equipped modern American liberalism with the ideas and the knowledge to construct a society where men will be both free and happy'.[18] Whatever Clio had taught liberals about 'happiness', she had obviously taught them little about cities or social change. The Federal Housing Act of 1949 and the Federal

[17] A. M. Schlesinger, Jr., *The Age of Jackson* (Boston, 1945), foreword.

[18] A. M. Schlesinger, Jr., *The Vital Center: The Politics of Freedom* (Boston, 1949), pp. vii–x, 219–42.

Highways Act of 1956 were designed, among other things to furnish 'decent housing' for all Americans, to renew the run-down cities and to circulate more of their urbane blessings by automobile and motor truck through the bucolic countrysides. In the event, they bull-dozed many 'humble people' out of their slum-sweet homes into more expensive sub-standard housing, accelerated the century-old peripheral sprawl of cities into the God-given greenbelts of metropolitan areas, and facilitated the removal of a dwindling rural remnant into the central city's core or to the bulging satellite centres of the metropolitan outer rings. Federal legislation provided an urban 'frontier' bonanza for real-estate speculators, construction industry mafia, corruptible politicians and civil servants, and not least the newly-growing planning profession.[19]

The improvised structures of the New Deal were already being undermined by their own obsolescence even before the situation deteriorated into what the mass media dubbed 'the urban crisis' of the 1960s. Even as federal pacification programmes multipled, the Blacks rebelled, the students rose up, the ethnic minorities revolted, and strident regiments of anguished middle-class women marched from the cities and suburbs in search of a human identity. No doubt, as Micawber-like consensus historians will remind us, all this will pass, even the vain pursuit of victory in Vietnam which stretches its bloody mindless strand across the third-quarter of the waning American century from 1949 to 1973. Modern liberal America seemed

---

[19] Almost 90 per cent of federal outlays on urban problems down to 1970 had been devoted to highways and subsidies to the largely middle class and segregated home-mortgage industry. Notwithstanding the promise of 'a decent home and a suitable living environment for every American family' in the 1949 Act, only one-fifth of housing built on renewal sites was required to be for 'low and moderate-income families'. Between 1937 and 1970 only 900,000 units of federally subsidized low cost housing units were built, although an array of other federal programmes contributed to the sale of a majority of new housing units. By 1970 more than 77 per cent of the 70 million housing units in the country were subject to the terms of Title VIII of the Fair Housing Act of 1968. Urban renewal programmes were originally designed to raise the tax base of local authorities and to make private real estate development more profitable. Such programmes also created jobs, especially for planners, whose expertise is mandatory since 1949. Membership in the American Institute of Planners rose from 240 in 1945 to 3,800 in 1965. Federal employment in housing agencies had climbed to *c.* 14,000 by 1965, when the U.S. Department of Housing and Urban Development was finally established. Proposals for such a federal department go back to the Roosevelt and Taft days before World War I. According to the *Housing Census of 1960*, nearly 12 million units were dilapidated or deteriorating. On 'abandonment' of federal housing, see *New York Times*, 13 Jan. 1972, pp. 1, 28; on widespread corruption in administration of some federal programmes, see admission by Secretary George Romney, *New York Times*, 28 March, 1972.

to have more ideas and knowledge about landing its children upon the
Moon than about building them a home in the city.

'Come Home America', called the minister's son from Mitchell, S.D.
But where indeed can Americans come home to? Where does America
reside in that vast land that belongs to you and me? Where every
fourth or fifth American now shifts his residence each year, perhaps
they are all destined to go on dwelling in the quagmire of their
collective importunity? What boots the capital gain? And where
is elusive Happiness? Perhaps it has already moved on to that
promised 'nonplace Urban Realm' where planners tell us technological
progress now permits the spatial separation of people in 'community
without propinquity'? Surely that must be *the* City upon a Hill for
which the American heart has so long prepared.

II

Clearly our present discontents belie Schlesinger optimism whether
of the father or the son. But whatever else the 'urban crisis' of the
1960s has revealed, it has made urban historiography unexpectedly
relevant. Whether he chooses to regard America's huge cup of
happiness as half-full or half-empty—and that has for long been the
measure of our historiographical differences, at least once chattel
slavery has been put down—the urban historian can now feel *engagé*.
The instant urban history that we are trying so industriously to write
can at last put the city in the foreground where it has always really
been, if we include London, Bristol, and Plymouth and all the latter-
day ports and hinterlands of emigrating Saints, Slaves, and Strangers.

In the balance of my time and space, I would like to sketch a broad
outline of the urbanization process which I call *the changing structure
of opportunities*. Then I would like to indicate how tenderfooted
Americans have followed an urban path along narrow lanes, broad
boulevards, and dead ends since they first entered the maze of the
Promised Land in the seventeenth century. This I call *the appropriation of the options*. Throughout it all there runs an implicit model of
system and adaptive behaviour.

The English planted their first settlements along the wilderness of
the trans-Atlantic seaboard throughout the seventeenth century. Of
course, wilderness is in the mind's eye of the beholder, and it was not
really a wilderness but the red man's home. Yet the English were
certain they had more to offer than their baubles and their bibles and,
besides, there was plenty of room; a man who did not know where he
was going in the new country might easily lose himself. And if *they*
had not seized the opportunity, there were the others, lesser breeds
without the imperial law: the French, the Spaniards, the Dutch.

Between them they would turn the blue Caribbean into a hell on earth. Unless a settler population clustered around some natural harbour or nestled along some navigable stream below the fall line, it was unlikely to grow beyond a mere village structure. Almost from the outset some villages and towns began serving the organized settlements that filled out the back country behind them as, what geographers call, 'a hierarchy of central places'. It was for long an unpretentious, minimal, and often interrupted hierarchy but it provided a focus. As the populations grew from their own natural increase or were irregularly supplemented by the 'excess' of other countries, when access to land improved and settlements became more secure, as the wilderness was turned into a garden, so the settlers tightened their grips upon particular physical environments, explored the natural properties, and commenced turning their God-given environments—physical and human—into productive resources. The new colonies grew in population and/or material wealth as they could severally participate in larger systems of trafficking that evolved around the Atlantic's shores.

The necessary lines of transport and communications crossed in the villages, towns, and the seaports cities. From this provenance came the system and the structure rather than from the laws of Parliament or instructions to Governors. Under conditions prevailing down into the early nineteenth century, in fact, interactions were closely circumscribed by what geographers term 'spatial biases' in the interlocal flows of commodities, persons, and information which gave some villages and towns—especially those at the existent terminals of maintravelled ocean, river, or coastal routes—a *positional* advantage over others of their kind. Sometimes this positional advantage proved transient and the geographer, Allan Pred, has argued that the different time-requirements for physical movement by water and land, together with the disparate volumes and frequencies of contact, among centres largely governed which places would grow in size and influence.[20] North America rapidly recapitulated the urban ontogeny of the city in European civilization: the stockade village, the agrarian town, the market city, and finally the industrial city. But because America unfolded in space as well as time, these characteristic phases, often misconceived as 'stages', were usually contemporary situations. This is consistent with what one would 'expect' to happen in a pre-

---

[20] A. R. Pred, 'Large-City Interdependence and the Pre-Telegraphic Diffusion of Innovations in the U.S.', *The New Urban History: Quantitative Exploration*, ed. L. F. Schnore (forthcoming). Also J. T. Lemon, 'Urbanization and the Development of 18th-Century Southeastern Pennsylvania and Adjacent Delaware', *Williams & Mary Quarterly*, xxiv (1967), pp. 501–42.

industrial market system in which frictions of distance, except over water, impose an almost insurmountable burden of 'costs'. Given market potential, with capital scarce, labour comparatively short, and other resources latently abundant, so much turned on the qualities and capacities of the human resources involved. Since there were few modes of enterprise which entailed much more than a man's skills, tools, and the energy with which he, his family, and his servants could employ them, the enterpriser needed only the favour of an alien and extreme Nature to get his dependents some sort of living. Every household was in varying degree a self-sufficient farmstead, manufactory, market place, and oasis. Savings could eventually be tied up in stocks of goods, in buildings and boats, in slaves, in financing indentures, and occasional manufactories, although almost any more ambitious and innovative venture, even in husbandry, would involve an acceptance of credit for variable intervals of time. In such communities there was little left over for 'infra-structure' or public goods and services but society, even a settler society, is always more than a market place and a life more than the livelihood. Localities collectively requisitioned the labour time for public goods in the traditional fashion, established a few mostly part-time public offices, or put the matter off until next season or never. There were lotteries, fees, and user charges; but taxes were correspondingly low.

Except for enthusiastic Saints, perhaps, many individuals—especially among the womenfolk—must have wondered at times whether the eventual gains in substance or status altogether outweighed the loss of other riches left forfeit in the villages, towns and seaports on the other side. But there were often neighbours from the old haunts; there were always the children, the future. How they must have cherished the intangibles lugged over in the cultural baggage, overprized them perhaps, discounted what they had abandoned, perhaps garbled the meanings of both. Within a few generations they were Americanized with material objects and treasured ways of their own; still recognizably English, or 'Dutch', or 'Scotch' to others, but with common intangibles no Englishman, German, Scot, or Ulsterman would ever have. *This* was home until opportunity beckoned on.

Colonial American development made an enormous impression on those who had grown up with it, whether native or foreign born. If some returned to the Old Country, they would not forget America, even though they distorted the reality of the New Found Land. 'Some few towns excepted,' wrote the repatriate Crèvecoeur in the third of his *Letters From an American Farmer*, published in France in 1782:

'we are all tillers of the earth, from Nova Scotia to West Florida. We are a people of cultivators scattered over an immense territory, communicating with each other by means of good roads and navigable rivers, united by the silken bands of mild government, all respecting the laws without dreading their power, because they are equitable. We are all animated with the spirit of industry, which is unfettered, and unrestrained, because each person works for himself . . . A pleasing uniformity of decent competence appears throughout our habitations . . . Lawyer or merchant are the fairest titles our towns afford; that of a farmer is the only appellation of the rural inhabitants of our country.'[21]

Here was a rural-agrarian model of settlement offered more as a parable of opportunity than as a paradigm for social change. This, and more, underlay the Jeffersonian heritage.

It was in the seaport cities which grew irregularly through the eighteenth century that the social and cultural nexus became more ramiform in their structures than Crèvecoeur had allowed. They were the cross routes and the crossroads. The great ports and their surrounds from Boston to Charles Town were the principal trading linkages with the outside world and transmitted the goods, persons, and intelligences to lesser places in between and up the valleys into the interiors. They were in time and due proportion the foci for innovation and diffusion of institutional and mechanical novelties, foreign and domestic, throughout their respective hinterlands. Their interaction with each other and the outside world controlled the locus and thrust of development, if not altogether of settlement. But here men and women could also live more readily by taking in each other's differentiated washing as long as wagons rolled, pack horses moved, and ships put to sea. Areas which had less to offer the larger systems by way or regional specialities—tobacco, rice, lumber, grain, furs, fish, or animal products—provided ships, ship services, mercantile connexions, and the crude or exquisite artifacts of their town and country crafts. Eventually debts were paid off, litigated over, gathered interest, or were written down.

The rhythms and regularities of such daily and seasonal rounds imparted a structure of opportunities within an inherited frame of law and local custom. As Adam Smith well knew, the division of labour and, in the aggregate the wealth of provinces and nations, depended on the extent of the market; the latter may be regarded as the spatial structure of opportunities. But opportunity occurs in time as well as space. Merchants and mechanics had known it long before the professor, but the risks were great and competition from near or far could only heighten uncertainties and anxiety. Hence the

21 *Letters From An American Farmer* (Dutton Paperback, New York, 1957), p. 36.

attempts—and not alone by Parliaments, Governors, or assemblies—
to warn off strangers, keep out encroachers and corrupters, and to
exclude as much as possible from the outside world. The corollary of
corporate barriers was that freemen of the boroughs, towns, parishes,
or districts should not take advantage of their co-inhabitants, but both
pressures from without as well as differences and tensions within,
would make it difficult to sustain the practices of restriction.[22]
Opportunity was with the system long before industrialization and
the price of functional independence or isolation was a loss of
momentum: stasis or stagnation. Not surprisingly, interrelations
among localities as well as individuals and families repeatedly
strained the frameworks of law and custom and contributed to the
transformation of the increasingly differentiated parts of the wider
whole.

Thus the process of social change in America, *pace* Crèvecoeur, was
not simply a repetition and enlargement of existing ways of life and
livelihood. Departures from prevailing patterns might also be reinforced by gain, amplified and confirmed by more *positive* feedbacks.
At other times the feedbacks were negative, the initiatives were
counteracted and activities returned within their prior restraints. But
as the scale of interactions among the systems' differentiated parts
shifted in volume or frequency, so varying degrees and levels of
structuring arose, persisted, dissolved, and were altered over again.
If social change in North America often appeared to be no more than
enlargement and growth along the existing parameters of westward
movement, it also involved a social learning process over time which
led to development, ultimately and unevenly to social transformation.
Whereas frontier development merely repeated itself with local
adaptations across the continent, the city's unfolding communicated
a dynamism and a shape to the whole of society.

But how does such a process occur? How do people serve it? Here
I must revert to my economist's categories, since I want to get to the
structure and motivation of collective behaviour beneath the integu-
mentary detail.[23]

---

[22] E. S. Griffith, *History of American City Government: The Colonial
Period* (New York, 1938); C. Bridenbaugh, *Cities in the Wilderness: The First
Century of Urban Life in America, 1625–1742* (New York, 1938); J. A.
Fairlie, *Essays in Municipal Administration* (New York, 1908), contains an
excellent study of colonial municipalities. On growth, see *The Growth of
Seaport Cities 1790–1825*, ed. D. T. Gilchrist (Charlottesville, Va., 1967).

[23] I apologize for my jargon but not for my models, who are the Scottish
moral philosopher, Adam Smith, the English political economist, Alfred
Marshall, and a necessary French sociologist, Emile Durkheim. I also need
a Canadian, Harold A. Innis, and his *The Bias of Communication* (Toronto,
1951), to complete my *entente intellectuelle*.

Urbanization, like any other patterned process of human settlement, may be adumbrated in terms of division of labour. If what we have described above accounts for the growth of a few major cities in the low productivity societies of North America, urbanization may be regarded as a societal process in which, among other things, factors of production, households and enterprises in town and country, and hence localities, become increasingly specialized and interdependent with respect to growing market areas and to each other. It involves the ways and means by which men have instituted and appropriated the economies and 'externalities' of scale.

With industrialization, and the greater accumulation of fixed capital goods and pertinent social infra-structures, the sequences of production become more prolonged and 'round about' in that a growing volume and share of specialized outputs represent, not final products for consumption, but the more or less specialized inputs for further processing or fabricating by others. Manufactories prefer to purchase, say, milling machines or textile machinery rather than to go on producing them on their own accounts. A similar option opens up for warehousing or haulage services, for borrowing rather than merely saving. The profitable reinforcement of such *transitive* connexions over time imparts a regular structure and integral character to continuing reorganizations of the division of labour in space: the changing structure of opportunities unfolds.

Erstwhile jacks-of-all-trades, sufficient households, or general merchants can begin to specialize the *full-use* of their time and means, if they can be assured of a sufficiently large and continuing market. Eventually they may become wholly specialized undertakings and rôles: jacks-of-one-trade, homes and factories, wholesalers, retailers, bankers, shippers, insurance men, etc. This progressive division and specialization of rôles and activities can thus yield higher returns (lower unit output costs) than were previously available to individuals, firms, localities, or to the system at large. The necessary scale shifts can be accomplished *either* by relocation of the new specialist in some particular environment that provides a large enough market for his more uniform product or service, *or*, through access to larger markets gained by innovations in transport and communications, he may, with consequent reductions in his unit market information and freight costs, preserve his existing location. Whether such returns to scale accrue internally to the enterprise or externally to the locality or industry, they provide a behavioural explanation for the growth of cities.[24]

[24] Lampard, 'Evolving System of Cities', *Issues in Urban Economics*, pp. 99–106. Already in the second quarter of the century, the system pivoted around three axes of transport and communication—the North-east coast

Early industrialization often involved a vertical reintegration of hitherto un-integrated or decentralized work processes into some more intensive scale of organization. The factories and similar installations, epitomized in American economic history by 'the Waltham System', illustrate the point. Water-powered cotton manufactories were instituted by Boston capitalists at several New England localities during the decade 1813–23. Many other examples might be given where mechanization or other special process consideration prompted similar integration and exploitation of scarce skills, expensive machines, or costly materials. The older, less integrated modes of comparatively unspecialized activities can no longer compete with the newer modes which enjoy higher returns to scale. Under the technical and organizational conditions of the early nineteenth century, the newer modes tended to concentrate around water-power sites. As fuel-burning machines became the more typical form of energy conversion, production was localized around coal sites as well.

The industrial revolution in the North-east tended to concentrate the newer and more productive jobs in the mill towns of New England and New York and the coke towns of Pennsylvania; they were often new foundations. In the older and larger seaport cities, the processing of regional raw materials and the fabricating of articles to meet the growing demands of commerce and local populations went on much as before; the accretion of newer modes and scales of organization developed more slowly and usually away from the central business districts. In the early Wests, barriers of mountains and distance protected the growth of local materials processing and even allowed some specialization along the main axes of communication but, with the transportation revolution during the second quarter of the century, small town activities tended to dwindle and the larger centres often contained the major part of their regions' more productive industries. By the postbellum decades, the bulk of manufactures in the Great Plains region was concentrated in the four or five largest cities.[25]

---

from Boston to Baltimore; the Ohio–Mississippi valleys from Pittsburgh to New Orleans; and the Great Lakes from Buffalo, N.Y., to Chicago. Southern ports from Norfolk to Mobile linked themselves more or less individually to the North-east coast rather than with each other. All regional sub-systems hinged on New York, R. G. Albion, *The Rise of New York Port* (New York, 1939); S. Buck, *The Development of the Organization of Anglo-American Trade, 1800–1850* (New Haven, 1925).

[25] Lampard, 'Evolving System of Cities', *Issues in Urban Economics,* pp. 116–24; H. A. Wooster, 'Manufacturer and Artisan', *Journal of Political Economy,* xxxiv (1926), pp. 61–72; P. Temin, 'Steam and Water Power in the Early 19th Century', *Journal of Economic History,* xxvi (1966), pp. 187–205; J. G. Williamson, 'Ante Bellum Urbanization in the American North-

One unfortunate consequence of the convenient textile stereotype of industrial revolution was to focus scholarly attention on the technical and fixed capital conditions of quantity production. The conditions for large-scale wholesale, financial, communications and other specialized types of intermediary rôle have been neglected, yet these were the functions that made the expanding systems work. Perhaps only transportation developments have yet received their due.[26] In any event, such intermediary rôles were usually located in the larger centres or their functions were organized from such points.

Just as increasing returns and its structural concomitant, integration of interdependent work processes, begot the factory as the *first level* of economic reorganization, so the greater enticements and menaces of the market later in the century gave rise to a *second level*: the vertically integrated business organization. Under the competitive conditions of the late nineteenth century, vast accumulations of capital were at stake. Businessmen—'Robber Barons' to the Progressives—sought to ensure control over their various inputs and/or the marketing of their outputs. Beginning on a regional level with consumer goods, the tendency had spread to certain raw materials production and to heavy manufactures on an interregional and continental scale. Some permissive state governments in the 1880s allowed virtually unrestricted business incorporation and the federal government joined in the 1890s with its anti-trust laws, which were designed, among other things, to eliminate the more radical and 'unfair' means of competition which threatened the capital accumulated and deployed by large organizations. Henceforth, the latter hoped not only to enhance their earnings' capacity but to preserve control over their investments under a legal umbrella of 'due process'.

---

east', *ibid.*, xxv (1965), pp. 592–608; R. B. Zevin, 'The Growth of Cotton Textile Production after 1815', *The Reinterpretation of American Economic History*, ed. R. W. Fogel and S. L. Engerman (New York, 1971), pp. 122–147; M. Walsh, *The Manufacturing Frontier: Pioneer Industry in Antebellum Wisconsin, 1830–1860* (Madison, Wis., 1972); H. S. Perloff *et al.*, *Regions, Resources, and Economic Growth* (Baltimore, 1960), pp. 122–221.

26 G. R. Taylor, *The Transportation Revolution, 1815–1860* (New York, 1951); E. F. Haites and J. Mak, 'Ohio and Mississippi River Transportation, 1810–1860', *Exploration in Economic History*, viii (1970–71); H. N. Scheiber, *The Ohio Canal Era, 1820–1861* (Athens, Ohio, 1969); A. Fishlow, *Railroads and the Transformation of the Ante-bellum Economy* (Cambridge, Mass., 1965); A. R. Pred, *The Spatial Dynamics of U.S. Urban-Industrial Growth, 1800–1914* (Cambridge, Mass., 1966), pp. 12–83; C. Goodrich, 'Internal Improvements Reconsidered', *Journal of Economic History*, xxx (1970), pp. 289–311.

Their strategies to control their business and financial environments appeared to work quite well until the collapse in 1929.[27]

Thereafter big business learned that the federal government was to be not merely a compliant partner, a crutch to firms engaged in interstate commerce, but the captain of the New Industrial State. Business, agriculture, and other sectors of society came to depend on government to furnish an environment of economic growth and stability. By the 1950s almost every articulate segment of society was potentially a client of Washington.

But the American system evolved in space as well as time. Through all these transformations of economic structures, there had been parallel and related transformations of social structures across the continent. These alterations reflected and fostered a reorganization of the territorial division of labour. Thus a *third level* of economic reorganization had emerged as the evolving system of cities which determined the spatial structure of opportunities. Territorial division of labour heightened the functional interdependence among towns, cities, and larger metropolitan areas up through a 'hierarchical' system with New York, so to speak, as the head office and Washington, D.C., as the long absentee, but increasingly interfering, 'boss'. The 1900 Census of Manufactures revealed the extent to which the coordinating activities of vertically integrated business organizations were already headquartered in New York City and, to a much lesser degree, in Chicago, while the rest of their interdependent members, the plants, packing houses, mills, mines—not to mention the chain stores and retail outlets—were scattered across the continent closer to the resource inputs and populations of consumers. Certainly all three levels of structural integration appear to be bound up with market forces, the exigencies of communications, and the contingencies of maintaining organizational coherence in the midst of rapid change.[28]

---

[27] A. D. Chandler, Jr., 'The Beginnings of "Big Business" in American Industry', *Business History Review*, xxxiii (1959), pp. 1–31; L. Herbert, 'A Perspective of Accounting', *Accounting Review*, xlvi (1971), pp. 433–40; E. B. Metcalf, 'Business Planning and Employment Stabilization, 1915–1960' (unpublished MA Thesis, University of Wisconsin, 1969). More generally, M. E. and G. O. Dimock, *Public Administration* (4th edn., New York, 1969), pt. iv.

[28] Of 185 industrial combinations, reported by 12th U.S. *Census*, 1900, vii, pt. i, p. lxxxvi, *et seq.*, no less than 70 headquarters were located in New York, 18 in Chicago, 16 in Pittsburgh, 6 in Cleveland, and 5 each in Philadelphia and San Francisco. No other city had more than four. Lampard, 'Evolving System of Cities', *Issues in Urban Economics*, 125–33. Also, B. Duncan and S. Lieberson, *Metropolis and Region in Transition* (Beverly Hills, Cal., 1970), which treats the changing metropolitan organization of manufactures and banking services. More generally, F. Lukermann, 'Empirical

Under industrialism, cities generate differential opportunities at a faster rate than the non-cities, even while the frontier process is still under way. The differential growth of cities, in turn, manifests the positional advantages which accrue to the most *accessible* places. The larger the number of business undertakings at any positionally-advantaged site, the larger its work force is likely to become, and hence the greater its population of households, whether from net migration or natural increase.

An innovating entrepreneur needs to know about the market access potentials of alternative locations and he has to anticipate how those possibilities are likely to change. Hence the growth structures of businesses and industries are intimately related to the differential growth structures of the city regions. Only when technical and organizational conditions for optimizing alter somewhat from those which obtained earlier in the industrial revolution do centripetal forces relax. With the adaptation of electrical energy and greater facility in its transmission, with rapid transit, telephonic means of communication and, auto-mobile means of transportation, the secular tendency for interest rates to decline with capital abundance, and with the explosive force of modern city problems and related tax burdens, the cities begin to disgorge their opportunities back to the country-sides—not back to rural America but to the outer rings of the metropolitan regions. During this century the urbanization of the countryside has gathered momentum on the perimeters of urban sprawl and the spatial structure of the classical industrial city has been radically re-formed.[29]

The evolving system of cities is an organized structure but, in behavioural terms, it is also an organized system of restraints. All three levels of structural integration discussed above are alike susceptible to diseconomies of scale, rising unit costs, and diminishing returns. Similarly, all integral constraints on scale are themselves subject to relaxation. Given incentives for innovation, the high profits and other gains which accrue to innovators in the short run—whether in knowledge, rôle playing, or other critical input in temporarily inelastic supply—will, assuming 'free' conditions of entry, entice

Expressions of Nodality and Hierarchy in a Circulation Manifold', *East Lakes Geographer*, ii (1966), pp. 17–43.

  [29] J. A. Swanson and J. G. Williamson, 'Firm Location and Optimal City Size in American History', *The New Urban History*, ed. Schnore (forthcoming); R. Vernon, *The Changing Economic Function of the Central City* (New York, 1959); *City and Suburbs: The Economics of Metropolitan Growth*, ed. B. Chinitz (Englewood Cliffs, N.J., 1964). More generally, J. Wolpert, 'The Decision Process in a Spatial Context', American Association of Geographers, *Annals*, liv (1964), pp. 537–58.

others to follow suit. The emulators will undertake similar productions or play comparable rôles at more 'normal' rates of profit either at the same site in competition with the innovator or at newer sites beyond the immediate range of effective competition from the locus of innovation. Somewhat paradoxically, therefore, the contagious effect of novel specialization is territorial diffusion throughout the system, which tends to make factory, business, and city-regional structures of the same approximate size functionally and structurally more like each other. Innovative behaviour which proves exceptionally profitable in the making leads first to differentiation within existing structures of opportunity, then to varying rates of diffusion and generalization as the novelty wears off at more 'normal' equilibrium rates of profit, and ultimately to varying degrees of convergence in behaviour, social, and spatial structures. As novelties catch on and eventually transform the structures which engendered them, social change occurs and new structures are formed. Consequently, places and people, however diverse and removed at their origins, are made more alike, if only on the surface, in their ultimate destinations.

Over time, minimum scales for innovation and rates of subsequent convergence become respectively lower and faster than in earlier phases of industrial revolution. Owing to the speed and spread of information networks, the entire system experiences *convergence* in space and time. Vertical integration still exists as an organizational brake, however temporary, on the dysfunctional acceleration of change. It is still a strategy for survival if those who control the structures can anticipate the vectors and absorb the magnitudes of change over time. Modern businesses develop their own research departments, diversify their holdings, take some of their capital eggs out of one line and incorporate a variety of investments in their new conglomerate baskets. Medium-sized cities grow more like large cities in their structures and surfaces; both one-product companies and one-industry towns are most vulnerable to the currents of social change.[30] Paradoxically again, the intelligent course of specialization seems to be diversification as many farmers found over a century ago.

Yet the cities have remained different, scarcely less so than their citizens, notwithstanding their comparable traits. Not before 1820 did New Orleans displace Charleston among the five great Atlantic ports and in the century of transformation after 1860 only 15 other cities moved ahead of New Orleans in point of size. Philadelphia,

---

[30] W. R. Thompson, 'The Future of the Detroit Metropolitan Area', *Michigan in the 1970's*, ed. W. Haber *et al.* (Ann Arbor, 1965), pp. 203–40. Also, M. L. Greenhut, *Plant Location in Theory and Practice: the Economics of Space* (Chapel Hill, N.C., 1956).

the second ranking city from 1790 to 1890, was not New York; Chicago, the second city between 1890 and 1970, was neither Philadelphia nor New York; Los Angeles the second city by 1970 is not Philadelphia, Chicago, or New York. Neither is Dallas like St Louis or Boston, Atlanta is not New Orleans, and all the world never was and never will be like Philadelphia. 'Each urban collective,' says Sartre, 'has its own physiognomy.'

III

Jefferson was right in 1809 to insist that merchants should not try 'to convert this great agricultural country into a city of Amsterdam'.[31] But a New Amsterdam had been planted in 1625 and the 'opportunity cost'—what was foregone and irretrievably relinquished—of allowing merchants and mechanics to build America's diverse metropolitan structures out of the incorporated micro-spaces of early nineteenth-century cities was the transformation of this potentially vast agricultural landscape many times over even before the 100th generation. What made this unmistakable collective choice so confusing to most contemporaries and so complex in its detail to all subsequent generations of agrarian sympathizers, whether on the farm or in the library, was the fact that America unfolded in its space as well as in its time. The work force on farms continued to grow in numbers across the country until around 1910, while it had continually declined in relative size after about 1810. It grew in absolute size right up to the very decade of the 1910s in which the national population—in the misleading terms of census enumeration—finally tilted towards the cities. Yet since 1810 the trend was to the city and both collectively and as an 'ideal type' the man with the hoe was grubbing his own grave.

[31] Jefferson, letter to Thomas Leiper, Jan. 21, 1809, *The Writings of Thomas Jefferson*, ed. A. A. Lipscomb and A. E. Bergh (Washington, D.C., 1904–5), xii, pp. 236–38. He refers to 1785 when he had published his *Notes on Virginia* in Paris; he went on, 'But who in 1785 could foresee the rapid depravity which was to render the close of that century the disgrace of the history of man? . . . We must now place the manufacturer by the side of the agriculturist . . . experience has taught me that manufactures are now as necessary to our independence as to our comfort'. He, nevertheless, thought that immigration would be 'as a drop in a bucket' compared to natural increase; he welcomed foreign settlers for the West, especially colonies of English farmers but he thought Germans should distribute themselves sparsely among the natives for 'quicker amalgamation': letter to George Flower, Sept. 12, 1817. In 1805, Jan. 4, his letter to J. Lithgow, rejects the idea of allowing 'dissolute and demoralized handicraftsmen' to enter and he wondered whether even 'good' craftsmen should not go to the culture of the earth: *The Writings*, ed. Lipscomb and Bergh, xv, pp. 139–42; xi, pp. 55–56.

At the Louisiana Purchase Centennial Exposition in the City of St Louis in 1904 Max Weber, no less, pronounced the American farmer to be an entrepreneur like any other. But he was almost always, even in the Old South, a small-scale enterpriser: there were no great scale advantages in most of nineteenth-century agriculture. This was at once a blessing and a curse since, unlike many small entrepreneurs located in the towns, the farmer was able to operate a family-sized business even under conditions of industrialization. Indeed, industrialization ought to have been a bonanza. The opportunity to supply a growing urban population at home and abroad prompted the farmer to enlarge his output at lower unit cost. After the Civil War, this course imposed increasing capital burdens in a period of secularly falling prices, only moderately rising land values, in a local milieu in which credit was comparatively expensive for his scale of operations. Even if his terms of trade with the non-agricultural sectors were seldom really adverse, this most 'independent' of American entrepreneurial types was almost entirely dependent upon transportation, marketing, and credit institutions over which he had little or no effective clout. He felt not only exploited but victimized, he saw himself as little better off than the slave made over into share-cropper in the contemporary New South.[32] The one thing cultivators had in common with the upstanding yeoman of the Jeffersonian heritage was their utter dependence upon the caprice of nature. They no longer had much sympathy for the declassed mechanics and small enterprisers in the cities who had been confronted with many of the same 'choices' and who had failed at the Hamiltonian game.

If indeed the farmer was an entrepreneur like any other, he was a very different one from the cultivator of Jefferson's or even Jackson's day. For one thing his average family had tended to get smaller in size since before the Civil War and was not much greater than that of the average townsman in the late nineteenth century. Not surprisingly, many of his sons and daughters went streaming down the roads to the cities, where they joined the sons and daughters of the displaced artisans and mixed in the city centres, at least, with the swarms of foreigners who had been inundating the towns even more than the countrysides since before mid-century. Even the opportunities that still opened up on the farms had long been subject to the city's sway. It was the higher productivity of city jobs on average—the

[32] Not all farmers were pathetic or polemical Populists. For the bumptious faith in science and economic progress of dairy leaders in the Upper Mississippi Valley, see E. E. Lampard, *The Rise of the Dairy Industry in Wisconsin: a Study of Agricultural Change, 1820–1920* (Madison, Wis., 1963), pp. 333–51. Also, A. G. Bogue, *From Prairie to Corn Belt* (Chicago, 1963). See M. P. Conzen, *Frontier Farming in an Urban Shadow* (Madison, Wis., 1971), for the influence of local urban growth on farming.

consequence of technical progress and improvements in the quality of institutional management and human resources—that made the economy so much richer, wages better, and kept people coming to the city.[33] But this was a *long-run* change and if the farm boy or immigrant happened to hit the city in the bad years around 1838, 1858, 1876-77, 1885, 1893-96, 1908, 1913, or 1930-34, he might wish that he had never left home. He might move on to another town, and there was always a great 'churning' and turnover of urban populations, but if he stuck it out and eventually joined the swim, he would not only earn a livelihood, but many of his children and grandchildren, if they survived infancy, might expect to better themselves.[34] In real income terms many of them would do better than their parents, particularly if they kept their families small, some would jump to petty properties in retailing or service industries, others might get into the professions, politics, or the civil service, a few would become an Andrew Carnegie, a John D. Rockefeller, or a Henry Ford. All this is part of the dream and, from the late nineteenth century, individual chances for career mobility are increasingly tied to formal educational attainment. The realities of family and schooling come to determine the level at which a person first enters the labour force structure and, since most career mobility is over comparatively short ranges, the level of entry closely determines a person's ultimate occupational destiny.

How did people come to exercise the options which the city's structures opened up? In oversimplified terms, of course, according to the demand for labour in the urban economy. But much always turned on the time and the place and we are deficient in our historical knowledge of the ways and whys of native American city dwellers. Many were born there, no doubt, and more probably came from the neighbouring towns and countrysides. Around 1850 in the larger cities

[33] E. E. Lampard, 'Historical Contours of Contemporary Urban Society', *Journal of Contemporary History*, iv (1969), pp. 3-25, for conditions of nineteenth-century rural-to-urban migration and problems in the analysis of 'occupational status' change. The use of national occupational 'prestige' ratings as a measure of individual status in diverse *local* contexts is further criticized in Lampard, 'Two Cheers for Quantitative History', *The New Urban History*, ed. Schnore (forthcoming), note 25.

[34] S. Thernstrom and P. R. Knights, 'Men in Motion: Some Data and Speculations about Urban Population Mobility in 19th-Century America', *Journal of Interdisciplinary History*, i (1970), pp. 7-35; L. E. Galloway and R. K. Vedder, 'Mobility of Native Americans', *Journal of Economic History*, xxxi (1971), pp. 613-49; J. E. Eblen, 'An Analysis of 19th-Century Frontier Populations', *Demography*, ii (1965), pp. 399-413. The fate of different cohorts of urban migrants needs to be interpreted in light of R. A. Easterlin, *Population, Labor Force and Long Swings in Economic Growth: the American Experience* (New York, 1968).

perhaps as many as half the citizens were native born of native parentage but less than half of the native parents would be native to the
city. Immigrants and their children made up the balance of the large
city populations and, if the children are classified by parentage rather
than by place of birth, then the census takers' 'foreign white stock'
probably made up a half to two-thirds of the large city residents.[35]

Boston or New York in the 1850s was probably not typical. But
by 1880 seven or eight of the largest cities had more than a third of
their census residents foreign born and only two, New York and
Jersey City, were on the North-east coast. San Francisco on the West
coast, with almost 45 per cent, was the most 'foreign' of cities in this
sense, but Chicago, Milwaukee, Detroit, Cleveland, and Buffalo,
N.Y., filled in the other ranks with New York itself in fourth place.
In all of the top 20 cities, the largest foreign-born groups in 1880 were
Irish and/or German born. The largest foreign contingent in any
one city was the 27 per cent German-born population of Milwaukee,
which Henry Villard called 'the German Athens'. By 1910 the cities
were even more foreign than they had been in 1880 or 1850. Thirteen
of the 20 largest places had more than a quarter of their inhabitants
foreign-born, ranging up from Philadelphia with 25 per cent to New
York with more than 40 per cent. If we include the children of immigrants and array the big cities by the proportions of their foreign white
stock, then the alien contribution stands out in starker relief. All of
the top twenty in 1910, with the exception of Washington, D.C. (21
per cent), had more than 30 per cent of such 'foreign' elements,
ranging up from New Orleans (30 per cent) to Milwaukee and New
York with more than 78 per cent and Chicago, Cleveland, Boston,
and Detroit with around 75 per cent close behind.[36]

Meanwhile, since the mid-1890s a majority of the immigrants had
been coming from regions in southern and eastern Europe. The term
'new' immigration had acquired a rather ugly connotation of 'unmeltable' and inferior, whereas immigrants stemming from 'old' northern
and western Europe or Canada now seemed comparatively agreeable,
even when the newcomer was a Roman Catholic or a German Jew.
Among the largest cities, populations from the Russian Empire
(chiefly Polish or 'Russian' Jewish) formed one of the three largest
foreign groups in New York, Chicago, Milwaukee, Pittsburgh, and
St Louis. Peoples from Austria-Hungary (also including Poles and
Jews) comprised one of the three largest foreign groups in Chicago,

[35] P. R. Knights, *The Plain People of Boston, 1830–1860: a Study in City
Growth* (New York, 1971), pp. 19–47. Only Milwaukee, Chicago, and St Louis
had foreign-born majorities.
[36] 10th U.S. *Census*, 1880, *Population*, pp. 471, 538–41; 13th U.S. *Census*,
1910, *Populations*, i, pp. 178, 826–28, 1007.

Milwaukee, and Pittsburgh; Italians were already one of the three major foreign groups in New York while Orientals, the only groups barred or limited in entry before World War I, formed one of the three major groups in San Francisco and Los Angeles. Only St Louis among the major cities had 'old' immigrants, German and Irish, comprising two of the three major foreign-born groups. Moreover, whereas Protestants of one sect or another had made up about 40 per cent of the immigration before 1870, they formed less than a quarter of those entering between 1870 and 1920; before 1870 only about one per cent of immigrant flows had been Jews but, from 1870 to 1920, perhaps as large a share as 20 per cent had been Jewish in their religious heritage.[37]

Up until 1910 most of the Negro urban movement had been towards cities of 'the New South'. Before the Civil War around 5 or 6 per cent of the slave labour force had lived in towns where they were usually far outnumbered by 'free' Negroes. In the 1850s Baltimore and New Orleans had contained the largest numbers of black urban residents, more than twice the size of New York's black population and almost half as many again as in Philadelphia in 1854. Male slave numbers had been falling in many Southern cities during the 1850s, possibly because it had become more profitable to sell off the unskilled to the countrysides, where slave prices were rising more rapidly with the fortunes of King Cotton. As late as 1880 large Negro populations in big cities comprised 26 per cent of the inhabitants of New Orleans, 13 per cent of Baltimore, 7 per cent of St Louis, less than 4 per cent of Philadelphia, and but 1·6 per cent of New York City. Whether from migration or annexation, black people were increasing their urban numbers faster than white people only in some of the Southern states before 1900.[38]

Thereafter black migration shifted to the North. During the dacade of World War I, the already quite large Negro population of New York (92,000) increased by more than a third; Chicago (44,000) far more than doubled, Cleveland (8,000) more than quadrupled, while Detroit (6,000) increased its black numbers by more than 600 per cent. Since 1940 the Negro migration has again gathered momentum and in the decade 1960–70 blacks increased their shares of total popu-

---

[37] *Ibid.* The estimates of religious affiliation are based on unpublished data provided by S. B. Warner, Jr. More generally, C. S. Rosenberg, *Religion and the Rise of the American City* (Ithaca, N.Y., 1971), on the religious roots of mid-nineteenth-century Urban reform movements.

[38] *Statistical View of the United States: A Compendium of the Seventh Census*, 1850, pp. 192–93, 395–98; *Compendium of the Tenth Census*, 1880, pt. I, pp. 380–405, 453–63. C. D. Goldin, 'An Economic Model to Explain the Relative Decline of Slavery in Cities, 1820–1860', *The New Urban History*, ed. Schnore (forthcoming). As late as 1850 only Charleston, S.C., and Wilmington, N.C., had black majorities.

lation in Detroit, Washington, D.C., Wilmington, Del., and Newark, N.J., by from 15 to 20 percentage points. By 1970 the nation's capital was 71 per cent black; Atlanta, Gary, and Newark more than 50 per cent black; Memphis, St Louis, Richmond, Birmingham, Wilmington, Detroit, New Orleans, and Baltimore ranged from 39 to 46 per cent black. Whereas the black proportion of the central cities in the nation's 67 largest metropolitan areas rose by nearly 6 percentage points, the black share in the same areas as a whole rose by less than a third of *one* percentage point. Thus the outward movement of blacks into the metropolitan 'suburban' rings during the ten-year span was no more than a trickle.[39]

Since World War II the black contribution to the city populations in many parts of the country has reached the proportions of the foreign stock in the years before World War I. The transformation of the immigrants into hyphenated Americans is commonly thought to provide a model for the native-born blacks, Tejidos, Chicanos, Indians and other 'Third World' elements. Although urban black and brown Americans comprise only a minority of those classified as below the federal 'poverty line', their absolute numbers are large while their age, sex and family structures diverge from the white majority of the poverty population. We know much less in detail about the foreign born at a comparable stage of their jumping on to the escalator of American urban mobility; and even if we knew more it would have to be recognized that labour market conditions are dramatically altered from even a quarter century ago. Nevertheless, the implication of the model is that they too mostly came in at the bottom and by dint of their own efforts climbed out of their 'ghettos' into the avenues of the industrial-urban structure. Their children now live in the 'suburbs' along with the 'old stock' Americans.[40] So confident are today's white majority populations that this was the way 'it really happened' for their kind that, insofar as the model now needs governmental assistance to make its processes work, the themes of this lecture have

[39] L. V. Kennedy, *The Negro Peasant Turns Cityward* (New York, 1930), pp. 23–40. Data from 19th U.S. *Census*, 1970, reported *New York Times*, 11, Feb. 1972, pp. 1, 24.

[40] Non-white families comprised only 10 per cent of all families in the 100 great metropolitan areas of 1960 but they contributed 72 per cent of families resident in census-demarcated 'poverty areas'; 28·5 per cent of families in such environmentally inferior areas were classified as below the federal 'poverty level'. The poverty areas covered almost a quarter of the surface area of the metropolitan central cities: U.S. Bureau of the Census, *Poverty Areas in the 100 Largest Metropolitan Areas*, Report PC(S1)–54, Nov. 1967. On housing conditions in 'poverty areas', see National Commission on Urban Problems, *Research Report*, no. 9 (Washington D.C., 1968). Also, D. P. Moynihan, 'Poverty in Cities', *The Metropolitan Enigma*, ed. J. Q. Wilson (Cambridge, Mass., 1968).

reached the heart of the current domestic policy debate. Indeed, the model of rural-to-urban-to-suburban mobility is held up to the world.

During the early nineteenth century America's young cities conformed to a fairly common spatial pattern of pre-industrial social-structural relations. The centres were pre-empted by the more well-to-do classes with the poorer and hence lower orders of the population, including many of the newcomers, living out towards the not yet distant perimeters. There was otherwise no marked spatial separation of residences or work along socio-economic lines. As numbers increased many of the back alleys of the hitherto 'garden' cities were converted into cheap dwellings. Artisans and labourers thus lived and worked in close contact and even comity with wealthier merchants and the few professionals, while even the very poor moved easily about their appointed lowly tasks.[41]

Foreign elements had been present in American cities from the beginning. Sometimes they had grouped in small residential clusters and at others had been dispersed among the general population. Even when floods of Irish and Germans moved in from the famines and political upheavals of Europe just prior to the mid-century, they too were well distributed among the natives, although our available measure—the index of residential separation, using political wards as the areal unit—is not refined enough to indicate whether, on a block or neighbourhood basis, the different national and religious elements enjoyed social as well as physical proximity in their everyday lives. The Negro was, likewise, no stranger and small numbers of 'free colored' were always to be found. When legal and social barriers in a few Northern cities were reduced somewhat in the antebellum decades, the blacks remained closely confined in residential pockets.[42]

[41] A. Kulikoff, 'The Progress of Inequality in Revolutionary Boston', *William & Mary Quarterly*, xxviii (1971), pp. 375–412; S. B. Warner, Jr., *The Private City: Philadelphia in Three Periods of Its Growth* (Philadelphia, 1968), pp. 49–62; E. Pessen, 'A Social and Economic Portrait of Jacksonian Brooklyn', *New York Historical Society Quarterly*, lv (1971); S. M. Blumin, 'Mobility and Change in Ante Bellum Philadelphia', *Nineteenth-Century Cities*, ed. S. Thernstrom and R. Sennett (New Haven, 1969), pp. 165–208; and Knights, *Plain People of Boston*, pp. 48–102. Also, R. A. Mohl, *Poverty in New York, 1783–1825* (New York, 1971), and E. Smolensky, 'The Past and Present Poor', *Reinterpretation of American Economic History*, pp. 84–96.

[42] 'A prejudice has existed in the community . . . against them on account of their color, and on account of their being descendents of slaves. They cannot obtain employment on equal terms with whites, and wherever they go a sneer is passed upon them, as if this sportive inhumanity were an act of merit . . . Thus, though their legal rights are the same as those of whites, their condition is one of degradation and dependence': Jesse Chickering, *A Statistical View of the Population of Massachusetts from 1765 to 1840* (Boston, 1846), p. 156. Chickering's sympathy did not extend to the Irish immigrants later in the decade.

Numbers of personal and domestic servants among them were spread out, particularly if they lived in with their employers.

During the latter half of the century the cities took on a more variegated residential structure with the trend set toward the socio-economic elevation of the periphery and deterioration of the core. The concurrent expansion of the central business districts also pressed harder on the crowded living spaces of the poor. With the development of horse-drawn streetcar lines, steam railroad commuter service, and more complex economic structures, the spread of cities accelerated locally as well as across the continent. The different national and sectarian elements began to separate out along socio-economic as well as transit lines. In the last third of the century, the different nationalities appear to have been congregating more together as they accommodated to American economic opportunities but chose to keep to their own kind in respect of residence and private affiliations.[43]

The so-called ethnic group was formed in America and not brought ready-made in the cultural baggage from Europe. The groups were 'a decompression chamber in which newcomers could, at their own pace, make a reasonable adjustment to the new forces of a society vastly different from that which they had known in the Old World'. Their newly found ethnic, even more than their inherited religious, organizations furnished 'the warmth, familiar ways, and sense of acceptance that prevented the saga of "uprooting" from becoming a dislocating horror'.[44] The ethnic sub-communities and their innumerable associations were the American-born institutional response which enabled families and individuals to survive the cold-heat of the melting pot. The advent of the polyglot populations and the forming of their sub-cultures and residential turfs allowed some class-mixing within the groups although, except on days of organized marches and

[43] S. B. Warner, Jr., *Streetcar Suburbs: The Process of Growth in Boston 1870–1900* (Cambridge, Mass., 1962). S. B. Warner, Jr., and C. Burke, 'Cultural Change and the Ghetto', *Journal of Contemporary History*, iv (1969), pp. 173–87, sharply modifies the traditional view of early immigrant 'ghetto' experience which D. P. Moynihan, among others, considers analogous to present-day Negro experience. See *Hearings*, Senate Committee on Government Operations on S–843, July 27, 1967, 90th Cong. I Sess. The classic source on the 'ghetto' process is O. Handlin, *The Uprooted: the Epic Story of the Great Migration that Made The American People* (New York, 1951), pp. 144–69. But see R. A. Easterlin, 'Influences in European Overseas Emigration Before World War I', *Reinterpretation of American Economic History*, pp. 384–95.

[44] M. M. Gordon, *Assimilation in American Life* (New York, 1965), *passim*. Also, B. McKelvey, 'Cities as Nurseries of Self-conscious Minorities', *Pacific Historical Review*, xxxix (1970), pp. 367–81. McKelvey seems to accept D. P. Moynihan's notion that Negroes are only *now* beginning to form ethnic separatist allegiances after the pattern of earlier 'minorities': Moynihan, *Maximum Feasible Misunderstanding: Community Action in the War on Poverty* (New York, 1969), p. 161.

processions, the practices of pluralism tended to emphasize real differences rather than emerging identities between different elements and classes of the city populations.

At no point were the city's municipal structures successfully adapted to the tasks of coping collectively with the newer 'urban' problems which affected all segments of the population in varying degree. The public streets, health, fire and police protection, schools, and eventually law and order, were the principal areas of civic concern.[45] During the second quarter of the century, new and more specialized 'professional' politicians were beginning to displace the 'amateur' mercantile city fathers who had hitherto mediated the interests and factions. But their party-politicization of ethnic and religious tensions—which had threatened to make some American cities like present-day Belfast or Derry—did little to ameliorate, let alone solve, the problems of the physical environment or to develop new, and increasingly necessary, municipal services.[46]

[45] The 20 colonial boroughs had lost their virtual 'home rule' after the Revolution and had become creatures of the states under their respective constitutional provisions; such large centres as Boston, Newport, R.I., and Charleston had never achieved municipal status. The development of administrative competence was subsequently frustrated by the incorporation of 'division of powers' and 'checks and balances' notions into new charter provisions. State legislatures continually intervened throughout the 19th-Century, variously redistributing authority among mayors, bicameral councils, and other branches, occasionally superseding local authority altogether. By the 1830s, moreover, local restrictions on white male voting were being removed in order to make local franchises more congruent with state provisions. State courts, meanwhile, generally denied that municipal corporations had retained any 'inherent' powers and most initiatives were made conditional on powers granted or implied in ordinary state legislation: J. F. Dillon, *The Law of Municipal Corporations* (5 vols, Boston, 1911, i, pp. 448–449. Spaulding *v.* Lowell, 23 *Pickering* (Mass.), 71, in J. H. Beale, *Selection of Cases on Municipal Corporations* (Cambridge, Mass., 1911), p. 240. Also, F. J. Goodnow, *Municipal Government* (New York, 1906), chapter on 'legal powers of municipalities'.

[46] F. Parkman, 'The Failure of Universal Suffrage', *North American Review*, cxxvii (1878), pp. 1–20, condemned the 'barbarism' that had overwhelmed the cities and made them 'a prey'. The barbarism was, of course, almost exclusively white adult male, native and foreign-born. On professionalization and ethno-religious electoral politics, see Warner, *The Private City*, pp. 79–157; S. J. Mandelbaum, *Boss Tweed's New York* (New York, 1965), pp. 1–58. On services, N. Blake, *Water for The Cities* (Syracuse, N.Y., 1956); R. Lane, *Policing the City, Boston, 1822–1885* (Cambridge, Mass., 1967); J. Richardson, *The New York Police: Colonial Times to 1901* (New York, 1970); M. Katz, *The Irony of Early School Reform* (Cambridge, Mass., 1967); C. Greer, *The Great School Legend* (New York, 1971); C. Rosenberg, *The Cholera Years* (Chicago, 1962); A Deutsch, *The Mentally Ill in America* (2nd edn, New York, 1949); W. G. Smillie, *Public Health: Its Promise For the Future, 1603–1914* (New York, 1955).

The ethno-political dealing of the professional politicians and their city-wide organization of the wards may well have diverted the social, if not the racial, antagonisms and conflicts into the routinized channels of partisan loyalties and voting blocs, but only at the price of institutionalizing 'the shame of the cities'. Settlement houses and neighbourhood missions may later have helped bring some sense of civility and possibility into the lives of some of the city's poor. To the extent that they fostered an ethnic self-consciousness and mutual awareness, and channelled these emotions into a richer flowering of pluralism, they also served the urban-mobility process. When they treated immigrants like children and warped them into joining the majority way, they may have exacerbated conditions and aggravated feelings. In either case, the settlements with their increasingly professionalized leadership would tend to lose their clientèles either by upward and outward mobility from the poorer neighbourhoods or backward into their exclusive sub-cultures and parochial separateness, mitigated only by the cohesive indoctrination which passed for public education. Since this avenue did not preclude eventual upward and outward mobility for some, the same end of assimilation to the functional structures of society was served, although acculturation to native outlook and behaviour may well have been slowed. The melting pot worked exceedingly slowly, if at all. What came to be called 'Anglo-Saxon' modes of family life, outlook, and behaviour remained distinctively foreign to a majority of immigrants almost without regard to their origins, socio-economic status, and achievements.[47]

It is sometimes forgotten that the native-American inheritance was also transformed by the industrial city and was in certain respects subject to prolonged and comparable strains. Native elements had to learn the new ways without benefit of the ethnic warmth. The foreigner, the Catholic, and the Negro were often convenient targets for their frustrations and animus; they were competitors for jobs and housing. Even when they worked alongside each other, the larger ethnic groups, as well as the smaller ones, tended to live further apart from each other and from the old American stock. By the early 1900's, the immigrants and their children had achieved much greater assimilation to the educational, economic and political structures of urban and rural America but, with improvements in rapid transit and the resulting space-time convergence on the local scene, the larger cities

---

47 M. K. Simkhovich, *Neighborhood: My Story of Greenwich House* (New York, 1938). On the perceptions and approaches of voluntary associations, see National Conference of Charities and Correction, 17th Annual *Proceedings* 1890 (Boston, 1890), *passim*. Also, D. Levine, *Jane Addams and The Liberal Tradition* (Madison, Wis., 1971); A. F. Davis, *Spearheads for Reform, 1890–1914* (New York, 1967); N. I. Huggins, *Protestants Against Poverty: Boston's Charities, 1870–1900* (Westport, Conn., 1970).

were characterized by residential stratification along more well-defined socio-economic lines.

The wages of the foreign born were not notably lower than those earned by natives in corresponding types of work. If newcomers were literate in their native languages, let alone competent in English, the remaining labour market differentials were rapidly eroded. The women lagged, of course, regardless of their origin or capability.[48] While it is true that native males were, on average, more represented in managerial, supervisory, and better white-collar jobs, and were contributing less to the heavy mining and manufacturing tasks, and little or nothing to the 'sweated' loft industries, many of foreign stock were moving up faster and further than some of the regionally-stranded native elements—white, brown, and black—who had not yet joined in the system. The socio-economic class polarization of the city's spaces had, in any case, begun long before the blacks and other native minorities had come to town in significant numbers to further pluralize the social landscape.

When considering the comparative entry conditions of yesterday's immigrants and today's old American coloured stocks, it should be remembered that the majority of foreign born never did pass through the teeming slums or grinding poverty that were, to be sure, the lot of many of their brethren. Not forgetting the social discrimination of local pecking-orders and legal disbarments at some places in earlier days, the vast majority of immigrants never experienced the 'ghetto' restrictions and bitter frustrations to which Negroes, 'Mexican', Orientals, and Indians were exposed long after they were the express beneficiaries of constitutional amendments and, in the case of freedmen, the *de jure* civil rights of 1866. They too had their subcultures but, not only were the inhabitants of the 'nigger towns' and 'mextowns' denied their *de facto* claims across the country, the whole apparatus of disenfranchisement and segregation in the reconstructed Southern states was established, and endorsed by federal courts, in

[48] I. A. Hourwich, *Immigration and Labor* (New York, 1912), is a useful corrective to contemporary and later stereotypes. See also R. Higgs, 'Race, Skills, and Earnings: American Immigrants in 1909', *Journal of Economic History*, xxxi (1971), pp. 420–28; S. Kuznets, 'Contribution of Immigration to the Growth of the Labor Force', *Reinterpretation of American Economic History*, pp. 396–401. On women's work, U.S. Bureau of Labor Statistics, *Bulletin 175*, (Washington D.C., 1915); E. Abbott and S. P. Breckinridge, 'Employment of Women in Industries', *Journal of Political Economy*, xiv (1906), pp. 14–40; R. W. Smuts, *Women and Work in America* (New York, 1959); E. F. Baker, *Technology and Woman's Work* (New York, 1964). On the greater contribution of women to incremental labour force growth after the end of unrestricted immigration and the lesser rôle of Negro migration, see A. R. Miller, 'Components of Labor Force Growth', *Journal of Economic History*, xxii (1962), pp. 47–58.

the last decades of the nineteenth century. The federal government allowed local segregation to be extended to its civil service as late as World War I. Yet regardless of their relative deprivation blacks, as Cable and Du Bois had contended at the time, still did better in the cities whether South or North.[49]

The social environments of the newer Western cities had also been easier on the foreign born than the older environments in the East. The early population of Milwaukee, for example, had been as much foreign as 'Yankee' from the outset. Foreigners had settled there at roughly the same time and in similar proportion to the native-born; they were alike migrants. In the 1850s the city of almost 50,000 residents was still a 'new town' with few established neighbourhoods and no older stock of housing to pass down to newcomers. The high degree of residential clustering that had developed among Germans, Irish, and natives (as well as a mixed dwelling area near the centre) was largely 'voluntary', except as the options of the poor were always limited by their incomes. The German and Polish 'sides' of town which were built later in the century were likewise new residential districts involving a high degree of home ownership and environmental self-determination. Poles often took in lodgers from among the new arrivals and the extra money was used for purchasing a 'working class' cottage. By the end of the century Milwaukee was no longer a 'new town' and the southern Italians inherited the eastern half of the old Third Ward from the Irish; their slums were reported to be worse than those of the 'Russian' Jews whose small enclave overlapped the edges of three wards. After World War I Milwaukee blacks also bought some hand-me-down housing but by 1960 the 66,000 of them were not living in a 'Black Athens' but in cramping 'ghettos' under daily assault from the bulldozers. Black migrants to Washington, D.C., and other cities also attempted the 'lodger' method of

---

[49] Carroll D. Wright's study of slum conditions was greatly restricted by reduced appropriations; he only developed data on four major cities. Some 360,000 people were classified as 'slum dwellers' in New York; 162,000 in Chicago, 35,000 in Philadelphia, and 25,000 in Baltimore, where 530 families were found domiciled each in one room. In New York 44·6 per cent of families lived in two rooms or less; 27·9 per cent in Baltimore, 19·4 per cent in Philadelphia, and 19·1 per cent in Chicago: U.S. Commissioner of Labor, *Special Report* no. 7 (Washington D. C., 1894). Also A. F. Weber, *The Growth of Cities in the Nineteenth Century* (New York, 1899), pp. 460–62. For contemporary concepts of housing reform, see R. Lubove, *The Progressives and the Slums, 1890–1917* (Pittsburgh, 1962). In Jones *v.* Meyer, 1968, the U.S. Supreme Court finally determined that the Civil Rights Act of 1866 had prohibited 'all racial discrimination, private as well as public, in the sale or rental of property'. *The Negro American Family*, W. E. B. DuBois, ed. (Atlanta, 1908), pp. 64–65. Also P. M. Gaston, *The New South Creed: a Study in Southern Mythmaking* (New York, 1970).

home-buying after the first World War and by 1930 a third of Los Angeles blacks owned their own homes.[50] For the blacks this last West was a much more hostile environment than for any European immigrants but, for all the deterioration which came with numbers, Watts was never like present-day Harlem, Bedford-Stuyvesant, Hough, or Roxbury-Dorchester.

By the kinds of measures we have, neither ethnic nor racial separation was much reduced with the passage of time. Indeed, economic betterment and the hardening of residential class differences may even have sustained the process. For all the intermingling in certain sectors of society, the major foreign-born elements of 1950 appeared to have been as separated residentially as they were in 1910 or 1880. Part of the change was, no doubt, a consequence of the fewer numbers of immigrants in the general population. The smaller a group's numbers, the more they seemed to need one another in order to cope with pressures of a fragmented city life. Since the 1940s optimists have been claiming that the white American Babel has been melting into a trinity of sectarian pots: Catholic, Protestant, and Jewish, an integrative process mediated by intra-faith marriage.[51] This view met

[50] K. N. Conzen, ' "The German Athens": Milwaukee and the Accommodation of its Immigrants, 1836–1860' (unpublished Ph.D. Dissertation, University of Wisconsin, 1972); and R. D. Simon, 'The Expansion of An Industrial City: Milwaukee, 1880–1910' (unpublished Ph.D. Dissertation, University of Wisconsin, 1971). Also, Z. L. Miller, 'Urban Blacks in the South, 1865–1920', *The New Urban History*, ed. Schnore (forthcoming). L. B. De Graaf, 'The City of Black Angels: Emergence of the Los Angeles Ghetto, 1890–1930', *Pacific Historical Review*, xxxix (1970), pp. 323–52. In contrast to the high level of black Angeleno home ownership in 1930, the figure for Detroit was 15 per cent, 10·5 per cent in Chicago, and 5·6 per cent in New York. Only six cities, 100,000 and over, exceeded the Los Angeles level of black ownership and none had a large Negro population. In 1930 the ratio of blacks to black-owned homes in L.A. was 10, compared with 8 whites per white-owned home. Ratios for Detroit were 31:10, Chicago 44:12, New York 77:15: U.S. Bureau of the Census, *Negroes in the U.S., 1920–1930* (Washington D.C., 1935), pp. 277–79. The 13th U.S. *Census*, 1910, reported the ratio of all home-owning families to be 33·7 per cent in Baltimore, 26·2 per cent in Chicago, 17·1 per cent in Boston, and 11·7 per cent in New York (13·1 per cent the Bronx, only 2·9 per cent Manhattan); 63 per cent of farm families owned their own farm homes.

[51] S. Lieberson, *Ethnic Patterns in American Cities* (New York, 1963), pp. 49–91, demonstrates the persistence of ethnic separation and shows the diffusion of groups to the 'suburbs'. Also, J. M. Beshers et al., 'Ethnic Congregation-Segregation, Assimilation, and Stratification', *Social Forces*, May 1964; R. J. R. Kennedy, 'Single or Triple Melting Pot? Inter-marriage in New Haven 1870–1940', *American Journal of Sociology*, xlix (1944), pp. 331–339; W. Herberg, *Protestant, Catholic, Jew* (New York, 1955); G. Lenski, *The Religious Factor: A Sociological Study of Religion's Impact on Politics, Economics, and Family Life* (New York, 1964). The *Yearbook of Churches*

the needs of the 1950s for demonstrative religiosity and was a reassurance to religious professionals of a brake on inter-faith first marriage, frowned on by pastors and psycho-therapists alike. But in expressing their options for home ownership, automobiles, less congested surroundings, and 'the church of their choice', system-oriented Americans in cities and suburbs are still 'sifting and sorting' themselves in terms of three structural-spatial attributes: (1) socio-economic class (2) ethnicity and colour, and (3) type of family (particularly in regard to early married years of heaviest child-bearing).

But Black America has always been in a segregated pot. In *Negroes in Cities*, published in 1965, the Taeubers showed that more than 60 per cent of the blacks in 207 cities would have to be *relocated* in order to achieve an unsegregated spatial distribution. Moreover, black disadvantages in schooling, in occupational achievement, and in incomes accounted for only a small part of their measurable segregation in urban space. The web of discrimination is the principal factor bringing about their inequitable exclusion, but the outmigration of whites also reinforces the position of blacks in their squalid isolation almost like the embattled farmers of the western wheat belts in the late nineteenth century. Blacks have very few options in choosing a home; quite apart from their inadequate resources, they get separated by the others. The Taeubers ended on a pessimistic note: 'Improving the economic status of Negroes is unlikely by itself to alter prevailing patterns of racial residential segregation.'[52]

1967 indicates that Jews comprised 4·5 per cent, Roman Catholics 37·0 per cent, and Protestants, 54·6 per cent of all church membership. Church members were said to constitute 64·3 per cent of the estimated population. In 1960 well over 20 million residents of the U.S. had a mother tongue other than English. Spanish and French were the other major 'colonial tongues' but 'maintenance prospects' for 21 other languages are discussed in *Language Loyalty in the United States*, ed. J. A. Fishman (The Hague, 1966).

[52] K. E. and A. F. Taeuber, *Negroes in Cities* (Chicago, 1965), pp. 52–5, 94–5. The Taeubers also give a critical discussion of the 'Index of Dissimilarity' technique for measuring group separation, pp. 43–62, 197–242. T. J. Woofter *et al.*, *The Problems of Negroes in Cities* (Garden City, N.Y., 1928). National Academy of Sciences, *Freedom of Choice in Housing: Opportunities and Constraints* (Washington D.C., 1972). Also, W. K. Tabb, *The Political Economy of the Black Ghetto* (New York, 1970). Small wonder that some poor young blacks are attracted to narcotics, like some of their better-off white counterparts. But American whites were hooked long before the blacks. See Dr D. Musto and A. Trachtenberg, 'As American As Apple Pie', *Yale Alumni Magazine*, Jan. 1972, pp. 17–21. Narcotic addiction was widespread in the U.S. before World War I; per capita consumption of opiates was about 18 times that of Germany or France and neither blacks nor Chinese could afford the habit. Musto attributes the source to pharmaceutical advertising and incompetent medical prescription.

Whatever may be the advantages and comforts of 'cultural pluralism', the territorial scale of modern metropolitan organization means that, outside the daytime districts of the central cities or on college campuses, the major part of inter-group stimulation must be taking place *via* commercial television and the glossy media. Most of the intercession is left to professional and political brokers. Americans remain spread out psychologically and physically even though more than 70 per cent are now jammed on to 2 per cent of the continental land area. America remains, as Henry James remarked of an earlier day and age, a very 'thin society'. In hyphenated subcultures, the living and society are doubtless thicker, if sometimes claustrophobic. But now there is no longer a recognizable and affirmative American without his hyphen. Now that the Sears Roebuck catalogue has scarcely more talismanic power than a McGuffey *Reader*; now that 'textbook Americanism,' the 'catalogue of Accepted Values and Favored Maxims', is no longer read, whence comes this American, this new urban man?[53] Clearly, the play of social forces in the city was creating opportunities and defining options. In the cities the older search for equality of opportunity developed its obverse, though no less seductive, face: the opportunity to become *unequal* and to express the greater option in social and residential separateness. The cities did not create all of their problems but, now that they are disintegrating, some pragmatic civilians regard them as the Republic's last best hope.

Mayor John V. Lindsay of New York recently proclaimed a vision of urban development which contrasts with Crèvecoeur's vision of rural settlement expressed nearly two centuries ago:

'It is the city that transforms displaced rural populations and immigrant populations. When immigrants need education and jobs and housing they have always come to the city. When the economy failed in the rural South, its victims came North to the city. It is

[53] P. Schrag, *The Decline of the Wasp* (New York, 1971), p. 14, and M. Novak, *The Rise of the Unmeltable Ethnics* (New York, 1971) are typical and symmetrical examples of the mutual disregard in which hyphenated Americans, especially sophisticated ones, have come to hold each other. The acronym 'Wasp' (from White Anglo-Saxon Protestant) is applied to more or less anything and anybody who is not obviously 'Catholic', 'Jewish', 'ethnic' or 'Third World'; it hyphenates the America that is descended from the 'old stock' and, while it allows for the settling of old scores and the projection of personal insecurities, it does not seem to make non-Wasps more amenable to each other. A more stinging social criticism is given by A. Hacker, *The End of The American Era* (New York, 1970), who locates his targets with greater precision. See also A. E. Parr, 'City and Psyche', *Yale Review*, lx (1965), pp. 71–85.

the city that gives human beings the education and skills and expectations that are the goals of the great urban working class and middle class.

'And when some of the successful graduates of the urban process move on to the suburbs they are inevitably . . . and properly replaced by the victims of whatever social ill plagues the nation—the failure of small farmers to compete, the mechanization of agriculture, unemployment among mine workers and discrimination against black people, or brown people, or ethnics, or women.

'The process of transformation is a costly one. It requires immense amounts of energy, and money, and faith. We have been denying our cities all three of these vital resources to carry on with the work of social progress. And when the big-city process breaks down, when the machine of social transformation no longer works, that burden is inevitably dispersed. And so our suburbs and our small towns now face the problems the big cities used to solve for them. This is the truth we can't avoid. This is the reality that can bring this country to its knees if we try to hide from it.'[54]

Notwithstanding the 'failures' of the Kennedy–Johnson 'War on Poverty' and the three or four hundred urban-related programmes initiated in recent decades, this is the Mayor's model and, one suspects, that of most concerned Americans. In so far as money is involved, this means federal money and here America begins to come apart at the seams of its consensus. The issue is not a partisan issue, since American party politics is about office and place, not policy. The policy question is whether to go on putting money, energy, and faith into the cities, by trying in Daniel P. Moynihan's phrase to 'gild the ghetto', or whether to put them where 'the solutions are'—in the suburban and satellite rings. This is where most of the new jobs are being generated, this is where most of the better schools are situated, this is where much of the private sector investment is located, and this is what the federal government has been subsidizing for decades, while it also gilded the central business areas. If Americans will not let 'the Urban Crisis' ride, will not endorse Moynihan's recommendation to relax the federal pressure and leave it to 'benign neglect', then the most salutary course is to disperse the 'ghettos', break up the hard cores of poverty and anti-social behaviour and parcel the poor out into suburban pockets where the honours' graduates of the urban process reside. An environment of the successful, although no longer silent, majority is more likely to lick the derelicts and the drop-outs

[54] From J. V. Lindsay, 'Cities Solve Problems', an address at Colorado College, *New York Times*, 14 Aug. 1972.

into shape than ever the rhetoric of Black Nationalists in the cores and on the campuses. Anyway, things are getting better.[55]

Lindsay and the other mayors disagree. Give us adequate financial tools, cooperate in programmes of our devising, end the murderous drain of Vietnam, and we can finish the job of the cities. No, say the policy scientists, the cities have had their chance, they are usually incompetent, if not always corrupt, the most they can do is cooperate more efficiently with state and federal agencies who will do what they can to revitalize the churning industrial-urban model. They have the constitutional powers and the fiscal resources to finish the job.[56]

By 1970 the populations of the outer rings outnumbered the central city populations of the nation's metropolitan areas. By census measures, the rings have been growing relatively faster than the central cities since 1920. Metropolitanites outside the central cities are more likely to agree with the mayors than with the technocrats, if the question were put. They do not want city problems dispersed to the suburbs; they have been *zoning* them out for half a century.[57] In

[55] A celebrated recommendation is Moynihan's 'Memorandum for the President' published by the *New York Times*, 1 March 1970, p. 69. Moynihan confirmed the document and expressed a hope that its content would be considered as a whole. It is remembered, however, for its advocacy of 'benign neglect' toward 'the issue of race'. Moynihan attributed the term to the Earl of Durham in 1839 but he apparently did not realize that 'Radical Jack' did not become a culture hero of *les Canadiens*. He recently confirmed his optimistic posture on the basis of proposed legislation to place a minimum $2,400 annual income floor under every family of four and to share the huge federal revenue deficit with state and local government: *New York Times*, 27 Sept. 1972, p. 47. See also W. Lilley III, 'Housing Report', Center for Political Research, *National Journal*, Oct. 17, 1970, pp. 2251–62. On dispersion, see A. Downs, *Opening Up The Suburbs* (New Haven, 1971); on revenue sharing, *Revenue Sharing and the City*, ed. II. S. Perloff and R. P. Nathan (Baltimore, 1968).

[56] Remarks of Mayor K. Gibson of Newark, N.J., Mayor F. W. Burke of Louisville, Ky, and Mayor T. A. Luken of Cincinnati, Ohio, cited by W. V. Shannon, *New York Times*, 25 June 1972. But there were also 14 million impoverished people left in rural America in the 1960s whose situation had not been improved by agricultural policies of the Kennedy–Johnson years: *The People Left Behind*, Report of the President's National Advisory Commission on Rural Poverty (Washington, D.C., 1967), p. ix.

[57] Statement of Housing and Urban Development Secretary George Romney to officials of Warren, Mich., 27 July 1970, on 'fair housing' as distinct from 'forced integration': HUD *News*, released 27 July 1970. With the Warren uprising, the 'suburbs' departed from the hard-won compliance indicated by suburban Dayton, Ohio, 1970: *New York Times*, 21 Dec. 1970, pp. 1, 42, Romney's earlier encounter with Mayor Ted Bates and Warren city council members is given in *The Detroit News*, 24 July 1970. On zoning and annexation, see S. I. Toll, *Zoned American* (New York, 1969), and M. Scott, *American City Planning since 1890* (Berkeley, 1969). In 1940 the suburban and satellite rings outside the central cities contained 27 million residents, or

an election year President Nixon has obviously got their message and so has the Congress. They have moved quickly against 'court-ordered bussing' as one of the strategems for better schooling, although it is not clear that they will immediately raise the money to commence re-gilding 'ghetto' education, even if they knew how.

Cities were, and perhaps as Mayor Lindsay affirms, still are great resources for social change. But it is easy for a city mayor in a college commencement address, or for a 'Fourth of July' orator, to reduce history to a formula, to compress the long drawn-out urbanization process into a teleological system. More ominous, perhaps, is the tough-talk of the policy scientist. It is distressing to hear that process so modelled and condensed as to be altogether too purposeful and exact. There is no slack left in the interstices of life, neither time nor place for what Randall Jarrell once called 'the dailiness' of living. There must be more than going on vacation or relaxing with a cold beer in front of the box. And is this how the American pursues happiness in the city? Either by leaving it or by isolating himself from it? Some critics suggest that he has already done both by decamping to the suburbs. Some planners say we do not really need the city any more or, at least, not in the recognizable shape we inherited from the late nineteenth century. Perhaps what Mayor Lindsay said was not the truth, not the reality any more, but only the nostalgia of someone who once wanted to be the Mayor, a brick-and-mortar Bryan who thought that politics was a way to keep memories alive.

---

2 out of every 10 Americans. By 1970 their 76 millions represented 4 out of every 10; their total *exceeded* the aggregate of central city dwellers by 12 millions. From 40 to 60 per cent of their working populations were employed in the rings. Two-thirds of all U.S. new residential construction value is located in the rings. These massive and, on the whole, focus-less 'free way' settlements are becoming the dominant ecological pattern. Some recent evidence from the 'outer-urbs' of Baltimore, Cleveland, Los Angeles, Houston, and Atlanta suggests that such settlements already have 'grave problems' of their own-making: *New York Times,* 30 May 1971, and four subsequent issues. A Los Angeles 'urbanologist', E. Contini, asserted that the 'suburban house' is 'the idealization of every immigrant's dream—the vassal's dream of his own castle'. Apparently, it was not the realization of the dream! Meanwhile, 'quiet decay erodes Downtown Areas of Small Cities', *New York Times,* 8 Feb. 1972. Many of these problems were foreshadowed and foreseen, with less urgency, in the 1920s, see R. D. McKenzie, 'The Rise of Metropolitan Communities', Report of the President's Research Committee, *Recent Social Trends in the U.S.* (New York, 1933), i, pp. 443–96. The cruel irony is that, according to the polls of the National Opinion Research Center, University of Chicago, white willingness to accept a high degree of integration in everything except mixed marriages and residential neighbourhoods has risen steadily since the 1940s: *New York Times,* 8 Dec. 1971.

But an enduring historiography is not to be written out of nostalgic memories and this holds for the up-rooted as it did for the up-raised. '*Ubi Panis, Ibi Patria* is the motto of all emigrants,' said Crèvecoeur, the now discredited author of the agrarian melting-pot model. The melting pot was to produce 'a new race of men', the western pilgrims. Men from all over Europe—Crèvecoeur omitted the Africans and those who were here before the first Pilgrims—'are incorporated into one of the finest systems of population which has even appeared'. The result of its process which 'tended to regenerate them: new laws, a new mode of living, a new social system', has turned out differently, at least in terms of self-identification, than the Frenchman had predicted; and Mayor Lindsay's urban pressure cooker has also developed a faulty gasket.[58]

The melting pot has not been the historical consensus for some time, and consensus historiography has, like the city, itself become controversial and abandoned by many. The most brilliant and generous of the consensus historians, Richard Hofstadter, shifted his ground, or perhaps only his focus, somewhat just prior to his untimely death. Hofstadter had found problems in American history which consensus historiography had not yet explained. One such problem was 'one of the most significant facts of American social life—the racial, ethnic, and religious conflict with which our country is saturated'. He agreed with the English historian, J. R. Pole, that: 'The idea of consensus was useful as a direction-finder.' It was not an explanation. Hofstadter suggested that the idea of consensus was useful when it helped pose 'a whole set of new questions about the extent to which agreement prevails in a society, who takes part in it and how it is arrived at'. He instanced the constitutional consensus where 'the overwhelming majority of the politically active public accepts the legitimacy of the legal-constitutional order'. He also wrote of the 'policy consensus' which exists 'when an issue moves out of the area of significant controversy'. He cited the eventual acceptance of the New Deal Social Security system as 'an established consensual position'. Hofstadter may, as J.R. Pole also remarked, have assumed 'a primarily urban standpoint when he wrote history'. One may doubt whether he was the first to do this. My candidate for such dubious distinction would be the elder Schlesinger, if not the now-disavowed Charles A. Beard. Hofstadter was no urban historian but he was, in the best sense, urbane and certainly had the urban dimension of the current crisis in mind when he indicated the need for 'a kind of moral consensus I would call comity'. 'Comity exists in a society,' he went

---

[58] Crèvecoeur, *Letters From An American Farmer*, pp. 39–40. For an optimistic appraisal, J. Burchard, 'The Culture of Urban America', *Environment and Change*, ed. W. Ewald, Jr. (Bloomington, Ind., 1968).

on, 'to the degree that those enlisted in its contending interests have a basic minimum regard for each other . . . civility is not abandoned' and even the most bitter opponents recognize each other's humanity and remember 'that a community life must be carried on after the ascerbic issues of the moment have been fought over and won'.[59]

Hofstadter concluded that 'the waxing and waning phases of comity shed considerable light on American history'. Yet they had not enlightened him as to the provenance of a comity adequate to America's current crisis. Nor did he recognize that the small 'politically active public' had often intensified the agonies of cities even when it lacked the first notions of an urban 'policy consensus'. It was still too easy for a crisis-managing 'technical elite' of lawyers and part-time professors to dismiss the illiberal ranting and rage of human underclasses as so much 'populist' noise and an earlier Hofstadter had unwittingly contributed to that ease. Certainly America's urbanized society had been coming apart before the 1960s and may even now be re-integrating itself in some, as yet, imperceptible form. Most Americans no longer find much happiness in the city, if they ever did, and many still pursue it vainly among the parking lots and crabgrass of the suburbs. A few have trekked even further out to locate it in some, as yet, undiscovered transcendental community, lost since the seventeenth century, perhaps never even 'Half-way' covenanted at all.

Community is both a method and a goal. Consensus implies agreement about something and, more loosely, it means a convergence of opinions. Comity is a means by which people find a way of diverging on goals but, in agreeing to differ, without their mutual destruction. There is little of comity or consensus on the American urban scene; there has always been much compromise, however, and usually at the expense of third and fourth weaker parties who are not fully represented in the discussion or the deal. If happiness is to be pursued in a fragmented community, it is still a long way off and the time is run-

[59] R. Hofstadter, *The Progressive Historians: Turner, Beard and Parrington* (New York, 1968), pp. 437–66. J. R. Pole, 'The American Past: is it Still Useable?', *Journal of American Studies*, i (1967), pp. 63–78; *idem* in *The Times*, London, a notice reprinted in *Columbia Forum*, xiii (1970), p. 8. As far back as 1963, however, Hofstadter, while arguing that 'a technical elite of lawyers and economists' had removed anti-trust policy out of the area of significant controversy, was gravely concerned that the economy seemed unable to free the 'urban mass society' from 'widespread poverty' and a deep 'malaise': *The Paranoid Style in American Politics and Other Essays* (New York, 1965), pp. 235–37. See also the perceptive review of Hofstadter's *Progressive Historians* by M. White in *American Historical Review*, lxxv (1969), pp. 601–3. But White continues to regard criticism of urban conditions as reflecting an 'anti-urban' bias and surely misses the mark on Charles Beard.

ning out. America has lost what Burke called 'the pleasing illusions, which made power gentle and obedience liberal'. The power of confident technocrats falls heavily on muddled human heads; their modern mace throttles the dissenting charm, they want compliant, if not passive, obedience.

There is neither the deference due to others nor a proper condescension in return. This eighteenth-century language is not altogether out of place even in a twentieth-century republic, however, for it envisages a not wholly vertical structure in human relationships that is more fixed, understood, and agreed upon than any consensus or comity that now obtains in the megacities of America. Their scale is too large and the disutilities and diseconomies of space-time convergence only too evident. Things are in the driving seat and movement is governed more by centrifugal forces than by centripetal ones. The city system is intact but its structures must bend. Another decade of American history may still work more than a cycle of Cathay. Liberal America characteristically leaves today's problems unsolved as it goes on to make tomorrow's; pragmatic America never really confronts itself and there is always new space at home, if only dwindling time.

Meanwhile, urban historians above all must not confront history or earlier historiography with what E. P. Thompson called 'the enormous condescension of posterity'. For regardless of whether one is an optimist or a pessimist about past and present outcomes, the industrial-urban transformation is to be understood and evaluated in terms of what it does to the quality of brief human lives.[60] Men and women still cry out for justice and the only enduring comity is justice done—not to 'groups' or 'quotas' but to persons. Justice done and seen to be done. That is perfect political art. And ultimately, wherever men and women pursue happiness, they will not find it anywhere until they first discover its meanings within themselves and among those

[60] 'In the long last, the probabilities are that, instead of adjusting automobiles to the city as it is, the city will be adjusted to the automobiles as they are, either by increasing the number of streets or by providing special thoroughfares for them. That would be in line with what took place when the automobiles proved destructive to the macadamed roads that once were so highly regarded. It was not the cars that were banished, but the paving that was changed': New York Times, 23 March 1923. 'Not long ago, a home meant something. It was the location of our birth . . . and where we held our family functions. Today . . . there is no tie to home and fireside . . . There is no neighborhood standard of conduct . . . Parents do not understand children, as they once did, however little that was; for the children react to changed life-conditions. There is need of inner control in the family, as against so much outside influence. It is all a question of adjustment and the right choice of "technique". Mr Damrosch hopes that the radio, by keeping people at home, will save family life from disruption by the automobile': New York Times, 13 June 1930,

with whom they are immediately and intimately inter-dependent. For of such is the pursuit of happiness in the countryside, in the city, the suburb, and in the wilderness without.

State University of New York,
Stony Brook

THE NEW HISTORY AND THE SENSE OF SOCIAL PURPOSE IN AMERICAN HISTORICAL WRITING

By J. R. Pole, M.A., Ph.D., F.R.Hist.S.

READ 20 OCTOBER 1972

HISTORIANS have often been inspired by the power of spiritually high ideals or socially good intentions, sometimes by both. Orosius, a disciple of Augustine, composed his *Seven Books of History Against the Pagans* to prove that nations which had submitted themselves to non-Christian rulers had thereby incurred a series of disasters. The legend that Brutus of Troy had founded Britain was thought useful by King James I. Both in the earlier and later stages of the development of concepts of verification with regard to historical records, the idea of a past whose example points the way to present and future conduct or which gives validity to the régime of the present has been an extraordinarily potent instrument of social policy. The social instrumentalists who emerged, among the political scientists, economists, sociologists, philosophers and historians of the western world about the end of the last century were hardly less ambitious than their predecessors. Among them, the American school was particularly confident of what could be achieved by wresting the study, teaching and writing of history from the hands of its orthodox exponents and redirecting the entire subject in the interests of social advance. There is an obvious temptation to describe this school as historical utilitarians, a word that suggests itself particularly because of their long emphasis on the use and usability of the past. But the term is inappropriate. Utilitarianism is a system which envisages the greatest good of the greatest number; whereas an instrumental view could be directed to special problems or be intended to promote the interests of a particular group.

The driving force of the school were those who proclaimed the New History. The phrase had been used several times before 1912, when James Harvey Robinson unfurled the banner bearing that device;[1] by 1938, after Robinson's death, Harry Elmer Barnes, the most pugnacious of the school's propagandists, who by this time had been obliged to recognize that the New History's intellectual pedigree could

[1] James Harvey Robinson, *The New History* (N.Y. 1912).

be traced back to Voltaire, was able to proclaim the outcome of the struggle in buoyant terms:

> Down to the present time the exponents of the new history have found it necessary to engage in a campaign of persistent propaganda and education . . . They have now definitely won the victory and can henceforth concentrate their energy upon perfecting the basis of the new history and on providing the training of those who will be competent to practice the new history.[2]

In view of this declaration, it seems important to recognize from the outset that several of the major figures of the period, including Osgood, Andrews, Morison, Wertenbaker, Miller and Nevins, were writing history that would probably have been exactly the same if the New History school had never existed; and later commentators, so far from accepting the triumph of the New History, came to the conclusion that, by at latest the end of World War II, its frontier of settlement had closed.[3] But if, as seems to be generally agreed, that impulse was spent, it would still be superficial to suppose that the influence was exhausted. The New Historians were one manifestation of the broader cultural phenomenon of the Progressive Movement, and in 1959 Henry May remarked that 'We still tend to see American history through the eyes of the Progressive Era'.[4] The Progressives, moreover, had powerful survivors and successors who carried the historical torch for the New Deal, and for a succession of reformers who seemed always to be struggling against those ever-renewed forces of reaction and oppression.

Thus although the phenomenon with which this paper is concerned lies in the past, it seems equally significant that by the time the nucleus of the New, or more broadly of Progressive, History, had spent its specific impulse, it had succeeded in infiltrating a much wider segment of the corporate body of historians in which it continued to live. The New History's aims could be summarized with a simplicity which does no injustice to its practitioners by saying that they proposed to convert history into a positive instrument of social progress through the clarification of the historical origins of current problems; and further, that the New History intended to enlist the full range of the more recent social sciences in an attempt to comprehend and interpret every aspect of the life of the past.

[2] Henry Elmer Barnes, *History of Historical Writing* (Norman, Okla., 1932).
[3] Richard Hofstadter, *The Progressive Historians: Turner, Beard, Parrington* (N.Y., 1968), p. 438; John Higham, *History: The Development of Historical Studies in the United States* (Englewood Cliffs, 1965), p. 131.
[4] Henry F. May, *The End of American Innocence* (London, 1960), p. 164.

It is the first of these aims that I have called 'instrumentalism'. The second aim seems to serve the first, but if it became an end in itself then it would seem to endanger the priority of the first. The details or logics of these priorities were not quite clearly established, even when set out by Barnes in his *History of Historical Writing* in 1938.

I doubt whether I should have come to write this paper if I were entirely satisfied that I agreed with the view that the New History, in all its manifestations, had passed away with its own generation of historians. There is, therefore, a sense in which I am exposed to the accusation of being engaged in a similarly instrumental activity myself. As an episode in the history of American thought, the New History calls for both identification and explanation; but the views that we develop are bound to be informed by the necessity for a critical consideration of the New History's longer-term intellectual consequences. Not that all the thinking that bears an instrumentalist stamp has necessarily been dedicated to social reform—a danger shrewdly seen, in 1935, by Theodore Clarke Smith,[5] who expressed his fears for the future if historians allowed themselves to be swayed by Charles Beard's presidential address to the American Historical Association, 'Written History as an Act of Faith'.[6] Smith observed that there was already Soviet History and Fascist History, and there would be national socialist history as soon as it could be manufactured, 'in each case based on a definite philosophy as an act of faith'. He foresaw that history would come to be permitted only as an entertainment or as a form of social control. Neither these words, nor the events of the next few years, appear to have supported the democratic faith of Conyers Read, who, as President of the Association in 1949,[7] disparaged those historians who interested themselves in the past for its own sake; in his view the liberal world, with its plurality of aims and values was a thing of the past, and for the future, 'we must clearly assume a militant attitude if we are to survive'. The theme of this militant attitude, involving the organization of resources and the disciplined interpretation of history, was to be the propagation of American doctrines. 'This sounds', he added, 'like the advocacy of one form of social control against another. In short, it is. But I see no alternative in a divided world.' He reassured his hearers that his concept of control meant 'no menace to essential freedoms', but left it to be inferred that the controllers of policy would decide which freedoms

---

[5] Theodore Clarke Smith, 'The Writing of American History in America from 1884 to 1934', *American Historical Review*, xl (April 1935).

[6] Charles A. Beard, 'Written History as an Act of Faith', *American Historical Review*, xxxix (January 1934).

[7] Conyers Read, 'The Social Responsibilities of the Historian', *American Historical Review*, lv (January 1950).

were essential. This programme was exceptional both in its extent and in the frankness with which it was avowed, at a time when the comparable views of Zhdanov still had the force of authority in Russia, and those of Goebbels were but a recent memory.

Social control in this organized sense has certainly never been an aim of historians writing in the general tradition of the New or Progressive History, but equally certainly it was within their compass to aim at the kind of intellectual influence that could help to shape social policy. The achievements of American historians were proclaimed by a Social Science Research Council Report of 1946, to have been 'frankly functional'.[8] As recently as 1966, Professor Eric Goldman is reported to have said on the 'Open Mind' television programme that 'most historians' were 'in agreement' that history was, to use his own word, a 'weapon'; and it was 'employed in determining peoples' ideas and attitudes'; he went further, for there was 'a certain measure of responsibility on the part of the historian for making sure that he writes history in such a way that it will bring about the kind of action that he wants'.[9] Mr Goldman's distinguished predecessors had chosen some sort of historical relativism, but it might be unfair to them to describe his assertion as lying logically at the end of that road. I don't think it does; it is better thought of as a wrong turning, but unfortunately it carries a great deal of traffic, some heavy, much light, and most of it noisy. Mr Goldman's statement is not better for being the counterpart of Conyers Read's presidential address, or of comparable declarations more recently from the New Left,[10] all of which stand before us as bleak warnings of what lies in store when the basic concept of historical truth has been discarded as irrelevant for the excellent reason that it has ceased to serve any useful purpose. They tend to justify Voltaire's cynical remark that history is nothing but a pack of tricks we play on the dead.

With these reverberations in mind, it will be timely to turn back to the beginnings of the school which claimed the rubric of the 'New History'. These historians were in fact not all of one mind, and were on occasion capable of differing from each other quite sharply. But on one common piece of ground they felt very firm: they had cleared away the dense undergrowth of pietistic rhetoric to uncover the nature of reality. The matter was stated by Arthur F. Bentley, with Charles

[8] J. H. Randall Jr. and George Haines IV, 'Controlling Assumptions', in *Theory and Practice in Historical Study: A Report of the Committee on Historiography*, ed. Merle Curti, SSRC Bulletin 54 (N.Y., 1946), p. 51.

[9] James J. Martin, 'History and Social Intelligence', in *Harry Elmer Barnes, Learned Crusader*, ed. Arthur Goddard (Colorado Springs, 1968), p. 241.

[10] For example, Howard Zinn, 'Abolitionists, Freedom-Riders and the Tactics of Agitation', in *The Anti-Slavery Vanguard: New Essays on the Abolitionists*, ed. Martin Duberman (Princeton, 1965).

Beard's warm approval: 'Reality is in group interests acting on political institutions, not in the hearts or minds or thoughts or feelings of the people'.[11] Similarly, Turner's preoccupation with the significance of the frontier amounted to a primitive form of geo-economic determinism. He was almost blindly unwilling to admit of the influence of ideas, of institutions, or of the cultural inheritances of language or religion; and, as Hofstadter observed, he never seriously applied himself to the problems of cultural transmission.[12] A little below the surface of agreement, his views were bound to separate from those of such social critics as the political scientists Bentley and Goodnow or the socialists Gustavus Myers and Algie Simons.

In its substance and style, the new movement was distinctly American, but it would be wrong to suppose that it grew out of a condition of intellectual isolation, or that its exponents were in any way confined to America. Charles Beard as an undergraduate at DePauw University had already read Arnold Toynbee's *Lectures on the Industrial Revolution* (1884), whose message was of formative importance for him:

> You must pursue facts for their own sake, but penetrated with a vivid sense of the problems of your own time. This is not a principle of perversion, but a principle of selection, and you could not have a better one than to pay special attention to the history of the social problems that are agitating the world now.[13]

The bibliography of Beard's first book, a little essay on the same subject—*The Industrial Revolution* (1901)—written during his years at Oxford and addressed to the British working classes, bore all the traces of his own intellectual debts to the new social consciousness in Britain; he listed *Fabian Essays*, and the works of the Webbs, of Hobson, and of Ruskin, who had moved him so deeply that he is said to have carried a copy of *Unto This Last* in his pocket for several years. The college which Beard helped to found was to be called Ruskin Hall. Behind all these, with their strong sense of social purpose, stood J. R. Green's famous *Short History of the English People* (1876), perhaps the first actual work of history to manifest the new historical spirit. Green, who disagreed with Freeman's dictum that 'History is past politics, politics is present history' and made it his

---

[11] In Beard's review of Arthur F. Bentley, *The Process of Government* (1908), *Political Science Quarterly*, xxiii (1908).

[12] Hofstadter, *The Progressive Historians*, p. 141.

[13] Burleigh Taylor Wilkins, 'Frederick York Powell and Charles A. Beard. A Study in Anglo-American Historiography and Social Thought', *American Quarterly*, xi (1959); Arnold Toynbee, *Lectures on the Industrial Revolution* (London, 1884).

aim to tell the story of the people as a whole, enjoyed enormous sales in the United States long before his approach had become acceptable to the more professional of American historians.

Beard dropped an oblique, perhaps unintended hint as to his own future direction when in 1906 he reviewed Jean Jaurès's new venture, the *Histoire socialiste*,[14] and remarked that the socialists had not yet made any great contributions to history because lengthy treatises did not serve the purposes of party propaganda. 'Nevertheless,' he significantly continued, 'the avowed purpose of the Socialists to force a disintegration of the intellectual synthesis on which the defence of the present order rests will compel them, in time, to open the whole question of historical interpretation and construction.' In the light of Beard's current beliefs about the nature of reality, one may wonder how fully he was aware of this implied commitment to the view that the defence of an economic and political order did in fact rest on an intellectual synthesis. But the prophetic quality of this observation seems to reveal as much about Beard's own prospective development as about that of the socialists. He might not have agreed that he ever intended 'to force a disintegration' of the American synthesis of his time, but as soon as he discovered the appropriate historical records he proved himself ready to deploy the resources of scholarship to expose the revered institutions of that order to the most sceptical and searching questions.

Yet Beard's iconoclasm was never unambiguously destructive. The tone of his short book, *The Supreme Court and the Constitution* (1912), which is constructed from sketchy evidence held together by faulty reasoning, is at least consistent with great respect for the Court, and it was meant to refute the allegation then current that judicial review was a usurped power. It thus seems reasonable to suppose that when Beard discovered the Treasury records showing the financial holdings of the Founders of the Constitution, which appreciated after its inauguration, the evidence may have influenced his views about their motives. But the influence, if so, was exerted on a mind that was already in a high state of susceptibility, and although his scrutiny was remarkably hasty and inconclusive, it was enough to satisfy him and, more surprisingly, for some forty years it satisfied an increasing proportion of his readers. His iconoclasm, in any case, was in keeping with the tone of the period, whose most devastating blast, perhaps surprisingly, had been sounded a few years earlier in England. In 1904 the English legal scholar Edward Jenks published in *The Independent Review* an astonishing article which denounced as a group of self-serving feudal reactionaries a body of strong-minded

---

[14] *Political Science Quarterly*, xxi (1906).

men who had for several centuries been honoured as the founders of the liberties of the English-speaking peoples. The article was called 'The Myth of Magna Carta'. By the time Beard, a close student of English history, reviewed Jaurès, he had read not only Jenks, but McKechnie's *Magna Carta* (1905), and took advantage of the opportunity to mention that Jaurès had not. Without imputing a direct line of connexion, one cannot but be struck by similarities of circumstance and tone. The peculiar role of the barons as the authors of a great and fundamental written charter of liberties was comparable, at least in a rhetorical sense, with that of the Founders of the Constitution in the history of the United States. When Beard came to write about the Founders he restrained his criticism to the level of innuendo; and he failed to resolve a certain ambivalence as to their achievement—for he never quite lost track of his own midwestern Republican background. But in his attribution of motives and in his scepticism towards their exalted reputations for disinterested service, Beard was as clear about the Founding Fathers as Jenks about King John's barons.

It was James Harvey Robinson who in 1912 proclaimed the arrival and outlined the programme of the New History in a book of essays under that title. Robinson's interest in the theme was not new. As early as 1892, when a junior faculty member at the University of Pennsylvania, he had been named to the National Educational Association's Committee of Ten to make suggestions about the teaching of history in schools, and this was the beginning of a connexion that lasted for twenty-five years. The Committee of 1892[15] (Woodrow Wilson was another member) stressed the importance of educating the majority of children who were not destined to go to college; the Committee felt strongly that all children should receive the same education, and that history and its allied subjects were 'better adapted than any other subject to promote the invaluable mental power we call the judgment'. They recommended the study of Greek, Roman, English, American and French history. From that time onwards, Robinson took a leading part in leading the N.E.A.'s advisory committees to recommend the reduction of time spent on ancient and medieval history, and the advancement in the curriculum of modern and American history; and by 1899 that view had got so strong a hold that the American Historical Association's Committee of Seven for that year went so far as to advise that 'It is not desirable that much time should be devoted to the colonial history.'[16] By 1911, a committee

---

[15] U.S. Bureau of Education, *Report of the Committee on Secondary School Studies at the Meeting of the National Educational Association, July 9 1892* (Washington, 1893).

[16] *The Study of History in Schools. Report to the American Historical Association of the Committee of Seven* (N.Y., 1899), pp. 74–75.

reporting to the American Historical Association advised that medieval history be dropped, and Robinson later stated that in all the conferences on historical instruction on which he had served he had always urged that history for students and readers be directed to the understanding of present conditions and problems.[17] The last curriculum committee in which he took part, which met in 1916, recommended a heavy reorientation of school studies towards civics, vocational studies and modern history. *The Social Studies in Secondary Education*, in which these proposals were made, quoted Robinson's *The New History* on the purpose of teaching history and showed much evidence of the influence of his views.

There can be no doubt of this Report's lasting influence on American school curricula; during the next ten years the United States Bureau of Education distributed 27,000 copies,[18] but the effects were by no means confined to the secondary schools. The university syllabus, or more accurately the courses offered for election, reflected a rising preoccupation with modern and recent history; and this tendency, as a result of which medieval and ancient history have had difficulty in holding any serious footing even in important universities, has never been effectively redressed. While it would be absurd to ascribe to Robinson's own influence the characteristic trend of the social as well as the intellectual life of the period, he was without doubt the most influential publicist and to that extent the most representative propagandist of these views. It becomes significant, therefore, that Robinson seems never to have differentiated seriously between the school, the university and the general public. History had for all of them the same purposive social utility, and it was in that spirit that he wrote, both for the students of the rising state universities and for the mass readership that his books gained. The didactic emphasis on recent history appeared in the text-book *The Development of Modern Europe* (1907–8) written jointly with Beard, the preface to which declared that,

> In preparing the volume in hand, the writers have consciously subordinated the past to the present. It has been their ever conscious aim to enable the reader to catch up with his own times; to read intelligently the foreign news in the morning paper; to know what was the attitude of Leo III towards the social democrats even if he has forgotten that of Innocent III towards the Albigenses.

[17] Luther Vergil Hendricks, *James Harvey Robinson, Teacher of History* (N.Y., 1946), pp. 53–56. Robinson's influence on the work of educational committees is traced on pp. 35–61.
[18] *Ibid.*, p. 63.

But in *The New History* Robinson's note was even more challenging:

> We must develop historical-mindedness upon a far more generous scale than hitherto, for this will add a still deficient element to our intellectual equipment and will promote rational progress as nothing else can do. The present has hitherto been the willing victim of the past; the time has now come when it should turn on the past and exploit it in the interests of advance.[19]

Historians, despite Robinson's belligerent tone, are generally rather fond of the past, whose inhabitants, as they get to know them, appear at least as attractive as some of the historians' own contemporaries. Robinson's strangely resentful and hostile attitude, suggesting an adversary relationship with the main object of his own vocation, requires some explanation. The reasons are to be found, I think, in the combination of his enthusiasm for social advance with his intellectual inheritance of a Darwinian sociology.

Since approximately the 1880s, the Darwinian analysis of society had been breaking into splinters, duly appropriated as weapons by opposing sides in the social struggle. Although the logical flaw that lies at the root of social Darwinist thinking consists in the mechanical transposition of methods belonging to the explanation of a biological process to the analysis of social processes of an entirely different kind, it must be said in fairness to the early social Darwinists that they had a distinguished exemplar: Charles Darwin, in *The Descent of Man,* agreed with the view that the progress of the United States was the result of natural selection and that the Anglo-Saxon emigration to the west was the climactic event of all history.[20] The language of social science was permeated with Darwinian ideas, while ideas of progress, in vague and unsystematic forms, were pervasive. For Beard, in his book on the Industrial Revolution, it was natural to argue that the unity of tendency to be found in the apparent confusion of history was that of the progressive control of man over his environment. For both Beard and Robinson this control was itself one of the themes of history, though Beard placed a heavier and more assured emphasis on democracy and the common man as the objects for whose benefit the control was to be directed—that was what made it progressive.

Robinson was aware of the intellectual risks he was inviting. In *The New History* he found room for an explicit warning against the fallacy of believing that historical lessons give direct solutions to present

[19] Robinson, *The New History*, p. 24.

[20] Cushing Strout, *The Pragmatic Revolt in American History. Carl Becker and Charles Beard* (New Haven, 1958), p. 17; Charles Darwin, *The Descent of Man* (London, 1871), i, p. 179.

problems;[21] he was well aware that every case differs and that past solutions hold good only for past problems. But as a historian Robinson did not go forward with his own programme; he seems to have been unable to commit himself to writing history in a way that would have exemplified his own thesis. In keeping with his own social convictions he involved himself in 1919 with the founding of the New School for Social Studies in New York; but his published work revealed no intellectual development. Ample in amount, and pitched as it was at the level of intelligent popularization, it became increasingly shallow and repetitive, sometimes drawing on materials that he had used twenty or thirty years earlier. His sales were enormous, and, a captive of the bestseller market, Robinson became a willing victim of the present.

When Robinson explained why historical studies were needed, he viewed the past as though the surviving evidence for its existence consisted largely of archaic relics forming stubborn, but reducible obstacles to social progress. 'If it be true,' he asked in *The New History*, ' . . . that opinion tends, in the dynamic age in which we live, to lag far behind our changing environment, how can we better discover the anachronisms in our views than by studying their origin?'[22] This was left as a rhetorical question; better ways might well be thought of, and history may need rather more subtle justifications for the claims that it makes on time and resources in a rapidly changing environment. In a later book, *The Mind in the Making*, which achieved immense sales in the 1920s, Robinson observed that the physics of Aristotle had been completely discarded, yet his ethics and politics were still considered to be works of profound value; and their continuing influence he regarded as an anomaly. This argument suggests certain limitations to evolutionism as a useful system of thought; an heir to both Darwin and the Utilitarians, it did not occur to Robinson or to those who thought like him that ethics might not be susceptible to evolutionary analysis; physics, after all, was undeniably a natural science, but Aristotle, whom Robinson had invoked, specifically held that ethics was not a science.

It was a fundamental tenet of the New History, propounded by Robinson and repeated enthusiastically by Barnes, that the evolutionary attitude would give men the power to resolve the social problems that resulted from the past. Barnes declared that the 'genetic attitude'—a term for evolutionism—had been taught to historians by biologists; he described 'the principle of development and the genetic attitude' as 'the cornerstone of the more vital phases of the new history'.[23] Barnes, even more explicitly than Robinson, insisted that

---

[21] Robinson, *The New History*, pp. 17–18.   [22] *Ibid.*, p. 103.
[23] Barnes, *History of Historical Writing*, p. 376.

historical mindedness would enable people to diagnose those obstacles left behind by the past, apparently somewhat resembling geological deposits that had somehow been carried along, as perhaps at the foot of a glacier; but the deepest consequences of these doctrines were, not the inculcation what they called historical mindedness, but a weakening of historical perspective. Robinson produced an analogy,[24] which Barnes fondly adopted, by which the age of the earth was depicted as on a clock with the beginning at midnight and the present at midday. By this way of measuring, Babylonian and Egyptian civilization had appeared on earth at about twenty minutes to twelve, while Greek literature, philosophy and science were about seven minutes old; Bacon's *Advancement of Learning* appeared at one minute to twelve, and not half a minute had elapsed since the first steam engine. To Robinson the inference from his imaginary time-scale led to firm and practical conclusions: 'This makes it obvious that those whom we call the ancients are really our contemporaries . . . They now belong to our own age.' It was Francis Bacon who first observed that there was something amiss about the traditional conception of the 'ancients'; they had really lived in the youth of the world. But Robinson was not interested in such subtleties. What he wanted to do was to annihilate all differences between antiquity and modernity. Yet an unusual burden seems to rest on his use of the word 'really'. Why, we may ask, are people who lived and died some thousands, or hundreds, of years ago, under different ecological systems, believing in different cosmologies, obeying different laws and worshipping different gods, 'really our contemporaries'? The human perspective, though enlarged by knowledge of geology, natural history and human development, is still contained in the human life-span, and the merging of past and present into one glutinous, undifferentiated mass is a form of *Gemütlichkeit* that is antipathetic to any genuinely historical vision.

That fundamental respect for the distance and differentness of the past, which is an indispensable element of the historical understanding, was absent from the historically innocent mind of Vernon Louis Parrington, whose influence was for a period greater even than that of Beard or Robinson. A poll taken in 1950 disclosed that, of books published between 1920 and 1950, Parrington's *Main Currents of American Thought* (1927–30) was the work most highly esteemed by the majority of historians working on American history.[25] Perhaps still more important is the lasting debt to Parrington that is warmly avowed by Henry Steele Commager.[26] Parrington, a professor of

---

[24] Robinson, *The New History*, p. 239.
[25] Hofstadter, *The Progressive Historians*, p. 350.
[26] H. S. Commager, *The American Mind* (N.Y., 1950), ix, p. 303; see Hofstadter, *op. cit.*, p. 350, n.2.

literature, had apparently received no historical training when he embarked on his ambitious history of American thought. He was not the first to accept the notion of an essential contemporaneity between past and present, or between different past periods, for Beard had argued that the late nineteenth century struggles of the Populist farmers of the West and South amounted to a virtual re-enactment of the great struggles a century earlier over the adoption of the Constitution, and Turner took a similar view. A kind of textually thinned and intellectually simplified whig view of history enabled Parrington to see the American past as a series of encounters between progress and privilege, enlightened democracy and obscurantist reaction, with an immediacy that transcended any necessity for the historical context of the problems. He was thus able to describe Roger Williams as 'contemporary with successive generations of prophets from his day to ours'. As for the colonists, with their up-to-date ideas of liberty and democracy, they were 'old-fashioned only in manners and dress'.[27] The point was that the issues they dealt with and the aims they strove for were modern.

The New Historians had an urgent message for their contemporaries; but their purposeful emphasis on recent history and their denigration of the significance of events more distant in time formed in the minds of their readers a dangerously shallow attitude to the past itself. This attitude has involved not only for them but for those who have been formed under their influence, a depreciation of the intellectual difficulties involved in historical understanding; as Henry May has remarked, 'In Robinson's exuberant pages there is little hint of skepticism, except about long dead traditions, and no whisper of doubt about our ability to understand what was happening.'[28]

The New Historians supposed themselves to be breaking away from a tradition of erudite but arid fact-gathering. Robinson, in this as in other things to be repeated by Barnes, was fond of replying to the great architect of orthodox history, Leopold von Ranke, by asserting that he had placed too much emphasis on history *'wie es eigentlich gewesen'* to the neglect of the more important question of *'wie es eigentlich geworden'*—how it came about.[29] But neither Ranke's American disciples, who thought of themselves as pure historical scientists, nor his American opponents, who believed themselves to be in revolt against orthodox nineteenth-century historical science, seem to have understood Ranke's meaning. They thought of facts as hard little nuggets deposited in the past; but Ranke thought of them

[27] Parrington, *Main Currents of American Thought*, i, pp. iv, vi, 62–75; Hofstadter, *The Progressive Historians*, ch. 2, esp. at p. 398.
[28] May, *End of American Innocence*, p. 161.
[29] Robinson, *New History*, p. 47.

as the agents of moral forces, possibly of divine origin.[30] When Ranke used his famous phrase, *'wie es eigenlich gewesen'*, which he did in distinguishing true historical values from such aims as romantic nationalism, what he meant to convey was the sense of what it was like at the time. The translation into our current idiom might be, 'tell it like it was'.

Assuredly the achievements of the school deserve to be measured against the more complacent assumptions of the orthodoxies to which they gave battle; and it is fair to say that they often wrote with style, verve and considerably wider learning than has been thought necessary by many of their intellectual heirs. Robinson inaugurated the course on European intellectual history which for many years attracted large attendances at Columbia, and the College catalogue for 1899–1900 indicates that a reading knowledge of French, German and Latin was required of undergraduates in his courses.[31] Progressives could reasonably argue that orthodox histories served their own instrumental purposes by protecting the reputations of established institutions;[32] and Progressives were more than merely narrow instrumentalists when they showed that history could be written with a sense of social commitment which would compel the attention of people who had not formerly been committed. But when these gains have been acknowledged, we may continue to ask whether the cogency of their theoretical arguments or their achievements as working historians earned these writers their remarkable and sustained influence over such an important sector of American intellectual life. For it cannot be said that the New History's excessive preoccupation with the recent past, and with the relevance of problems that seem to lie in a direct line to current affairs, has served them well, or has done much to deepen the respect felt by American students for the comparative aspects of the past or the different qualities of other cultures. Judgments about recently current affairs may in a sense be just as important as those about the more remote past, but they rest on a shorter time-scale and tend to be much more rapidly superseded. Robinson's own example, put forward in the preface to *The Development of Modern Europe*, rebounds upon him; for some of the gravest problems of the authoritarian age into which he survived, and which grew more forbidding after his death, would probably gain more

---

[30] I depend here on Cushing Strout, *The Pragmatic Revolt in America: Carl Becker and Charles Beard* (New Haven, 1958), p. 20; Morton G. White, *Social Thought in America: The Revolt against Formalism* (N.Y., 1947), pp. 221–222.

[31] Hendricks, *James Harvey Robinson*, p. 14.

[32] See Barnes's attack on 'good taste' as a handicap to contemporary historical writing; *History of Historical Writing*, p. 273.

illumination from studying Innocent III's crusade against the Albigenses than Leo III's attitude to the social democrats.

When the early proponents of new aims and methods demanded a major transformation of both, they strongly implied that their predecessors' intellectual foundations had been misconceived. Were orthodox historians working with correct methods but improper aims? Or were they the victims of a philosophical misconception about the nature of historical knowledge itself? Very few of the new school allowed themselves to be detained, still less deflected, by these questions; the impulses that bore them forward were social, not philosophical. Carl Becker, an ambiguous ally, was the only contemporary, apart from the philosopher Frederick J. Teggart—who wrote some of the most interesting discussions of the whole problem—to apply himself at all systematically to the investigation of the logical consequences of adopting a consistent position of philosophical relativism. Becker's teacher, Turner, had said in a sentence as early as 1891 all that most of the Progressive or New Historians thought it necessary to say by way of philosophical justification. In his essay, 'The Significance of History', Turner observed that 'Each age writes the history of the past anew with reference to the conditions uppermost in its own times.[33] When reduced to its elements this statement was not a very careful expression of so important a principle; but it would do. People were already thinking in such terms, and Toynbee's lectures had made a similar point seven years earlier. Both were preceded by F. H. Bradley's *Presuppositions of Critical History*, published in 1874, the year of Beard's birth. Bradley argued that each period was capable of historical knowledge only to the extent made possible by the limits of its own assumptions. 'Inference,' he explained, 'depends on the character of our general consciousness—and so the past varies with the present, and can never do otherwise, since it is always the present on which it rests.'[34]

Turner does not seem to have read Bradley, although he may have done; but certainly he was offering a sharp hint that a new way of looking at both the aims and the subject matter of history might be at hand. The relativism implied by this turn of thought, however, contained hidden traps for the confident exponents of the newly fashionable geographical and economic determinism. It has already been observed that they were optimistically sure of their sense of reality—it was interests, economics, brute facts, that made history, not ideals or principles or thoughts. Beard and his contemporaries did not pause to ask themselves why a thought should be something less than

[33] F. J. Turner, 'The Significance of History', can be found, *inter alia*, in *The Varieties of History*, ed. Fritz Stern (N.Y., 1956).
[34] F. H. Bradley, *Presuppositions of Critical History* (Oxford, 1874), p. 15.

a reality if it were in truth a real thought, or why, by prescribing modes of action, it should not contribute to the next set of material realities.

Turner had referred to 'each age' as though ages possessed general characters. Carl Becker, whose thinking in these matters appears to have owed much to Bradley, went on to develop a much fuller view of the characteristics of a historical age. J. B. Bury remarked that 'Ideas have their intellectual climates'.[35] Earlier, William James had argued for the recognition of a 'specious present' in which ideas encountered the tests of pragmatism. Becker believed A. N. Whitehead to have been the source of his own concept, but it was Becker himself who thought out the idea of 'climates of opinion' as virtual determinants of thought and knowledge. (We shall perhaps be fortunate if we escape without hearing them called paradigms.) Becker also took further than his American contemporaries the difficult enquiry into the status of the historical fact; he was the first of them to take seriously the problems arising from the observation that all knowledge of the past is necessarily present knowledge. However, Becker too was concerned to harness history to social improvement, and probably owed more to American pragmatism than to European idealism; his thinking at times suggested that he was heading for a form of epistemological relativism which would have kept very uneasy company with Beard's or Robinson's hard-headed kind of interest in social advance; yet he withdrew sharply from the implication of solipsism that seemed to lie along that road. After his famous presidential address, 'Everyman His Own Historian', Becker found himself obliged to reply to the criticism of William E. Dodd, who told him that he was afraid the address had undermined younger members of the profession in their confidence in the validity of historical research. Becker explained that he had tried to say that it was the duty of the historian 'to keep Mr. Everyman's history, so far as possible, in reasonable harmony with what actually happened'. In a critique of Maurice Mandelbaum he made clear that he did, after all, believe that historical knowledge was objectively ascertainable: the truth was to be searched for.[36]

This late recruit to the school of Ranke had at least taken the debate on to slightly higher ground. He had always been a little sceptical of

[35] J. B. Bury, *The Idea of Progress* (London, 1920).

[36] Carl Becker, *Everyman His Own Historian* (N.Y., 1935); Charlotte Watkins Smith, *Carl Becker: On History and the Climate of Opinion* (Ithaca, N.Y., 1956), pp. 64, 69–76, 86. Burleigh Taylor Wilkins, *Carl Becker: A Biographical Study in American Intellectual History* (Cambridge, Mass., 1961), pp. 88–89, 194–95, 198, 205. On Becker's debt to pragmatism, David Noble in *Ethics*, lxvii (1957). A distinction between evolution and progress in Becker's thoughts is suggested by David Noble, *The Paradox of Progressive Thought* (Minneapolis, 1958), pp. 18–33.

the New Historians, and when he reviewed Robinson in 1912 he raised the question as to what was meant by 'progress', suggesting that a scientific definition was needed before action followed.[37] Becker was also sceptical about the novelty of the New History, and it was he who obliged his contemporaries to notice that the *philosophes* had proclaimed their own 'New History' in order to disengage from the past the elements having universal validity which, conforming to the essential nature of man, would act as guiding principles for social regeneration. For Becker, historical thinking was an intrinsic part of any given society's intellectual process, and one of his more imaginative expressions suggested the needs to which he thought the process answered: 'The past' he said, 'is a kind of screen upon which each generation projects its vision of the future, and so long as hope springs in the human breast the 'new history' will be a recurring phenomenon'.[38]

Becker was not alone in perceiving that ideas had, after all, their place in historical studies. That thought—for it was a thought, and no doubt a real one—began to trouble Charles Beard by 1926, when he hinted at his own waverings towards relativism in his presidential address to the American Political Science Association.[39] By 1932, in writing an introduction to the American edition of Bury's *Idea of Progress*, Beard could admit that 'the world is largely ruled by ideas, whether true or false'. This was a graver concession for Beard than it could have been for Robinson, who taught a course in intellectual history, or for Becker, to whom in any case it was obvious. Even in his celebrated interpretation of the Constitution, however, Beard had left unresolved problems of interpretation; he never clarified or appeared to recognize the distinction between economic determinism and economic interpretation; nor did he clear up the problems of moral responsibility involved in these views. But he had struck a resounding blow against time-honoured institutional certainties, and in his flashes of scepticism as in his profound conviction of the strength and future of democracy he always showed how deeply he shared the Progressive faith.

Faith became the theme of his pronouncement when he told the American Historical Association, in 1933, that he had lost his determinism but had gained a philosophy.[40] When he called written history 'an act of faith' he was as much concerned with the future as with the past. In a manner very like that of H. G. Wells, whom the New

---

[37] Smith, *op. cit.*, pp. 61–62. [38] Becker, *op. cit.*, p. 170.
[39] C. A. Beard, 'Time, Technology and the Creative Spirit in Political Science', *The American Political Science Review*, xxi (Feb. 1927).
[40] Charles Beard, 'Written History as an Act of Faith', *American Hist. Rev.*, xxxix (1934).

Historians tended to regard as one of their own,[41] Beard maintained that the correctness of the historian's judgment about the past was to be measured by the extent to which his predictions about the future were verified by the course of events. Beard's own faith was pitched on the advance of democracy and the interests of the common man; his historical vision revealed to him that this was the course that history had progressively followed. This expansive statement failed to provide any guide to the explanation of specific historical problems. In later years Beard pursued these questions further, but he never seems to have been completely clear about the logical distinction between an analysis of a given historical situation based on a hypothesis, and a prior judgment of value which actually controls the historian's findings and opinions. The manifest courage with which Beard in his later years tackled these problems, attempting to enlist the names of Croce, Heussi and Rietzler in his columns, does not help to establish that he understood them. His subsequent essays display his unfailing energy, his deep commitment to history as a hope for the solution of human problems, and his basic lack of comprehension of the differences between the types of problem involved. Croce was engaged with the problem of defining history as a mode of knowledge; Beard was never far removed from the question of how one was to interpret general or specific issues, how one was to come to terms with the admitted relativity of one's own judgment.[42]

The New History was not an exclusively American phenomenon, nor were its early standard-bearers fighting in pure intellectual isolation. Robinson's *Mind in the Making* had a preface by H. G. Wells, of whom a signed photograph appeared as the frontispiece; Barnes acknowledged a host of Europeans as pioneers and contemporaries of a common movement. Yet it is curious that while so much of the work of the Americans was frankly hortatory and propagandist, their British compeers were writing of the history of trade unions and local government, of the town and village labourer, and of the agrarian movement in the sixteenth century. There were significant national differences in emphasis, in the content of the work, perhaps even in aim; but there was also an international movement.

Karl Lamprecht of Leipzig was probably the first to bear the message in person. His book, *What is History?* was published in English in 1905, after he had lectured both at the 150th anniversary celebrations of Columbia University and at the World Fair in St Louis.

---

[41] See Barnes, *History of Historical Writing*, p. 142.
[42] The debate was continued in C. A. Beard, 'That Noble Dream', *American Hist. Rev.*, xli (1935); C. A. Beard and Alfred Vagts, 'Currents of Thought in Historiography', *ibid.*, xlii (1937). For a bibliography, see Hofstadter, *The Progressive Historians*, p. 484.

Lamprecht, whom Becker, it is comforting to note, found incomprehensible, announced that history was primarily a socio-psychological science. In the nineteenth century, he said, speaking of Germany, 'when the nation yearned with every fibre of its being for the long coveted political unity', political history could be an instrument of national purposes—a statement which at least established the instrumental nature of history and the fact that its subject might change with different aims. The quality which Lamprecht wished history to recapture from the past was nothing less than a nation's soul-life,[43] a task for which the American profession was not perfectly equipped. But a sort of *Kulturgeschichte* was in fact attractive to the New Historians. Turner himself was excited by the spirit of American society, and in 1909 he wrote to Max Farrand that 'The new line for the future is the history of the development of American *society*, ideals, etc.[44] The 'etc.' is not without pathos. Turner, proceeding with feverish enthusiasm into his labyrinths of research, could never quite specify the relationships between his ever exciting discoveries and his general ideas; his ideas were too general, his details too detailed. He seldom seems to have known precisely what question he was trying to answer.

Yet his one famous essay on the frontier influenced more than a generation of scholars; Beard's sketchy and inconclusive tract on the Constitution had almost captured the field by the mid-1930s; Robinson's books sold by the hundreds of thousands. These successes deserve explanation, and an explanation should in turn depend on and help to reveal the more general character of American culture. When the proponents of the new approach began their work, the historical profession in America was still of recent growth. The various men of letters who had taken it upon themselves to write histories, usually in many volumes, during the nineteenth century, had often been men of independent means; few of them owed their opportunities for scholarship to university chairs. In fact posts of any sort were exceedingly sparse; in 1884 there were only about twenty full-time teachers of history in the 400 or so American institutions of higher education, and as late as 1907, when the Mississippi Valley Historical Association was founded, only 250 candidates had taken the degree of Ph.D. in history in all American universities.[45] The popular readership for history actually declined towards the end of the century, and in face of the rise of the social and political sciences, members of the historical profession had some reason to feel that their calling was in

---

[43] Karl Lamprecht, *What is History?* (New York and London, 1905).
[44] W. R. Jacobs, *The World of Frederick Jackson Turner* (New Haven, 1968), p. 99.
[45] Hofstadter, *The Progressive Historians*, p. 35; Higham, *History* p. 19.

a defensive position.[46] The economic, social and psychological problems which beset the country in the 1890s, which included such material events as the economic depression of 1893 and the closing of the frontier of settlement, did not dispose people to believe that the solution of their difficulties lay in the study of history. This state of affairs gives Turner's essay its special significance, not only for the theme it proposed to the American imagination, but for the historical perspective it cast on the present. Turner's message was that the crisis that would arise from the closing of the frontier could be understood only in the light of history, and this brilliant, if somewhat discoloured, flash of illumination gave new life to the hopes and self-respect of historians.

Turner, for the time being, had spent his force. It was far from clear that the detailed filling-in of the landscape he had lit up would be enough to serve the needs of the present, but professional history still tended to be the home of political and economic orthodoxy. When Robinson in due course demanded that history be written to serve the cause of social advance, he not only failed, as Becker pointed out, to specify his meaning of progress in general, but he failed to explain precisely what kind of advance was needed and in what ways the study of history might serve it. Robinson, abetted in this by Beard, was satisfied to declare the aim of promoting history as the study of modern problems; they never seriously addressed their attention to the working out of the problems of method which their programme implied. But the concept of instrumentalism in history accommodates profound differences as to the aims which historical study may serve. It was one thing to believe, as Robinson, who actually declined to admit that he was a social reformer, could reasonably have maintained, that the general character of modern industrial problems called for knowledge of the history of the modern industry. It was another thing to identify some specific problems whose existence was due to the survival of mistaken beliefs or anachronistic institutions. Both Robinson and Barnes, in their optimism about the solvent powers of historical knowledge, seemed unwilling to face the fact that the obstacles to social advance possess a recrudescent character. They renew themselves and spring up afresh even in some cases as a result of the kind of progress that progressives desire. The critical problems for American society in their period were posed not by the legacy of the medieval church (of which Robinson was well aware) but by the new power of the trusts—in which he showed much less interest.

The New Historians only occasionally probed problems of this sort. Considered as historians, they were in fact substantially orthodox;

[46] Higham, *op. cit.*, p. 71.

nor did they contribute any refinements of technique. But their comprehensive embrace of the social sciences caused grave offence to those members of the profession who had spent their lives establishing the reputability of history in face of dangerous academic competition. George Burton Adams, one of the chief patrons of this school, gave vent to his feelings in a presidential address to the American Historical Association in 1908,[47] in which he defended history as an independent science of investigation against the encroachments of political scientists, geographers, economic interpreters, sociologists and social psychologists. He asked whether the profession was moving from an age of investigation to one of speculation? Those interested in theories of aggression will note his use of the idea that what had happened was an 'invasion of territory'. Much the same point was made by William Sloane, the Low Professor at Columbia, in a memorandum to President Butler and the Trustees directed against the activities of Robinson and James T. Shotwell. They were accused of having departed from Columbia traditions in history by establishing courses in the history of thought and culture, 'in which courses they teach didactically from a modernist point of view . . . everything except history as understood by their colleagues'. According to him, the departments of economics and sociology had been disturbed by the 'trespass'.[48]

Yet the New History came increasingly into possession of the field, a process reflected in the increasing modernism of courses and a foreshortening of the perspectives of time. The explanation could not lie exclusively in the internal politics of the profession and its conflict of interest with other disciplines. In the broadest sense, the New History has to be understood in its relation to the emerging material of American culture. As early as 1892, the National Educational Association's Committee of Ten made a remark which reflected the peculiarity as well as the urgency of the social problem facing American education in general. 'An additional responsibility,' said the Report, 'is thrown on the American system of education by the great number of children of foreigners, children who must depend on the schools for their notions of American institutions, or of anything outside their contracted circle.'[49] Mass immigration, on a scale out of all proportion to the experience of other countries, produced a complex of problems of which the most basic was that of language. It is not altogether sur-

[47] G. B. Adams; 'History and the Philosophy of History', *American Hist. Rev.*, xiv (1909).
[48] Richard Hofstadter, 'The Department of History', in R. G. Hoxie, *History of the Faculty of Political Science, Columbia University* (N.Y., 1955), p.227.
[49] *The Study of History in Schools*, pp. 167–68.

prising that educators should have begun to concern themselves with the problems not only of instruction and content but of communication in its broadest sense.

Robinson and Beard both felt that history could be useful to an industrial working class, of whose alienation they were clearly apprehensive, by explaining to them such mechanisms as the division of labour, by which the workers had come, through the growth of industry, to be contributors to a mighty system of which they were beneficiaries as well as servants.[50] These needs did not present themselves to such teachers as involving difficult philosophical questions about the status of historical knowledge; all that concerned them was their right to use history, recognizing the properly scientific methods for ascertaining facts, in their own way, to make it do what they wanted it to do.

All this was less new than it seemed to them. As Commager has argued, Americans had begun from an early date to shape their knowledge of American history into what he has called 'a usable past'.[51] The New History defined itself in relation to the conventions of subject matter and teaching that had established themselves in the small number of genuine institutions of higher learning, during a period of only some thirty years. Its practitioners might have established their claims with more conviction if they had spent more of their efforts in the writing of history as they conceived that it ought to be written, and correspondingly less in what Barnes frankly called 'propaganda'. As it was, the body of their work, when measured against the achievements of their less socially inspired contemporaries, does not seem to possess great powers of endurance. Yet their mood was in tune with the wider audience of the mass universities, their impatience with the remote past was more characteristic, their sense of relevance was constantly merging into their sense of what was American. The cast of mind was discerned, in another connexion, by Momigliano,[52] who has remarked that 'The trust with which Americans welcome foreign historians who import new knowledge and ideas . . . must not conceal the fact that, in the end, the testing ground for the validity of historical theories of any kind is, in America, American history.' The phase of American culture to which these reflections applied as imperatives may, however, have begun to come to a close; there have been increasing and deep signs of a standpoint from which the historian, without feeling compelled to disengage himself from his own society, feels less driven by that society's immediate

---

[50] Cf. Beard, *The Industrial Revolution*; and Robinson, 'History for the Common Man', in *The New History*.

[51] H. S. Commager, *The Search for a Usable Past* (N.Y., 1967).

[52] A. D. Momigliano, *Studies in Historiography* (London, 1966), p. 231.

presence to take a functional and foreshortened view of the past. But that is only one view of the possible future, and I have no intention of committing myself to an act of faith.

Churchill College, Cambridge

PRESIDENTIAL ADDRESS

By R. W. Southern, M.A., D.Litt., F.B.A.

ASPECTS OF THE EUROPEAN TRADITION OF HISTORICAL WRITING: 4. THE SENSE OF THE PAST

READ 24 NOVEMBER 1972

I

IN the first three of these papers I have examined three aspects of the European historical tradition—aspects which I may briefly characterize as classical, early scientific, and prophetic. The models for all these modes were derived from the ancient world, and all three have played an important part in the development of western attitudes to history. Yet no one who looks dispassionately at the works produced by these three modes of studying history will think that they are the main sources of our modern ways of thinking about and writing history. So we must now ask whether it is possible to identify any central tradition in historical study leading to the practice and assumptions of most historians today.

It may help to clear the ground for our enquiry if we begin by asking what were the aims of the historians of the three types which we have so far examined. The brief answer to this question is that the aim of the classical imitators was to exemplify virtues and vices for moral instruction, and to extract from the confusion of the past a clear picture of the destinies of peoples. The aim of the scientific students of universal history was to exhibit the divine plan for mankind throughout history, and to demonstrate the congruity between the facts of history revealed in the Bible and the facts provided by secular sources. As for the prophetic historians, their aim was first to identify the historical landmarks referred to in prophetic utterances, then to discover the point at which history had arrived, and finally to predict the future from the still unfulfilled portions of prophecy.

These purposes cover all the main aims traditionally put forward to justify the study of history. But one has only to mention them to know that they are not those of modern historians. If we ask what these are, no doubt widely different answers can be given. But there is one aim which, whether as an end in itself, or as a means to other ends, nearly all historians will either acknowledge or in practice pursue. This is the aim of reconstituting the thoughts and experiences of the past in their total environment of social relationships and material and mental resources. The hope of success in this task is something new in modern historical writing, and it has created a new relationship between past and present. Even though the historian may reject the thoughts and experiences he describes, and would find them very repellent in practice, yet the act of understanding them creates a bond between past and present, which is all the stronger if these thoughts and experiences are in some sense his own. Whether or not this is the fundamental aim of modern historical study, it is a condition of success in any further aim which the historian may have, and it requires a careful and deliberate cultivation of what we may call a sense of the past.

As an avowed aim of historical study this cultivation of a sense of the past is a fairly recent development. In its most articulate form it is a product of the breakdown of the relatively stable intellectual system which had been created in the Middle Ages and remained substantially operative till the mid-nineteenth century. When the breakdown of this inherited system became widely apparent, and when as a consequence the past ceased to be a repository of true doctrines and became an incoherent heap of errors and inhumanities, sensitive people were threatened with the most serious alienation from their past in the whole course of European history. One remedy for this threatened alienation was an increasingly vigorous and sensitive cultivation of historical understanding. The result of this was to replace intellectual certainty by an emotional cohesion within which all the experiences of the past could coexist. The doctrines of the past might be false, but the experiences which had given rise to the doctrines were indubitably true. By the imaginative appropriation of these experiences, people could still possess the past, while rejecting the intellectual structure which it had once been the rôle of the historical process to hand down intact from age to age.

This struggle between alienation and desire for union with the past provided the impetus—so it seems to me—for the great outburst of historical activity of which we are the heirs. An appreciation of the therapeutic value of this historical activity was not confined to historians. Indeed it was non-historians who rejoiced most abundantly in the cure which it worked; and, since history was a cure for alienation, it is not surprising that it was aliens and exiles who experienced most vividly its healing power. Among these none were more eloquent than Kipling and Henry James. It was the returned exile Kipling—in my view the most gifted historical genius this country has ever produced—who created the most vivid imaginative pictures of the successive phases of life in England going back to a remote antiquity. But it was Henry James I think—and the wide sweep of the historical impulse can be seen in its powerful effect on a man so different in taste and character from Kipling—who first used the phrase 'the sense of the past' to denote the impact of an immensely complicated and varied scene on a historically sensitive mind. He certainly expressed with greater sensitivity than any other writer the mixture of alienation and desire for union which underlies a great mass of late nineteenth-century historical work. This mixture is to be found in innumerable passages, but a single example will suffice. When Nick Dormer in *The Tragic Muse* looked over the estate which he would never inherit, what came over him was

> simply the sense of England—a sort of apprehended revelation of his country. The dim annals of the place appeared to be in the air (foundations bafflingly early, a great monastic life, wars of the Roses, with battles and blood in the streets, and then the long quietude of the respectable centuries, all cornfields and magistrates and vicars) and these things were connected with an emotion that arose from the green country, the rich land so infinitely lived in, and laid on him a hand that was too ghostly to press and yet somehow too urgent to be light. It produced a throb that he could not have spoken of, it was so deep, and that was half imagination and half responsibility.

One could go on for ever in this vein, and of course Henry James virtually did. But, however embarrassing these effusions may seem out of their context, they are valuable witnesses to the consoling sense of continuity and peace which historical studies everywhere in Europe brought to minds bruised by the perplexities of Darwinism, Socialism, and industrial society. This consolation may now seem a feeble thing to minds toughened by long familiarity with these perplexities. The cultivation of a sense of the past now appears rather as a private luxury than as the medicine for the universal ill. But a hundred years ago, the study of history offered a sense of stability, permanence, and the gentleness of change, in place of a long vista of meaningless and inhuman errors. Hence it became the most cultivated area of intellectual activity for the better part of a century.

Historical study has now lost this position, though I am not persuaded that the task which it took up in the mid-nineteenth century, is either completed or unnecessary today. On the contrary, it has only started. It is not, however, my intention tonight to provide an exhibition of the historian as propagandist or prophet. I have mentioned the immediate past not as a basis for prophecy, but as a starting point for looking further back. I want to ask whether situations of alienation in the past have produced outbursts of historical activity similar to that which we find in the nineteenth century, to examine the nature of these outbursts and the effect they have had in forming our habits of historical work.

If we look back with these questions in mind, it is at once clear that there are two periods which require attention. The first is from about 1090 to 1130 and the second from about 1560 to 1620. These are both periods of a conspicuous renewal in historical studies, when there was an abundance of activity among a relatively large number of workers, and when their methods of work were substantially new. Both periods, moreover, came after a crisis in national affairs, which seemed to alienate men from their past. To these periods I now turn.

II

The first historical revival began about twenty-five years after the Norman Conquest of England. The features in the situation which provoked it were these. The old English aristocracy had disappeared; the English language, which had recently been the medium of all social life and a surprisingly large area of religious life, was no longer in use in the upper strata of society. The literature, educational manuals, prayers, rituals, laws, and legal procedures, which had employed this language, were rapidly becoming unintelligible curiosities. At the level of literate and aristocratic society, no country in Europe, between the rise of the barbarian kingdoms and the twentieth century, has undergone so radical a change in so short a time as England experienced after 1066. The distant eye of the historian can detect many signs of continuity, but to cultivated contemporaries these signs must have been very inconspicuous. The main reaction of men who had known pre-Conquest England was one of outrage, resentment, and nostalgia. As late as 1120 William of Malmesbury, who was only half English and no enemy to the Normans, could write of the state of England:

It is the habitation of strangers and the domination of foreigners. There is today no Englishman who is either earl, bishop or abbot. The newcomers devour the riches and entrails of England, and there is no hope of the misery coming to an end.[1]

[1] William of Malmesbury, *Gesta Regum* (ed. W. Stubbs, Rolls Series, 1887), i, p. 278.

And this was not an isolated voice. It was the voice of a whole generation of literate men who had English ancestors.

The only people who were in a position to observe, feel, and express their reaction to these changes, were Benedictine monks in monasteries sufficiently old and wealthy to evoke an acute sense of the difference between the present and the past. The members of these communities lived among the evidences of ancient greatness, and they were exposed more continuously than any others to the dangers of the present in the multiple forms of the loss of lands, the destruction of rituals, the plundering of ancient treasures, and the overturning of old habits of life. Many, probably most, members of ancient monasteries in 1100 were men of English descent. They were the lucky Englishmen of their generation, for compared with their relatives who belonged to the dispossessed or depressed aristocracy, they had survived with their way of life relatively intact. They were not unaware or ungrateful for their good fortune, but it made them all the more sensitive to the places where the shoe pinched most. Most irksome of all, they felt their exclusion from all promotion. This was one cause of internal tension within monastic communities, and it drew English monks together in defence of their past.

The men of English speech in the monasteries felt themselves the special custodians of the monastic past, and this gave them some compensation for their exclusion from high office. Besides being bound to the past by blood, they were the only members of the community who could understand the documents in which much of the evidence of the past was preserved. Yet it must not be thought that they were the only members of monastic communities who valued the past greatness of their monasteries. Everyone who lives in an ancient community is sooner or later drawn into the task of defending it against all comers. In the last resort commitment to the community knows no limits. But in the post-Conquest monasteries the threat of the outside world evoked responses of varying degrees of intensity. The crudest threat was to the monastic lands, and all members could combine wholeheartedly to resist this. The many intruders into monastic estates could be repelled only by constant vigilance and frequent reference to early documents. In making these documents available for instant use, the English monks were doing a service which all their brethren would applaud. They could be less sure of applause in their efforts to repel the threats to local rituals, to domestic legends, to traditional claims to respect and authority. On these points the newcomers in the community required instruction, and we can sometimes see with extraordinary clarity how the English monks set about this task—surreptitiously at first, and then with growing confidence and success. Superficially, the written evidence at their disposal was not impressive. There were many silent shrines:

> This is a state of affairs which you will find in many places in England: the evidence has been destroyed by the violence of enemies, so that only the names of saints remain and their modern miracles, if any.[2]

In the days of their prosperity the old monasteries had relied on established usage, on the support of kings and nobles, and on popular veneration, to preserve all that they valued in their way of life. Consequently the evidence was scattered, fragmentary, and difficult to interpret. Yet there was an abundance of ancient charters; the bodies of the saints lay thick on the ground; although many manuscripts had been destroyed or stolen, there were still ancient volumes which preserved the outlines of the old monastic culture. All these documents told something about the ancient saints and patrons of the community, and there were many legends which enforced the intimate connexion between the prosperity of the kingdom and the greatness of the monasteries. The task of bringing this fragmentary and widely dispersed material together, and extracting from it a story which would impress hostile or indifferent contemporaries, was very urgent, but it was also very difficult.

It was not only in England that Benedictine monks felt their position threatened in the early twelfth century. In Germany, especially, there were monks, like Rupert of Deutz, who bitterly resented their depreciation by the world and expressed this bitterness very copiously. Rupert of Deutz tried to restore the scholarly reputation of the monasteries by undertaking vast works of Biblical and liturgical interpretation, and by engaging in ill-advised controversy with scholastic theologians.[3] There is nothing like this in England. The English reaction was peculiar in its strong historical bias, and there was an obvious reason for this. The Norman Conquest provided an event in the past to which every evil could be traced: 'the fatal day for England, the mournful end of the sweet country, the coming of the new lord'.[4] All hope of revival, all hope of resistance to further depre-

---

[2] William of Malmesbury, *Gesta Pontificum* (ed. N. E. S. A. Hamilton, Rolls Series, 1870), p. 202.

[3] The monastic reaction in Germany has been intensively studied in recent years, especially in the persons of Rupert of Deutz and Gerhoh of Reichersberg. For the former, see especially the remarkable article of H. Grundmann, 'Der Brand von Deutz 1128 in der Darstellung Abt Ruperts von Deutz', *Deutsches Archiv*, xxii (1966), pp. 385–471; also R. Haacke, 'Die Überlieferung der Schriften Ruperts v. Deutz', *ibid.*, xvi (1960), pp. 397–436, and H. Silvestre, 'La lettre d'Anselme de Laon à Héribrand de St-Laurent', *Recherches de Théologie ancienne et médiévale*, xxvii (1961), pp. 5–26.

[4] *Gesta Regum*, ii, p. 304.

ciation, depended on reanimating the pre-Conquest past and showing that the Conquest was no more than a tremor in a long development. It was from this situation that the English historical movement developed. It developed spontaneously in monasteries which were widely separated geographically, but they all had the same problem and all possessed similar material for dealing with it. Canterbury, Malmesbury, Worcester, Evesham, and Durham were the outstanding places in the movement; but Abingdon, Rochester, Glastonbury, Thorney, Peterborough, and Ramsey all made a contribution. The movement had its great names—Eadmer, William of Malmesbury, Symeon of Durham, Wulfstan, Florence and John of Worcester, chief among them—but it was not inspired by the personal tastes of a few antiquaries. It drew its inspiration and gained its momentum from the necessities of corporate survival—at the lowest level mere physical survival; at the highest, the survival of an ancient monastic culture, a religious and intellectual tradition, and a position in the world. What was important for success in this task was the cumulative weight of many men working on similar material for similar purposes in many different places. It was this that gave consistency to the historical work of the period. Circumstances forced scholarly monks all over England to become historians, to examine the historical content of material which had never been used in this way before, and to extract from unpromising documents a new picture of antiquity.

The mistake is often made of looking for evidence of a historical revival only in the histories which it produces; and this mistake has obscured the character of the work done by these monastic scholars. Just as the finest work of the modern historical movement is to be found in editions of texts, catalogues of materials, and critical notes on sources, symbols, and social habits, so in the twelfth century the historical revival is to be seen as a continuous process of collecting and arranging charters, transcribing documents, and carrying out minute investigations into chronology and topography, studying monastic buildings and inscriptions, assembling the texts of ancient learning, writing estate-histories, chronicles, and biographies—and only at the end of the day the histories which we all know.

The initial impulse was sternly practical, but the work diverged in different directions according to the needs and resources of the community, and the scholarly talent which each community contained. At Worcester the practical impulse is very clearly expressed in the preface to the collection of charters made by the monk Hemming in about 1095:

Wulfstan, bishop of this see, caused this book to be written to teach his successors about the things which have been committed to their care, and to show them which lands justly belong (or ought to belong) to the church, and which have been unjustly seized by evil men—first, during the Danish invasions; later, by unjust royal officials and tax collectors; and most recently, by the violence of Normans in our own time, who by force, guile and rapine have unjustly deprived this holy church of its lands, villages and possessions, until hardly anything is safe from their depredations.[5]

It would be hard to think of anything more practical than this. Yet bare practicality can scarcely have inspired research into the depredations of Danish invaders two centuries earlier, or of royal officials in the tenth and eleventh centuries. By no conceivable process of law could these losses be made good, and very few of the documents in Hemming's cartulary can ever have been produced in a court of law. In its totality the collection provides, not a practical handbook, but a complete picture of past glories, most of them beyond human powers to restore, but all of them laid up in heaven and apprehensible on earth only by the historical imagination. This imaginative reconstruction of the monastic past inevitably grew out of the initial impulse to regain lost lands and to save those which remained. It was part of a large effort to make the past alive in the present. Even in the act of stating his practical aim Hemming at Worcester illustrates the extension of purpose which was common to all ancient monastic communities.

Worcester, however, also illustrates a quite different historical extension taking place at the same time. Bishop Wulfstan, who promoted the collection of charters, also promoted the enlargement of monastic history from a local to a universal setting. The process of enlargement can be observed in the manuscript of the Worcester chronicle preserved at Corpus Christi College, Oxford (MS. 157). The volume starts with a historical account of the origin of the see of Worcester and of the possessions given to it between 679 and 1093. Then after various other preliminary matters—lists of consuls, popes and bishops, genealogies of kings, Easter Tables, sacred sites (the basic materials of universal history)—the manuscript contains the most learned of all contemporary attempts to fit the facts of English history into a universal chronology. It is worth noting that this scholarly purpose, and consequently the whole movement of thought which the Worcester volume represents, is wholly obscured in the only generally available edition. The editor—true to the tradition which regarded

---

[5] *Hemingi Chartularium Ecclesiae Wigorniensis* (ed. T. Hearne, Oxford, 1723), ii, p. 391. For the composition of the cartulary see N. R. Ker, 'Hemming's Cartulary', *Studies in Medieval History presented to F. M. Powicke* (Oxford, 1948), pp. 49–75.

medieval chronicles simply as repositories of facts and not as evidence of the minds and intentions of their authors—printed only the insertions relating to English history and entirely ignored the body on to which they were grafted. To get a truer picture we have to go back to the edition of 1592, and only a photographic edition could adequately represent the various streams of thought which converged to make up this volume.[6] It was not a mechanical task which the compiler undertook; it required an elaborate series of chronological decisions, a wide learning, and a continuous search for new sources. The Corpus manuscript with its many corrections and changes of hand brings us into immediate contact with the long continued effort which these processes entailed, and it makes intelligible the fame of the monk (in the phrase of his contemporary admirer) 'whose subtle learning and laborious scholarship made this composite chronicle pre-eminent over all others'.

If Worcester illustrates the historical movement at its two extremes of territorial intensity and universal extension, Durham illustrates a different kind of movement. Here too the practical impulse of self-protection is very conspicuous, but the historical manifestations of a single character, St Cuthbert, stand out more clearly than anything else in the past. No community had more physical objects which recalled its past than Durham, and the most important of these were associated with the many journeys of the saint's body in the centuries from 875 to 1070. In the cemetery there was the stone cross made by Bishop Ethelwold in about 730, broken by the Vikings in 793, repaired, and carried with the body of St Cuthbert till it finally came to rest at Durham. On the altar there was the Gospel Book written by Bishop Eadfrith about 700, bound by his successor Bishop Aethelwold, and ornamented by Billfrith the anchorite. This too had accompanied the saint from Lindisfarne, and it bore the traces of its miraculous survival after immersion in the sea in the course of these travels. Beside it on the altar there lay the Book of Life, with the names of monks, friends, and benefactors of St Cuthbert begun in the eighth century and continued to the present day. Outside, on the monastic estates, there still lived descendants of the men who had carried the body from 875 to 883 and could trace their genealogies back to the years of travel. And most impressive of all, there were the

---

[6] The main part of the manuscript was probably written between 1120 and 1122, with corrections and additions to 1130. The chronicle of Marianus Scotus on which is was based was brought to England by Robert, bishop of Hereford 1079–1095, and no doubt introduced to Worcester by Wulfstan. Unfortunately no manuscript takes us back to the early stages of compilation at Worcester before the death of Florence, the original compiler, in 1118; but the corrections and additions vividly illustrate the continuing tradition of historical work after Florence's death.

many gifts of lands, books, and ornaments given by King Athelstan in recognition of St Cuthbert's help in uniting the kingdom under his rule.[7]

These may seem small matters, scarcely worth detaining the Society for the length of time it takes to tell them, but taken together they built up a complicated sense of the past, which must always be made up of small things vividly perceived.

The post-Conquest historical revival was very rich in historical perceptions. Each community added some feature of its own. At Christ Church, Canterbury, the main corporate interest was at first concentrated on the great collection of saints' bodies which lay around in disarray. The writing of their biographies, the authentication of their miracles, the preservation of their Feasts, were the primary tasks of historical effort. Here too, as elsewhere, the charters were collected, annotated, and transcribed, to resist attack. Too often, more often and more radically than elsewhere, they were brought up to date, for at Canterbury new problems had arisen for which the past could provide an answer only by being taken firmly in hand. The fatal dispute about the primacy and the great political issues of St Anselm's time gave a new direction to the historical interests of the community, and especially of Eadmer its best historian. He had as great a love of the English past as anyone, but he was spoilt as a researcher by his opportunities for observing the present. As the companion of Archbishop Anselm he had moved more freely among the great men and isssues of his day than any of his contemporary monks. These experiences altered his view of the past. He looked for contemporary issues in past events, and his *Historia Novorum* was an explicit attempt to provide the kind of evidence he would have liked to find:

> When [he wrote] I see men of the present time, hard-pressed by misfortunes, anxiously scanning the deeds of their predecessors for consolation and strength, and unable to get as much as they wish, I conceive it will be a great service to posterity to commit to writing the deeds of the present for the use of the future.[8]

The objects of research were everywhere influenced by locality. At Glastonbury, the oldest of the English monasteries, the main interest of the monks lay in extending their history backwards as far as it

[7] For the objects associated with the journey of St Cuthbert's body see *Symeonis Monachi Opera Omnia* (ed. T. Arnold, Rolls Series, 1882), i, pp. 39, 57, 64, 66, 67, 74–75, 79–80; and for Athelstan's gifts, i, pp. 75, 211. For the Durham MSS mentioned above see R. A. B. Mynors, *Durham Cathedral Manuscripts* (Oxford, 1939), nos 5, 13, 15, 16.

[8] Eadmer, *Historia Novorum*, ed. M. Rule (Rolls Series, 1884), p. 1. For historical studies and their background at Canterbury, see R. W. Southern, *St. Anselm and his Biographer* (Cambridge, 1963), pp. 229–336.

would go—to St Patrick, and ultimately to King Arthur.[9] At Abingdon the main interest was in the history of the estates;[10] at Evesham in the miracles of the saints.[11] Thorney and Peterborough did most for the revival of Anglo-Saxon scientific learning.[12] At Rochester the monk who put together and transcribed the monastery's charters also made the fullest collection of Old English laws and legal texts, stretching from the laws of Aethelberht in about 600 to Henry I's Coronation Charter in 1100. The arrangement and correct transcription of these texts in Old English was a notable scholarly achievement, and the impulse behind it can only have been the desire, which the compiler shaded with his English monastic contemporaries, to demonstrate that the Norman Conquest had only shaken, but not interrupted, a long development.[13]

Finally there is the community which produced the most talented of all the researchers of this period: William of Malmesbury.[14] Unlike Eadmer, his only rival as a historian, William never deviated from the corporate monastic purpose of recreating the Old English past, and of all the monastic scholars of his day he knew best how to use ancient materials.

His virtuosity can best be studied in his small work on the antiquity of Glastonbury, which was once the most despised of all the historical productions of this time. Armitage Robinson, nearly fifty years ago, restored it to respectability, though not to the fame which it deserves,

[9] See below, p. 254, no. 15.

[10] The essential text is British Museum, Cotton MS. Claudius C ix, ff. 105–203, badly edited by J. Stevenson, *Chronicon Monasterii de Abingdon*, 2 vols. (Rolls Series, 1858), and first given its due importance by F. M. Stenton, *The Early History of the Abbey of Abingdon* (Reading, 1913).

[11] The most important writer at Evesham was Prior Dominic, on whom see J. C. Jennings, 'The Writings of Prior Dominic of Evesham', *English Historical Review*, lxxvii (1962), pp. 298–304, and 'The Origins of the "Elements Series" of the Miracles of the Virgin', *Mediaeval and Renaissance Studies*, vi (1968), pp. 84–93; also the texts in *Chronicon Abbatiae de Evesham* (ed. W. D. Macray, Rolls Series, 1863), pp. 1–100.

[12] The main manuscripts are St John's College, Oxford, MS. 17 with British Museum Cotton MS. Nero C vii from Thorney, written (with additions) in the period from 1085 to 1125 (see N. R. Ker, *British Museum Quarterly*, xii (1938), p. 131); and B.M. Cotton Tiberius C i, ff. 2–42 with Harleian 3667 from Peterborough, written in 1121–22. For the Easter Tables in the Thorney MS. with their uniquely long series of annals from 528 to 1536, see C. Hart, 'The Ramsey Computus', *English Historical Review*, lxxxv (1970), pp. 29–44.

[13] The works of this most expert of all post-Conquest students of Anglo-Saxon can now be studied in a facsimile edition with a full analysis and introduction, by Peter Sawyer, *Early English Manuscripts in Facsimile* (1957), vii (*Textus Roffensis*, Pt. i), and xi (1962) (*Textus Roffensis*, Pt. ii).

[14] For a recent survey of his life and works, see H. Farmer in *Journal of Ecclesiastical History*, xiii (1962), pp. 39–54.

by freeing it from later imaginative accretions.[15] It was in its origin a polemical work, designed to show that the earliest of the post-Conquest Canterbury historians had been wrong in saying that Dunstan in 942 was the first abbot of Glastonbury. The monks of Glastonbury gave William access to all their materials and he had no difficulty in proving his main point. But the peculiar excellence of his work lies in the way in which he used his materials. Eight hundred and fifty years before J. H. Round he discovered how to use charters as a historian.

Several monastic scholars of the day discovered that a history of the monastic estates could be extracted from charters, but William alone saw how many-sided this history could be. He read charters with an eye open for every hint they could give him. He saw that they told a story, not only of losses and gains throughout the centuries, but also of kings and bishops with intelligible wills and purposes. He used witness lists to establish the succession of bishops and abbots. He drew on them for archaeological details. He noticed the nationality of early donors, whether they were British or Saxon, and he remarked that Cadwalla, while he was still a pagan, already used the sign of the cross to authenticate his charters. And to the evidence of the charters, he added the evidence of tombs and inscriptions, crosses, reliquaries, books, and ornaments. From the whole mass of fragments he constructed a history in which local men known only by their names mingled with some of the greatest names in English history. By the standards of modern scholarship William was a primitive operator, but he had grasped the essential principle that in studying a period for which there is little evidence no detail and no kind of evidence are unimportant.

The methods which he employed in his history of Glastonbury are to be found in all his works. He himself thought that his ecclesiastical survey of England, his *Gesta Pontificum*, was his most original work, and in this he was right, though not altogether for the reasons he gives. He thought that his originality consisted in doing something which no one had previously attempted:

> Here I am destitute of all help; I feel the palpable darkness of ignorance, and I have no lantern of an earlier history to guide my footsteps.[16]

---

[15] The contaminated text is printed in T. Hearne, *Adami de Domerham Historia de rebus Glastoniensibus* (Oxford, 1727), pp. 1–122. For the original text see J. Armitage Robinson, *Somerset Historical Essays* (Oxford, for the British Academy, 1921), pp. 1–25, and his later study, *Two Glastonbury Legends: King Arthur and Joseph of Arimathea* (Cambridge, 1926).

[16] *Gesta Pontificum*, p. 2.

All this is fine and true. But his more important originality lay in extending to the whole kingdom the corporate aims of each monastic researcher of his day. He used the materials of every monastery he could visit, or from which he could get information—their chronicles, charters, legends, ornaments, inscriptions, and buildings—to make a survey of the whole kingdom. He travelled widely to gather material for his book, and he is the first of a long line of historians whose sense of the English past has been developed in the course of extensive journeys, notebook in hand, recording inscriptions, examining charters, and writing descriptions of the places he visited.[17] His brief descriptions of Canterbury, Rochester, Glastonbury, London, Hereford, York, Durham, Crowland, Thorney, the vale of Gloucester, and the fens, are the first accounts of ancient places in this country seen through the eyes of a man with a critical and developed sense of the past.

If his *Gesta Pontificum* is the most original of his works, the account it contains of Aldhelm, the founder of his own monastery, is his masterpiece of historical method, doing for a single man of the late seventh century what he had earlier done for the monastery at Glastonbury through several centuries. The attempt to evoke a figure of so distant a past from such fragmentary materials—for he had no contemporary biography to guide him—was a daunting task. He had to rely on a mixture of charters, inscriptions, archaeological remains, pictures, legends, and chronicles; and to these he added Aldhelm's own theological writings and letters. In its complicated texture, its critical assessment of the evidence, and its total use of the evidence, it is—in the whole body of medieval historical writing—the piece which leaves the strongest impression of modernity.

William was well aware that he was writing history in a manner widely different from that of historians writing in the rhetorical tradition. He inveighed against the use of rhetoric to add bulk to an exiguous work: he had made it a rule, he said, to add nothing except to put the meaning of an old author in a clearer light. He denounced the commonest of all rhetorical devices, the introduction of imaginary speeches: 'the memory of the *deeds* of the past has scarcely come down to us', he wrote; 'how much less the *volatile* words?'[18] He had a strict idea of what he meant by *integritas* in historical writing: it meant the frequent quotation of texts and a close reliance on his

[17] Most of William's descriptions of places throughout England occur in his *Gesta Pontificum*, and it seems likely that he did most of his travelling in preparation for this work between the completion of the *Gesta Regum* in about 1120–1 and the *Gesta Pontificum* in 1125.

[18] *Memorials of St Dunstan* (ed. W. Stubbs, Rolls Series, 1874), pp. 287–88, 317.

sources. If his ideas of relevance and of the relative importance of events sometimes seem very bizarre to us, we must remember that the whole school of scholars to which he belonged would have rejected our notion of importance. What mattered to them was the web of associations which made objects or events, however trivial, part of the life of the community. Every object in the church and every portion of land, and all their associations with past events and people, had a place in the composite picture. The prime object was to connect the community with its past by making its physical being a vehicle for the remembrance of a great army of benefactors, craftsmen, saints, and enemies. The aim was a total recall of the past in order to give the community its identity in the present.

The historical scholars who worked for this end were inspired by ideals quite different from those of classical, universal, or prophetic historians. They rejected both the form and the rhetoric of classical models. They accepted unpredictable confusion as the ordinary state of men in history, and they found a uniting thread, not in the working out of a grand design, but in the memories of small communities accumulating over several centuries. Their only contribution to universal history was to fit these microscopically small events into the system of earlier scholars. They took no account of the end of the world, which (in their sense) ended where the monastic property began. By way of compensation for their limitations, they had a vivid interest in the texts of old documents and an eagerness in collecting and scrutinizing them. Their whole effort was anchored in the countryside and in the defence of a long established way of life. Out of their local knowledge and their local materials they created the image of a phase of English history which would scarcely have existed without their efforts: substantially they were responsible for bringing Anglo-Saxon history into existence.

III

If time and ability allowed I should have liked to show how the methods and aims of the early twelfth-century monks, and the necessities which moved them to undertake their work, were revived in the antiquaries of the sixteenth and seventeenth centuries. From this point one could trace the stages by which their work became the foundation of modern historical studies. But the time for such a survey has not yet come. Despite all the work that has been done in recent years, the bulk of unexplored material is still very large. Instead of losing myself and my audience in this jungle, let me simply offer a slight sketch of a Tudor researcher at work, with a few remarks on the type he represents.

For my sketch I choose neither the most original nor the most influential—neither, on the one hand, Laurence Nowell, who revived the study of Anglo-Saxon at the point where it had been abandoned in the early twelfth century, nor on the other, a great entrepreneur like Camden—but a man between Nowell and Camden in time and influence: William Lambarde.[19] Nowell was his master in Anglo-Saxon; Camden his supplanter in fame. He came from the level of society which produced most of the hard-working antiquaries of the next hundred years, and he displays most of the features of the type. He was a small Kentish landowner, the newest of the newcomers in his class, for his father—a London draper and alderman—had bought the small manor at Greenwich, which his son inherited, only ten years before he died. William was eighteen when he succeeded his father in 1554. Before he was thirty he was a member of the House of Commons, where he narrowly escaped being associated with Peter Wentworth.[20] When he was forty-one he became a bencher of Lincoln's Inn and two years later a J.P. At fifty-five he was appointed a Master in Chancery, at sixty-one Deputy Keeper of the Rolls, and at sixty-five Keeper of the Records in the Tower.[21] His last appointment was in 1601, and he died in the same year. For a brief period in Parliament, and for a long time in local affairs, at Quarter Sessions, and in the Court of Chancery, he was a very busy man, but it is as a historian that I commemorate him now.

[19] The best accounts of his career are Conyers Read, *William Lambarde and Local Government* (Ithaca, N.Y., 1962), and Wilbur Dunkel, *William Lambarde, Elizabethan Jurist, 1536–1601* (New Brunswick, 1956). Robin Flower, 'Laurence Nowell and the Discovery of England in Tudor Times', *Proceedings of the British Academy*, xxi (1935), pp. 47–73, has a valuable account of the relations between Lambarde and Nowell, based on the Nowell transcripts (which belonged to Lambarde) in British Museum, Additional MSS. 43703–10, but he exaggerates the importance of Nowell in Lambarde's development. Lambarde is scarcely noticed in F. S. Fussner, *The Historical Revolution: English Historical Writing and Thought, 1580–1640* (London, 1962), where his contemporaries are discussed at length.

[20] For Lambarde's career in Parliament as member for Aldborough (Yorks) in 1563 and 1566, see J. E. Neale, *Elizabeth I and her Parliaments, 1559–1581* (1953). The main evidence for the identification of William Lambarde with the Mr Lambert, who made a speech in Parliament on the succession in 1566 is a small treatise on Parliament (in *Harleian Miscellany*, v (1810), pp. 258–67), which gives an account of the speech of 1566 made by 'this writer, W. L.' The treatise and (more especially) the collection of documents of which it forms part clearly reflect William Lambarde's manner of composition. The title 'Some certaine notes of the Order, Proceedings, Punishments, and Priviledges of the Lower house of Parliament Gathered by W. Lambert', generally given to the treatise, really refers to the whole collection in British Museum Add. MS. 5123, in which the treatise is only one item.

[21] The dates are provided by the family diary which Lambarde started, printed in *Miscellanea Genealogica et Heraldica*, ii (1876), pp. 99–101.

He was not an antiquary of the type which became common in the eighteenth century, when men of abundant leisure took an interest —more or less profound according to their abilities—in every kind of curious or ancient object. With Lambarde it was his business, not his leisure, that made him a historian. In all phases of his life he felt an intense urge to give his position a historical dimension. In the 1560s, before he had settled down and when he was briefly active in Parliament, he took all England as his theme, and he then planned an ambitious 'description and History of our whole Realm'. Then,

after such time as it had pleased my good God, by marriage of a wife, to bestow me in Kent, I resolved for sundry just respects to draw out of that my Topographical storehouse a particular discourse of Kent.

This resolve produced, in 1571, his *Perambulation of Kent*, the first of our county histories.[22] Nine years later, on 6 August 1579, he was put on the Commission of the Peace in Kent, and at once began 'in greedy haste' to study the history of his new Office. The first draft of his work on this subject bears the date of the very month of his appointment. It was published two years later, in 1581, as *Eirenarcha, or of the Office of Justices of Peace*, and for the next twenty years he continuously revised it, thickening his illustrations from the past and enlarging his views of the future.[23] His work as a Justice led him to probe more deeply into the lower offices of the shire, and to produce in 1583 a volume on the duties of 'Constables, borsholders, tithingmen, and such other lowe Ministers of the Peace'.[24] Having, in the

[22] The work was not printed until 1576, when Thomas Wotton (the father of Sir Henry) published it with a dedication to the 'Gentlemen of Kent'. Lambarde had sent it to Wotton on 31 January 1571 with a letter, which is printed in the second edition of 1596. A draft of the letter to Wotton with Lambarde's numerous corrections for the second edition is in the Bodleian copy of the *Perambulation* (4° Rawl. 263). Another copy with an autograph letter from Lambarde to Sir Henry Sydney, dated 1 June 1576, explaining the circumstances of the composition and publication of the work, is also in the Bodleian (4° Rawl. 587). It is from this letter that I have taken (with slight abbreviation and modernization of spelling) the extract quoted above. Lambarde, of course, had an estate in Kent before his marriage, but there is no evidence that he ever lived on it. After 1570 he divided his time between the Kentish family-estates of his wives and Lincoln's Inn.

[23] The original draft of 1579 is British Museum Add. MS. 41137. The title page has Lambarde's signature (in Anglo-Saxon characters) with the date August 1579 followed by notes of the revisions to 1594. For a full description of the manuscript see B. H. Putnam, 'The earliest form of Lambard's 'Eirenarcha' and a Kent Wage Assessment of 1563', *English Historical Review*, xli (1926), pp. 260–73. For Lambarde's work as a J.P., see J. H. Gleason, *The Justices of Peace in England 1558–1604* (Oxford, 1969).

[24] As with most of his works, Lambarde continued to revise and to produce enlarged editions (1587, 1594, 1599) until the end of his life.

course of these studies, become convinced that 'the base courts of the Shires, Hundreds, Boroughs and Manors do yet remain in a manner the same in substance that they then (in Anglo-Saxon times) were' he turned his attention to the Courts of King's Bench, Star-Chamber, Constable's Court, Admiralty, etc., and showed (as he thought) that they had all sprung from the same root in the King's court.[25] By this time he was becoming closely associated with the central legal administration, and a few months before his appointment as a Master in Chancery he produced his *Archeion, or a Commentary upon the High Courts of Justice in England*, in which he traced the history of the various branches of the royal courts of justice.[26] Meanwhile his experiences in the House of Commons led him to make a collection of ancient treaties and notes on the proceedings of Parliament.[27] And, in his last years, his work as a lawyer in the Court of Chancery caused him to collect precedents, which were later published as a volume 'out of the labours of Master William Lambert'.[28] Everywhere he discovered that the roots of his daily work were hidden in deep layers of the past. *Periit et inventa est:* this motto on his volume of 1583 might apply to his whole search for the past—'It was lost, and is found'.

His life provides as perfect a conjunction of history and practice as we can find. Yet a man's thoughts always range more widely than his business. In the sixteenth, as in the twelfth century, practical and psychological needs might provide the initial impetus, but the result was a new vision of the past beyond all the claims of necessity. We can follow the growth of Lambarde's vision most clearly in his notebooks and annotations. They are the raw material for his printed works, and they show how widely he ranged and how varied were his sources and his friends. His earliest extracts seem to have been chiefly from chronicles, often transcribed in collaboration with his 'dearest friend' Laurence Nowell. The earliest date in these notebooks is 1560, when Lambarde made extracts from Gerald of Wales's *Itinerary* and

---

[25] For his conclusions on the development of these courts, see *Archeion* (1635), pp. 21, 27.

[26] The manuscript of the work which Lambarde sent to Sir Robert Cecil in 1591, with the dedicatory letter in his own hand, is in the Bodleian, Carte MS. 174. The work was not printed until 1635. There is a modern edition by C. H. McIlwain and P. L. Ward (Cambridge, Mass., 1957).

[27] See above, p. 257, n. 20.

[28] *Reports of Causes in Chancery Collected by Sir George Cary one of the Masters of the Chancery in Anno 1601 out of the labours of Master William Lambert* (printed 1650). There is an important study of the collection of material from which these 'Reports' were drawn, by P. L. Ward, 'William Lambarde's Collections on Chancery', *Harvard Library Bulletin*, vii (1953), pp. 271–98. For Lambarde's work as a Master in Chancery, see W. J. Jones, *The Elizabethan Court of Chancery* (Oxford, 1967), pp. 103–17.

Topography of Wales.[29] Later, his interests expanded to include records of many kinds—Perambulations of the Forest, fiscal returns, surveys of the courts of Chancery and Exchequer, lists of castles, and land-owners in Kent who had obtained an alteration in the terms of their tenure. One of his manuscripts contains taxation records for Knights' Fees and ecclesiastical benefices from 1483 to 1581. In another he constructed an imitation of an Anglo-Saxon Easter Table from 1571 to 1600 with all the appropriate apparatus of Indictions, Epacts, Golden Numbers, Sunday Letters, and Feast Days. The latest dated transcript of his I have seen is a copy of a fourteenth-century treatise on the coinage made in 1588.[30]

Anything that was old and English, especially if it was also Kentish, was noted, extracted, and indexed. But it was long a puzzle to him to know how to use all his material. At first he thought of bringing everything together in a Topographical Dictionary of England.[31] The book on Kent was an experimental volume extracted from his material. He sent this at the beginning of 1571 to his fellow Kentish landowner Thomas Wotton with a letter explaining his method and his hope of expanding the work into 'a description and story of the most famous places throughout the Realm'. For several years he continued to collect material for the large work, but his hopes of completing it (if indeed they were still alive) were dashed in 1585 when he received a pre-publication copy of Camden's *Britannia*, which anticipated his own plan. In its first edition, Camden's *Britannia* was a jejune and inferior performance but it had the merit of having actually appeared, which Lambarde's would probably never have done. Lambarde's letter of thanks is a model for anyone who finds himself in a similar position:

> In reading these your painful topographies I have been contrarily affected; one way taking singular delight and pleasure in the perusing of them; another way by sorrowing that I may not now, as I wonted, dwell in the meditation of the same things that you are occupied withal. And yet I must confess that the delectation which I reaped by your labours recompensed the grief that I conceived of mine own bereaving from the like: notwithstanding that

[29] Bodleian Library MS. Rawlinson B 471, ff. 1–13. This MS. also contains a text and translation of Walter of Henley, an analysis of the members and officials of the Court of Chancery, and extracts from Bracton, etc., on the 'writing and making of Deeds or Muniments in Law'.

[30] Bodleian MS. Rawlinson B 198. The other MSS mentioned in this paragraph are British Museum, Cotton MSS Vespasian A v and Julius C ix, and Add. MS. 43705. The Easter Table is in Bodleian MS. Hatton 41.

[31] The notes for this work were printed by Fletcher Gyles in 1730. The last addition which can be dated was made in 1577 (p. 410).

in time past I have preferred the reading of antiquities before any sort of study that ever I frequented. . . . To be plain, I seem to myself not to have known Kent till I knew Camden.[32]

After this act of renunciation, he went on in the second edition of his *Perambulation* to express an opinion which is a charter for all later work undertaken by county historians:

Nevertheless, being assured that the inwards of each place may best be known by such as reside therein, I cannot but still encourage some one able man in each shire to undertake his own.[33]

Lambarde's discovery that history is best written from inside, and that it was his own task to write it in this way, came at the end of a long search. In 1577 he was still engaged on his Topography 'digging and raking together the antiquities of this realm which (as metall conteyned within the bowells of the earth) lie hidden in old books hoarded up in corners'. But he may in the end not have been sorry to find that Camden had forestalled him, and that his own task was to be confined to the countryside he knew best, and to the history of the offices and courts with which he was familiar through personal experience.

IV

This is the picture of a Tudor researcher at work. There had been a few—a very few—like him in the hundred years before 1550, but he and his friends, and the similar groups who were beginning to appear in other parts of the country, were the first body of workers since the historical revival of the early twelfth century to devote themselves to a systematic examination of records and chronicles over a wide area of country. They turned over great masses of unexplored documents searching for material of historical interest. They analysed and transcribed indefatigably; and they exchanged their results. As in the earlier period, so in the sixteenth century, the writing of great histories was not the primary aim. These workers felt (as Lambarde described himself) like miners digging great masses of ore out of the earth, casting it into rude lumps, and then looking round to see what they could make of it. Slowly the books began to emerge, but the first aim was simply (in Lambarde's words) 'to attayne to some knowledge and understanding of the antiquities of this realme'.

---

[32] See the memoirs of William Lambarde Esq. in *Bibliotheca Topographica Britannica* (1790), i, p. 512.

[33] *Perambulation of Kent* (1596), pp. 526–27. The drafts for this passage, which show Lambarde's anxiety to give Camden his full due, are in the Bodleian copy (4° Rawl. 587), p. 378.

If we ask why they wanted to do this, the reason seems to be that—
like the English monks nearly five hundred years earlier—they were
the fortunate but uneasy survivors of a great upheaval, and they
wanted to overcome the sense of alienation from the past, which was
threatened by the destruction of old institutions and the growing
unintelligibility of old books and records. This desire to make the
present intelligible by linking it with the past affected all men of a
certain position in society. The dedications and acknowledgments in
Lambarde's books tell us who they were. Above all they were the
'Gentlemen of England'. Most of them had landed property; many
were beneficiaries of monastic estates; some had ancient documents on
their hands; and all were surrounded by many evidences of past life
and institutions. These evidences were at first sight obscure and
repulsive, but if attacked with sufficient determination, they proved
that local and national affairs had for centuries followed a pattern
which was still familiar and could be stabilized if it was understood. It
is unlikely that antiquarian research was motivated, as it had been in
the twelfth century, by the need to defend titles to land, but in a more
general way it satisfied a need to understand the offices and title-deeds
of a large class of men: the nature of their tenures, their position in
society, and the claims of their families, however recently established,
to a respectable antiquity. Men newly established in county society
and in ancient titles and functions, wanted to feel at home in their
properties, to understand their dignity and offices, and to be identified with the landscape. These were needs which historical research
alone could satisfy.

The researchers of the period after 1560 were the secular successors
of the post-Conquest monks. They were engaged in the same task of
bridging a gap between past and present which made them uneasy and
diminished their stature in society. But at this point an important
difference has to be noticed. The post-Conquest monks were sure that
they had a great past, but they were uncertain of their present and
future. Their post-Reformation secular successors were relatively
sure of the present but uncertain of their past. The monks felt the
danger of losing their lands; the new landowners felt the danger of
holding their lands without having the ancient respectability which
would give dignity and stability to their position. The monastic
antiquaries searched the records to give detail and lucidity to their
inherited conviction of greatness; the secular antiquaries searched to
discover what it was they had inherited. Hence their interest in family
history, and the consequent importance of the College of Heralds in
the historical researches of the Tudor and Stuart periods. Hence also
their interest in institutions and in the descent of landed property, and
the consequent importance of lawyers in the historical movement.

Heralds and lawyers were the men who handled ancient documents as part of their daily work, and they became the interpreters of these documents to their generation, just as the English monks in the post-Conquest monasteries had been the interpreters in their time.

Despite the difference of emphasis, the researchers into the past in the two periods had a similar function; but their work had a different fate. The researchers of the earlier period had fulfilled their purpose and exhausted their material within a period of about thirty years. By 1130 their work was done. In historical research they had no successors. The monastic historians of the later Middle Ages abandoned historical research for contemporary journalism, and relied on their predecessors for their record of the past. Even a laborious scholar like Ranulf Higden regarded the past as an accumulation of compilations from which he made his own mountainous abridgment. The Tudor researchers had a better fortune. The methods they revived and the materials they unearthed have continued to attract workers from that time to this. The various stages in the evolution of this work, from being the absorbing passion of a whole generation to becoming the pleasing habit of a leisured clergy and gentry, cannot concern us now; but even in the mid-nineteenth century, when a new and much more powerful impulse than ever before stirred men to historical study, the tradition of research, which had been started in the twelfth century and renewed in the sixteenth, was still strong enough to give a distinctive character to English historical writing. Stubbs learnt to be a historian by studying family history at Knaresborough and by compiling lists of bishops at Navestock. Maitland learnt by copying legal documents in a conveyancer's office in London. They were starting where Hemming had started at Worcester and Lambarde in Kent. This starting point has the great merit of beginning with the ordinary needs of life, and not with any intellectual programme whatsoever. Therefore, in the end, it proved stronger than any of the other traditions of historical scholarship which we have examined. So far as there is a central tradition in our historical writing, it arises from this recurrent need to understand and stabilize the present by reviving the experience of the past.

THE ROYAL HISTORICAL SOCIETY

REPORT OF COUNCIL, SESSION 1971-72

THE Council of the Royal Historical Society has the honour to present the following Report to the Anniversary Meeting.

A conference on 'History and the Arts' was held at the University of Durham from 20 to 22 September 1971. The papers read were:

> 'Politics and Art: Inigo Jones and the Ideas of Personal Rule'. By Dr. Roy Strong.
> 'The Gregorian Reform and the Visual Arts: a problem of Method'. By Professor Ernst Kitzinger.
> 'Art and the Counter-Reformation before 1600'. By Professor Ellis Waterhouse.
> 'Art and Society in England and France in the mid-nineteenth Century'. By Mr. Alan Bowness.

Fifty-eight members of the Society and twelve guests attended. The University held a reception for them and they had the opportunity to visit the excavation sites at Jarrow and Monkwearmouth. The success of this second conference has caused Council to arrange for a conference to be held at St. John's College, Oxford, from 14 to 16 September 1972, on the topic 'Urban Civilization'.

Council made a submission to the Department of the Environment concerning the Department's proposals for the reorganization of local government boundaries, and in particular on such aspects of the reorganization as would affect historians, viz. the possible fragmentation of collections, the redistribution of records amongst repositories, the proliferation of small record offices and the destruction of records. Council also made a submission to the Department of Education and Science, protesting at the Government's proposals to revise the regulations governing the Export Control of Documents and urging that, as Council suggested in its submission of 16 March 1970, much stricter control should be exercised.

The representation of the Society upon various bodies was as follows: Professor G. E. Aylmer and Mr. A. T. Milne on the Joint Anglo-American Committee exercising a general supervision over the production of the *Bibliographies of British History*; the President, Professor C. N. L. Brooke, Professor Sir Goronwy Edwards, Professor J. C. Holt and Professor the Rev. M. D. Knowles on the Advisory Committee of the new edition of Gross, *Sources and Literature of English History*; Professor G. W. S. Barrow, Dr. P. Chaplais and

Professor P. H. Sawyer on the Joint Committee of the Society and the British Academy established to prepare an edition of Anglo-Saxon charters; Dr. E. B. Fryde on a committee to regulate British co-operation in the preparation of a new repertory of medieval sources to replace Potthast's *Bibliotheca Historica Medii Aevi*; Professor P. Grierson on a committee to promote the publication of photographic records of the more significant collections of British coins; Professor A. G. Dickens on the Advisory Council on the Export of Works of Art; the President and Professor C. H. Wilson on the British National Committee of the International Historical Congress; Professor Sir Goronwy Edwards on the Council of the British Records Association; Professor A. M. Everitt on the Standing Conference for Local History; Professor D. A. Bullough on the Ordnance Survey Archaeological Advisory Committee. Council received reports from these representatives.

The President is *ex officio* a Trustee of the *Spectator*.

After serving for 25 years as the Society's representative on the Committee to advise the publishers of the *Annual Register*, Professor W. N. Medlicott resigned in June 1972. Council wishes to place on record its appreciation of his services. He was replaced on the Committee by Professor M. R. D. Foot. Professor Medlicott continues to represent the Society on the Court of the University of Exeter.

At the Anniversary Meeting on 26 November 1971 the Vice-Presidents retiring under By-Law XVI were Professor C. R. Cheney and Miss K. Major. Dr. P. Chaplais and Professor Denys Hay were elected to replace them. The members of Council retiring under By-Law XIX were Professor R. Ashton, Mr. R. H. Ellis, Professor J. Lynch and Professor J. S. Roskell. Mr. T. H. Aston, Professor J. McManners, Professor P. H. Sawyer and Professor F. M. L. Thompson were elected to fill the vacancies. Messrs. Beeby, Harmar and Co. were appointed auditors for the year 1971-72.

Publications, and Papers Read

The following works were published: *Transactions*, Fifth Series, volume 21; *Camden*, Fourth Series, volume 9, *Camden Miscellany XXIV*.

Other volumes in the press were *Transactions*, Fifth Series, volume 22, and *Camden*, Fourth Series, volume 10, *Herefordshire Militia Assessments, 1663*, edited by M. A. Faraday.

At the ordinary meetings of the Society the following papers were read:

'Britain and France in 1940'. By Professor D. W. J. Johnson. (22 October 1971.)

'The King's Affinity in the Polity of Yorkist England'. By D. A. L. Morgan. (4 February 1972.)

'The French Origins of the "Right" '. By Dr. J. M. Roberts. (10 March 1972.)

'Age at Marriage in England from the late seventeenth to the nineteenth century'. By Dr. R. B. Outhwaite. (12 May 1972.)

At the Anniversary Meeting on 26 November 1971, the President, Dr. R. W. Southern, delivered an address on 'Aspects of the European Tradition of Historical Writing': III. 'History as Prophecy'.

The Alexander Prize was awarded to Mr. Ian d'Alton for his essay on 'Southern Irish Unionism: A Study of Cork City and County Unionists, 1884–1914'; *proxime accessit*: Mrs. Rosemary O'Day for her essay 'The Ecclesiastical Patronage of the Lord Keeper: 1558–1640', both of which will be published in *Transactions*, Fifth Series, volume 23; and honourable mention: Mr. Patrick Williams for his essay 'Spanish Government Restored: Philip III, the Duke of Lerma, and the councils of State, War and Finance, 1598–1602'.

Membership

Council records with regret the death of 19 Fellows since 30 June 1971. Among these Council would especially mention Professor E. F. Jacob and Professor Francis Wormald, Honorary Vice-Presidents, Lady Stenton, a former Vice-President, and Professor A. Browning. Council has accepted with gratitude the bequest to the Society by Professor Browning of his residuary estate. The resignation of 3 Fellows, 1 Associate and 8 Subscribing Libraries was received.

71 Fellows and 9 Associates were elected, and 23 Subscribing Libraries were admitted. The membership of the Society on 30 June 1972 comprised 1144 Fellows (including 130 Life Fellows), 35 Corresponding Fellows, 142 Associates and 734 Subscribing Libraries (1095, 35, 134 and 719 respectively on 30 June 1971). The Society exchanged publications with 20 societies, British and foreign.

Finance

The Treasurer reports that despite an increase in income from all sources of £679, there was a deficit on Income and Expenditure Account for the year of £1,172. This compares with a surplus in the preceding year of £2,702. The turn round of £4,553 is attributable partly to the publication of three volumes instead of only two, but more seriously, and despite all possible economies, to a continuing severe increase in costs, and not least those of book production.

Since inflation continues at a lively pace, the deficit in prospect for 1972/73 will be substantially larger than that for the current year, unless the programme of publications is curtailed, which would undoubtedly be a matter for general regret. In 1973/74, V.A.T. will impose a substantial additional burden on the Society's resources, and other tax changes will reduce revenue from covenants by $22\frac{1}{2}$ per cent.

Council has consequently under active consideration the need to increase the rates of subscription, which in the case of Fellows and Associates have remained unchanged since 1958.

THE ROYAL HISTORICAL SOCIETY
BALANCE SHEET AS AT 30 JUNE 1972

30.6.71 £	£		£	£
		ACCUMULATED FUNDS		
		GENERAL FUND		
38,886		As at 1 July 1971		43,495
		Royalties from reprints of the Society's publications		
	1,800	received in the year and treated as capital . .	1,594	
		Royalties from *Essays on Medieval and Modern History*		
	107	(Macmillan, 1968)	15	
	———		———	1,609
	1,907			
				45,104
	—	*Add* Profit on Sale of Investments in year . .		226
1,907	———			
				45,330
		Less Excess of Expenditure and Provisions over Income		
2,702 *(surplus)*		for year		1,172
———				———
43,495				44,158
13,571		SIR GEORGE W. PROTHERO BEQUEST		
		As at 1 July 1971	13,571	
		Add Profit on Sale of Investments . . .	281	
			———	13,852
5,000		REDDAWAY FUND		5,000
———				———
£62,066				£63,010

		REPRESENTED BY:		
51,283		INVESTMENTS—at cost		59,115
		Market Value £109,554 (1971: £87,916)		
		SUM DUE ON SURRENDER OF LEASE of 96 Cheyne Walk		
	6,250	As at 1 July 1971	5,000	
	1,250	Paid in year	1,250	
		(Payable in annual instalments of £1,250)		
5,000	———		———	3,750
		CURRENT ASSETS		
		Balances at Bank:		
	2,049	Current Accounts	1,794	
	8,498	Deposit Account	5,072	
	7	Cash in Hand.	37	
	———		———	
	10,554		6,903	
		Less CURRENT LIABILITIES		
	595	Subscriptions received in advance .	506	
	62	Conference Fees received in advance .	94	
	323	Sundry Creditors	108	
	2,600	Provision for Publications in Hand .	6,050	
	1,191	*Writings on British History* . .	—	
	4,771		———	6,758
5,783	———			145
———				———
£62,066				£63,010

NOTE: The cost of the Society's Library, Furniture and Office Equipment, and the Stock of its own publications, has been written off to Income and Expenditure Account as and when acquired.

THE ROYAL HISTORICAL SOCIETY
Income & Expenditure Account for the Year Ended 30 June 1972

30.6.71 £	£		£	£
		INCOME		
205		Subscriptions for 1971/72: Associates	198	
2,226		Libraries	2,227	
3,587		Fellows	3,896	
6,018				6,321
		(The Society also had 130 Life Fellows at 30 June 1972)		
655		Tax Recovered on Covenanted Subscriptions . .		765
317		Arrears of Subscriptions Recovered in year . . .		501
3,544		Interest and Dividends received and Income Tax recovered		3,661
64		Prothero Royalties and Reproduction Fees . .		86
83		Donations and Sundry Receipts		26
£10,681				£11,360

		EXPENDITURE		
		Secretarial & Administrative Expenses		
	3,298	Salaries, Pension Contributions and National Insurance .	3,940	
	488	General Printing and Stationery	266	
	316	Postage, Telephone and Sundries.	347	
	204	Accountancy and Audit	223	
	213	Office Equipment	—	
	63	Insurance	127	
	172	Meeting and Conference Expenses	96	
	4,754		4,999	
	900	*Less* Charged to Library and Publications Accounts .	900	
3,854				4,099
		Publications		
	187	Directors' Honoraria and Expenses	163	
		Publishing Costs in the year:		
		Transactions, Fifth Series, Vol. 21 (total cost)	2,236	
		Camden, Fourth Series, Vol. 8 (balance of cost:		
		total £1,627).	567	
		Vol. 9 (total cost) . . .	2,235	
			5,038	
	1,130	*Less* Provision made 30 June 1971 .	2,600	
			2,438	
	219	Warehousing, Packing and Postage	31	
		Provision for Publications in Progress:		
	2,100	*Transactions*, Fifth Series, Vol. 22 . .	2,550	
	500	Camden, Fourth Series, Vol. 10 . .	3,500	
			6,050	
	750	Proportion of Secretarial and Administrative Expenses .	750	
	4,886		9,432	
	1,653	*Less* Sales of Publications	1,618	
3,233				7,814
7,087		*Carried forward*		11,913

270

EXPENDITURE (contd.) £ £

<table>
<tr><td>30.6.71</td><td></td><td></td><td></td><td></td></tr>
<tr><td>£7,087</td><td></td><td>*Brought forward*</td><td></td><td>11,913</td></tr>
<tr><td></td><td></td><td>WRITINGS ON BRITISH HISTORY 1901–33</td><td></td><td></td></tr>
<tr><td></td><td></td><td>Subsidies towards cost of publication paid in year:</td><td></td><td></td></tr>
<tr><td></td><td>1,191</td><td>Final instalment, Vol. V . . . . .</td><td>—</td><td></td></tr>
<tr><td></td><td>1,275</td><td>Balance of Provision no longer required . . .</td><td>—</td><td>—</td></tr>
<tr><td>(84)</td><td></td><td></td><td></td><td></td></tr>
<tr><td></td><td></td><td>LIBRARY AND ARCHIVES</td><td></td><td></td></tr>
<tr><td></td><td>442</td><td>Purchase of Books and Publications . . . .</td><td>238</td><td></td></tr>
<tr><td></td><td>148</td><td>Library Assistance and Equipment . . . .</td><td>170</td><td></td></tr>
<tr><td></td><td>590</td><td></td><td>408</td><td></td></tr>
<tr><td></td><td>150</td><td>Proportion of Secretarial and Administrative Expenses</td><td>150</td><td></td></tr>
<tr><td></td><td>740</td><td></td><td>558</td><td></td></tr>
<tr><td></td><td>—</td><td>*Less* Sales of Surplus Books in year . . . .</td><td>23</td><td></td></tr>
<tr><td>740</td><td></td><td></td><td></td><td>535</td></tr>
<tr><td></td><td></td><td>OTHER CHARGES</td><td></td><td></td></tr>
<tr><td></td><td>18</td><td>Alexander Prize and expenses . . . . .</td><td>19</td><td></td></tr>
<tr><td></td><td>84</td><td>Subscriptions to other bodies . . . . .</td><td>15</td><td></td></tr>
<tr><td></td><td>—</td><td>Prothero Lecture fee and expenses . . . .</td><td>50</td><td></td></tr>
<tr><td>102</td><td></td><td></td><td></td><td>84</td></tr>
<tr><td></td><td></td><td>PROVISION FOR ADDITIONAL REMOVAL EXPENSES</td><td></td><td></td></tr>
<tr><td>134</td><td></td><td>Cost of Removal of stocks of publications . . .</td><td>—</td><td></td></tr>
<tr><td>7,979</td><td></td><td>TOTAL EXPENDITURE . . . .</td><td></td><td>12,532</td></tr>
<tr><td>10,681</td><td></td><td>INCOME AS ABOVE . . . .</td><td></td><td>11,360</td></tr>
<tr><td>£2,702 (*surplus*)</td><td></td><td>EXCESS OF EXPENDITURE AND PROVISIONS OVER INCOME FOR THE YEAR</td><td></td><td>£1,172</td></tr>
</table>

R. W. SOUTHERN, *President.*

G. R. C. DAVIS, *Treasurer.*

We have examined the foregoing Income and Expenditure Account and Balance Sheet with the books and vouchers of the Society. We have verified the Investments and Bank Balances appearing in the Balance Sheet. In our opinion the above Balance Sheet and annexed Income and Expenditure Account are properly drawn up so as to exhibit a true and fair view of the state of the affairs of the Society according to the best of our information and the explanations given to us and as shown by the Books of the Society.

BEEBY, HARMAR & CO.,
Chartered Accountants, Auditors

FINSBURY COURT,
FINSBURY PAVEMENT,
LONDON E.C.2.
4th August 1972

THE DAVID BERRY TRUST
Receipts and Payments Account for the Year Ended 30 June 1972

1971		*Receipts*		
		BALANCE IN HAND 30 June 1971:		
		Cash at Bank:		
90		Current Account	45	
43		Deposit Account	56	
1		Cash in Hand	—	
564	430	410 Shares Charities Official Investment Fund . .	430	531
64		DIVIDEND ON INVESTMENT Per Charity Commissioners .		66
2		INTEREST RECEIVED ON DEPOSIT ACCOUNT . . .		2
£630				£599

		Payments		
21		EXAMINERS FEES		—
50		DAVID BERRY PRIZE		—
27		DAVID BERRY MEDAL		—
1		POSTAGE AND SUNDRIES		25
		BALANCE IN HAND 30 June 1972		
		Cash at Bank:		
	56	Current Account	6	
	45	Deposit Account	38	
		483.63 Shares Charities Official Investment		
531	430	Fund (Market Value 30.6.72 £647)	530	574
£630				£599

We have examined the above account with the books and vouchers of the Trust and find it to b[e]
in accordance therewith.

FINSBURY COURT,
FINSBURY PAVEMENT,
LONDON E.C.2.
4th August 1972

BEEBY, HARMAR & CO.,
Chartered Accountants, Auditor

The late David Berry, by his Will dated 23rd day of April, 1926, left £1,000 to provide in ever[y]
three years a gold medal and prize money for the best essay on the Earl of Bothwell or, at th[e]
discretion of the Trustees, on Scottish History of the James Stuarts I to VI in memory of hi[s]
father, the Late Rev. David Berry.

The Trust is regulated by a scheme sanctioned by the Chancery Division of the High Court o[f]
Justice dated 23rd day of January, 1930, and made in an action 1927 A.1233 David Anderso[n]
Berry Deceased, Hunter and another *v.* Robertson and another.

The Royal Historical Society is now the Trustee. The Investment held on Capital Accoun[t]
consists of 634 Charities Official Investment Fund Shares (Market Value £848).

The Trustee will in every second year of the three year period advertise in *The Times* invitin[g]
essays.

ALEXANDER PRIZE

The Alexander Prize was established in 1897 by L. C. Alexander, F.R.Hist.S. It consists of a silver medal awarded annually for an essay upon some historical subject. Candidates may select their own subject provided such subject has been previously submitted to and approved by the Literary Director. The essay must be a genuine work of original research, not hitherto published, and one which has not been awarded any other prize. It must not exceed 6,000 words in length and must be sent in on or before 1 January 1974. The detailed regulations should be obtained in advance from the Secretary.

LIST OF ALEXANDER PRIZE ESSAYISTS (1889–1972)[1]

1898. F. Hermia Durham ('The relations of the Crown to trade under James I').

1899. W. F. Lord, BA ('The development of political parties in the reign of Queen Anne').

1901. Laura M. Roberts ('The Peace of Lunéville').

1902. V. B. Redstone ('The social condition of England during the Wars of the Roses').

1903. Rose Graham ('The intellectual influence of English monasticism between the tenth and twelfth centuries').

1904. Enid M. G. Routh ('The balance of power in the seventeenth century').

1905. W. A. P. Mason, MA ('The beginnings of the Cistercian Order').

1906. Rachel R. Reid, MA ('The Rebellion of the Earls, 1569').

1908. Kate Hotblack ('The Peace of Paris, 1763').

1909. Nellie Nield, MA ('The social and economic condition of the unfree classes in England in the twelfth and thirteenth centuries').

1912. H. G. Richardson ('The parish clergy of the thirteenth and four-teenth centuries').

1917. Isobel D. Thornley, BA ('The treason legislation of 1531–1534').

1918. T. F. T. Plucknett, BA ('The place of the Council in the fifteenth century').

1919. Edna F. White, MA ('The jurisdiction of the Privy Council under the Tudors').

1920. J. E. Neale, MA ('The Commons Journals of the Tudor Period').

1922. Eveline C. Martin ('The English establishments on the Gold Coast in the second half of the eighteenth century').

1923. E. W. Hensman, MA ('The Civil War of 1648 in the east midlands').

[1] No award was made in 1900, 1907, 1910, 1911, 1913, 1914, 1921, 1946, 1948, 1956, 1969. The prize Essays for 1909 and 1919 were not published in the *Transactions*. No Essays were submitted in 1915, 1916, and 1943.

1924. Grace Stretton, BA ('Some aspects of mediæval travel').
1925. F. A. Mace, MA ('Devonshire ports in the fourteenth and fifteenth centuries').
1926. Marian J. Tooley, MA ('The authorship of the *Defensor Pacis*').
1927. W. A. Pantin, BA ('Chapters of the English Black Monks, 1215–1540').
1928. Gladys A. Thornton, BA, PhD ('A study in the history of Clare, Suffolk, with special reference to its development as a borough').
1929. F. S. Rodkey, AM, PhD ('Lord Palmerston's policy for the rejuvenation of Turkey, 1839–47').
1930. A. A. Ettinger, DPhil ('The proposed Anglo-Franco-American Treaty of 1852 to guarantee Cuba to Spain').
1931. Kathleen A. Walpole, MA ('The humanitarian movement of the early nineteenth century to remedy abuses on emigrant vessels to America').
1932. Dorothy M. Brodie, BA ('Edmund Dudley, minister of Henry VII').
1933. R. W. Southern, BA ('Ranulf Flambard and early Anglo-Norman administration').
1934. S. B. Chrimes, MA, PhD ('Sir John Fortescue and his theory of dominion').
1935. S. T. Bindoff, MA ('The unreformed diplomatic service, 1812–60').
1936. Rosamond J. Mitchell, MA, BLitt ('English students at Padua, 1460–1475').
1937. C. H. Philips, BA ('The East India Company "Interest", and the English Government, 1783–4').
1938. H. E. I. Phillips, BA ('The last years of the Court of Star Chamber, 1630–41').
1939. Hilda P. Grieve, BA ('The deprived married clergy in Essex, 1553–61').
1940. R. Somerville, MA ('The Duchy of Lancaster Council and Court of Duchy Chamber').
1941. R. A. L. Smith, MA, PhD ('The *Regimen Scaccarii* in English monasteries').
1942. F. L. Carsten, DPhil ('Medieval democracy in the Brandenburg towns and its defeat in the fifteenth century').
1944. Rev. E. W. Kemp, BD ('Pope Alexander III and the canonization of saints').
1945. Helen Suggett, BLitt ('The use of French in England in the later middle ages').
1947. June Milne, BA ('The diplomacy of Dr John Robinson at the court of Charles XII of Sweden, 1697–1709').
1949. Ethel Drus, MA ('The attitude of the Colonial Office to the annexation of Fiji').
1950. Doreen J. Milne, MA, PhD ('The results of the Rye House Plot, and their influence upon the Revolution of 1688').
1951. K. G. Davies, BA ('The origins of the commission system in the West India trade').

1952. G. W. S. Barrow, BLitt ('Scottish rulers and the religious orders, 1070–1153').

1953. W. E. Minchinton, BSc(Econ) ('Bristol—metropolis of the west in the eighteenth century').

1954. Rev. L. Boyle, OP ('The *Oculus Sacerdotis* and some other works of William of Pagula').

1955. G. F. E. Rudé, MA, PhD ('The Gordon riots: a study of the rioters and their victims').

1957. R. F. Hunnisett, MA, DPhil ('The origins of the office of Coroner').

1958. Thomas G. Barnes, AB, DPhil ('County politics and a puritan *cause célèbre*: Somerset churchales, 1633').

1959. Alan Harding, BLitt ('The origins and early history of the Keeper of the Peace').

1960. Gwyn A. Williams, MA, PhD ('London and Edward I').

1961. M. H. Keen, BA ('Treason trials under the law of arms').

1962. G. W. Monger, MA, PhD ('The end of isolation: Britain, Germany and Japan, 1900–1902').

1963. J. S. Moore, BA ('The Domesday teamland: a reconsideration').

1964. M. Kelly, PhD ('The submission of the clergy').

1965. J. J. N. Palmer, BLitt ('Anglo-French negotiations, 1390–1396').

1966. M. T. Clanchy, MA, PhD ('The Franchise of Return of Writs').

1967. R. Lovatt, MA, DPhil ('The *Imitation of Christ* in late medieval England').

1968. M. G. A. Vale, MA, DPhil ('The last years of English Gascony, 1451–1453').

1970. Mrs Margaret Bowker, MA, BLitt ('The Commons Supplication against the Ordinaries in the light of some Archidiaconal Acta').

1971. C. Thompson, MA ('The origins of the politics of the Parliamentary middle group, 1625–1629').

1972. I. d'Alton, BA ('Southern Irish Unionism: A study of Cork City and County Unionists, 1884–1914').

DAVID BERRY PRIZE

The David Berry Prize was established in 1929 by David Anderson-Berry in memory of his father, the Reverend David Berry. It consists of a gold medal and money prize awarded every three years for Scottish history. Candidates may select any subject dealing with Scottish history within the reigns of James I to James VI inclusive, provided such subject has been previously submitted to and approved by the Council of the Royal Historical Society. The essay must be a genuine work of original research not hitherto published, and one which has not been awarded any other prize. The essay must not exceed 50,000 words. It must be sent in on or before 31 October 1973.

LIST OF DAVID BERRY PRIZE ESSAYISTS (1937–1970)[1]

1937. G. Donaldson, MA ('The polity of the Scottish Reformed Church c. 1560–1580, and the rise of the Presbyterian movement').

1943. Rev. Prof. A. F. Scott Pearson, DTh, DLitt ('Anglo-Scottish religious relations, 1400–1600').

1949. T. Bedford Franklin, MA, FRSE ('Monastic agriculture in Scotland, 1440–1600').

1955. W. A. McNeill, MA (' "Estaytt" of the king's rents and pensions, 1621').

1958. Prof. Maurice Lee, PhD ('Maitland of Thirlestane and the foundation of the Stewart depotism in Scotland').

1964. M. H. Merriman ('Scottish collaborators with England during the Anglo-Scottish war, 1543–1550').

1967. Miss M. H. B. Sanderson ('Catholic recusancy in Scotland in the sixteenth century').

1970. Athol Murray, BA, MA, LLB, PhD ('The Comptroller, 1425–1810').

[1] No Essays were submitted in 1940. No award was made in 1946, 1952 and 1961.

LIST OF FELLOWS OF THE ROYAL HISTORICAL SOCIETY

(CORRECTED TO 31 DECEMBER 1972)

Names of Officers and Honorary Vice-Presidents are printed in capitals. Those marked* have compounded for their annual subscriptions.

Abbott, A. W., CMG, CBE, Frithys Orchard, West Clandon, Surrey.
Adair, J. E., MA, PhD, Crockford Park Road, Addlestone, Surrey.
Adam, R. J., MA, Cromalt, Lade Braes, St Andrews, Fife.
Addison, W. W., FSA, 6 Ravensmere, Epping, Essex.
*Addleshaw, The Very Rev. Canon G. W. O., MA, BD, FSA, The Deanery, Chester.
Ahmad, Mr Justice M. B., MA, MLitt, 58 Cherry Road, Enfield, Middx.
Ainsworth, Sir John, Bt, MA, c/o National Library, Kildare Street, Dublin 2, Eire.
Akrigg, Professor G. P. V., BA, PhD, Dept of English, University of British Columbia, Vancouver 8, B.C., Canada.
Albion, Rev. Canon Gordon, DSc (Louvain), Sutton Park, Guildford.
Alcock, L., MA, FSA, 32 Cyncoed Road, Cardiff.
Alderman, G., MA, DPhil, 43 Walsingham Road, Clapton, London E5.
Alexandrowicz, Professor C. H., LLD, DrJur, 8 Rochester Gardens, Croydon, Surrey.
Allan, D. G. C., MSc(Econ), FSA, 1 Victoria Rise, Clapham Common, London SW4 0PB
Allen, Professor H. C., MC, MA, School of English and American Studies, University of East Anglia, University Plain, Norwich, NOR 88C.
Allen, W. E. D., OBE, FSA, Whitechurch House, Cappagh, Co. Waterford, Eire.
Allmand, C. T., MA, DPhil, 59 Menlove Avenue, Liverpool L18 2EH.
Altschul, Professor M., PhD, Case Western University, Cleveland, Ohio, 44106, U.S.A.
Anderson, Professor M. S., MA, PhD, London School of Economics, Houghton Street, WC2A 2AE.
Anderson, Mrs O. R., MA, BLitt, Westfield College, NW3.
*Anderson, R. C., MA, LittD, FSA, 9 Grove Place, Lymington, Hants.
Andrews, K. R., BA, PhD, Dept of History, University of Hull, Cottingham Road, Hull HU6 7RX.
Andrews, Rev. Canon P. J., OBE, DD, Redbourne, De Moulham Road, Swanage, Dorset.
Anglo, S., BA, PhD, Dept of History of Ideas, University College, Swansea.
Annan, Lord, OBE, MA, DLitt, DU, University College, Gower Street, WC1E 6BT.
Appleby, J. S., Little Pitchbury, Brick Kiln Lane, Great Horkesley, Colchester, Essex.
Armstrong, Miss A. M., BA, 7 Vale Court, Mallord Street, SW3.

Armstrong, C. A. J., MA, FSA, Hertford College, Oxford.
Armstrong Professor F. H., PhD, University of Western Ontario, London 72, Ontario.
Armstrong, W. A., BA, PhD, Eliot College, The University, Canterbury, Kent.
Ashton, Professor R., PhD, The Manor House, Brundall, near Norwich.
Ashworth, Professor W., BSc(Econ), PhD, Dept of Econ. and Soc. History, The University, Bristol.
Aston, Mrs M. E., Castle House, Ongar, Essex.
Aston, T. H., MA, FSA, Corpus Christi College, Oxford.
Auchmuty, Professor J. J., MA, PhD, MRIA, University of Newcastle, N.S.W., Australia.
Avery, D. J., MA, BLitt, 6 St James's Square, London, SW1.
Axelson, Professor E. V., DLitt, University of Cape Town, Rondebosch, S. Africa.
*Aydelotte, Professor W. O., PhD, State University of Iowa, Iowa City, Iowa, U.S.A.
Aylmer, Professor G. E., MA, DPhil, University of York, Heslington, York YO1 5DD.

Bagley, J. J., MA, 10 Beach Priory Gardens, Southport, Lancs.
Bagshawe, T. W., FSA, c/o Luton Museum, Wardown Park, Luton, Bedfordshire.
Bahlman, Dudley W. R., PhD, Dept of History, Williams College, Williamstown, Mass., U.S.A.
Baillie, H.M.G., MA, 12B Stanford Road, W8 3QJ.
Baily, L. W. A., 29 Saxon Way, Saffron Walden, Essex.
Bailyn, Professor B., MA, PhD, LittD, LHD, Widener J, Harvard University, Cambridge, Mass. 02138, U.S.A.
Baker, L. G. D., MA, BLitt, Dept of Medieval Hist., The University, Edinburgh.
Baker, T. F. T., BA, Camden Lodge, 50 Hastings Road, Pembury.
*Bales, P. G., MC, MA, Selwyn House, Fakenham, Norfolk.
Balfour, Professor M. L. G., CBE, MA, 5B Prince Albert Road, NW3.
Ballhatchet, Professor K. A., MA, PhD, 4 Windmill Hill, Hampstead, NW3.
Bargar, Professor B. D., PhD, University of South Carolina, Columbia, S.C., 29208, U.S.A.
Barker, Professor T. C., MA, PhD, Minsen Dane, Brogdale Road, Faversham, Kent.
Barkley, Professor the Rev. J. M., MA, DD, 2 College Park, Belfast, N. Ireland.
Barley, Professor M. W., MA, FSA, 66 Park Road, Chilwell, Nottingham.
*Barlow, Professor F., MA, DPhil, FBA, Middle Court Hall, Kenton, Exeter.
*Barnes, Professor D. G., MA, PhD, 2300 Overlook Road, Cleveland, Ohio, 44106, U.S.A.
Barnes, Miss P. M., PhD, Public Record Office, Chancery Lane, WC2.
Barnes, Professor T. G., AB, DPhil, University of Califorina, Berkeley, Calif., 94720, U.S.A.
*Barnes, Professor Viola F., MA, PhD, LLD, (address unknown).
Barratt, Miss D. M., DPhil, The Corner House, Hampton Poyle, Kidlington, Oxford.
Barron, Mrs C. M., MA, PhD, 35 Rochester Road, NW1.

BARROW, Professor G. W. S., MA, DLitt (*Literary Director*), University of Newcastle, Newcastle upon Tyne.
Bartlett, C. J., PhD, 5 Strathspey Place, West Ferry, Dundee.
Batho, G. R., MA, The University, Sheffield 10.
Baxter, Professor S. B., PhD, 608 Morgan Creek Road, Chapel Hill, N.C., U.S.A.
Baylen, Professor J. O., MA, PhD, Georgia State University, 33 Gilmer Street S.E., Atlanta, Georgia, U.S.A.
Beales, D. E. D., MA, PhD, Sidney Sussex College, Cambridge.
Bean, Professor J. M. W., MA, DPhil, 711 Hamilton Hall, History Department, Columbia University, New York, N.Y. 10027.
Beardwood, Miss Alice, BA, BLitt, DPhil, 415 Miller's Lane, Wynnewod, Pa., U.S.A.
Beasley, Professor W. G., PhD, FBA, 172 Hampton Road, Twickenham, Middlesex.
Beaumont, H., MA, Silverdale, Severn Bank, Shrewsbury.
Beckett, Professor J. C., MA, 19 Wellington Park Terrace, Belfast 9, N. Ireland.
Beckingsale, B. W., MA, 8 Highbury, Newcastle upon Tyne.
Beddard, R. A., MA, DPhil, Oriel College, Oxford.
Beeler, Professor J. H., PhD, 1302 New Garden Road, Greensboro, N.C. 27410, U.S.A.
*Beer, E. S. de, MA, DLitt, FBA, FSA, 31 Brompton Square, SW3.
Begley, W. W., 17 St Mary's Gardens, SE11.
Behrens, Miss C. B. A., MA, Dales Barn, Barton, Cambridge.
Bell, P. M. H., BA, BLitt, The School of History, The University, P.O. Box 147, Liverpool.
Beller, E. A., DPhil, Dept of History, Princeton University, N.J., 08540, U.S.A.
Beloff, Professor M., MA, BLitt, All Souls College, Oxford.
Bennett, Captain G. M., RN(ret), DSC, 33 Argyll Road, W8.
Bennett, Rev. Canon G. V., MA, DPhil, FSA, New College, Oxford.
Bennett, R. F., MA, Magdalene College, Cambridge.
Bethell, D. L. T., MA, Dept of Medieval History, University College, Dublin 4, Ireland.
Bethell, L. M., PhD, University College, Gower Street, WC1E 6BT.
Biddle, M., MA, FSA, Winchester Research Unit, 13 Parchment Street, Winchester.
Bindoff, Professor S. T., MA, 5 Carlton Road, New Malden, Surrey.
*Bing, H. F., MA, 45 Rempstone Road, East Leake, nr Loughborough, Leics.
Binney, J. E. D., DPhil, 6 Pageant Drive, Sherborne, Dorset.
Birch, A., MA, PhD, University of Hong Kong, Hong Kong.
Bishop, A. S., BA, PhD, 254 Leigham Court Road, Streatham, SW16 2RP.
Bishop, T. A. M., MA, The Annexe, Manor House, Hemingford Grey, Hunts.
Blair, P. Hunter, MA, Emmanuel College, Cambridge.
Blake, E. O., MA, PhD, Roselands, Moorhill Road, Westend, Southampton.
Blake, Professor J. W., CBE, MA, DLitt, Willow Cottage, Mynoe, Limavady, Co. Londonderry, N. Ireland.
Blake, Lord, MA, FBA, The Provost's Lodgings, The Queen's College, Oxford.
Blakemore, H., PhD, 43 Fitzjohn Avenue, Barnet, Herts.

*Blakey, Professor R. G., PhD, c/o Mr Raymond Shove, Order Dept, Library, University of Minnesota, Minneapolis, Minn., U.S.A.

Blakiston, H. N., BA, 6 Markham Square, SW3.

Blomfield, Mrs K., 8 Elmdene Court, Constitution Hill, Woking, Surrey.

Blunt, C. E., OBE, FBA, FSA, Ramsbury Hill, Ramsbury, Marlborough, Wilts.

*Boase, T. S. R., MC, MA, FSA, 6 Atherton Drive, SW19.

*Bolsover, G. H., OBE, MA, PhD, 7 Devonshire Road, Hatch End, Middlesex.

Bolton, Professor G. C., MA, DPhil, University of Western Australia, Nedlands, Western Australia.

Bolton, Professor W. F., AM, PhD, F.S.A., Douglass College, Rutgers University, New Brunswick, N.J. 08903, U.S.A.

Bond, M. F., OBE, MA, FSA, 19 Bolton Crescent, Windsor, Berks.

Bond, Mrs S. M., MA, 19 Bolton Crescent, Windsor, Berks.

Borrie, M. A. F., BA, 14 Lancaster Gate, W2.

Bossy, J. A., MA, PhD, The University, Belfast.

*Botha, Lieut-Colonel C. Graham, VD, MA, LLD, FSA, Nairn, Isabel Avenue, Newlands, C.P., S. Africa.

Boulton, Professor J. T., BLitt, PhD, School of English Studies, The University, Nottingham.

Bowker, Mrs M., MA, BLitt, 5 Spens Avenue, Cambridge.

Bowyer, M. J. F., 32 Netherhall Way, Cambridge.

*Boxer, Professor C. R., DLitt, FBA, Ringshall End, Little Gaddesden, Berkhamsted, Herts.

Boyle, Professor the Rev. L. E., DPhil, STL, Pontifical Institute of Mediaeval Studies, 59 Queen's Park, Toronto 181, Canada.

Boynton, L. O. J., MA, DPhil, FSA, Westfield College, NW3.

Bramsted, E. K., PhD, DPhil, Fauran, 16 Barham Close, Weybridge, Surrey.

Breck, Professor A. D., MA, PhD, University of Denver, Denver, Colorado 80210, U.S.A.

Brentano, Professor R., DPhil, University of California, Berkeley, Calif., U.S.A.

Brett-James, E. A., MA, Royal Military Academy, Sandhurst, Camberley, Surrey.

Bridenbaugh, Professor C., MA, PhD, LittD, 364 Benefit Street, Providence, R.I. 02903, U.S.A.

Bridge, F. R., PhD, The Poplars, Radley Lane, Radley, Leeds.

Briers, Miss P. M., BLitt, 58 Fassett Road, Kingston-on-Thames, Surrey.

Briggs, Professor A., BSc(Econ), MA, DLitt, University of Sussex, Stanmer House, Stanmer, Brighton.

Briggs, R., MA, All Souls College, Oxford.

Brock, M. G., MA, 31 Linton Road, Oxford.

Brock, Professor W. R., MA, PhD, Department of History, University of Glasgow, Glasgow 2.

Brodie, Miss D. M., PhD, 137 Roberts Road, Pietermaritzburg, Natal, South Africa.

Brogan, D. H .V., MA, St John's College, Cambridge.

Brogan, Professor Sir Denis W., MA, LLD, FBA, Peterhouse, Cambridge.

*Bromley, Professor J. S., MA, Merrow, Dene Close, Upper Bassett, Southampton.

*Brooke, Professor C. N. L., MA, FBA, FSA, 28 Wood Lane, Highgate, N6 5UB.
Brooke, J., BA, 63 Hurst Avenue, Chingford, E4 8DL.
Brooke, Mrs R. B., MA, PhD, 28 Wood Lane, Highgate, N6 5UB.
Brooks, F. W., MA, FSA, The University, Hull.
Brooks, N. P., BA, DPhil, The University, St Andrews, Fife.
Brown, A. L., MA, DPhil, The University, Glasgow 2.
Brown, G. S., PhD, 1720 Hanover Road, Ann Arbor, Mich., 48103, U.S.A.
Brown, Judith M., MA, PhD, Dept of History, The University, Manchester M13 9PL.
Brown, Miss L. M., MA, PhD, 93 Church Road, Hanwell, W7.
Brown, Professor M. J., MA, PhD, 333 South Candler Street, Decatur, Georgia 30030, U.S.A.
Brown, P. R. Lamont, MA, FBA, Hillslope, Pullen's Lane, Oxford.
Brown, R. A., MA, DPhil, FSA, King's College, Strand, WC2.
*Browning, Professor A., MA, DLitt, Durie House, 6 West Abercromby Street, Helensburgh, Dunbartonshire.
Bruce, J. M., MA, 28 Lime Tree Grove, Shirley, Croydon.
Bruce, Professor M., BA, 22 Chorley Drive, Sheffield.
Bryant, Sir Arthur W. M., CH, CBE, LLD, 18 Rutland Gate, SW7.
Buckland, P. J., MA, PhD, 6 Rosefield Road, Liverpool L25 8TF.
Bueno de Mesquita, D. M., MA, PhD, Christ Church, Oxford.
Bullock, A. L. C., MA, DLitt, FBA, St Catherine's College, Oxford.
Bullough, Professor D. A., MA, FSA, The University, Nottingham NG7 2RD.
Burke, U. P., MA, 15 Lower Market Street, Hove, Sussex, BH3 1AT.
Burleigh, The Rev. Principal J. H. S., BD, 4 Braid Avenue, Edinburgh.
Burns, Professor J. H., MA, PhD, 39 Amherst Road, W.13.
Burroughs, P., PhD, Dalhousie University, Halifax, Nova Scotia, Canada.
Burrow, J. W., MA, PhD, Sussex University, Falmer, Brighton.
Bury, J. P. T., MA, Corpus Christi College, Cambridge.
*Butler, Professor Sir James R. M., MVO, OBE, MA, Trinity College, Cambridge CB2 1TQ.
Butler, Professor L. H., MA, DPhil, Dept of Medieval History, St Salvator's College, St Andrews.
Butler, R. D'O., CMG, MA, All Souls College, Oxford.
BUTTERFIELD, Professor Sir Herbert, MA, LLD, DLitt, DLit, LittD, FBA, 28 High Street, Sawston, Cambridge.
Bythell, D., MA, DPhil, University College, The Castle, Durham.

Cabaniss, Professor J. A., PhD, University of Mississippi, Box No. 153, University, Mississippi, U.S.A.
Calvert, P. A. R., MA, PhD, AM, Dept of Politics, University of Southampton, Highfield, Southampton SO9 5NH.
Cameron, Professor K., PhD, The University, Nottingham.
Campbell, Professor A. E., MA, PhD, School of History, University of Birmingham, P.O. Box 363, Birmingham B15 2TT.
*Campbell, Miss A. M., AM, PhD, 190 George Street, Brunswick, N.J., U.S.A.
Campbell, Major D. A., FSAScot, An Cladach, Achnacree Bay, Connel, Argyll.
Campbell, J., MA, Worcester College, Oxford.

*Campbell, Professor Mildred L., PhD, Vassar College, Poughkeepsie, N.Y., U.S.A.
Campbell, R. H., MA, PhD, University of Stirling, Scotland.
Campbell, Miss Sybil, OBE, MA, Drim-na-Vulun, Lochgilphead, Argyll.
Cant, R. G., MA, The University, St Andrews, Fife.
Capp, B. S., MA, DPhil, Dept of History, University of Warwick, Coventry, Warwickshire CV4 7AL.
Cargill-Thompson, W. D. J., MA, PhD, Dept of Ecclesiastical History, King's College, Strand, WC2.
*Carlson, Professor L. H., PhD, Southern California School of Theology, 1325 College Avenue, Claremont, Calif., U.S.A.
Carman, W. Y., FSA, 94 Mulgrave Road, Sutton, Surrey.
Carr, A. R. M., MA, St Antony's College, Oxford.
Carr, W., PhD, 16 Old Hay Close, Dore, Sheffield.
Carrington, Miss Dorothy, 3 Rue Emmanuel Arene, 20 Ajaccio, Corsica.
Carter, Mrs A. C., MA, 12 Garbrand Walk, Ewell, Epsom, Surrey.
Cartlidge, Rev. J. E. G., Sunnyside House, Snowhill, St George's, Oakengates, Salop.
*Carus-Wilson, Professor E. M., MA, FBA, FSA, 14 Lansdowne Road, W11.
Cassar, P., MD, PhC, BSc, DPM, St Luke, Pope Alexander VII Junction, Balzan, Malta.
Catto, R. J. A. I., MA, Oriel College, Oxford.
Chadwick, Professor W. O., DD, DLitt, FBA, Selwyn Lodge, Cambridge.
Challis, C. E., MA, PhD, 14 Ashwood Villas, Headingley, Leeds 6.
Chambers, D. S., MA, DPhil, Warburg Institute, Woburn Square, WC1.
Chandaman, Professor C. D., BA, PhD, St David's University College, Lampeter, Cardiganshire.
Chandler, D. G., MA, Hindford, Monteagle Lane, Yately, Camberley, Surrey.
Chandler, G., MA, 23 Dowsefield Lane, Calderstones, Liverpool 18.
Chaplais, P., PhD, FSA, Wintles Farm House, 36 Mill Street, Eynsham, Oxford.
Charles-Edwards, T. M., DPhil, Corpus Christi College, Oxford.
*Chart, D. A., ISO, LittD, 29 Cambourne Park, Upper Malone, Belfast.
*Cheney, Professor C. R., MA, DLitt, FBA, 236 Hills Road, Cambridge.
Chew, Miss H. M., MA, PhD, Seven Hills Nursing Home, St Margaret's Road, St Marychurch, Torquay.
Chibnall, Mrs Marjorie, MA, DPhil, 6 Millington Road, Cambridge.
Child, C. J., OBE, MA, PhM, 94 Westhall Road, Warlingham, Surrey CR3 9HB.
Chorley, The Hon. G. P. H., BA, 52 Warwick Gardens, W14.
Chrimes, Professor S. B., MA, PhD, LittD, University College, Cathays Park, Cardiff.
*Christie, Mrs, St George's Retreat, Ditchling Common, Burgess Hill, Sussex.
Christie, Professor I. R., MA, 10 Green Lane, Croxley Green, Herts.
Church, R. A., BA, PhD, The University, Birmingham.
Cirket, A. F., 71 Curlew Crescent, Bedford.
Clanchy, M. T., MA, The University, Glasgow, W2.
Clark, A. E., MA, 32 Durham Avenue, Thornton Cleveleys, Blackpool.
Clark, G. S. R. Kitson, MA, LittD, DLitt, Trinity College, Cambridge CB2 1TQ.

Clarke, P. F., MA, PhD, Dept of History, University College, Gower Street, WC1E 6BT.

*CLAY, Sir Charles T., CB, MA, LittD, FBA, FSA, 30 Queen's Gate Gardens, SW7.

Clementi, Miss D., MA, DPhil, Flat 7, 43 Rutland Gate, SW7.

Clemoes, Professor P. A. M., BA, PhD, Emmanuel College, Cambridge.

Clough, C. H., MA, DPhil, School of History, The University, 8 Abercromby Square, Liverpool 7.

Clover, Mrs V. Helen, MA, PhD, New Hall, Cambridge.

Cobb, H. S., MA, FSA, 1 Child's Way, Hampstead Garden Suburb, NW11.

Cobb, Professor R. C., MA, FBA, Worcester College, Oxford.

Cobban, A. B., MA, PhD, School of History, The University, 8 Abercromby Square, Liverpool 7.

Cocks, E. J., MA, Middle Lodge, Ardingly, Haywards Heath, Sussex.

*Code, Rt Rev. Monsignor Joseph B., MA, STB, ScHistD, DLitt, 1112 Orleans Avenue, Keokuk, Iowa, U.S.A.

Cohn, H. J., MA, DPhil, University of Warwick, Coventry.

Cohn, Professor N., MA, DLitt, 61 New End, NW3.

Cole, Lieut-Colonel H. N., OBE, TD, DL, FRSA, 4 Summer Cottages, Guildford Road, Ash, nr Aldershot, Hants.

Coleman, Professor D. C., BSc, PhD, FBA, Over Hall, Cavendish, Sudbury, Suffolk.

Collier, W. O., MA, FSA, 34 Berwyn Road, Richmond, Surrey.

Collieu, E. G., MA, BLitt, Brasenose College, Oxford.

Collins, Mrs I., MA, BLitt, School of History, 8 Abercromby Square, Liverpool 7.

Collinson, Professor P., MA, PhD, Department of History, University of Sydney, N.S.W. 2006, Australia.

Colvin, H. M., CBE, MA, FBA, St John's College, Oxford.

Conacher, Professor J. B., MA, PhD, 151 Welland Avenue, Toronto 290, Ontario, Canada.

Congreve, A. L., MA, FSA, Orchard Cottage, Cranbrook, Kent.

Connell, K. H., BSc(Econ), MA, PhD, Queen's University, Belfast.

Connell-Smith, G. E., PhD, 7 Braids Walk, Kirkella, Hull, Yorks.

Constable, G., PhD, 25 Mount Pleasant Street, Cambridge, Mass., U.S.A.

Conway, Professor A. A., MA, University of Canterbury, Christchurch 1, New Zealand.

Coolidge, Professor R. T., MA, BLitt, 27 Rosemount Avenue, Westmount, Quebec, Canada.

Cooper, J. P., MA, Trinity College, Oxford.

Cornwall, J. C. K., MA, 1 Orchard Close, Copford Green, Colchester, Essex.

Corson, J. C., MA, PhD, Mossrigg, Lilliesleaf, Melrose, Roxburghshire.

Cowan, I. B., MA, PhD, University of Glasgow, Glasgow, W2.

Cowdrey, Rev. H. E. J., MA, St Edmund Hall, Oxford OX1 4AR.

Cowie, Rev. L. W., MA, PhD, 38 Stratton Road, Merton Park, S.W.19.

Cowley, F. G., PhD, 17 Brookvale Road, West Cross, Swansea.

Cowling, M. J., MA, Peterhouse, Cambridge B2 1RD.

Cox, A. D. M., MA, University College, Oxford.

Craig, R. S., BSc(Econ), 99 Muswell Avenue, N10.

Cramp, Professor Rosemary, MA, BLitt, FSA, Department of Archaeology, The Old Fulling Mill, The Banks, Durham.

Cranfield, L. R., 31a Clara Street, South Yarra, Victoria, Australia.
*Crawley, C. W., MA, 1 Madingley Road, Cambridge.
Cremona, The Hon. Mr Justice Professor J. J., DLitt, PhD, LLD, 5 Victoria Gardens, Sliema, Malta.
Crittall, Miss E., MA, FSA, 16 Downside Crescent, NW3.
Crombie, A. C., BSc, MA, PhD, Trinity College, Oxford.
Crompton, J., MA, BLitt, FSA, Digby Hall, Stoughton Drive South, Leicester LE2 2NB.
*Cromwell, Miss V., MA, University of Sussex, Falmer, Brighton, Sussex.
Cross, Miss M. C., MA, PhD, University of York, York.
Crowder, C. M. D., MA, DPhil, Queen's University, Kingston, Ontario, Canada.
Crowe, Miss S. E., MA, PhD, St Hilda's College, Oxford.
Cruickshank, C. G., MA, DPhil, 15 McKay Road, Wimbledon Common, SW20.
Cumming, Professor I., MEd, PhD, The University, Auckland, New Zealand.
Cummins, J. S., PhD, University College, Gower Street, WC1E 6BT.
Cumpston, Miss I. M., MA, DPhil, Birkbeck College, Malet Street, WC1.
Cunliffe, Professor M. F., MA, BLitt, Dept of American Studies, University of Sussex, Falmer, Brighton.
Cunningham, Professor A. B., MA, PhD, Simon Fraser University, Burnaby 2, B.C., Canada.
Curtis, M. H., PhD, Scripps College, Claremont, Calif., U.S.A.
Cushner, Rev. N. P., SJ, MA, Canisius College, Buffalo, New York 14208, U.S.A.
*Cuttino, Professor G. P., DPhil, Department of History, Emory University, Atlanta, Ga., U.S.A.

Dakin, D., MA, PhD, 7 Langside Avenue, SW15.
Darlington, Professor R. R., BA, PhD, FBA, FSA, Warrenhurst, Twyford, Reading.
Davies, Professor Alun, MA, 46 Eaton Crescent, Swansea.
Davies, C. C., MA, PhD, 100 Divinity Road, Oxford.
Davies, C. S. L., MA, DPhil, Wadham College, Oxford.
Davies, R. R., DPhil, University College, Gower Street, WC1E 6BT.
*DAVIS, G. R. C., MA, DPhil, (*Treasurer*), 214 Somerset Road, SW19 5JE.
Davis, Professor R. H. C., MA, FSA, 56 Fitzroy Avenue, Harborne, Birmingham.
*Dawe, D. A., 46 Green Lane, Purley, Surrey.
*Day, P. W., MA, 2 Rectory Terrace, Gosforth, Newcastle upon Tyne.
Deane, Miss Phyllis M., MA, Newnham College, Cambridge.
*Deanesly, Professor Margaret, MA, FSA, 196 Clarence Gate Gardens, NW1.
*Deeley, Miss A. P., MA, 41 Linden Road, Bicester, Oxford.
Denton, J. H., BA, PhD, The University, Manchester.
Dickens, Professor A. G., MA, DLit, FBA, FSA, Institute of Historical Research, University of London, Senate House, WC1.
Dickinson, H. T., MA, PhD, Dept of Modern History, The University, Edinburgh.
Dickinson, Rev. J. C., MA, FSA, The University, Birmingham 15.
Dickinson, P. G. M., FSA, The Willows, Wyton, Huntingdon PE17 2AD.

Dickson, P. G. M., MA, DPhil, St Catherine's College, Oxford.
Diké, Professor K. O., MA, PhD, Dept of History, Harvard University, Cambridge, Mass. 02138, U.S.A.
Dilks, Professor D. N., BA, Dept. of International History, The University, Leeds.
Dilworth, Rev. G. M., OSB, PhD, The Abbey, Fort Augustus, Inverness-shire.
Dobson, R. B., MA, DPhil, Department of History, The University, Heslington, York.
Dockery, Rev. J., MA, The Friary, Forest Gate, E7.
*Dodwell, Miss B., MA, The University, Reading.
Dodwell, Professor C. R., MA, PhD, FSA, History of Art Department, The University, Manchester.
Dolley, R. H. M., BA, MRIA, FSA, 48 Malone Avenue, Belfast 9.
Don Peter, The Very Rev. W. L. A., MA, PhD, Aquinas College, Colombo 8, Ceylon.
Donald, Professor M. B., MSc, Rabbit Shaw, Stagbury Avenue, Chipstead, Surrey.
*Donaldson, Professor G., MA, PhD, DLitt, 24 East Hermitage Place, Edinburgh EH6 8AD.
*Donaldson-Hudson, Miss R., BA, (address unknown).
Dore, R. N., MA, Holmrook, Chapel Lane, Hale Barns, Altrincham, Cheshire.
Douglas, Professor D. C., MA, DLitt, FBA, 4 Henleaze Gardens, Bristol.
Douie, Miss D. L., BA, PhD, FSA, Flat A, 2 Charlbury Road, Oxford.
Doyle, A. I., MA, PhD, University College, The Castle, Durham.
*Drus, Miss E., MA, The University, Southampton.
Du Boulay, Professor F. R. H., MA, Broadmead, Riverhead, Sevenoaks, Kent.
Duckham, B. F., MA, Hillhead Cottage, Balfron, Stirlingshire.
Duggan, C., PhD, King's College, Strand, WC2.
Dugmore, The Rev. Professor C. W., DD, King's College, Strand, WC2.
Dunbabin, J. P. D., MA, St Edmund Hall, Oxford.
Duncan, Professor A. A. M., University of Glasgow, 29 Bute Gardens, Glasgow, W2.
Dunham, Professor W. H., PhD, 200 Everit Street, New Haven, Conn. 06511, U.S.A.
Dunlop, Mrs A. I., PhD, DLitt, Torwood, 73 London Road, Kilmarnock, Ayrshire.
Dunning, Rev. P. J., CM, MA, PhD, St Patrick's College, Armagh, Northern Ireland.
Dunning, R. W., BA, PhD, FSA, 16 Comeytrowe Rise, Taunton, Somerset.
Durack, Mrs I. A., MA, PhD, University of Western Australia, Crawley, Western Australia.
Dykes, D. W., MA, 64 Windsor Avenue, Radyr, Cardiff.
Dyos, Professor H. J., BSc(Econ), PhD, 16 Kingsway Road, Leicester.

Eastwood, Rev. C. C., PhD, Heathview, Monks Lane, Audlem, Cheshire.
Eckles, Professor R. B., PhD, P.O. Box 3035, West Lafayette, Indiana, 47906, U.S.A.
Ede, J. R., MA, Public Record Office, Chancery Lane, WC2.
Edmonds, Professor E. L., MA, PhD, Dean of Education, Univ. of Prince Edward Island, Charlottetown, Prince Edward Island, Canada.

Edwards, F. O., SJ, FSA, 114 Mount Street, W1Y 6AH.
EDWARDS, Professor Sir J. Goronwy, MA, DLitt, LittD, FBA, FSA, 35 Westmoreland Road, SW13.
Edwards, Miss K., MA, PhD, FSA, Dunbar Cottage, 10 Dunbar Street, Old Aberdeen.
Edwards, Professor R. W. D., MA, PhD, DLitt, 31 Castle Avenue, Clontarf, Dublin.
Ehrman, J. P. W., MA, FBA, FSA, Sloane House, 149 Old Church Street, SW3 6EB.
Elliott, Professor J. H., MA, PhD, FBA, King's College, Strand, WC2.
Ellis, R. H., MA, FSA, Cloth Hill, 6 The Mount, NW3.
Ellul, M., BArch, DipArch, 'Pauline', 55 Old Railway Road, Birkirkara, Malta.
Elrington, C. R., MA, FSA, Institute of Historical Research, Senate House, WC1.
Elton, Professor G. R., MA, PhD, LittD, FBA, 30 Millington Road, Cambridge CB3 9HP.
Elvin, L., 10 Almond Avenue, Swanpool, Lincoln.
*Emmison, F. G., MBE, PhD, FSA, Bilbury, Links Drive, Chelmsford.
d'Entrèves, Professor A. P., DPhil, Strada Ai Ronchi 48, Cavoretto, Torino, Italy.
Erickson, Charlotte J., PhD, London School of Economics, Houghton Street, WC2.
*Erith, E. J., Shurlock House, Shurlock Row, Berkshire.
Erskine, Mrs A. M., MA, BLitt, 44 Birchy Barton Hill, Exeter.
Evans, Mrs A. K. B., PhD, FSA, White Lodge, 25 Kingleton Grange Road, Leicester.
Evans, Sir David L., OBE, BA, DLitt, 2 Bay Court, Doctors Commons Road, Berkhamsted, Herts.
Evans, Miss Joan, DLitt, DLit, LLD, LittD, FSA, Thousand Acres, Wotton-under-Edge, Glos.
Evans, The Very Rev. S. J. A., MA, FSA, The Old Manor, Fulbourne, Cambs.
Everitt, Professor A. M., MA, PhD, The University, Leicester.
Eyck, Professor U. F. J., MA, BLitt, 24 Norman Avenue, Abingdon, Berks.

Fage, Professor J. D., MA, PhD, Dept of African History, The University, Birmingham.
Fagg, J. E., MA, 47 The Avenue, Durham.
Farmer, D. F. H., BLitt, FSA, The University, Reading.
Farr, M. W., MA, FSA, 12 Emscote Road, Warwick.
Fearn, Rev. II., MA, PhD, Holy Trinity Vicarage, 6, Wildwood, Northwood, Middlesex.
Fellows, A. E., MA, 69 Lonsdale Road, SW13.
Fenn, Rev. R. W. D., MA, BD, FSAScot, Glascwm Vicarage, Llandrindod Wells, Radnorshire.
Fieldhouse, D. K., MA, Nuffield College, Oxford.
Finberg, Professor H. P. R., MA, DLitt, FSA, 151 Park Road, W4.
Finer, Professor S. E., MA, University of Manchester, Dover Street, Manchester 13.
Finlayson, G. B. A. M., MA, BLitt, The University, Glasgow, W2.
Finley, Professor M. I., MA, PhD, 12 Adams Road, Cambridge.
Fisher, D. J. V., MA, Jesus College, Cambridge.

Fisher, Professor F. J., MA, London School of Economics, Houghton Street, WC2.

Fisher, F. N., Duckpool, Ashleyhay, Wirksworth, Derby DE4 4AJ.

Fisher, Professor S. N., PhD, Box 162, Worthington, Ohio 43085, U.S.A.

Fitch, M. F. B., FSA, c/o Phillimore & Co. Ltd, Shopwyke Hall, Chichester, Sussex.

*Fletcher, The Rt Hon. The Lord, P. C., BA, LLD, 9 Robin Grove, N6.

Flint, Professor J. E., MA, PhD, Dalhousie University, Halifax, Nova Scotia, Canada.

Foot, Professor M. R. D., MA, BLitt, The University, Manchester M13 9PL.

Forbes, D., MA, 89 Gilbert Road, Cambridge.

Ford, W. K., 48 Harlands Road, Haywards Heath, Sussex.

Forrester, E. G., MA, BLitt, Spring Cottage, Pebble Lane, Brackley, Northants.

Forster, G. C. F., BA, The University, Leeds 2.

Fowler, K. A., BA, PhD, 2 Nelson Street, Edinburgh 3.

Fox, L., OBE, DL, LHD, MA, FSA, FRSL, Silver Birches, 27 Welcombe Road, Stratford-upon-Avon.

Francis, A. D., CBE, MVO, MA, 21 Cadogan Street, SW3.

Franklin, R. M., BA, All Souls College, Oxford.

*Fraser, Miss C. M., PhD, 39 King Edward Road, Tynemouth, North Shields NE30 2RW.

Fraser, Miss Maxwell, MA, Crowthorne, 21 Dolphin Road, Slough, Bucks SL1 1TF.

Fraser, P., BA, PhD, The University, Manchester 13.

Frend, Professor W. H. C., MA, DPhil, DD, FSA, Marbrae, Balmaha, Stirlingshire.

Fryde, E. B., DPhil, 1 Plas Danycoed, Aberystwyth, Cards.

*Fryer, Professor C. E., MA, PhD (address unknown).

Fryer, Professor W. R., BLitt, MA., 68 Grove Avenue, Chilwell, Beeston, Notts.

Frykenberg, Professor R. E., MA, PhD, 1840 Chadbourne Avenue, Madison, Wis. 53705, U.S.A.

*Furber, Professor H., MA, PhD, History Department, University of Pennsylvania, Philadelphia, Pa., U.S.A.

Fussell, G. E., DLitt, 55 York Road, Sudbury, Suffolk, CO10 6NF.

Fyrth, H., BSc(Econ.), Dept of Extra Mural Studies, University of London, 7 Ridgemount Street, WC1.

Gabriel, Professor A. L., PhD, FMAA, CFIF, CFBA, Box 578, University of Notre Dame, Notre Dame, Indiana 46556, U.S.A.

*Galbraith, Professor J. S., BS, MA, PhD, University of California, Los Angeles, Calif. 92204, U.S.A.

GALBRAITH, Professor V. H., MA, DLitt, LittD, FBA, 20A Bradmore Road, Oxford.

Gale, Professor H. P. P., OBE, PhD, 6 Nassau Road, SW13.

Gale, W. K. V., 19 Ednam Road, Goldthorn Park, Wolverhampton WV4 5BL.

Gann, L. H., MA, BLitt, DPhil, Hoover Institution, Stanford University, Stanford, Calif., U.S.A.

Ganshof, Professor F. L., 12 Rue Jacques Jordaens, Brussels, Belgium.

Gash, Professor N., MA, BLitt, FBA, Gowrie Cottage, 73 Hepburn Gardens, St Andrews.

Gee, E. A., MA, DPhil, FSA, 28 Trentholme Drive, The Mount, York.

Gerlach, Professor D. R., MA, PhD, University of Akron, Akron, Ohio 44325, U.S.A.

Gibbs, G. C., MA, Birkbeck College, Malet Street, WC1.

Gibbs, Professor N. H., MA, DPhil, All Souls College, Oxford.

Gibson, Margaret T., MA, DPhil, School of History, The University, Liverpool L69 3BX.

Gifford, Miss D. H., PhD, FSA, Public Record Office, Chancery Lane, WC2.

Ginter, D. E., AM, PhD, Dept of History, Sir George Williams University, Montreal 107, Canada.

Girtin, T., MA, Butterfield House, Church Street, Old Isleworth, Kent.

*Glover, Professor R. G., MA, PhD, Carleton University, Ottawa 1, Canada.

*Godber, Miss A. J., MA, FSA, Mill Lane Cottage, Willington, Bedford.

*Godfrey, Professor J. L., MA, PhD, (address unknown).

Goldthorp, L. M., MA, Wilcroft House, Pecket Well, Hebden Bridge, Yorks.

Goodman, A. E., MA, BLitt, Dept of Medieval History, The University, Edinburgh.

Goodspeed, Professor D. J., BA, 164 Victoria Street, Niagara-on-the-Lake, Ontario, Canada.

Goodwin, Professor A., MA, Windsor Court, 12 Hound Street, Sherborne, Dorset.

*Gopal, S., MA, DPhil, 30 Edward Elliot Road, Mylapore, Madras, India.

Gordon, Professor D. J., MA, PhD, Wantage Hall, Upper Redlands Road, Reading.

Gordon-Brown, A., Velden, Alexandra Road, Wynberg, C.P., South Africa.

Gorton, L. J., MA, 41 West Hill Avenue, Epsom, Surrey.

Gosden, P. H. J. H., MA, PhD, The University, Leeds.

Gough, J. W., MA, DLitt, Oriel College, Oxford.

Gowing, Professor Margaret M., BSc(Econ), Linacre College, Oxford.

*Graham, Professor G. S., MA, PhD, Hobbs Cottage, Beckley, Sussex.

Gransden, Mrs A., MA, PhD, 51 Burlington Road, Sherwood, Nottingham.

Grassby, R. B., MA, Jesus College, Oxford.

Graves, Professor Edgar B., 318 College Hill Road, Clinton, New York 13323, U.S.A.

Gray, J. W., MA, Dept of Medieval History, Queens University, Belfast BT7 1NN.

Greaves, Professor R. W., MA, DPhil, 1920 Hillview Road, Lawrence, Kansas, U.S.A.

Greaves, Mrs R. W., PhD, 1920 Hillview Road, Lawrence, Kansas, U.S.A.

Green, H., BA, Rhinog Brands Hill Avenue, High Wycombe, Bucks.

Green, Rev. V. H. H., MA, DD, Lincoln College, Oxford.

Greenhill, B. J., CMG, National Maritime Museum, Greenwich, SE10 9FN.

Greenleaf, Professor W. H., BSc(Econ), PhD, University College, Singleton Park, Swansea, Glam.

Grenville, Professor J. A. S., PhD, University of Birmingham, P.O. Box 363, Birmingham 15.
Grierson, Professor P., MA, LittD, FBA, FSA, Gonville and Caius College, Cambridge.
Grieve, Miss H. E. P., BA, 153 New London Road, Chelmsford, Essex.
Griffiths, J., MA, Springwood, Stanley Road, New Ferry, Cheshire.
Griffiths, R. A., PhD, University College, Singleton Park, Swansea.
Grimble, I., PhD, 111 Downton Avenue, SE2.
Grimm, Professor H. J., PhD, Department of History, 216 North Oval Drive, The Ohio State University, Columbus, Ohio, U.S.A.
Grisbrooke, W. J., MA, 14 The Vale, Edgbaston Park Road, Edgbaston, Birmingham 5.
*Griscom, Rev. Acton, MA, (address unknown).
Gum, Professor E. J., PhD, 5116 Grant Street, Omaha, Nebraska 68104, U.S.A.
Gundersheimer, Professor W. L., MA, PhD, 507 Roumfort Road, Philadelphia, Pa. 19119, U.S.A.

Habakkuk, H. J., MA, FBA, Jesus College, Oxford.
Haber, Professor F. C., PhD, Dept of History, University of Maryland, College Park, Md. 20742, U.S.A.
*Hadcock, R. N., DLitt, FSA, Winchcombe Farm, Briff Lane, Bucklebury, Reading.
Haffenden, P. S., PhD, 36 The Parkway, Bassett, Southampton.
Haigh, C. A., BA, PhD, Dept of History, The University, Manchester M13 9PL.
Haight, Mrs M. Jackson, PhD, 8 Chemin des Clochettes, Geneva, Switzerland.
Haines, Professor R. M., MA, MLitt, DPhil, FSA, Dalhousie University, Halifax, N.S., Canada.
Hair, P. E. H., MA, DPhil, The School of History, The University, P.O. Box 147, Liverpool.
Halcrow, Miss E. M., MA, BLitt, Achimota School, Achimota, P.B.11, Ghana, West Africa.
Hale, Professor J. R., MA, FSA, University College, Gower Street, WC1.
Haley, Professor K. H. D., MA, BLitt, 15 Haugh Lane, Sheffield 11.
Hall, Professor A. R., MA, PhD, 23 Chiswick Staithe, W.4.
Hall, Professor B., MA, University of Manchester, M13 9PL.
*Hall, C. S., MA, Flat 16, Petersgath, Moorhead Lane, Shipley, Yorks.
Hall, Professor D. G. E., MA, DLit, 4 Chiltern Road, Hitchin, Herts.
Hall, G. D. G., MA, The President's Lodgings, Corpus Christi College, Oxford.
Hallam, H. E., MA, PhD, University of Western Australia, Nedlands, Western Australia.
Hamilton, B., BA, PhD, The University, Nottingham NG7 2RD.
Hammersley, G. F., BA, University of Edinburgh, William Robertson Building, George Square, Edinburgh.
Hampson, Professor N., MA, D. de l'Univ., The University, Newcastle upon Tyne.
Hand, G. J., MA, DPhil, Woodburn, Sydney Avenue, Blackrock, Co. Dublin, Ireland.
Handover, Miss P. M., MA, 3 Lyon House, 14 Aldersey Road, Guildford, Surrey.

Hanham, Professor H. J., MA, PhD, Harvard University, Cambridge, Mass. 02138, U.S.A.

Hanke, Professor L. U., PhD, University of Massachusetts, Amherst, Mass. 01002, U.S.A.

Hanna, A. J., PhD, 6 Cliffe Road, Barton-on-Sea, Hants.

Harding, A., MA, BLitt, 3 Tantallon Place, Edinburgh.

Harding, F. J. W., MA, BLitt, FSA, Brynrhos, 187 Mayals Road, Swansea.

Harding, H. W., BA, LLD, 39 Annunciation Street, Sliema, Malta.

Hargreaves, Professor J. D., MA, 146 Hamilton Place, Aberdeen.

Hargreaves-Mawdsley, Professor W. N., MA, DPhil, FSA, The University, Brandon, Manitoba, Canada.

Harman, Rev. L. W., Hardingstone Vicarage, Northampton.

Harris, Professor J. R., MA, PhD, The University, P.O. Box 463, Birmingham.

Harrison, Professor B., MA, University of British Columbia, Vancouver 8, Canada.

Harrison, B. H., MA, DPhil, Corpus Christi College, Oxford.

Harrison, C. J., BA, St John's College, Oxford.

Harriss, G. L., MA, DPhil, Magdalen College, Oxford.

Hart, C. J. R., MA, MB, BS, Goldthorns, Stilton, Peterborough.

Hart, Mrs J. M., MA, St Anne's College, Oxford.

Hartwell, R. M., MA, DPhil., Nuffield College, Oxford.

Harvey, Miss B. F., MA, BLitt, Somerville College, Oxford.

Harvey, Margaret M., MA, DPhil, St Aidan's College, Durham.

Harvey, P. D. A., MA, DPhil, FSA, 9 Glen Eyre Close, Bassett, Southampton.

Harvey, Sally P. J., MA, PhD, School of History, The University, Leeds, LS2 9JT.

Haskell, Professor F. J., MA, FBA, Trinity College, Oxford.

Haskins, Professor G. L., AB, LLB, JD, MA, University of Pennsylvania, The Law School, 3400 Chestnut Street, Philadelphia, Pa. 19104 U.S.A.

Haslam, E. B., MA, 5 Pymers Mead, Dulwich, SE21 8NQ.

Hassall, W. O., MA, DPhil, The Manor House, 26 High Street, Wheatley, Oxford OX9 1XX.

Hastings, Professor Margaret, PhD, Douglass College, Rutgers University, New Brunswick, N.J. 08903, U.S.A.

Hattersley, Professor A. F., MA, DLitt, 1 Sanders Road, Pietermaritzburg, S. Africa.

Hatton, Professor Ragnhild M., PhD, London School of Economics, Houghton Street, WC2.

*Havinden, Eric, MA, 30 Park Avenue, Solihull, Warwickshire.

Hay, Professor D., MA, DLitt, FBA, Department of History, The University, Edinburgh EH8 9JY.

Hazlehurst, G. C. L., BA, DPhil, Institute of Advanced Study, Australian National University, Box 4, P.O. Canberra, A.C.T.

Headlam-Morley, Miss A., BLitt, MA, St Hugh's College, Oxford.

Hearder, H., PhD, University College, Cathays Park, Cardiff.

Hembry, Mrs P. M., PhD, Flat 24, Thorncliffe, Lansdown Road, Cheltenham GL51 6PZ.

Hemleben, S. J., MA, DPhil, (address unknown).

Henderson, A. J., AB, AM, PhD, 247 North Webster, Jacksonville, Ill. 62650, U.S.A.

Henning, Professor B. D., PhD, Saybrook College, Yale University, New Haven, Conn., U.S.A.

Highfield, J. R. L., MA, DPhil, Merton College, Oxford.

HILL, Sir Francis, CBE, MA, LLD, LittD, FSA (Hon Solicitor), The Priory, Lincoln.

Hill, J. E. C., MA, DLitt, FBA, The Master's Lodgings, Balliol College, Oxford.

*Hill, Miss M. C., MA, County Record Office, Shirehall, Shrewsbury.

*Hill, Professor Rosalind M. T., MA, BLitt, FSA, Westfield College, Hampstead, NW3.

Hilton, Professor R. H., DPhil, University of Birmingham, P.O. Box 363, Birmingham 15.

*Hinsley, Professor F. H., MA, St John's College, Cambridge.

*Hodgett, G. A. J., MA, King's College, Strand, WC2.

*Hogg, Brigadier O. F. G., CBE, FSA, 1 Hardy Road, Blackheath, SE3.

Holdsworth, C. J., MA, PhD, West End House, Totteridge Lane, N20.

Hollaender, A. E. J., PhD, FSA, 110 Narbonne Avenue, South Side, Clapham Common, SW4.

*Hollingsworth, L. W., PhD, Flat 27, Mayfair, 74 Westcliff Road, Bournemouth.

Hollis, Patricia, MA, DPhil, 30 Park Lane, Norwich.

Hollister, Professor C. Warren, MA, PhD, University of California, Santa Barbara, Calif. 93106, U.S.A.

Holmes, G. A., MA, PhD, 431 Banbury Road, Oxford.

Holmes, G. S., MA, BLitt, Tatham House, Burton-in-Lonsdale, Carnforth, Lancs.

Holt, Miss A. D., Fasga-na-Coille, Nethy Bridge, Inverness-shire.

Holt, Professor J. C., MA, DPhil, FSA, University of Reading, Whiteknights Park, Reading, Berks.

Hope, R. S. H., 25 Hengistbury Road, Southbourne, Bournemouth, Hants.

Horwitz, Professor H. G., BA, DPhil, White Horses, Kingsdown, nr Deal, Kent.

*Howard, C. H. D., MA, 15 Sunnydale Gardens, NW7.

*Howard, M. E., MC, MA, FBA, The Homestead, Eastbury, Newbury, Berks.

Howarth, Mrs J. H., MA, St Hilda's College, Oxford.

Howat, G. M. D., MA, BLitt, Old School House, North Moreton, Berks.

Howell, Miss M. E., MA, PhD, 10 Highland Road, Charlton Kings, Cheltenham, Glos. GL53 9LT.

Howell, R., MA, DPhil, Bowdoin College, Brunswick, Maine 04011, U.S.A.

Hudson, G. F., MA, St Antony's College, Oxford.

Huehns, Miss G., PhD, 35A Sterling Avenue, Edgware, Middlesex.

Hufton, Miss O. H., PhD, 10 Belmont Drive, Maidenhead, Berks.

Hughes, Professor J. Q., BArch, PhD, Loma Linda, Criccieth, Caernarvons.

Hughes, Miss K. W., MA, PhD, FSA, Newnham College, Cambridge.

Hull, F., BA, PhD, Roundwell Cottage, Bearsted, Maidstone, Kent.

Hulton, P. H., BA, FSA, 46 St Paul's Road, N1.

HUMPHREYS, Professor R. A., OBE, MA, PhD, DLitt, LittD, 13 St Paul's Place, Canonbury, N1 2QE.

Hunnisett, R. F., MA, DPhil, 54 Longdon Wood, Keston, Kent BR2 6EW.
Hurnard, Miss N. D., 40c Park Town, Oxford.
Hurst, M. C., MA, St John's College, Oxford.
Hurstfield, Professor J., DLit, 7 Glenilla Road, NW3.
Hurt, J. S., BA, PhD, BSc(Econ), 14 The Avenue, Barnet, Herts EN5 4EN.
Hurwitz, Professor S. J., LLB, AM, PhD, Brooklyn College of the City University of New York, 11210, U.S.A.
*Hussey, Professor Joan M., MA, BLitt, PhD, FSA, Royal Holloway College, Englefield Green, Surrey.
Hyams, P. R., MA, DPhil, Pembroke College, Oxford.
Hyde, Professor F. E., MA, PhD, Savanna, Caldy Road, West Kirby, Cheshire.
*Hyde, H. Montgomery, MA, DLit, Westwell, Tenterden, Kent.
Hyde, J. K., MA, PhD, The University, Manchester.

Ingham, Professor K., MA, DPhil, The Woodlands, 94 West Town Lane, Bristol 4.
Ives, E. W., PhD, 214 Myton Road, Warwick.

Jack, Professor R. I., MA, PhD, University of Sydney, Sydney, N.S.W., Australia.
Jackman, Professor S. W., PhD, FSA, 1065 Deal Street, Victoria, British Columbia, Canada.
Jackson, E. D. C., FSA, (address unknown).
Jaffar, Professor S. M., BA, Khudadad Street, Peshawar City, N.W.F. Province, W. Pakistan.
James, M. E., MA, University of Durham, 43–45 North Bailey, Durham.
Jarvis, R. C., ISO, FSA, Shelley, Station Road, Hockley, Essex.
Jasper, Rev. Canon R. C. D., MA, DD, 1 Little Cloister, Westminster Abbey, SW1.
Jeffs, R. M., MA, DPhil, 25 Lawson Road, Sheffield S10 5BU.
Jenkins, D., MA, LLM, Dept of Law, University College of Wales, Aberystwyth, Cards., SY23 2DB.
Jeremy, D. J., BA, MLitt, 523 Osgood Street, North Andover, Mass. 01845, U.S.A.
John, Professor A. H., BSc(Econ), PhD, London School of Economics, Houghton Street, WC2.
John, E., MA, The University, Manchester 13.
Johnson, D. J., BA, 41 Cranes Park Avenue, Surbiton, Surrey.
Johnson, Professor D. W. J., BLitt, University College, Gower Street, WC1E 6BT.
Johnson, H. C., CB, CBE, MA, Hawthorns, 39 Algarth Rise, Pocklington, York.
*Johnson, J. H., MA, Whitehorns, Cedar Avenue, Chelmsford.
Johnson, W. Branch, FSA, Hope Cottage, 22 Mimram Road, Welwyn, Herts.
Johnston, Miss E. M., MA, PhD, The University, Sheffield 10.
Johnston, Lieut-Colonel G. R., RA, FRSA, Wood Corner, Lankhills Road, Winchester.
Johnston, Professor S. H. F., MA, Fronhyfryd, Llanbadarn Road, Aberystwyth.

Jones, G. A., MA, PhD, Dept of History, Faculty of Letters, University of Reading, Whiteknights, Reading, Berks.
Jones, G. H., PhD, Mayflower House, Acrefield Drive, Cambridge.
Jones, G. J., The Croft, Litchard Bungalows, Bridgend, Glam.
*Jones, Professor G. P., MA, Spa House, Witherstack, via Grange-over-Sands, Lancs.
Jones, H. W., MA, PhD, 32 Leylands Terrace, Bradford 9.
Jones, Professor I. G., MA, 12 Laura Place, Aberystwyth, Cards.
Jones, Professor J. R., MA, PhD, School of English and American Studies, University Plain, Norwich.
Jones, Professor M. A., MA, DPhil, Dept of History, University College, Gower Street, WC1E 6BT.
Jones, M. C. E., MA, DPhil, The University, Nottingham.
Jones, The Rev. Canon O. W., MA, The Vicarage, Builth Wells, Breconshire.
Jones, P. E., LLB, FSA, 18 Wansunt Road, Bexley, Kent.
Jones, P. J., DPhil, Brasenose College, Oxford.
Jordan, Professor P. D., PhD, LLD, 26 Cascade Terrace, Burlington, Iowa 52601, U.S.A.
*Judges, Professor A. V., BA, DSc(Econ), Oliver House, 53A Strand-on-the-Green, W4.
Jukes, Rev H. A. Ll., MA, The Vicarage, Tilney All Saints, nr King's Lynn, Norfolk.

Kamen, H. A. F., MA, DPhil, The University, Warwick CV4 7AL.
*Kay, H., MA, 16 Bourton Drive, Poynton, Stockport, Cheshire.
Kearney, Professor H. F., MA, PhD, Edinburgh University, Old College, South Bridge, Edinburgh 8.
Keen, M. H., MA, Balliol College, Oxford.
Kellaway, C. W., MA, FSA, 2 Grove Terrace, NW5.
Kelly, Professor T., MA, PhD, 55 Freshfield Road, Formby, nr Liverpool.
Kemp, Miss B., MA, FSA, St Hugh's College, Oxford.
Kemp, B. R., BA, PhD, 12 Redhatch Drive, Earley, Reading, Berks.
Kemp, The Very Rev. E. W., DD, The Deanery, Worcester WR1 2LH.
Kemp, Lt-Commander P. K., RN, Malcolm's, 51 Market Hill, Maldon, Essex.
Kennedy, J., MA, 1 The Grove, Abbot's Way, Newcastle-under-Lyme, Staffs.
Kent, Rev. J. H. S., MA, PhD, Dept of Theology, University of Bristol, Senate House, Bristol BS8 1TH.
Kenyon, Professor J. P., PhD, Nicholson Hall, Cottingham, Yorks.
Ker, N. R., MA, DLitt, FBA, FSA, Slievemore, Foss, by Pitlochry, Perthshire.
Kerling, Miss N. J. M., PhD, 26 Upper Park Road, NW3.
Kerridge, E. W. J., PhD, 9 Cross Green, Upton by Chester, Cheshire.
Kershaw, Ian, BA, DPhil, 6 Cranston Drive, Sale, Cheshire.
Ketelbey, Miss D. M., MA, 18 Queen's Gardens, St Andrews, Fife.
Khan, M. Siddiq, MA, LLB, University Bungalow No 28, P.O. Ramna, Dacca, Bangladesh.
Khanna, Kahan Chand, MA, PhD, 3-B Mathura Road, New Delhi 14, India.
Kiernan, Professor V. G., MA, University of Edinburgh, William Robertson Building, George Square, Edinburgh.

*Kimball, Miss E. G., BLitt, PhD, Drake's Corner Road, Princeton, N.J., U.S.A.

King, E. J., MA, PhD, Dept of History, The University, Sheffield S10 2TN.

King, P. D., BA, PhD, Lancaster View, Bailrigg, Lancaster.

Kingsford, Rev. M. R., MA, BLitt, STM, R.R.2, Madoc, Ontario, Canada.

Kingsford, P. W., BSc(Econ), PhD, Hatfield Polytechnic, Bayfordbury, Hertford, Herts.

Kinsley, Professor J., MA, PhD, DLitt, FBA, University of Nottingham, Nottingham NG7 2RD.

Kirby, D. P., MA, PhD, Manoraven, Llanon, Cards.

Kirby, J. L., MA, FSA, 22 Bardwell Court, Bardwell Road, Oxford.

Klibansky, Professor R., MA, PhD, DPhil, FRSC, McGill University, Montreal, Canada.

Knecht, R. J., MA, 22 Warwick New Road, Leamington Spa, Warwickshire.

*Knight, L. Stanley, MA, Little Claregate, 1 The Drive, Malthouse Lane, Tettenhall, Wolverhampton.

Knowles, C. H., PhD, University College, Cathays Park, Cardiff.

*KNOWLES, Professor the Rev. M. D., MA, DD, LittD, DLitt, DLit, FBA, FSA, 9 Old House Close, Church Road, SW19.

Kochan, L. E., BA, PhD, 237 Woodstock Road, Oxford.

Koenigsberger, Professor H. G., PhD, Department of History, Cornell University, Ithaca, New York, USA.

Koeppler, Professor H., OBE, DPhil, Wilton Park, Wiston House, Steyning, Sussex.

Kossmann, Professor E. H., DLitt, Rijksuniversiteit te Groningen, Groningen, The Netherlands.

Lambert, M. D., MA, 17 Oakenwood Road, Henleaze, Bristol.

Lamont, W. M., PhD, 9 Bramleys, Kingston, Lewes, Sussex.

Lancaster, Miss J. C., MA, FSA, 43 Craigmair Road, Tulse Hill, SW2.

Landa, Professor L. A., AM, PhD, Princeton University, Princeton, N.J., U.S.A.

Lander, J. R., MA, MLitt, Middlesex College, University of Western Ontario, London, Ont., Canada.

Landes, Professor D. S., PhD, Widener 97, Harvard University, Cambridge, Mass. 02138, U.S.A.

*Langton, Rev. E., DD, Delamere, 43 Glandon Drive, Cheadle Hulme, nr Stockport.

La Page, J., FSA, Craig Lea, 44 Bank Crest, Baildon, Yorkshire.

Laprade, Professor W. T., PhD, 1108 Monmouth Avenue, Durham, N. Carolina, U.S.A.

Larkin, Professor the Rev. J. F., CSV, PhD, University College, De Paul University, 25E Jackson Blvd., Chicago, Ill. 60604, U.S.A.

Larner, J. P., MA, The University, Glasgow, W2.

Latham, Professor R. C., MA, Magdalene College, Cambridge.

Lawrence, Professor C. H., MA, DPhil, Bedford College, Regent's Park, NW1.

*Laws, Lieut-Colonel M. E. S., OBE, MC, Bank Top Cottage, Seal Chart, Sevenoaks, Kent.

Leddy, J. F., MA, BLitt, D Phil, University of Windsor, Windsor, Ontario, Canada.

Lee, Professor M. du P., PhD, Douglass College, Rutgers University, New Brunswick, N.J. 08903, U.S.A.

Lees, R. McLachlan, MA, Kent College, Harbridge, Ringwood, Hants.

Legge, Professor M. Dominica, MA, BLitt, David Hume Tower, George Square, Edinburgh.

Lehmberg, Professor S. E., PhD, Dept of History, University of Minnesota, Minneapolis, Minn. 55455, U.S.A.

Lenanton, Lady, MA, FSA, Bride Hall, nr Welwyn, Herts.

Le Patourel, Professor J. H., MA, DPhil, D. de l'Univ., Westcote, Hebers Ghyll Drive, Ilkley, Yorks.

Leslie, Professor R. F., BA, PhD, 23 Grove Park Road, W4.

Lewis, Professor A. R., MA, PhD, History Dept, University of Massachusetts, Amhurst, Mass. 01003, U.S.A.

Lewis, Professor B., PhD, FBA, 55 Springfield Road, NW8.

Lewis, C. W., BA, FSA, University College, Cathays Park, Cardiff.

Lewis, E. D., MA, DSc, Glamorgan College of Education, Buttrils Road, Barry, Glam.

Lewis, P. S., MA, All Souls College, Oxford.

Lewis, R. A., PhD, University College of North Wales, Bangor.

Leyser, K., MA, Magdalen College, Oxford.

Lhoyd-Owen, Commander J. H., RN, 37 Marlings Park Avenue, Chislehurst, Kent.

Liebeschütz, H., MA, DPhil, Dockenhuden, Marines Road, Liverpool 23.

*Lindsay, Mrs H., MA, PhD, Girton College, Cambridge.

Linehan, P. A., MA, PhD, St John's College, Cambridge.

Lipman, V. D., DPhil, Flat 14, 33 Kensington Court, W8.

Livermore, Professor H. V., MA, Sandycombe Lodge, Sandycombe Road, St Margarets, Twickenham.

Loades, D. M., MA, PhD, Oatlands, Farnley Mount, Durham.

Lobel, Mrs M. D., BA, FSA, 16 Merton Street, Oxford.

Lockhart, L., MA, LittD, PhD, Cedarwood House, West Green, Barrington, Cambridge CB2 5SA.

Lockie, D. McN., MA, Chemin de la Panouche, Saint-Anne, Grasse, Alpes Maritimes, France.

Loewenberg, Professor B. J., MA, PhD, 15 Center Knolls, Bronxville, New York, U.S.A.

Logan, Rev. F. D., MA, MSD, Emmanuel College, 400 The Fenway, Boston, Mass. 02115, U.S.A.

London, Miss Vera C. M., MA, Underholt, Westwood Road, Bidston, Birkenhead, Cheshire.

Longford, The Right Honble The Countess of, MA, DLitt, Bernhurst, Hurst Green, Sussex.

Longrais, Professor F. Joüon des, D.-en-droit, L.-ès-L., 4 rue de la Terrasse, Paris XVII, France.

Loomie, Rev. A. J., SJ, MA, PhD, Fordham University, New York, N.Y. 10458, U.S.A.

Lourie, Elena, MA, DPhil, 66 Brandeis Street, Tel-Aviv, Israel.

Lovatt, R. W., MA, DPhil, Peterhouse, Cambridge.

Lovell, J. C., BA, PhD, Eliot College, University of Kent, Canterbury.

Lowe, P. C., BA, PhD, The University, Manchester.

Loyn, H. R., MA, FSA, 196 Fidlas Road, Llanishen, Cardiff.

Luft, The Rev. M., MA, MLitt, Merchant Taylor's School, Crosby, Liverpool 23.

*Lumb, Miss S. V., MA, Flat 309, 112 King's Head Hill, Chingford, E4 7ND.
Luscombe, Professor D. E., MA, PhD, 129 Prospect Road, Totley Rise, Sheffield.
Luttrell, A. T., MA, DPhil, British School at Rome, Via Gramsci 61, 00197 Rome.
Lynch, Professor J., MA, PhD, University College, Gower Street, London, WC1E 6BT.
Lyons, Professor F. S. L., MA, PhD, LittD, Eliot College, University of Kent, Canterbury.
Lyttelton, The Hon. N. A. O., BA, St Antony's College, Oxford.

Mabbs, A. W., Public Record Office, Chancery Lane, WC2.
MacCaffrey, Professor W. T., PhD, 745 Hollyoke Center, Harvard University, Cambridge, Mass. 02138, U.S.A.
McConica, Professor J. K., OSB, MA, DPhil, Pontifical Institute of Medieval Studies, 59 Queen's Park Crescent, Toronto 181, Ont., Canada.
McCord, N., PhD, 7 Hatherton Avenue, Cullercoats, North Shields, Northumberland.
McCracken, Professor J. L., MA, PhD, New University of Ulster, Coleraine, Co. Londonderry, N. Ireland.
McCulloch, Professor S. C., MA, PhD, 2121 Windward Lane, Newport Beach, Calif. 92660, U.S.A.
Macdonald, Professor D. F., MA, DPhil, Queen's College, Dundee.
McDonald, Prof. T. H., MA, PhD, Idaho State University, Pocatello, Idaho 83201, U.S.A.
McDowell, R. B., PhD, Trinity College, Dublin.
Macfarlane, A., MA, DPhil, King's College, Cambridge CB2 1ST.
Macfarlane, L. J., PhD, FSA, King's College, University of Aberdeen, Aberdeen.
McGrath, P. V., MA, University of Bristol, Bristol.
MacGregor, D. R., BA, 99 Lonsdale Road, SW13.
McGurk, J. J. N., BA, MPhil, 12 Sunninghill Court, Ascot, Berks.
McGurk, P. M., PhD, Birkbeck College, Malet Street, WC1E 7HX.
Machin, G. I. T., MA, DPhil, Queen's College, Dundee.
MacIntyre, A. D., MA, DPhil, Magdalen College, Oxford.
McKenna, Professor J. W., MA, PhD, Haverford College, Haverford, Pa. 19041, U.S.A.
Mackesy, P. G., MA, Pembroke College, Oxford.
*Mackie, Professor J. D., CBE, MC, MA, LLD, FSAScot, 67 Dowanside Road, Glasgow W2.
McKinley, R. A., MA, 42 Boyers Walk, Leicester Forest East, Leics.
McKisack, Professor May, MA, BLitt, FSA, 59 Parktown, Oxford.
Maclagan, M., MA, FSA, Trinity College, Oxford.
Maclean, J. N. M., BLitt, PhD, 61 Learmonth Court, Edinburgh 4.
*McManners, Professor J., MA, University of Leicester, Leicester.
MacMichael, N. H., FSA, 2B Little Cloister, Westminster Abbey, SW1.
MacNiocaill, G., PhD, Dept of History, University College, Galway, Ireland.
McNulty, Miss P. A., BA, St George's Hall, Elmhurst Road, Reading.
MacNutt, Professor W. S., MA, University of New Brunswick, Fredericton, N.B., Canada.
McRoberts, Rt Rev. Monsignor David, STL, FSA, Chaplain's House, St Charles', Carstairs Junction, Lanarkshire.

Madariaga, Miss Isabel de, PhD, 27 Southwood Lawn Road, N6.
Madden, A. F. McC., D Phil, Nuffield College, Oxford.
Maddicott, J. R., MA, DPhil, Exeter College, Oxford.
Maehl, Professor W. H., PhD, University of Oklahoma, Norman, Oklahoma 73069, U.S.A.
Magnus-Allcroft, Sir Phillip, Bt, CBE, FRSL, Stokesay Court, Craven Arms, Shropshire SY7 9BD.
Mahoney, Professor T. H. D., AM, PhD, MPA, Massachusetts Institute of Technology, Cambridge, Mass. 02138, U.S.A.
*Major, Miss K., MA, BLitt, LittD, FSA, 21 Queensway, Lincoln.
Malone, Professor J. J., PhD, 207 Eisenhower Hall, Kansas State University, Manhattan, Kansas 66502, U.S.A.
Mann, Miss J. de L., MA, The Cottage, Bowerhill, Melksham, Wilts.
Manning, B. S., MA, DPhil, The University, Manchester.
Manning, Professor R. B., PhD, 2848 Coleridge Road, Cleveland Heights, Ohio 44118, U.S.A.
Mansergh, Professor P. N. S., DPhil, DLitt, The Lodge, Little Shelford, Cambridge.
Marchant, Rev. R. A., PhD, BD, Paxfield Vicarage, Woodbridge, Suffolk.
Marder, Professor A. J., PhD, University of California, Irvine, Calif. 92664, U.S.A.
Markham, F. M. H., MA, Hertford College, Oxford.
Markus, R. A., MA, PhD, The University, 8 Abercromby Square, Liverpool.
Marriner, Sheila, MA, PhD, Social Studies Building, Bedford Street South, Liverpool.
Marsden, A., BA, PhD, 9 Fort Street, Dundee.
Marshall, Miss D., MA, PhD, University College, Cathays Park, Cardiff.
Marshall, J. D., PhD, 16 Westgate, Morecambe, Lancs.
Marshall, P. J., MA, DPhil, King's College, Strand, WC2.
Martin, Professor G. H., MA, DPhil, 21 Central Avenue, Leicester.
Marwick, Professor A. J. B., MA, BLitt, Dept of History, The Open University, Walton Hall, Walton, Bletchley, Bucks.
Mason, F. K., 147 London Road, St Albans, Hertfordshire.
Mason, J. F. A., MA, DPhil, Christ Church, Oxford.
Mason, T. W., MA, DPhil, St Peter's College, Oxford OX1 2DL.
Mather, F. C., MA, 69 Ethelburg Avenue, Swaythling, Southampton.
*Mathew, The Most Rev. Archbishop D. J., MA, LittD, FSA, Stonor Park, Henley-on-Thames.
Mathias, Professor P., MA, All Souls College, Oxford.
*Mathur-Sherry, Tikait Narain, BA, LLB, 17/254 Chili-Int-Road, Agra (U.P.), India.
Matthew, D. J. A., MA, DPhil, The University, Durham.
Mattingly, Professor H. B., MA, Dept of Ancient History, The University, Leeds.
Mayr-Harting, H. M. R. E., MA, DPhil, St Peter's College, Oxford.
Medlicott, Professor W. N., MA, DLit, DLitt, 2 Cartref, Ellesmere Road, Weybridge, Surrey.
Meekings, C. A. F., MA, 42 Chipstead Street, SW6.
Merson, A. L., MA, The University, Southampton.
Metcalf, D. M., MA, DPhil, Ashmolean Museum, Oxford.
Meyer, Professor C. S., PhD, 3 Seminary Terrace, St Louis, Mo. 63105, U.S.A.
Micklewright, Rev. F. H. A., MA, 228 South Norwood Hill, SE25.

Midgley, Miss L. M., MA, 84 Wolverhampton Road, Stafford.
Miller, Professor E., MA, 18 Rutland Park, Sheffield 10.
Miller, E. J., BA, 37 Aldbourne Road, W.12.
Miller, Miss H., MA, 32 Abbey Gardens, NW8.
Milne, A. T., MA, 9 Dixon Close, SE21.
Milne, Miss D. J., MA, PhD, King's College, Aberdeen.
Milsom, Professor S. F. C., MA, FBA, London School of Economics, Houghton Street, WC2.
Minchinton, Professor W. E., BSc(Econ), The University, Exeter.
Mingay, Professor G. E., PhD, Mill Field House, Selling Court, Selling, nr Faversham, Kent.
Mitchell, C., MA, BLitt, (Address unknown)
Mitchell, L. G., MA, DPhil, University College, Oxford.
Mitchison, Mrs R. M., MA, 6 Dovecot Road, Edinburgh 12.
*Moir, Rev. Prebendary A. L., MA, 55 Mill Street, Hereford.
Momigliano, Professor A. D., DLitt, FBA, University College, Gower Street, WC1E 6BT.
Moody, Professor T. W., MA, PhD, Trinity College, Dublin.
Moore, B. J. S., BA, University of Bristol, 67 Woodland Road, Bristol.
*Moorman, Mrs, MA, Bishop Mount, Ripon, Yorks.
Morey, Rev. Dom R. Adrian, OSB, MA, DPhil, Benet House, Mount Pleasant, Cambridge.
Morgan, B. G., BArch, PhD, ARIBA, 29 Gerard Road, Wallasey, Cheshire.
Morgan, K. O., MA, DPhil, The Queen's College, Oxford OX1 4BH.
*Morrell, Professor W. P., MA, DPhil, 16 Skibo Street, Kew, Dunedin, SW1, N.Z.
Morris, The Rev. Professor C., MA, 53 Cobbett Road, Bitterne Park, Southampton.
Morris, G. C., MA, King's College, Cambridge.
Morris, J. R., BA, PhD, Little Garth, Ashwell, nr Baldock, Herts.
Morton, Miss C. E., MA, MLS, 30 Prospect Road, Tunbridge Wells, Kent.
Morton, Professor W. L., MA, BLitt, LLD, DLitt, Champlain College, Peterborough, Ontario, Canada.
Mosse, Professor W. E. E., MA, PhD, Dawn Cottage, Ashwellthorpe, Norwich, Norfolk.
MULLINS, E. L. C., OBE, MA (*Librarian*), Institute of Historical Research, University of London, Senate House, WC1.
Muntz, Miss J. Hope, FSA, 30 Prospect Road, Tunbridge Wells, Kent.
Murphy, J., MA, PhD, Fellview, Heathwaite Manor, Windermere, Westmorland.
Murray, A., BA, BPhil, The University, Newcastle upon Tyne.
Murray, Athol L., BA, MA, LLB, PhD, 33 Inverleith Gardens, Edinburgh.
Murray, Miss K. M. E., BA, BLitt, FSA, Upper Cranmore, Heyshott, Midhurst, Sussex.
Myers, Professor A. R., MA, PhD, FSA, Rosemount, 3 Cholmondeley Road, West Kirby, Wirral, Cheshire.
Myres, J. N. L., MA, LLD, DLitt, DLit, FBA, PSA, Christ Church, Oxford.

Naidis, Professor M., PhD, 10847 Canby Avenue, Northbridge, California 91324.

Nath, Dwarka, MBE, 30 Crowther Road, South Norwood, SE25.
*NEALE, Professor Sir John E., MA, DLitt, LittD, LHD, FBA, Adare, Penn Road, Beaconsfield, Bucks.
Nef, Professor J. U., PhD, University of Chicago, Chicago, Ill., U.S.A.
New, Professor J. F. H., Dept of History, Waterloo University, Waterloo, Ontario, Canada.
Newman, A. N., MA, DPhil, 33 Stanley Road, Leicester.
Newsome, D. H., MA, Christ's Hospital, Horsham, Sussex.
Newton, K. C., MA, 82 Dorset Road, Maldon, Essex.
Nicholas, Professor H. G., MA, FBA, New College, Oxford.
Nicholl, D., MA, 2 Church Plantations, Keele, Staffordshire.
Nicol, Professor D. M., MA, PhD, King's College, London WC2R 2LS.
Nobbs, D., MA, 51 Craiglockart Avenue, Edinburgh 11.
Norman, E. R., MA, PhD, Jesus College, Cambridge.
*Nunn, W., Gillgrass, Gosforth, Cumberland.

Oakeshott, W. F., MA, FBA, FSA, Lincoln College, Oxford.
Obolensky, Prince Dimitri, MA, PhD, FSA, Christ Church, Oxford.
O'Connell, Professor D.P., All Souls College, Oxford.
*Offler, Professor H. S., MA, 28 Old Elvet, Durham.
O'Gorman, F., BA, PhD, The University, Manchester M13 9PL.
*Orr, J. E., MA, ThD, DPhil, 11451 Berwick Street, Los Angeles, Cal. 90049, U.S.A.
Oschinsky, Dorothea, DPhil, PhD, The University, Liverpool L69 3BX.
Otway-Ruthven, Professor A. J., MA, PhD, 7 Trinity College, Dublin, Eire.
Outhwaite, R. B., BA, PhD, The University, Leicester.
Owen, A. E. B., MA, 79 Whitwell Way, Coton, Cambridge.
Owen, C. V., The Vicarage, Addlestone, Surrey.
Owen, Mrs D. M., MA, FSA, 79 Whitwell Way, Coton, Cambridge.
Owen, G. D., MA, PhD, Casa Alba, Wray Lane, Reigate, Surrey.
Owen, J. B., MA, BSc, DPhil, The University, Calgary 44, Alberta, Canada.

*Packard, Professor S. R., PhD, 126 Vernon Street, Northampton, Mass., U.S.A.
Pakeman, Professor S. A., MC, MA, 45 Kensington Mansions, Trebovir Road, SW5.
Pallister, Anne, BA, PhD, Dept of History, University of Reading, Whiteknights, Reading, Berks.
Pantin, W. A., MA, DLitt, FBA, FSA, Oriel College, Oxford.
Parker, R. A. C., MA, DPhil, The Queen's College, Oxford OX1 4BH.
Parker, The Rev. Dr T. M., MA, DD, FSA, University College, Oxford.
*Parkinson, Professor C. N., MA, PhD, Les Caches House, St Martins, Guernsey, C.I.
Parry, E. Jones, MA, PhD, 3 Sussex Mansions, Old Brompton Road, SW7.
Parry, Professor J. H., MA, PhD, Pinnacle Road, Harvard, Mass. 01451, U.S.A.
Parsloe, C. G., BA, 1 Leopold Avenue, SW19.
Patterson, Professor A. T., MA, Orchard Cottage, South Mundham, Chichester.
Paul, J. E., PhD, 24 Portsdown Avenue, Drayton, nr Portsmouth, Hants.
Pearl, Mrs V. L., MA, DPhil, 70 Holden Road, Woodside Park, N12.

Pearn, B. R., OBE, MA, The White House, Beechwood Avenue, Aylmer-
ton, Norfolk.
Peaston, Rev. A. E., MA, BLitt, The Manse, Dromore, Co. Down,
N. Ireland.
Peek, Miss H. E., MA, FSA, FSAScot, Taintona, Moreton hampstead,
Newton Abbot, Devon TQ13 8LG.
Pegues, Professor F. J., PhD, 71 Acton Road, Columbus, Ohio 43214,
U.S.A.
Pelham, R. A., MA, PhD, The Court House, West Meon, Hants.
Pennington, D. H., MA, Balliol College, Oxford.
*Percy-Smith, Lieut-Colonel H. K., 13 Beechvale, Hillview Road,
Woking, Surrey.
Perkin, Professor H. J., MA, Borwicks, Caton, Lancaster.
Petrie, Sir Charles, Bt, CBE, MA, 190 Coleherne Court, SW5.
Philip, I. G., MA, FSA, 28 Portland Road, Oxford.
Philips, Professor C. H., MA, PhD, DLitt, 3 Winterstoke Gardens,
NW7.
Phillips, Sir Henry E. I., CMG, MBE, MA, 34 Ross Court, Putney Hill,
SW15.
Pitt, H. G., MA, Worcester College, Oxford.
Platt, C. P. S., MA, PhD, FSA, 24 Oakmount Avenue, Highfield, South-
ampton.
Platt, Professor D. C. St M., MA, DPhil, St Antony's College, Oxford.
Plumb, Professor J. H., PhD, LittD, FBA, FSA, Christ's College, Cam-
bridge.
Pole, J. R., MA, PhD, 6 Cavendish Avenue, Cambridge.
Porter, B. E., BSc(Econ), PhD, Dept of International Politics, University
College of Wales, Aberystwyth SY23 3DB.
Porter, H. C., MA, PhD, Selwyn College, Cambridge.
Postan, Professor M. M., MA, FBA, Peterhouse, Cambridge CB2 1RD.
*Potter, Professor G. R., MA, PhD, FSA, Herongate, Derwent Lane,
Hathersage, Sheffield S30 1AS.
Powell, W. R., BLitt, MA, FSA, 2 Glanmead, Shenfield Road, Brent-
wood, Essex.
Powicke, Professor M. R., MA, University of Toronto, Toronto 5, Ont.,
Canada.
Prest, J. M., MA, Balliol College, Oxford.
Prest, W. R., MA, DPhil, Dept of History, University of Adelaide,
Adelaide, S. Australia 5001.
Preston, Professor A. W., PhD, R.R.3, Bath, Ontario, Canada.
*Preston, Professor R. A., MA, PhD, Duke University, Durham, N.C.,
U.S.A.
Prestwich, J. O., MA, The Queen's College, Oxford.
Prestwich, Mrs M., MA, St Hilda's College, Oxford.
Prestwich, M. C., MA, DPhil, Dept of Medieval History, The University,
St Andrews, Fife.
Price, F. D., MA, BLitt, FSA, Keble College, Oxford.
Price, Professor Jacob M., AM, PhD, University of Michigan, Ann
Arbor, Michigan 48104, USA.
Pritchard, Professor D. G., PhD, 11 Coedmor, Sketty, Swansea, Glam.
Proctor, Miss Evelyn E. S., MA, Little Newland, Eynsham, Oxford.
Pronay, N., BA, School of History, The University, Leeds.
Prothero, I. J., BA, PhD, The University, Manchester.
*Pugh, Professor R. B., MA, DLitt, FSA, 67 Southwood Park, N.6.

Pugh, T. B., MA, BLitt, 28 Bassett Wood Drive, Southampton.
Pullan, Professor B. S., MA, PhD, The University, Manchester M13 9PL.
Pulzer, P. G. J., MA, PhD, Christ Church, Oxford OX1 1DP.

Quinn, Professor D. B., MA, PhD, DLit, DLitt, 9 Knowsley Road, Cressington Park, Liverpool 19.

Rabb, Professor T. K., MA, PhD, Princeton University, Princeton, N.J. 08540, U.S.A.
Radford, C. A. Ralegh, MA, FBA, FSA, Culmcott, Uffculme, Cullompton, Devon EX15 3AT.
*Ramm, Miss A., MA, Somerville College, Oxford.
*Ramsay, G. D., MA, DPhil, St Edmund Hall, Oxford OX1 4AR.
Ramsey, Professor P. H., MA, DPhil, Taylor Building, King's College, Old Aberdeen.
Ranft, Professor M. McL., MA, DPhil, 16 Eliot Vale, SE3.
Ranger, Miss F., MA, 1 Mazoe Close, Bishop's Stortford, Hertfordshire.
Ransome, Miss M. E., MA, 16 Downside Crescent, NW3.
Rathbone, Eleanor, PhD, Flat 5, 24 Morden Road, SE3.
Rawley, Professor J. A., PhD, University of Nebraska, Lincoln, Nebraska 68508, U.S.A.
Read, D., BLitt, MA, Darwin College, University of Kent, Westgate House, Canterbury, Kent.
Reader, W. J., BA, PhD, 67 Wood Vale, N10 3DL.
Rees, Professor W., MA, DSc, DLitt, FSA, 2 Park Road, Penarth, Glam.
Reese, T. R., PhD, Institute of Commonwealth Studies, 27 Russell Square, WC1.
Reeves, Miss M. E., MA, PhD, 38 Norham Road, Oxford.
Reid, Professor L. D., MA, PhD, College of Arts and Science, 127 Switzler Hall, University of Missouri, Columbia, Mo. 65201, U.S.A.
Reid, Professor W. S., MA, PhD, University of Guelph, Guelph, Ontario, Canada.
Renold, Miss P., MA, 6 Forest Side, Worcester Park, Surrey.
Reynolds, Miss S. M. G., MA, 26 Lennox Gardens, SW1.
Rich, Professor E. E., MA, St Catharine's College, Cambridge.
Richards, Professor G. M., MA, PhD, FSA, University College of North Wales, Bangor.
Richards, Rev. J. M., MA, BLitt, STL, Heythrop College, 11–13 Cavendish Square, W1M 0AN.
*Richards, R., MA, FSA, Gawsworth Hall, Gawsworth, Macclesfield, Cheshire.
*Richardson, H. G., MA, BSc, FBA, The Grange, Goudhurst, Kent.
Richardson, K. E., MA, PhD, Dept of Politics and History, Lanchester Polytechnic, Priory Street, Coventry.
Richardson, Professor W. C., MA, PhD, Louisiana State University, Baton Rouge, Louisiana, USA.
Rigold, S. E., MA, FSA, 2 Royal Crescent, W11.
Riley, P. W. J., BA, PhD, The University, Manchester.
Riley-Smith, J. S. C., MA, PhD, 53 Hartington Grove, Cambridge.
Rimmer, Professor W. G., MA, PhD, University of New South Wales, P.O. Box 1, Kensington, N.S.W. 2033, Australia.
Ritcheson, Professor C. R., DPhil, c/o Dept of History, University of Southern California, University Park, Los Angeles 90007 U.S.A.
Roach, Professor J. P. C., MA, PhD, 1 Park Crescent, Sheffield 10.

Robbins, Professor Caroline, PhD, Bryn Mawr College, Bryn Mawr, Pa., U.S.A.
Robbins, Professor K. G., MA, University College of North Wales, Bangor.
Roberts, J. M., MA, DPhil, Merton College, Oxford.
Roberts, Professor M., MA, DPhil, FilDr, FBA, The Queen's University, Belfast BT7 1NN.
Roberts, Brigadier M. R., DSO, Merton Lodge, Nackington, Canterbury, Kent.
Roberts, P. R., MA, PhD, FSA, Eliot College, University of Kent, Canterbury.
Roberts, R. C., PhD, 284 Blenheim Road, Columbus, Ohio 43214, U.S.A.
Roberts, Professor R. S., PhD, University of Rhodesia, Salisbury, P.B. 167H, Rhodesia.
*Robinson, Professor Howard, MA, PhD, LLD, 75 Elmwood Place, Oberlin, Ohio, U.S.A.
Robinson, K. E., CBE, MA, DLitt, LLD, The Old Rectory, Church Westcote, Kingham, Oxford.
Robinson, R. A. H., BA, PhD, School of History, The University, Birmingham.
Robinton, Professor Madeline R., MA, PhD, 210 Columbia Heights, Brooklyn, New York, U.S.A.
*Rodkey, F. S., AM, PhD, 152 Bradley Drive, Santa Cruz, Calif., U.S.A.
Rodney, Professor W., MA, PhD, 14 Royal Roads Military College, Victoria, B.C., Canada.
Roe, F. Gordon, FSA, 19 Vallance Road, N22.
Rogers, A., MA, PhD, The Firs, 227 Plains Road, Mapperley, Nottingham.
Rolo, Professor P. J. V., MA, The University, Keele, Staffordshire.
Roots, Professor I. A., MA, University of Exeter, Exeter.
Roper, M., MA, Public Record Office, Chancery Lane, WC2.
Rose, Professor P. L., MA, Dept of History, New York University, 19 University Place, New York, N.Y. 10003, U.S.A.
Roseveare, H. G., King's College, Strand, WC2.
Roskell, Professor J. S., MA, DPhil, FBA, The University, Manchester M13 9PL.
Roskill, Captain S. W., CBE, DSC, RN(ret), Frostlake Cottage, Malting Lane, Cambridge.
Ross, C. D., MA, DPhil, Wills Memorial Building, Queens Road, Bristol.
Rothney, Professor G. O., PhD, St John's College, University of Manitoba, Winnipeg 19, Canada.
Rothrock, Professor G. A., MA, PhD, University of Alberta, Edmonton, Alberta, Canada.
Rothwell, Professor H., PhD, Hill House, Knapp, Ampfield, nr Romsey, Hants.
*Routh, Miss E. M. G., c/o Glyn Mills & Co., Childs Bank, 1 Fleet Street, EC4.
*Rowe, Miss B. J. H., MA, BLitt, St Anne's Cottage, Winkton, Christchurch, Hants.
Rowe, W. J., DPhil, 20 Seaview Avenue, Irby, Wirral, Cheshire.
Rowland, Rev. E. C., 239 Murray Road, Preston, Australia, 3072.
Rowse, A. L., MA, DLitt, DCL, FBA, All Souls College, Oxford.
Roy, Professor R. H., MA, PhD, 2841 Tudor Avenue, Victoria, B.C., Canada.

Rubens, A., FRICS, FSA, 16 Grosvenor Place, SW1.
Rubini, D. A., DPhil, Temple University, Philadelphia, Penn., U.S.A.
Rubinstein, N., PhD, Westfield College, Hampstead, NW3.
Ruddock, Miss A. A., PhD, FSA, Birkbeck College, Malet Street, WC1.
Rudé, Professor G. F. E., MA, PhD, Sir George Williams University, Montreal 107, P.Q., Canada.
*RUNCIMAN, The Hon. Sir Steven, MA, LLD, LittD, DLit, FBA, FSA, Elieshields, Lockerbie, Dumfriesshire.
Rupp, Rev. E. G., MA, DD, FBA, The Principal's Lodge, Wesley House, Cambridge.
Russell, C. S. R., MA, Bedford College, NW1.
Russell, Mrs J. G., MA DPhil, St Hugh's College, Oxford.
Russell, Professor P. E., MA, 23 Belsyre Court, Woodstock Road, Oxford.
Ryan, A. N., MA, University of Liverpool, 8 Abercromby Square, Liverpool 7.
Ryder, A. F. C., MA, DPhil, University of Ibadan, Nigeria.

Sainty, J. S., MA, 22 Kelso Place, W8.
*Salmon, Professor E. T., MA PhD, McMaster University, Hamilton, Ontario, Canada.
Salmon, Professor J. H. M., PhD, Bryn Mawr College, Bryn Mawr, Pa. 19101, U.S.A.
*Saltman, A., MA, PhD, Bar Ilan University, Ramat Gan, Israel.
Saltmarsh, J., MA, FSA, King's College, Cambridge, CB2 1ST.
Sammut, E., LLD, 4 Don Rue Street, Sliema, Malta.
Samuel, E. R., 8 Steynings Way, N12.
Sanders, I. J., MA, DPhil, Ceri, St Davids Road, Aberystwyth.
Sanderson, Professor G. N., Dept of Modern History, Royal Holloway College, Englefield Green, Surrey.
Sawyer, Professor P. H., MA, The University, Leeds, LS2 9JT.
Sayers, Miss J. E., MA, BLitt, FSA, 17 Sheffield Terrace, Campden Hill, W8.
Scammell, G. V., MA, Pembroke College, Cambridge.
Scammell, Mrs J. M., BA, 137 Huntingdon Road, Cambridge.
Scarisbrick, Professor J. J., MA, PhD, 35 Kenilworth Road, Leamington Spa, Warwickshire.
Schenck, H. G., MA, DPhil, DrJur, University College, Oxford.
Schoeck, Professor R. J., PhD, Folger Shakespeare Library, Washington, D.C., 20003, U.S.A.
Schofield, A. N. E. D., PhD, LittD, FSA, 15 Westergate Corfton Road, W5.
Schofield, R. S., MA, PhD, Cambridge Group for History of Population, 20 Silver Street, Cambridge.
Scouloudi, Miss I. C., MSc(Econ), FSA, 67 Victoria Road. W8.
Seaborne, M. V. J., MA, Chester College, Cheyney Road, Chester CH1 4BJ.
Seary, Professor E. R., MA, PhD, Memorial University of Newfoundland, St John's, Newfoundland, Canada.
Seton-Watson, C. I. W., MC, MA, Oriel College, Oxford.
Seton-Watson, Professor G. H. N., MA, FBA, Dept of Russian History, School of Slavonic Studies, London WC1.
Shannon, R. T., MA, PhD, 84 Newmarket Road, Norwich, Norfolk.
Sharp, Mrs M., PhD, 59 Southway, NW11 6SB.
Shaw, I. P., MA, 3 Oaks Lane, Shirley, Croydon, Surrey CR0 5HP.

*Shaw, R. C., MSc, FRCS, FSA, Orry's Mount, Kirk Bride, nr Ramsey, Isle of Man.
Shead, N.F., MA, BLitt, 16 Burnside Gardens, Clarkston, Glasgow.
Shennan, J. H., PhD, Glenair, Moorside Road, Brookehouse, Caton, nr Lancaster.
Sheppard, F. H. W., MA, PhD, FSA, 55 New Street, Henley-on-Thames, Oxon.
Sherborne, J. W., MA, 26 Hanbury Road, Bristol.
Sigsworth, Professor E. M., BA, PhD, The University, Heslington, York.
Sillery, A., MA, DPhil, 24 Walton Street, Oxford.
Simmons, Professor J., MA, The University, Leicester.
*Simpson, Rev. F. A., MA, Trinity College, Cambridge.
Simpson, G. G., MA, PhD, FSA, Taylor Building, King's College, Old Aberdeen.
Siney, Professor Marion C., MA, PhD, 2676 Mayfield Road, Cleveland Heights, Ohio 44106, U.S.A.
Singhal, Professor D. P., MA, PhD, University of Queensland, St Lucia, Brisbane, Queensland, Australia 4067.
Skinner, Q. R. D., MA, Christ's College, Cambridge.
Slack, P. A., MA, DPhil, Exeter College, Oxford OX1 3DP.
Slade, C. F., PhD, FSA, 28 Holmes Road, Reading.
Slater, A. W., MSc(Econ), 146 Castelnau, SW13.
Slatter, Miss M. D., MA, 5 Inglewood Court, Liebenrood Road, Bath Road, Reading.
Slavin, Professor A. J., PhD, University of California, Los Angeles, Calif., U.S.A.
Smail, R. C., PhD, Sidney Sussex College, Cambridge.
*Smalley, Miss B., MA, PhD, FBA, 5c Rawlinson Road, Oxford.
Smith, A. G. R., MA, PhD, 40 Stanley Avenue, Paisley, Renfrewshire.
Smith, E. A., MA, York House, The Street, Swallowfield, nr Reading.
Smith, Professor Goldwin A., MA, PhD, DLitt, Wayne State University, Detroit, Michigan, 48202 U.S.A.
Smith, J. Beverley, MA, University College, Aberystwyth.
Smith, Professor L. Baldwin, PhD, Northwestern University, Evanston, Ill. 60201, U.S.A.
Smith, P., MA, DPhil, 42 Oak Tree Close, Ealing, W5.
Smith, S., BA, PhD, Les Haies, Oatlands Road, Shinfield, Berks.
Smith, W. J., MA, 5 Gravel Hill, Emmer Green, Reading, Berks.
Smout, Professor T. C., MA, PhD, Dept of Econ History, Edinburgh University.
*Smyth, Rev. Canon C. H. E., MA, 12 Manor Court, Pinehurst, Cambridge.
Snell, L. S., MA, FSA, Newman College, Bartley Green, Birmingham 32.
Snow, Professor V. F., MA, PhD, University of Nebraska, Lincoln, Nebraska, U.S.A.
Snyder, Professor H. L., MA, PhD, 1324 Strong Avenue, Lawrence, Kansas 66044, U.S.A.
Soden, G. I., MA, DD, Buck Brigg, Hanworth, Norfolk.
Somers, Rev. H. J., JCB, MA, PhD, St Francis Xavier University, Antigonish, Nova Scotia.
Sosin, Professor J. M., PhD, History Dept, University of Nebraska, Lincoln, Nebraska 68508, U.S.A.
SOUTHERN, R. W., MA, DLitt, LittD, FBA (President), The President's Lodgings, St John's College, Oxford OX1 3JP.

Southgate, D. G., BA, DPhil, 40 Camphill Road, Broughty Ferry, Dundee, Scotland.
Speck, W. A., MA, DPhil, The University, Newcastle upon Tyne.
Spencer, B. W., BA, FSA, 6 Carpenters Wood Drive, Chorleywood, Herts.
Spooner, Professor F. C., MA, PhD, The University. 23 Old Elvet, Durham.
Spufford, P., MA, PhD, The University, Keele, Staffs.
Stanley, Professor G. F. G., MA, BLitt, DPhil, Library, Mount Allison University, Sackville, New Brunswick, Canada.
Steefel, Professor L. D., MA, PhD, 3549 Irving Avenue South, Minneapolis, Minn. 55408, U.S.A.
Steel, A. B., OBE, MA, LittD, LLD, Wrangbrook, Lisvane Road, Cardiff.
Steele, E. D., MA, PhD, The University, Leeds.
Steer, F. W., MA, FSA, 63 Orchard Street, Chichester, Sussex.
Steinberg, J., MA, PhD, Trinity Hall, Cambridge.
Steiner, Mrs Zara S., MA, PhD, New Hall, Cambridge.
Stéphan, Rev. Dom John, OSB, FSA, St Mary's Abbey, Buckfast, Buckfastleigh, Devon.
Stephens, W. B., MA, PhD, FSA, 37 Batcliffe Drive, Leeds 6.
Steven, Miss M. J. E., PhD, University of Western Australia, Perth, W. Australia.
Stone, E., MA, DPhil, FSA, Keble College, Oxford.
Stone, Professor L., MA, Princeton University, Princeton, N.J., U.S.A.
*Stones, Professor E. L. G., PhD, FSA, 70 Oakfield Avenue, Glasgow W2.
Storey, R. L., MA, PhD, 19 Elm Avenue, Beeston, Nottingham.
*Stoye, J. W., MA, DPhil, Magdalen College, Oxford.
Street, J., MA, PhD, 6 Thulborn Close, Teversham, Cambridge.
Strong, R., BA, PhD, FSA, National Portrait Gallery, St Martin's Place, WC2.
Styles, P., MA, FSA, 21 Castle Lane, Warwick.
Stuart C. H., MA, Christ Church, Oxford.
Supple, Professor B. E., BSc(Econ), PhD, Dept of Econ and Social History, The University of Sussex, Falmer, Brighton BN1 9QQ.
Surman, Rev. C. E., MA, 4 Holly Lane, Erdington, Birmingham 24.
Sutherland, Professor D. W., DPhil, State University of Iowa, Iowa City, Iowa, U.S.A.
SUTHERLAND, Dame Lucy, DBE., MA, DLitt, LittD, DCL, FBA, Lady Margaret Hall, Oxford.
Sutherland, N. M., MA, PhD, St John's Hall, Bedford College, NW1.
Swart, Professor K. W., PhD, LittD, University College, Gower Street, WC1E 6BT.
Sydenham, M. J., PhD, Carleton University, Ottawa 1, Canada.
Syrett, Professor D., PhD, 46 Hawthorne Terrace, Leonia, N.J. 07605, U.S.A.
Talbot, C. H., PhD, BD, FSA, 47 Hazlewell Road, SW15.
Tanner, J. I., MA, PhD, Flat One, 57 Drayton Gardens, SW10.
Tanner, L. E., CVO, MA, DLitt, FSA, 32 Westminster Mansions, Great Smith Street, Westminster SW1P 3BP.
Tarling, Professor P. N., MA, PhD, University of Auckland, Private Bag, Auckland, New Zealand.
Taylor, Arnold J., MA, DLitt, FSA, 56 Langham Road, Teddington, Middlesex.
Taylor, Professor Arthur J., MA, The University, Leeds LS2 9JT.

Taylor, J., MA, The University, Leeds LS2 9JT.
Taylor, J. W. R., 36 Alexandra Drive, Surbiton, Surrey.
Taylor, W., MA, PhD, FSAScot, 25 Bingham Terrace, Dundee.
Temple, Nora C., BA, PhD, University College, Cardiff.
Templeman, G., MA, PhD, FSA, 22 Ethelbert Road, Canterbury, Kent.
Thirsk, Mrs I. J., PhD, St Hilda's College, Oxford.
Thistlethwaite, F., MA, University of East Anglia, Earlham Hall, Norwich NOR 88C.
Thomas, Professor H. S., MA, University of Reading, Reading.
Thomas, Rev. J. A., MA, PhD, 164 Northfield Lane, Brixham, Devon.
THOMAS, K. V., MA, (Literary Director), St John's College, Oxford OX1 3JP.
Thomas, P. D. G., MA, PhD, University College, Aberystwyth SY23 2AU.
Thomas, W. E. S., MA, Christ Church, Oxford OX1 1DP.
Thomis, M. I., MA, PhD, 28 Keir Street, Bridge of Allan, Stirlingshire.
Thompson, A. F., MA, Wadham College, Oxford.
Thompson, Mrs D. K. G., MA, School of History, The University, Birmingham.
Thompson, E. P., MA, Warwick University, Coventry.
Thompson, Professor F. M. L., MA, DPhil, Bedford College, Regent's Park, NW1.
Thomson, J. A. F., MA, DPhil, The University, Glasgow, W2.
*Thomson, T. R. F., MA, MD, FSA, Cricklade, Wilts.
Thorne, Professor S. E., MA, LLB, FSA, Harvard Law School, Cambridge, Mass., U.S.A.
Thornton, Professor A. P., MA, DPhil, 11 Highbourne Road, Toronto 7, Canada.
Thorpe, Prof. Lewis, BA, LésL, PhD, DdeL'U, 26 Parkside, Wollaton Vale, Nottingham.
*Thrupp, Professor S. L., MA, PhD, University of Michigan, Ann Arbor, Mich., U.S.A.
Thurlow, A. G. G., MA, FSA, Dean of Gloucester, The Deanery, Gloucester.
Tibbutt, H. G., FSA, 12 Birchdale Avenue, Kempston, Bedford.
Titow, J. Z., PhD, Dept of Economic History, The University, Nottingham.
Titterton, Commander G. A., RN(ret), Flat 4, Clarence House, 8 Granville Road, Eastbourne, Sussex.
Tomkeieff, Mrs O. G., MA, LLB, King's College, Newcastle upon Tyne 2.
Tooley, Miss M. J., MA, The Guest House, St Mary's Convent, Burlington Lane, W4.
Toynbee, Miss M. R., MA, PhD, FSA, 22 Park Town, Oxford.
Trebilcock, R. C., MA, Pembroke College, Cambridge.
*Trevor-Roper, Professor H. R., MA, FBA, Oriel College, Oxford.
Trickett, Professor the Rev. A. S., MA, PhD, 509 South 58th Street, Omaha, Nebraska 68106, U.S.A.
Tyler, P., BLitt, MA, DPhil, University of Western Australia, Nedlands, Western Australia, 6009.

Ugawa, Professor K., BA, MA, PhD, 1008 Ikebukuco, 2 Chome, Tokyo 171, Japan.
Ullmann, Professor W., MA, LittD, Trinity College, Cambridge.
Underhill, C. H., The Lodge, Needwood, Burton upon Trent, Staffs.

Upton, A. F., MA, 5 West Acres, St Andrews, Fife.
Urry, W. G., PhD, FSA, St Edmund Hall, Oxford.

Vale, M. G. A., MA, DPhil, Dept of History, The University, Heslington, York.
Van Caenagem, Professor R. C., LLD, Veurestraat 18, Afsnee, Belgium.
Van Cleve, Professor T. C., MA, PhD, DLitt, Bowdoin College, Brunswick, Maine, U.S.A.
*Varley, Mrs J. M. A., FSA, 164 Nettleham Road, Lincoln.
Vaughan, Professor Sir G. Edgar, c/o Division of the Social Sciences, University of Saskatchewan, Regina Campus, Regina, Sask., Canada.
Véliz, Professor C., BSc, PhD, Dept of Sociology, La Trobe University, Melbourne, Victoria, Australia.
Villiers, Lady de, MA, BLitt, 4 Church Street, Beckley, Oxford.
Vincent, Professor J. R., MA, PhD, The University, Bristol.
Virgoe, R., BA, PhD, University of East Anglia, Norwich.

Waddell, Professor D. A. G., MA, DPhil, University of Stirling, Stirling.
*Wagner, Sir Anthony R., KCVO, MA, DLitt, FSA, College of Arms, Queen Victoria Street, EC4.
*Wake, Miss Joan, CBE, MA, LLD, FSA, 11 Charlbury Road, Oxford.
Walcott, Professor R., MA, PhD, The College of Wooster, Wooster, Ohio 44691 U.S.A.
Waley, D. P., MA, PhD, Dept of Manuscripts, British Museum, WC1B 3DG.
Walford, A. J., MA, PhD, FLA, 45 Parkside Drive, Watford, Herts.
Walker, Rev. D. G., DPhil, FSA, University College, Swansea.
Walker, J., MA, PhD, Ashlynne, 33 Heaton Road, Huddersfield.
*Walker, Miss M. I., Boynecliff, Bridgetown, Totnes, S. Devon.
Wallace, Professor W. V., MA, New University of Ulster, Coleraine, Northern Ireland.
Wallace-Hadrill, J. M., MA, DLitt, FBA, Merton College, Oxford.
Wallis, Miss H. M., MA, DPhil, FSA, 96 Lord's View, St John's Wood Road, NW8 7HG.
Wallis, P. J., MA, 27 Westfield Drive, Newcastle upon Tyne 3.
Walne, P., MA, FSA, County Record Office, County Hall, Hertford.
Walters, (W.) E., MA, Burrator, 355 Topsham Road, Exeter.
Wangermann, E., MA, DPhil, The University, Leeds.
*Ward, Mrs G. A., PhD, FSA, Unsted, 51 Hartswood Road, Brentwood, Essex.
Ward, Professor W. R., DPhil, University of Durham, 43 North Bailey, Durham.
*Warmington, Professor E. H., MA, 48 Flower Lane, NW7.
Warren, W. L., MA, DPhil, The Queen's University, Belfast, N. Ireland.
*Waterhouse, Professor E. K., CBE, MA, AM, FBA, Overshot, Badger Lane, Hinksey Hill, Oxford.
*Waters, Lt-Commander D. W., RN, FSA, Jolyons, Bury, West Sussex.
Watkin, Rev. Dom Aelred, OSB, MA, FSA, Downside Abbey, Stratton-on-the-Fosse, nr Bath BA3 4RJ.
WATSON, A. G., MA, BLitt, FSA, (Secretary), University College, Gower Street, WC1.
Watson, J. S., MA, The University, College Gate, North Street, St Andrews, Fife, Scotland.

Watt, Professor D. C., MA, London School of Economics, Houghton Street, WC2.

Watt, D. E. R., MA, DPhil, Dept of Mediaeval History, St Salvator's College, St Andrews, Fife, Scotland.

Watt, J. A., BA, PhD, The University, Hull.

Webb, J. G., MA, 11 Blount Road, Pembroke Park, Old Portsmouth, Hampshire PO1 2TD.

Webster, (A.) Bruce, MA, FSA, 5 The Terrace, St Stephens, Canterbury.

Webster, C., MA, BSc, MSc, Corpus Christi College, Oxford.

Wedgwood, Dame Veronica, OM, DBE, MA, LittD, DLitt, LLD, 22 St Ann's Terrace, St John's Wood, NW8.

Weinbaum, Professor M., PhD, 133–33 Sanford Avenue, Flushing, N.Y. 11355, U.S.A.

Weinstock, Miss M. B., MA, 26 Wey View Crescent, Broadway, Weymouth, Dorset.

Wernham, Professor R. B., MA, Worcester College, Oxford.

*Weske, Mrs J. R., AM, PhD, Oakwood, Sandy Spring, Maryland, U.S.A.

West, Professor F. J., PhD, Dept of Pacific History, Australian National University, P.O. Box 4, Canberra, Australia, 2600.

*Whatmore, Rev. L. E., MA, St Wilfred's, South Road, Hailsham, Sussex.

Whelan, Rev. C. B., OSB, MA, Belmont Abbey, Hereford.

White, Professor B. M. I., MA, DLit, FSA, 3 Upper Duke's Drive, Eastbourne, Sussex BN20 7XT.

*Whitelock, Professor D., CBE, MA, LittD, FBA, FSA, 30 Thornton Close, Cambridge.

Whiteman, Miss E. A. O., MA, DPhil, FSA, Lady Margaret Hall, Oxford.

*Whitfield, Professor A. S., BLitt, PhD, Plas Benar, Dyffryn Ardudwy, Merioneth.

Wilkinson, Rev. J. T., MA, DD, Brantwood, Farrington Lane, Knighton, Radnorshire.

Wilks, M. J., MA, PhD, Dept of History, Birkbeck College, Malet Street, WC1.

*Willan, Professor T. S., MA, DPhil, The University, Manchester M13 9PL.

Williams, Professor C. H., MA, 6 Blackfriars, Canterbury.

Williams, D., MA, PhD, DPhil, University of Calgary, Calgary, Alberta, Canada, T2N 1N4.

Williams, E. T., CB, CBE, DSO, MA, Rhodes House, Oxford.

Williams, Professor Glanmor, MA, DLitt, University College, Swansea.

Williams, Glyndwr, BA, PhD, Queen Mary College, Mile End Road, E1.

Williams, Professor G. A., MA, PhD, Dept of History, The University, York YO1 5DD.

Williams, J. A., MA, BSc(Econ), 44 Pearson Park, Hull, E. Yorks.

Williams, N. J., MA, DPhil, FSA, 57 Rotherwick Road, NW11.

Williams, P. H., MA, DPhil, New College, Oxford.

*Williams, T. G., MA, 63 Eardley Crescent, SW5.

Willson, Professor D. H., PhD, 1881 Fairmount Avenue, St Paul, Minn. 55105 U.S.A.

*Wilson, Professor A. McC, MA, PhD, 1 Brookside, Norwich, Vermont, U.S.A.

Wilson, Professor C. H., MA, FBA, Jesus College, Cambridge.

Wilson, H. S., BLitt, The University, Heslington, York.

Wilson, Professor T., MA, DPhil, Dept of History, University of Adelaide, Adelaide, South Australia.
Winks, Professor R. W. E., MA, PhD, 648 Berkeley College, Yale University, New Haven, Conn. 06520 U.S.A.
Wiswall, F. L., PhD, 23 Richmond Drive, Darien, Conn. 06820 U.S.A.
Wittke, Professor Carl, AM, PhD, 2232 Harcourt Drive, Cleveland, Ohio 44106, U.S.A.
Wolffe, B. P., MA, BLitt, DPhil, Highview, 19 Rosebarn Avenue, Exeter.
*Wood, Rev. A. Skevington, PhD, Ridgeway, Curbar, Sheffield.
Wood, Mrs S. M., MA, BLitt, St Hugh's College, Oxford.
Woodfill, Professor W. L., PhD, University of California, Davis, Calif. 95616, U.S.A.
Wood-Legh, Miss K. L., BLitt, PhD, DLitt, 49 Owlstone Road, Cambridge.
Woods, J. A., MA, PhD, The University, Leeds 2.
Woolf, S. J., MA, DPhil, The University, Whiteknights, Reading.
Woolrych, Professor A. H., BLitt, MA, Patchetts, Caton, nr Lancaster.
Wormald, B. H. G., MA, Peterhouse, Cambridge.
Wright, Professor E., MA, Institute of United States Studies, 31 Tavistock Square, London WC1H 9EZ.
Wroughton, J. P., MA, 11 Powlett Court, Bath, Somerset BA2 6QJ.

Youings, Miss J. A., PhD, University of Exeter, Exeter.
Young, Brigadier P., DSO, MC, MA, FSA, Bank House, Ripple, Tewkesbury, Glos.

Zeldin, T., MA, DPhil, St Antony's College, Oxford OX2 6JF.

ASSOCIATES OF THE
ROYAL HISTORICAL SOCIETY

Addy, J., MA, 66 Long Lane, Clayton West, Huddersfield.

Baird, Rev. E. S., BD, The Vicarage, Harrington, Workington, Cumberland.
Begley, M. R., 119 Tennyson Avenue, King's Lynn, Norfolk.
Bird, E. A., 29 King Edward Avenue, Rainham, Essex.
Bratt, C., 65 Moreton Road, Upton, Wirral, Cheshire.
Brigg, Mrs M., The Hollies, Whalley Road, Wilpshire, Blackburn, Lancs.
Bryant, W. N., MA, PhD, College of S. Mark and S. John, King's Road, SW10.
Bullivant, C. H., FSA, Sedgemoor House, Warden Road, Minehead, Somerset.
Burton, Commander R. C., RN(ret), Great Streele Oasthouse, Framfield, Sussex.
Butler, Mrs M. C., MA, 19 Menelik Road, NW2.

Cairns, Mrs W. N., MA, Alderton House, New Ross, Co. Wexford, Eire.
Carter, F. E. L., CBE, MA, The Leys, London N2 0HE.
Cary, R. H., BA, 23 Bath Road, W4.
Chandra, Shri Suresh, MA, MPhil, 90–36, 155th Street, Jamaica, New York 11432.
Cook, Rev. E. T., 116 Westwood Park, SE23 3QH.
Cooper, Miss J. M., MA, 49 Park Town, Oxford.
Cox, A. H., Winsley, 11A Bagley Close, West Drayton, Middlesex.
Creighton-Williamson, Lt-Col D., 90 Lloyds Bank Ltd, Cox & Kings (F.Sec.), 6 Pall Mall, SW1.

Dawson, Mrs, 5 Sinclair Street, Nkana/Kitwe, Zambia.
Dewar, Rev. M. W., MA, PhD, Magherally Rectory, Banbridge, Co. Down, N. Ireland.
Dowse, Rev. I. R., Y Caplandy (The Chaplain's House), Cathedral Close, Bangor, Caerns.
Draffen of Newington, George, MBE, KLJ, MA, Meadowside, Balmullo, Leuchars, Fife KY16 0AW.
Drew, J. H., 19 Forge Road, Kenilworth, Warwickshire.
Driver, J. T., MA, BLitt, 25 Abbot's Grange, Off Liverpool Road, Chester.

Emberton, W. J., Firs Lodge, 13 Park Lane, Old Basing, Basingstoke, Hants.
Emsden, N., Strathspey, Lansdown, Bourton-on-the-Water, Cheltenham, Glos. GL54 2AR.

Fawcett, Rev. T. J., BD, PhD, 4 The College, Durham DH1 3EH.
Ferguson, J. T., MA, Fayerweather Hall, Columbia University, New York, N.Y., U.S.A.
Field, C. W., The Twenty-Sixth House, Robertsbridge, Sussex.

Fitzwilliam, B. R., ACP, ThA, Rockhampton Grammar School, Archer Street, Rockhampton, Queensland 4700, Australia.
Flitcroft, Rev. J., MA, Hulme Hall, Victoria Park, Manchester 14
Fryer, J., BA, Greenfields, Whitemore, nr Congleton, Cheshire.

Gardner, W. M., Chequertree, Wittersham, nr Tenterden, Kent.
Granger, E. R., Bluefield, Blofield, Norfolk.
Grattan-Kane, P., 12 St John's Close, Helston, Cornwall.
Greatrex, Mrs J. G., MA, Dept of History, St Patrick's College, Carleton University, Ottawa, Canada.
Green, P. L., MA, 9 Faulkner Street, Gate Pa, Tauranga, New Zealand.
Griffiths, Rev. G. Ll., MA, BD, Rhiwlas, 10 Brewis Road, Rhos-on-Sea, Colwyn Bay, Denbighs.

Haines, F. D., PhD, Southern Oregon College, Ashland, Oregon, U.S.A.
Hall, P. T., Accrington College of Further Education, Sandy Lane, Accrington, Lancs.
Hannah, L., BA, St John's College, Oxford.
Harding, Rev. F. A. J., BSc(Econ), 74 Beechwood Avenue, St Albans.
Hardy, Rev. P. E., The Manse, 20 Victoria Road, Hanham, Bristol.
Harte, N. B., BSc(Econ), University College, Gower Street, WC1E 6BT.
Hawtin, Miss G., BA, FSAScot, Honey Cottage, 5 Clifton Road, SW19.
Heath, P., BA, 17 Lodge Road, West Croydon, Surrey.
Henderson-Howat, Mrs A. M. D., 7 Lansdowne Crescent, Edinburgh 12.
Henriques, Miss U. R. Q., BA, BLitt, 4 Campden Hill Square, W11.
Hoare, E. T., 70 Addison Road, Enfield, Middx.
Hope, R. B., MA, MEd, PhD, 5 Partis Way, Newbridge Hill, Bath, Somerset.
Hopewell, S., MA, 133 Barnstaple Road, Thorpe Bay, Essex.
Hughes, R. G., 'Hafod', 92 Main Road, Smalley, Derby.
Hunt, E. D., BA, 5 Mason Road, Woodford Green, Essex.
Hunt, J. W., MA, 123 Park Road, Chiswick, W4.

Jarvis, L. D., Middlesex Cottage, 86 Mill Road, Stock, Ingatestone, Essex.
Jermy, K. E., MA, 8 Thelwall New Road, Thelwall, Warrington, Lancs.
Jerram-Burrows, Mrs L. E., Parkanaur House, 88 Sutton Road, Rochford, Essex.
Johnston, F. R., MA, 20 Russell Street, Eccles, Manchester.
Johnstone, H. F. V., 96 Wimborne Road, Poole, Dorset.
Jones, E. W., 54 Walker Road, Blackley Estate, Manchester 9.
Joy, E. T., MA, BSc(Econ), The Rotunda, Ickworth, Bury St Edmunds, Suffolk.

Keen, Rev. Canon D. A. R., MA, FSA, 6 College Green, Gloucester.
Keen, L. J., 14 Fairfield's Close, Roe Green, NW9.
Keir, Mrs G. I., BA, 21 Raleigh Road, Richmond, Surrey.
Kennedy, M. J., BA, Dept of Medieval History, The University, Glasgow W2.
Kitching, C. J., BA, 54 Compayne Gardens, NW6.
Knight, G. A., BA, 46 Bold Street, Pemberton, Wigan, Lancs WN5 9E2.
Knowlson, Rev. G. C. V., St John's Vicarage, Knutsford Road, Wilmslow, Cheshire.

Laws, Captain W. F., MLitt, University of Otago, P.O. Box 56 Dunedin, New Zealand.
Lea, R. S., MA, 29 Crestway, SW15.
Lewin, Mrs J., MA, 3 Sunnydale Gardens, Mill Hill, NW7.
Lewis, F., 23 Berwick Road, Rainham, Essex.
Lewis, Professor N. B., MA, PhD, 8 Westcombe Park Road, SE3.
Loach, Mrs J., MA, Somerville College, Oxford.

McIntyre, Miss S. C., BA, Lady Margaret Hall, Oxford.
McLeod, D. H., BA, PhD, School of History, The University, P.O. Box 363, Birmingham B15 2TT.
Mansfield, Major A. D., 38 Churchfields, West Mersea, Essex.
Marshall, F. R. D., The Lodge, New Place, Park Road, Banstead, Surrey.
Mathews, E. F. J., BSc(Econ), PhD, 2 Park Lake Road, Poole, Dorset.
Maycock, Rev. J., MA, PhD, Moorcroft, Brown Moor, Kirtlebridge, Lockerbie.
Meatyard, E., BA, DipEd, Guston, Illtyd Avenue, Llantwit Major, Glam. CF6 9TG.
Mills, H. J., MA, BSc, Old Timbers, The Square, Wickham, Hants.
Morgan, D. A. L., MA, Virginals, The Green, Richmond, Surrey.

Newman, L. T., HND, LRIC, 12 Gay Bowers, Hockley, Essex.
Nicholls, R. E., MA, PhD, Glenholm, Hook Road, Surbiton, Surrey.

Obelkevich, J., MA, (address unknown).
O'Day, Mrs M. R., BA, PhD, Flat 8, 174 Frankley Beeches Road, Birmingham B31 5LW.
Oggins, R. S., PhD, c/o Dept of History SM, State University of New York, Binghampton 13901, U.S.A.
Oldham, C. R., MA, Te Whare, Walkhampton, Yelverton, Devon.
Orme, N. I., MA, DPhil, University of Exeter, Exeter.

Palliser, D. M., MA, DPhil, Flat D, The Hawthorns, Keele, Staffs.
Partridge, Miss F. L., BA, 17 Spencer Gardens, SW14 7AH.
Pasmore, H. S., MB, BS, 21 Edwardes Square, W8.
Paton, L. R., 49 Lillian Road, Barnes, SW13.
Paulson, E., BSc(Econ), 11 Darley Avenue, Darley Dale, Matlock, Derbys.
Perry, E., 10 Shield Street, Oldham, Lancs.
Pitt, B. W. E., Flat 4, Red Roofs, Bath Road, Taplow, Maidenhead, Berks.
Priestley, E. J., MA, 10 Kent Close, Bromborough, Wirral, Cheshire.

Rankin, Colonel R. H., 6203 Beachway Drive, Falls Church, Va. 22041, U.S.A.
Reeve, H. F., 12 Station Road, Pontnewydd, nr Newport, Mon.
Rendall, Miss J., BA, Alcuin College, University of York, Heslington, York.
Richards, N. F., PhD, 376 Maple Avenue, St Lambert, Prov. of Quebec, Canada.
Richmond, C. F., DPhil, 268 Horwood Flats, The University, Keele, Staffs.

Sabben-Clare, E. E., MA, c/o The University Registry, Clarendon Building, Broad Street, Oxford.
Sainsbury, F., 16 Crownfield Avenue, Newbury Park, Ilford, Essex.
Saksena, D. N., Ministry of Education, New Delhi 1, India.
Sandell, Miss E. M., 12 Avenue Court, 2 Westwood Road, Southampton.
Scott, The Rev. A. R., MA, BD, PhD, Ahorey Manse, Portadown, Co. Armagh, N. Ireland.
Seddon, P. R., BA, PhD, The University, Nottingham.
Sellers, J. M., MA, 9 Vere Road, Pietermaritzburg, Natal, S. Africa.
Sharpe, F., FSA, Derwen, Launton, Bicester, Oxfordshire.
Shores, C. F., ARICS, 40 St Mary's Crescent, Hendon, NW4.
Sloan, K., BEd, MPhil, 13 Fernwood, Park Villas, Roundhay, Leeds 8.
Smith, C. D., MA, PhD, 416 Hall of Languages, Syracuse University, Syracuse, N.Y. 13210, U.S.A.
Smith, D. M., Borthwick Institute of Historical Research, St Anthony's Hall, York.
Sondheimer, Mrs J. H., MA, PhD, 51 Cholmeley Crescent, N6.
Sorensen, Mrs M. O., MA, 8 Layer Gardens, W3.
Sparkes, I. G., FLA, 124 Green Hill, High Wycombe, Bucks.
Stafford, D. S., BA, 10 Highfield Close, Wokingham, Berks.
Stitt, F. B., BLitt, William Salt Library, Stafford.

Thewlis, J. C., BA, Van Mildert College, Durham.
Thomas, Miss E. J. M., 8 Ravenscroft Road, Northfield End, Henley-on-Thames, Oxon.
Thompson, L. F., Orchard House, Stanford Road, Orsett, nr Grays, Essex.
Thorold, M. B., 15 Park Walk, SW10 0AJ.
Tracy, J. N., BA, MPhil, PhD, c/o P. Huth Esq, 6 Chaucer Court, 28 New Dover Road, Canterbury, Kent.
Tristram, B., DipEd, (address unknown).
Tuffs, J. E., 360 Monega Road, Manor Park, E12.

Waldman, T. G., MA, 131 Riverside Drive, New York, N.Y. 10024, U.S.A.
Wall, Rev. J., BD, MA, Ashfield, 45 Middleton Lane, Middleton St George, nr Darlington, Co. Durham.
Wallis, K. W., BA, 48 Berkeley Square, W1.
Warrillow, E. J. D., MBE, FSA, Hill-Cote, Lancaster Road, Newcastle, Staffs.
Westman, Mrs B. H., MA, PhD, 512½ Midvale Avenue, Los Angeles, Calif. 90024, U.S.A.
Whiting, J. R. S., MA, 18 College Green, Goucester.
Wilkinson, F. J., 40 Great James Street, Holborn, London WC1N 3HB.
Williams, A. R., MA, 5 Swanswell Drive, Granley Fields, Cheltenham, Glos.
Williams, H., (address unknown).
Williams, Miss J. M., MA, History Dept, University of Auckland, Private Bag, Auckland, New Zealand.
Windrow, M. C., 40 Zodiac Court, 165 London Road, Croydon, Surrey.
Wood, A. W., 11 Blessington Close, SE13.
Wood, J. O., BA, MEd, Fountains, Monument Gardens, St Peter Port, Guernsey, C.I.
Woodall, R. D., BA, Bethel, 7 Wynthorpe Road, Horbury, nr Wakefield, Yorks.

Woodfield, R., BD, MTh, 43 Playfield Crescent, SE22.
Worsley, Miss A. V., BA, (address unknown).
Wright, J. B., White Shutters, Braunston, Rutland.

Yates, W. N., BA, 29 Ystrad Drive, Johnstown, Carmarthen, S. Wales.

Zerafa, Rev. M. J., St Dominic's Priory, Valletta, Malta.

CORRESPONDING FELLOWS

Andersson, Ingvar, FilDr, Engelbrektsgátan 6A IV, Stockholm, Sweden.

Bartoš, Professor F. M., PhDr, II. Jihozápadní 7, Praha-Spořilov, Czechoslovakia.

Bischoff, Professor B., DLitt, 8033 Planegg C. München, Ruffini-Allee 27, Germany.

Botha, Lieut-Colonel C. Graham, MA, LLD, FSA, Nairn, Isabel Avenue, Newlands, C.P., South Africa.

Braudel, Professor F., École Pratique des Hautes Études, 20 rue de la Baume, Paris VIIIᵉ, France.

Cárcano, M. A., Centeno 3131, Buenos Aires, Argentina.

Coolhaas, Professor W. P., Gezichtslaan 71, Bilthoven, Holland.

Creighton, Professor D. G., MA, DLitt, LLD, University of Toronto, Toronto, Canada.

Donoso, R. Presidente de la Sociedad Chilena de Historia y Geografía, Casilla 1386, Santiago, Chile.

Dvornik, Professor the Rev. F., DD, D-ès-Lettres, DLit, Harvard University, Dumbarton Oaks, 1703 32nd Street, Washington, D.C., U.S.A.

Ganshof, Professor F. L., 12 rue Jacques Jordaens, Brussels, Belgium.

Giusti, Rt Rev. Mgr M., JCD, Prefect Archivio Segreto Vaticano, Vatican City, Italy.

Glamann, Professor K., DrPhil, Frederiksberg, Bredegade 13A, 2000 Copenhagen, Denmark.

Gouber, Professor A., Moscow State University, Moscow, U.S.S.R.

Gwynn, Professor the Rev. A., SJ, MA, DLitt, Milltown Park, Dublin 6, Eire.

Halecki, Professor O., DrPhil, (address unknown).

Hancock, Professor Sir Keith, KBE, MA, DLitt, FBA, Australian National University, Box 4, P.O., Canberra, A.C.T., Australia.

Heimpel, Professor Dr H., DrPhil, Direktor des Max Planck-Instituts für Geschichte, Göttingen, Düstere Eichenweg 28, Germany.

Inalcik, Professor Halil, PhD, The University of Ankara, Ankara, Turkey.

Kuttner, Professor S., MA, JUD, SJD LLD, Institute of Medieval Canon Law, University of California, Berkeley, Calif. 94720, U.S.A.

Langer, Professor W. L., PhD, LLD, DPhil, LHD, 16 Dunster Street, Cambridge, Mass., U.S.A.

Morison, Professor S. E., PhD, LittD, Harvard College Library, 417 Cambridge, Mass., U.S.A.

Ostrogorsky, Professor G., (address unknown).

Peña y Cámara, J. M. de la, Juan del Castillo, 5, 2°, Seville, Spain.
Perkins, Professor D., MA, PhD, LLD, University of Rochester, Rochester, N.Y., U.S.A.
Perroy, Professor E. M. J., D-ès-L, 5 rue Monticelli, Paris XIVe, France.

Rau, Professor Virginia, MA, Universidade de Lisbon, Lisbon, Portugal.
Renouvin, Professor P., D-ès-L, 2 Boulevard Saint Germain, Paris, France.
Rodrígues, Professor José Honório, Rua Paul Redfern, 23, ap. C.O.1, Rio de Janeiro, Gb. ZC—37, Brasil.

Santifaller, Professor L., DrPhil, DrTheol, DrJur, Österreichische Akademie der Wissenschaften, Wien 1, Dr Ignaz Seipel Platz 2, Austria.
Sapori, Professor A., Università Commerciale Luigi Bocconi, Via Sabbatini 8, Milan, Italy.

Van Houtte, Professor J. A., PhD, FBA, Termunkveld, Groeneweg 51, Egenhoven, Heverlee, Belgium.
Verlinden, Professor C., PhD, 8 Via Omero (Valle Giulia), Rome, Italy.

Zavala, S., LLD, Mexican Embassy, 9 rue de Longchamp, Paris XVIe, France.

TRANSACTIONS AND PUBLICATIONS
OF THE
ROYAL HISTORICAL SOCIETY

The annual publications of the Society issued to Fellows and Subscribing Libraries include the *Transactions*, supplemented since 1897 by a continuation of the publications of the Camden Society (1838–1897) as the *Camden Series*, and since 1937 by a series of *Guides and handbooks*. The Society also began in 1937 an annual bibliography of *Writings on British History*, for the continuation of which the Institute of Historical Research accepted responsibility in 1965; it publishes, in conjunction with the American Historical Association, a series of *Bibliographies of British History*; and from time to time it issues miscellaneous publications. Additional copies of the *Transactions*, the *Camden Series*, the *Guides and handbooks*, and the 'Miscellaneous publications' may be obtained by Fellows and Subscribing Libraries at the prices stated below. The series of annual bibliographies of *Writings on British history* and the *Bibliographies of British history* are not included among the volumes issued to subscribers, but may be obtained by them at the special prices stated below by ordering from a bookseller or from the publishers. Associates, while receiving only the *Transactions* in return for their subscription, are entitled to purchase at a reduction of 25 per cent one copy of other volumes issued to Fellows and Subscribing Libraries and one copy of each of the volumes of the *Writings on British history* and the *Bibliographies of British history* at the special price.

N.B. Current volumes of the *Transactions* and *Camden Series* (*i.e.* those for the current year and two years preceding) are not sold by the Society to the public, but are available only to members on application to the Society.

Back issues of both series are obtainable from Wm. Dawson & Sons Ltd, Cannon House, Folkestone, Kent, and *Guides and handbooks* from Dawsons of Pall Mall at the same address.

TRANSACTIONS

Additional copies of *Transactions* may be had for £2·50. (Special price to members, who should order from the Society, £1·87.)

Volumes out of print in *Transactions, Old, New and Third Series* may be obtained from Kraus-Thomson Organisation Ltd.

Old series, 1872–1882. Vols. I to X.
New series, 1884–1906. Vols. I to XX.
Third series, 1907–1917. Vols. I to XI.
Fourth series, 1918–1950. Vols. I to XXXII.
Fifth series, 1951–   . Vols. I–XXII.

MISCELLANEOUS PUBLICATIONS

Copies of the following, which are still in print, may be obtained from the Society, with the exception of *The Domesday Monachorum of Christ Church, Canterbury* and *The Royal Historical Society, 1868–1968*, which can be ordered from Dawsons of Pall Mall, Cannon House, Folkestone, Kent, and *Essays in Medieval History* and *Essays in Modern History*, which are obtainable from Macmillan and Co., Ltd.

Domesday studies. 2 vols. Edited by P. E. Dove. 1886. £3.50. (Vol. 1 out of print.)

German opinion and German policy before the War. By G. W. Prothero. 1916. 75p.

The *Domesday monachorum* of Christ Church, Canterbury. 1944. £15.

Essays in Medieval History, selected from the Transactions of the Royal Historical Society. Edited by R. W. Southern. 1968. London, Macmillan. *p.b.*, £1.25.

Essays in Modern History, selected from the Transactions of the Royal Historical Society. Edited by Ian R. Christie. 1968. London, Macmillan. £2.75, *p.b.*, £1.50.

The Royal Historical Society, 1868–1968. By R. A. Humphreys. 1969. £1.25.

BIBLIOGRAPHIES ISSUED IN CONJUNCTION WITH THE AMERICAN HISTORICAL ASSOCIATION

Copies of the following cannot be supplied by the Society, but may be ordered through a bookseller.

Bibliography of British history: Tudor Period, 1485–1603. Edited by Conyers Read. 1st ed. 1933; 2nd ed. 1959. Oxford Univ. Press £3.75. (Special price, £2.80.)

Bibliography of British history: Stuart period, 1603–1714. 2nd ed. Edited by Mary F. Keeler, 1970. Oxford Univ. Press. £5. (Special price, £3.75.)

Bibliography of British history: 1714–1789. Edited by S. M. Pargellis and D. J. Medley. 1951. Oxford Univ. Press. (Out of print.) Supplement, edited by A. T. Milne and A. N. Newman, *in preparation*.

Bibliography of British history: 1789–1851. Edited by Ian R. Christie and Lucy M. Brown, *in preparation*.

Bibliography of British history: 1851–1914. Edited by H. J. Hanham, *in preparation*.

ANNUAL BIBLIOGRAPHIES

Copies of the following cannot be supplied by the Society, but may be ordered from a bookseller or Jonathan Cape.

Writings on British history, 1901–1933 (5 vols. in 7); Vol 1–3, 1968, Vol. 4, 1969, Vol. 5, 1970. London, Jonathan Cape. Vol. 1, £5.25 (special price £4.58); Vol. 2, £3.15 (special price £2.75); Vol. 3, £5.25 (special price £4.58); Vol. 4 (in two parts), £7.35 (special price £6.40); Vol. 5 (in two parts), £8.40 (special price £7.35).

Writings on British history, 1934. Compiled by A. T. Milne. 1937. London, Jonathan Cape, £1.75. (Special price, £1.50.)

Writings on British history, 1935. Compiled by A. T. Milne. 1939. London, Jonathan Cape, £1·75. (Special price, £1·50.)
Writings on British history, 1936. Compiled by A. T. Milne. 1940. London, Jonathan Cape, £1·75. (Special price, £1·50.)
Writings on British history, 1937. Compiled by A. T. Milne. 1949. London, Jonathan Cape, £1·75. (Special price, £1·50.)
Writings on British history, 1938. Compiled by A. T. Milne. 1951. London, Jonathan Cape, £1·75. (Special price, £1·50.)
Writings on British history, 1939. Compiled by A. T. Milne. 1953. London, Jonathan Cape. (Out of print.)
Writings on British history, 1940–1945. 2 vols. Compiled by A. T. Milne. 1960. London, Jonathan Cape, £6·30. (Special price, £5·50.)

GUIDES AND HANDBOOKS

1. Guide to English commercial statistics, 1696–1782. By G. N. Clark, with a catalogue of materials by Barbara M. Franks. 1938. £1·50.
2. Handbook of British chronology. Edited by F. M. Powicke and E. B. Fryde, 1st ed. 1939; 2nd ed. 1961. £4·50.
3. Medieval libraries of Great Britain, a list of surviving books. Edited by N. R. Ker, 1st ed. 1941; 2nd ed. 1964. £4·50.
4. Handbook of dates for students of English history. By C. R. Cheney. 1970. £1·50.
5. Guide to the national and provincial directories of England and Wales, excluding London, published before 1856. By Jane E. Norton. 1950. £2·00.
6. Handbook of Oriental history. Edited by C. H. Philips. 1963. £2·25.
7. Texts and calendars: an analytical guide to serial publications. Edited by E. L. C. Mullins. 1958. £4·50.
8. Anglo-Saxon charters. An annotated list and bibliography. Edited by P. H. Sawyer. 1968. £5·25.

Provisionally accepted for future publication:

A Handbook of British Currency. Edited by P. Grierson and C. E. Blunt.
Texts and calendars: an analytical guide to serial publications. Supplement, 1958–1968. By E. L. C. Mullins.
A Guide to the Local Administrative Units of England and Wales. Edited by F. A. Youngs.
A Register of Parliamentary Poll Books, c. 1700–1870. Edited by E. L. C. Mullins.
A Guide to Cabinet Ministers' papers, 1900–1951. Edited by Cameron Hazlehurst and Christine Woodland.

THE CAMDEN SERIES

Camdens published before the *Fourth Series* are listed in A. T. Milne's *A Guide to the Publications of the Royal Historical Society.*
Additional copies of volumes in the *Camden Series* may be had for £3·00. (Special price to members £2·25.)
Volumes out of print in the *Camden Old* and *New Series* may be obtained from Johnson Reprint Co. Ltd. Orders for out-of-print volumes in *Camden Third* and *Fourth Series* should be placed with Wm. Dawson & Sons, Ltd., Cannon House, Folkestone, Kent.

FOURTH SERIES

1. Camden miscellany, Vol. XXII: 1. Charters of the Earldom of Hereford, 1095–1201. Edited by David Walker. 2. Indentures of Retinue with John of Gaunt, Duke of Lancaster, enrolled in Chancery, 1367–1399. Edited by N. B. Lewis. 3. Autobiographical memoir of Joseph Jewell, 1763–1846. Edited by A. W. Slater. 1964.
2. Documents illustrating the rule of Walter de Wenlock, Abbot of Westminster, 1283–1307. Edited by Barbara Harvey. 1965.
3. The early correspondence of Richard Wood, 1831–1841. Edited by A. B. Cunningham. 1966. (Out of print.)
4. Letters from the English abbots to the chapter at Cîteaux, 1442–1521. Edited by C. H. Talbot. 1967.
5. Select writings of George Wyatt. Edited by D. M. Loades. 1968.
6. Records of the trial of Walter Langeton, Bishop of Lichfield and Coventry (1307–1312). Edited by Miss A. Beardwood. 1969.
7. Camden miscellany, Vol. XXIII: 1. The Account Book of John Balsall of Bristol for a trading voyage to Spain, 1480. Edited by T. F. Reddaway and A. A. Ruddock. 2. A parliamentary diary of Queen Anne's reign. Edited by W. A. Speck. 3. Leicester House politics, 1750–1760, from the papers of John, second Earl of Egmont. Edited by A. N. Newman. 4. The Parliamentary diary of Nathaniel Ryder, 1764–67. Edited by P. D. G. Thomas. 1969.
8. Documents illustrating the British Conquest of Manila, 1762–1763. Edited by Nicholas P. Cushner. 1971.
9. Camden Miscellany, Vol. XXIV: 1. Documents relating to the Breton succession dispute of 1341. Edited by M. Jones. 2. Documents relating to Anglo-French negotiations, 1439. Edited by C. T. Allmand. 3. A 'Fifteenth century chronicle' at Trinity College, Dublin. Edited by G. L. Harriss.
10. Herefordshire Militia Assessments of 1663. Edited by M. A. Faraday.
11. The early correspondence of Jabez Bunting, 1820–1829. Edited by W. R. Ward.

Provisionally accepted for future publication:

British diplomatic representatives, 1509–1688. Ed. by C. H. Carter.
Wentworth papers, 1597–1628. Edited by J. P. Cooper (*in the press*).
The Account Book of Beaulieu Abbey. Edited by S. F. Hockey.
Select documents illustrating the internal crisis of 1296–1298 in England. Edited by Michael Prestwich.
The *Acta* of Archbishop Hugh of Rouen (1130–1164). Edited by T. Waldman.
Cartularies of Reading Abbey. Edited by B. R. Kemp.
A calendar of Western Circuit Assize Orders, 1629–1652. Edited by J. S. Cockburn.
The Parliamentary Diary of John Clementson, 1770–1804. Edited by P. D. G. Thomas.
J. B. Pentland's Report on Bolivia, 1827. Edited by J. V. Fifer.
The Letters of William, Lord Paget. Edited by Barrett L. Beer and Sybil Jack.
The Letter Book of Thomas Bentham, Bishop of Coventry and Lichfield. Edited by M. Rosemary O'Day and J. A. Berlatsky.

Lawrence Squibb, A Booke of all the Severall Officers of the Court of the Exchequer (1642). Edited by W. H. Bryson.

A Breviat of the Effectes devised for Wales. Edited by P. R. Roberts.

Letters of Henry St John to Charles, Earl of Orrery, 1709–1711. Edited by H. T. Dickinson.

Correspondence of Henry Cromwell, 1655–1659. Edited by Clyve Jones.

Correspondence of William Camden. Edited by Richard DeMolen.

Gervase Markham, The Muster-Master. Edited by Charles L. Hamilton.